MODEL THEORY
AND ITS APPLICATIONS

This book is a part of the

ALLYN AND BACON SERIES IN ADVANCED MATHEMATICS

Consulting Editors: Irving Kaplansky
Charles De Prima

Other books in the series:

James Dugundji, *Topology*
Horst Herrlich and George E. Strecker, *Category Theory*
Irving Kaplansky, *Commutative Rings*
Irving Kaplansky, *Linear Algebra and Geometry: A Second Course*
Irving Kaplansky, *Set Theory and Metric Spaces*
Joseph J. Rotman, *The Theory of Groups: An Introduction*

MODEL THEORY AND ITS APPLICATIONS

Ralph Kopperman

Associate Professor of Mathematics
City College of New York

ALLYN AND BACON, INC.
BOSTON

Printed in the United States of America
Library of Congress Catalog Card No. 76-144144

To Poopsie

Contents

Acknowledgments

This text, along with my knowledge of model theory, had its origin in a class taught by Professor Michael Rabin, and much of Chapter 1 and a bit of Chapter 2 are based on that course. In particular, the idea of introducing and motivating the compactness theorem long before its proof was suggested by Rabin.

After the initial class, I taught several courses on the subject. Two students from my classes are responsible for much of the readability of the text. David Saltman, as a freshman, knew more mathematics than most top graduating seniors and found scores of mistakes in the notes. Martin Ellis has the finest eye for counterexample I have ever seen in a student, and he used it to find numerous other errors and unclear passages later, after I thought the manuscript had been picked clean. Other suggestions which resulted in changes in the text were offered by my office mate, Professor Martin Zuckerman, and by the following members of my classes: Professor George Brown, Alan Cooper, Simon Ellberger, Howard Hamburger, Bruce Horowitz, Robert Lax, David Scherr, David Shulman, and Ivan Stux.

In writing the text, I borrowed wholesale from the works of Professors H. Jerome Keisler, Simon Kochen, and Abraham Robinson, as well as Professors James Ax, Abraham Bernstein, W. A. J. Luxemburg, Michael Morley, and Robert Vaught, and also other giants in the field of logic and model theory. I don't mention their names because my borrowing from them was less direct.

Professors Allen R. Bernstein and Rohit Parikh read the text and offered many suggestions.

While the contributions of all these people should assure excellence in the final manuscript, I must take the full responsibility for any degree to which it might fall short. I should be happy to have any additional suggestions you may have for consideration in any possible future edition.

Ralph Kopperman

MODEL THEORY
AND ITS APPLICATIONS

Introduction and Prerequisites

In order to understand many of the proofs in this text the reader should have a one-semester background in set theory, including discussions of ordinal numbers, general Cartesian products, cardinal arithmetic, and several forms of the axiom of choice.

For an understanding of the examples and an appreciation of the theory developed, a background of at least one semester of algebra is essential; a year is more useful. The reader should know the definitions of *group*, *ring*, *field*, *vector space*, and *Boolean algebra*, and have a good knowledge of the concepts of homomorphism and isomorphism. Simple recognition of the above terms is insufficient, however; considerable practice in their use is essential.

A knowledge of formal logic is not essential to the study of this text.

We now proceed to look at certain notations and points of view adopted in the text. Our set theory could have either of the two most standard axiomatizations: Zermelo-Frankel (treated, for example, in Suppes and Abian) or Gödel-Bernays-Von Neumann (treated in Rubin or Kelley). However, we use it loosely on occasion: For example, at the beginning of Section 1.6, we refer to $\equiv$ as an equivalence relation when it is not a relation at all in Zermelo-Frankel; earlier, near the beginning of Section 1.3, we discuss EC, EC_Δ, which are "collections" of proper classes, thus not classes even in Gödel-Bernays-Von Neumann set theory. But any abuses are only apparent; what we want can be said within these theories.

We always assume the axiom of choice, and later in the introduction list several equivalent forms that are actually used.

For any set A, $\mathscr{P}A = \{B \mid B \subset A\}$, where $\subset$ denotes not-necessarily-proper subset. R is a relation iff for some $A_1, \ldots, A_n$, $R \subset A_1 \times \cdots \times A_n$, the Cartesian product of $A_1, \ldots, A_n$. If $D \subset A_1 \times \cdots \times A_m$, $m \leq n$, then $R \mid D = R \cap (D \times A_{m+1} \times \cdots \times A_n)$; if $m < n$,

$$R[D] = \{\langle a_{m+1}, \ldots, a_n\rangle \mid \text{for some } \langle a_1, \ldots, a_m\rangle \in D, \langle a_1, \ldots, a_n\rangle \in R\}.$$

By $\mathscr{D}R$ we mean

$$\{\langle a_1, \ldots, a_{n-1}\rangle \mid \text{for some } a_n, \langle a_1, \ldots, a_n\rangle \in R\}, \qquad \mathscr{R}R = R[\mathscr{D}R].$$

An operation is a relation R such that

$$\text{if} \quad \langle a_1, \ldots, a_n\rangle, \langle a_1, \ldots, a_{n-1}, b\rangle \in R, \qquad \text{then} \quad a_n = b.$$

If $n = 2$,

$$R^{-1} = \{\langle a, b\rangle \mid \langle b, a\rangle \in R\};$$

and, a binary operation is called a function. If A, B are sets, then $\mathfrak{I}_A = \{\langle a, a\rangle \mid a \in A\}$ is the identity function on A, and $B^A = \{f\colon A \to B\}$ is the set of functions with domain A and range contained in B.

If $A_1 = \cdots = A_n = A$ above, we call R a relation on A, or n-ary relation on A; if R is also an operation and $\mathscr{D}R = A^{n-1}$, we may call R an operation on A, or n-1-ary operation on A. If here $C \subset A$, then $R \upharpoonright C = R \mid C^n$.

A function on an ordinal may be denoted $\langle a_0, a_1, \ldots\rangle$, where $a_\alpha = a(\alpha)$, and may be referred to as a β-sequence if it has domain β. An ω-sequence is simply referred to as a sequence, where ω is the first infinite ordinal, therefore the set of all natural numbers $\{0, 1, 2, \ldots\}$; and a β-sequence is called a finite sequence if its domain is a natural number. More generally, any function may be denoted by $\langle a_i\rangle_{i \in I}$, where I is its domain and, if the function is a, $a_i = a(i)$, and in this form may be referred to as an indexed set. We often use the notation $\langle a, a_i\rangle_{i \in I}$ and call the result an *indexed set*; we mean the ordered pair $\langle a, \langle a_i\rangle_{i \in I}\rangle$, where $\langle a_i\rangle_{i \in I}$ is an indexed set as described above. If $\langle A_i\rangle_{i \in I}$ is an indexed set and for each i, A_i is a set, then $\prod_I A_i$ will denote the Cartesian product of the A_i.

The result in cardinal arithmetic we use most often asserts that if $\mathfrak{m}$, $\mathfrak{n}$ are two cardinals, at least one of which is infinite and neither of which is 0, then $\mathfrak{m}\mathfrak{n} = \mathfrak{m} + \mathfrak{n} = \max\{\mathfrak{m}, \mathfrak{n}\}$. By $\mathfrak{m}^+$ we mean the smallest cardinal larger than $\mathfrak{m}$. A set A is called countable iff $c(A) \leq \omega$, where $c(A)$ denotes the cardinality of A (see form (c) of the axiom of choice later in the introduction). Lower case German letters will denote cardinals with these exceptions: ω denotes the first infinite cardinal; and cardinals known to be finite are denoted by lower case Roman letters. Lower case Greek letters denote ordinals (however γ, δ sometimes denote elements of index sets Γ, Δ; and φ, ψ and some others may denote functions); but if they are finite, lower case Roman letters may be used. A directed set A is a set partially ordered by some relation $<$ such that if $a, b \in A$ then for some $c \in A$, $a < c$ and $b < c$.

We use the following forms of the axiom of choice:

(a) If A is partially ordered by $<$ and every chain B in A is bounded, then A has maximal elements. (Here B is a chain in A iff $< \upharpoonright B$ totally orders B; B is bounded iff for some $a \in A$, if $b \in B$, then $b \leq a$; and $a \in A$ is maximal iff there is no $b \in A$ such that $a < b$.) We refer to this form as *Zorn's lemma*, although it would probably be more proper to credit it to Tukey.

(b) Every set can be well ordered.

(c) Every set can be put in one-one correspondence with a cardinal (a *cardinal* is an ordinal not admitting a one-one function into a smaller ordinal).

(d) If $R \subset A_1 \times A_2$ is a relation, there is a function $f \subset R$ such that $\mathscr{D}f = \mathscr{D}R$.

(e) If for each $i \in I$, $A_i \neq \phi$, then $\prod_I A_i \neq \phi$.

(f) If A, B are any two sets, there is a function f that is one-one, and such that $f: A \to B$ or $f: B \to A$.

A unified discussion of several equivalent forms of the axiom of choice, including those listed above, is given in Suppes, and over 100 forms of the axiom of choice are discussed in Rubin and Rubin.

All topics listed in the second paragraph of our introduction are covered in Birkhoff and MacLane and in Jacobson coupled with a satisfactory linear algebra text.

We now glance at two set-theoretic topics not treated in standard texts. Let $<$ be a total ordering of a set A; if $B \subset A$, then

$$\text{seg}(B) = \{x \in A \mid \text{for some } y \in B, x \leq y\},$$

and B is called cofinal in A iff $\text{seg}(B) = A$. If C is totally ordered by $<'$, a cofinality map from C into A is a strict order-preserving map $\varphi: C \to A$ (i.e., if $x <' y$, then $\varphi(x) < \varphi(y)$) such that $\mathscr{R}\varphi$ is cofinal in A.

It is simple to check that any composition of cofinality maps is a cofinality map and that a union of a chain of strict order-preserving maps is a strict order-preserving map.

Lemma. Let $<$ be a total order on A, μ an ordinal, $g: \mu \to A$, $\mathscr{R}g$ cofinal in A. Then for some ordinal $\alpha \leq \mu$ there is a cofinality map $f: \alpha \to A$.

Sketch of proof: For each ordinal $\beta \leq \mu$, we define an ordinal $\alpha_\beta \leq \beta$ and a strict order-preserving map $f_\beta: \alpha_\beta \to A$ by ordinal induction as follows: $\alpha_0 = 0, f_0 = \phi$; if $\beta = \gamma + 1$ and f_γ is not a cofinality map, let

$$\alpha_\beta = \alpha_\gamma + 1, \qquad f_\beta = f_\gamma \cup \{\langle \alpha_\gamma, g(\tau)\rangle\}$$

for the least τ such that

$$g(\beta) \leq g(\tau) \qquad \text{and} \qquad g(\tau) \in A \sim \text{seg}(\mathscr{R}f_\gamma);$$

if $\beta = \gamma + 1$ and f_γ is a cofinality map, let $\alpha_\beta = \alpha_\gamma$ and $f_\beta = f_\gamma$. In either case, f_β is a strict order-preserving map, and in the second case a cofinality map. If β is a limit ordinal, then

$$\alpha_\beta = \bigcup_{\gamma<\beta} \alpha_\gamma, \qquad f_\beta = \bigcup_{\gamma<\beta} f_\gamma;$$

once again $\alpha_\beta \leq \beta$, f_β is strictly order-preserving. Also note that for $\delta < \beta$, $f_\beta(\delta) = f_{\delta+1}(\delta) \geq g(\delta)$; thus $\mathrm{seg}(g[\beta]) \subset \mathrm{seg}(f_\beta[\alpha_\beta])$.

Now consider $f_\mu \colon \alpha_\mu \to A$. It is a strict order-preserving map; finally

$$A = \mathrm{seg}(g[\mu]) \subset \mathrm{seg}(f_\mu[\alpha_\mu]),$$

so f_μ is a cofinality map and $\alpha_\mu \leq \mu$.

In particular, if $\mathfrak{m} = c(A)$, there is an onto $g\colon \mathfrak{m} \to A$, thus a cofinality map $f\colon \alpha \to A$ for some $\alpha \leq \mathfrak{m}$. Thus there is an ordinal with a cofinality map into A, therefore a least such ordinal; call that least ordinal the cofinality of A, $cf(A)$.

$cf(A)$ must always be a cardinal, for if $f\colon \alpha \to A$ is a cofinality map, $\mathfrak{m} = c(\alpha) \leq \alpha$, then there is a cofinality map $g\colon \beta \to \alpha$ for some $\beta \leq \mathfrak{m}$; so $f \circ g\colon \beta \to A$ is a cofinality map; but if $\alpha = cf(A)$, then $\alpha \leq \beta$, so $\mathfrak{m} = \alpha$. In addition, by the previous paragraph, $cf(A) \leq c(A)$, so for ordinals $cf(\alpha) \leq \alpha$.

Note that the above lemma can now be restated: If for some $g\colon \mu \to A$, $\mathscr{R}g$ is cofinal in A, then $cf(A) \leq \mu$.

A cardinal $\mathfrak{m}$ is called regular if $cf(\mathfrak{m}) = \mathfrak{m}$. If $\omega \leq \mathfrak{m}$, $\mathfrak{m}^+$ is regular: Let $g\colon \alpha \to \mathfrak{m}^+$, $\alpha < \mathfrak{m}^+$ (thus $c(\alpha) \leq \mathfrak{m}$). Then $\mathfrak{m}^+ = \bigcup_{\gamma<\alpha} g(\gamma)$, but $c(g(\gamma)) \leq \mathfrak{m}$, so

$$c\left(\bigcup_{\gamma<\alpha} g(\gamma)\right) \leq \sum_{\gamma<\alpha} c(g(\gamma)) \leq c(\alpha)\mathfrak{m} \leq \mathfrak{m}^2 = \mathfrak{m} < \mathfrak{m}^+,$$

a contradiction.

Our second topic is the construction for each cardinal $\mathfrak{m}$ of a cardinal $\mathfrak{p}$ such that $\mathfrak{m} < cf(\mathfrak{p})$ and for $\mathfrak{n} < \mathfrak{p}$, $2^{\mathfrak{n}} < \mathfrak{p}$, properties used in Section 2.8. For this construction we define for each ordinal α a cardinal Ω_α by transfinite induction as follows: $\alpha_0 = \omega$, given Ω_γ, $\Omega_{\gamma+1} = 2^{\Omega_\gamma}$, and for limit ordinals, $\Omega_\alpha = \bigcup_{\beta<\alpha} \Omega_\beta$. Let $\mathfrak{m}$ be an infinite cardinal, thus a limit ordinal:

(1) If $\mathfrak{n} < \Omega_\mathfrak{m}$, then $\mathfrak{n} \leq \Omega_\alpha$ for some $\alpha < \mathfrak{m}$; thus $2^{\mathfrak{n}} < \Omega_{\alpha+2} \leq \Omega_\mathfrak{m}$.

(2) $cf(\mathfrak{m}) = cf(\Omega_\mathfrak{m})$, for if $f\colon \mu \to \Omega_\mathfrak{m}$ is a cofinality map, let $g\colon \mu \to \mathfrak{m}$ be defined by $g(\beta) = \min\{\gamma \mid f(\beta) < \Omega_\gamma\}$. If $\delta \in \mathfrak{m}$, since f is a cofinality map there is a $\gamma < \alpha$ such that $f(\gamma) \geq \Omega_\delta$; thus $g(\gamma) > \delta$, so $\delta \in \mathrm{seg}(\mathscr{R}g)$; thus $\mathscr{R}g$ is cofinal in $\mathfrak{m}$, so $cf(\mathfrak{m}) \leq \mu$. However, if $h\colon \eta \to \mathfrak{m}$ is a cofinality

map, let $k: \eta \to \Omega_{\mathfrak{m}}$ be defined by $k(\alpha) = \Omega_{h(\alpha)}$ for $\alpha < \eta$; $\mathscr{R}k$ is cofinal in $\Omega_{\mathfrak{m}}$ because if $\beta \in \Omega_{\mathfrak{m}}$ then for some $\gamma < \mathfrak{m}$, $\beta \leq \Omega_\gamma$; but if $\gamma < h(\alpha)$, $\Omega_\gamma \leq \Omega_{h(\alpha)}$ so $\beta \leq \Omega_{h(\alpha)}$, thus $cf(\Omega_{\mathfrak{m}}) \leq \eta$.

Thus $\mathfrak{p} = \Omega_{\mathfrak{m}^+}$ satisfies the conditions $\mathfrak{m} < \mathfrak{m}^+ = cf(\mathfrak{p})$, and for $\mathfrak{n} < \mathfrak{p}$, $2^{\mathfrak{n}} < \mathfrak{p}$.

The text is organized as follows. Chapter 1 concentrates on basic definitions and those parts of model theory that can be considered without an overwhelming temptation to use the ultraproduct construction. Section 1.8 is written as a climax to that chapter and is of little use thereafter. Chapter 2 introduces ultraproducts, ultralimits, limit ultraproducts, and the author's Q-relations, which can be used to unify several preservation theorems. It is written so that essentially only the first three sections are prerequisites to later work. In Chapter 3, the completeness theorem is proved. This chapter depends on nothing beyond Section 1.3 other than a statement of the compactness theorem, and nothing depends on it. Chapter 4 is devoted to some of the recent incursions of model theory into algebra and Chapter 5 is similarly related to analysis. Thus several possible courses can be carved out of the book, depending on the interests of the students and of the teacher. The latter should keep in mind the fact that it takes two to three class hours to cover comfortably the average section, particularly since many of the problems are an intrinsic part of the text; some proofs depend on their results. The accompanying diagram illustrates the interdependence of sections of the book.

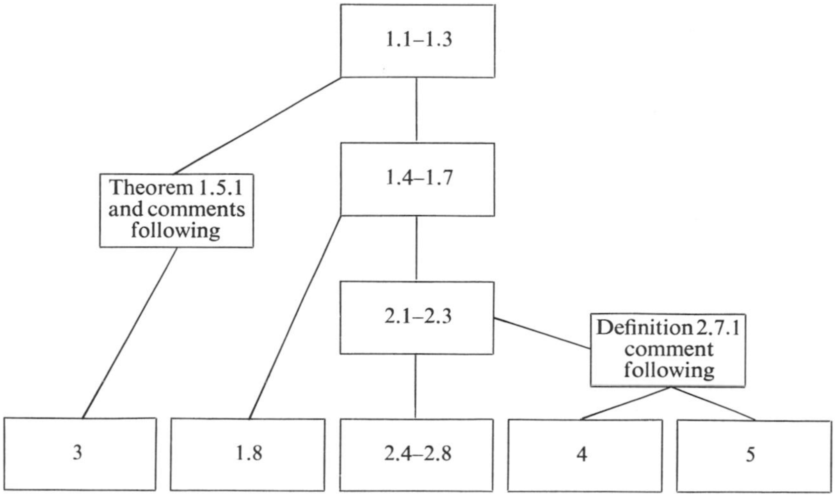

1

Classical Work

1.1 Structures

The purpose of model theory is to discover relationships that hold between sets of axioms and the structures that satisfy them. Our first duty, therefore, is to define the pertinent terms in the above sentence, namely, *axiom*, *structure*, and *satisfaction*.

We deal first with structures. Most systems encountered in algebra (groups, rings, or ordered sets, for example) consist of a set together with a collection of operations and relations on it and perhaps some distinguished elements (such as 0 and 1) from it. Every operation is a relation (see the introduction), so we do not mention operations specifically in our formal definition.

DEFINITION 1.1.1. A structure is an indexed set $\langle A, R_i \rangle_{i \in I}$ together with a function $t\colon I \to \omega$ such that $A \neq \phi$, and for each $i \in I$, if $t(i) = 0$, then $R_i \in A$, and if $t(i) > 0$, then $R_i \subset A^{t(i)}$.

Despite the above, we often assume t known and simply refer to $\langle A, R_i \rangle_{i \in I}$ as the "structure." It should be noted, however, that even though t is understood, it is not completely determined by $\langle A, R_i \rangle_{i \in I}$ in every case. For example, the Boolean algebra $\langle \mathscr{P}B, \bigcup, \bigcap, ', \phi \rangle$ is understood to be of type $\langle 3, 3, 2, 0 \rangle$, but $\phi \subset B^n$ for each positive integer n, so if we did not understand ϕ to be a distinguished element, our type might equally well be $\langle 3, 3, 2, n \rangle$ for any integer n. Note that we have also used a convention here to avoid explicitly mentioning I, and it is a convention that we shall often use in the future. We assume that $I = 4 = \{0, 1, 2, 3\}$; then t can be written as a sequence, i.e., as $\langle 3, 3, 2, 0\rangle$ rather than $\{\langle 0, 3\rangle, \langle 1, 3\rangle, \langle 2, 2\rangle, \langle 3, 0\rangle\}$, its true form. Further conventions are introduced as we need them.

Examples: A group is generally considered to be a nonempty set A together with a binary operation $\circ$ and a distinguished element e. The operation and element are supposed to have some properties we cannot yet formally express. In our work with groups, we consider instead of the binary operation $\circ$ the ternary relation

$$R = \{\langle a, b, c\rangle \mid a \circ b = c\} \subset A^3.$$

Thus we define a group as a structure of the form $\mathfrak{A} = \langle A, R, e\rangle$ satisfying certain axioms to be stated later, when we have more machinery at our disposal.

Note that the above choice is somewhat arbitrary. For example, we could have listed e before R, discarded e (since it can be defined in terms of R), or added a relation $^{-1}$.

An ordered set is a pair $\mathfrak{A} = \langle A, \leq\rangle$, where $A \neq \phi$, $\leq \subset A^2$, and $\leq$ satisfies axioms to be stated later.

NOTATION. As in the above examples, we generally use capital German letters to denote structures and often use the corresponding Roman capital to denote the domain of the structure (the set on which the relations are defined). For example, $\mathfrak{A} = \langle A, R_i\rangle_{i \in I}$ has domain A, and in fact, unless otherwise noted, by $\mathfrak{A}$ we mean $\langle A, R_i\rangle_{i\in I}$; by $\mathfrak{B}$, $\langle B, S_i\rangle_{i\in I}$; and by $\mathfrak{C}$, $\langle C, T_i\rangle_{i\in I}$. We do not feel bound by the notation R_i and often denote relations or distinguished elements by R, e, 0, 1, $+$, $\cdot$, $<$, or any other symbol that seems appropriate. In particular, if $t(i) = 0$, we often set $R_i = e_i \in A$.

When attempting to compare two structures, we encounter a basic problem. Given two groups, we find it meaningful to ask and often useful to discover whether one is a subgroup of the other or whether they are isomorphic. We are puzzled, though, when asked to decide whether a given group is a subgroup of (or isomorphic to) a given ring, and in deep trouble when asked to decide whether a given ordered set is isomorphic to a given group.

One of the grossest possible distinctions between structures will allow us to decide whether or not a pair of structures can be compared.

DEFINITION 1.1.2. A type is a function whose range is a subset of ω. Let $\mathfrak{A}$ be a structure. The type of $\mathfrak{A}$ is the function introduced in Definition

1.1.1, and denoted by $t_{\mathfrak{A}}$ or simply t. Two structures $\mathfrak{A}$, $\mathfrak{B}$ are said to be similar iff $t_{\mathfrak{A}} = t_{\mathfrak{B}}$. If $t_{\mathfrak{A}} = t$, then $\mathfrak{A}$ is said to be of type t.

To see that it is meaningful to attempt to compare similar structures, we now formulate definitions for the concepts of substructure and isomorphism, as well as some other concepts.

Definition 1.1.3. Let $\mathfrak{A}$, $\mathfrak{B}$ be similar structures. Then $\mathfrak{A}$ is a substructure of $\mathfrak{B}$, a relationship denoted by $\mathfrak{A} \subset \mathfrak{B}$, iff

(i) $A \subset B$; and
(ii) if $t(i) = 0$, $R_i = S_i$. Otherwise

$$R_i = S_i \upharpoonright A = S_i \cap A^{t(i)}.$$

Let $X \subset A$ contain all the distinguished elements of $\mathfrak{A}$. Then

$$\mathfrak{A} \mid X = \langle X, R_i \upharpoonright X \rangle_{i \in I}.$$

The notation $\mathfrak{A} \mid X$ can only be used for such X.

Note that the above definition entails the fact that if $S_i \in B$ then $S_i \in A$. This is consistent with a practice often followed in algebra. For example, the definition of subring for a ring with identity generally states that the subring must contain the identity element (see Problem 1.1.1). Our definition, as a whole, however, is not always the one used in algebra (see Problems 1.1.2 and 1.1.3).

Definition 1.1.4. Throughout this definition let $\mathfrak{A}$, $\mathfrak{B}$ be similar structures. An isomorphism $f\colon \mathfrak{A} \to \mathfrak{B}$ is a one–one onto function $f\colon A \to B$ such that

(i) if $t(i) > 0$, then

$$S_i = \{\langle f(a_1), \ldots, f(a_{t(i)})\rangle \mid \langle a_1, \ldots, a_{t(i)}\rangle \in R_i\},$$

and

(ii) if $t(i) = 0$, then $f(R_i) = S_i$.

In this case we also write $f\colon \mathfrak{A} \cong \mathfrak{B}$. $\mathfrak{A}$ is isomorphic to $\mathfrak{B}$ iff there is an isomorphism $f\colon \mathfrak{A} \cong \mathfrak{B}$ (and we write $\mathfrak{A} \cong \mathfrak{B}$). f is an automorphism of $\mathfrak{A}$ iff $f\colon \mathfrak{A} \cong \mathfrak{A}$. $f\colon A \to B$ is an imbedding of $\mathfrak{A}$ into $\mathfrak{B}$ iff for some $\mathfrak{C} \subset \mathfrak{B}$, $f\colon \mathfrak{A} \cong \mathfrak{C}$.

A function $f\colon A \to B$ is a homomorphism of $\mathfrak{A}$ onto $\mathfrak{B}$ iff $f[A] = B$,

(i′) if $t(i) > 0$ and $\langle a_1, \ldots, a_{t(i)}\rangle \in R_i$, then $\langle f(a_1), \ldots, f(a_{t(i)})\rangle \in S_i$, and (ii) of the definition of isomorphism is satisfied by f. If there is a homomorphism f of $\mathfrak{A}$ onto $\mathfrak{B}$, then $\mathfrak{B}$ is called a homomorphic image of $\mathfrak{A}$. A function $f\colon A \to B$ is a homomorphism of $\mathfrak{A}$ into $\mathfrak{B}$ iff whenever $t(i) = 0$, $S_i \in f[A]$ and f is a homomorphism of $\mathfrak{A}$ onto $\mathfrak{B} \mid f[A]$.

Let us see how the above definition applies to rings. Let $\mathfrak{A} = \langle A, R_0, R_1, R_2, R_3\rangle$ and $\mathfrak{B} = \langle B, S_0, S_1, S_2, S_3\rangle$, where

$$\begin{aligned} R_0 &= \{\langle a, b, a + b\rangle \mid a, b \in A\},\\ R_1 &= \{\langle a, b, a \cdot b\rangle \mid a, b \in A\},\\ R_2 &= 0,\\ R_3 &= 1, \end{aligned}$$

and the S_i are defined similarly. Then $\mathfrak{A}$ and $\mathfrak{B}$ are isomorphic iff we can find $f\colon A \to B$ (one-one, onto) such that $\langle a, b, c\rangle \in R_0$ iff

$$\langle f(a), f(b), f(c)\rangle \in S_0,$$

i.e., $a + b = c$ iff $f(a) +' f(b) = f(c)$, and similarly $a \cdot b = c$ iff $f(a) \cdot' f(b) = f(c)$, $f(0) = 0'$, and $f(1) = 1'$. The usual definition of isomorphism differs only in that it abbreviates the first two conditions to $f(a + b) = f(a) +' f(b)$ and $f(a \cdot b) = f(a) \cdot' f(b)$ and eliminates the third and fourth, which are implied by the first two. That the two sets of conditions are equivalent is simple to verify, using the fact that S_0, S_1 are operations (see Problem 1.1.4).

Notation. By $c(\mathfrak{A})$ we mean the cardinality of A, the domain of the structure $\mathfrak{A}$. This is the second time (and it will not be the last) that we take a property of the domain of $\mathfrak{A}$ and "abuse" our notation by attributing it to $\mathfrak{A}$. We have previously written $f\colon \mathfrak{A} \to \mathfrak{B}$ instead of $f\colon A \to B$ for functions that obviously do the latter.

Definition 1.1.5. Let $\mathfrak{A}$, $\mathfrak{B}$ be similar structures with the property that if $t_{\mathfrak{A}}(i) = 0$ $(= t_{\mathfrak{B}}(i))$, then $R_i = S_i$. Then $\mathfrak{A} \cup \mathfrak{B} = \langle A \cup B, T_i\rangle_{i \in I}$, where $T_i = R_i \cup S_i$ if $t_{\mathfrak{A}}(i) > 0$, and $T_i = R_i = S_i$ if $t_{\mathfrak{A}}(i) = 0$. More generally, let $\mathscr{S}$ be a set of similar structures, and for $\mathfrak{A} \in \mathscr{S}$ set $\mathfrak{A} = \langle A_{\mathfrak{A}}, R_i^{\mathfrak{A}}\rangle_{i \in I}$. If whenever $t_{\mathfrak{A}}(i) = 0$ we have $R_i^{\mathfrak{A}} = R_i^{\mathfrak{B}}$ for every $\mathfrak{A}$, $\mathfrak{B} \in \mathscr{S}$, we define $\bigcup \mathscr{S} = \langle C, T_i\rangle_{i \in I}$, where $C = \bigcup \{A_{\mathfrak{A}} \mid \mathfrak{A} \in \mathscr{S}\}$; if $t_{\mathfrak{A}}(i) > 0$, then $T_i = \bigcup \{R_i^{\mathfrak{A}} \mid \mathfrak{A} \in \mathscr{S}\}$; and if $t_{\mathfrak{A}}(i) = 0$, $T_i = R_i^{\mathfrak{A}}$ for any $\mathfrak{A} \in \mathscr{S}$. The definition of $\bigcap$ is similar.

The above definition, even on the restricted class of sets of structures for which it holds, does not imply either of the relations $\mathfrak{A} \subset \mathfrak{A} \cup \mathfrak{B}$ or

$\mathfrak{A} \cap \mathfrak{B} \subset \mathfrak{B}$. For example, let $A \neq \phi$, $\mathfrak{A} = \langle A, \phi \rangle$, $\mathfrak{B} = \langle A, A \rangle$, both structures of type $\langle 1 \rangle$ that satisfy the conditions of the definition. Then

$$\mathfrak{A} = \mathfrak{A} \cap \mathfrak{B} \not\subset \mathfrak{B} = \mathfrak{A} \cup \mathfrak{B}.$$

DEFINITION 1.1.6. A set $\mathscr{S}$ of similar structures is directed by inclusion iff for every $\mathfrak{A}, \mathfrak{B} \in \mathscr{S}$, there is a $\mathfrak{C} \in \mathscr{S}$ such that $\mathfrak{A} \subset \mathfrak{C}$ and $\mathfrak{B} \subset \mathfrak{C}$. $\mathscr{S}$ is inversely directed by inclusion iff for every $\mathfrak{A}, \mathfrak{B} \in \mathscr{S}$ there is a $\mathfrak{C} \in \mathscr{S}$ such that $\mathfrak{C} \subset \mathfrak{A}$ and $\mathfrak{C} \subset \mathfrak{B}$.

We note that if $\mathfrak{A}$, $\mathfrak{B}$, and $\mathfrak{C}$ are such that $\mathfrak{A} \subset \mathfrak{C}$ and $\mathfrak{B} \subset \mathfrak{C}$ (or $\mathfrak{C} \subset \mathfrak{A}$ and $\mathfrak{C} \subset \mathfrak{B}$) and if $t(i) = 0$, then $R_i = T_i = S_i$. Thus $\bigcap$ and $\bigcup$ are defined for sets directed or inversely directed by inclusion.

THEOREM 1.1.7. If $\mathscr{S}$ is directed by inclusion, then for every $\mathfrak{A} \in \mathscr{S}$, $\bigcap \mathscr{S} \subset \mathfrak{A} \subset \bigcup \mathscr{S}$. If $\mathscr{S}$ is inversely directed by inclusion, then for every $\mathfrak{A} \in \mathscr{S}$, $\bigcap \mathscr{S} \subset \mathfrak{A}$.

Proof: We show here that if $\mathscr{S}$ is directed by inclusion, then for every $\mathfrak{A} \in \mathscr{S}$, $\mathfrak{A} \subset \bigcup \mathscr{S}$. We leave the rest for the reader. Set $\bigcup \mathscr{S} = \langle C, T_i \rangle_{i \in I}$ and for $\mathfrak{A} \in \mathscr{S}$ set $\mathfrak{A} = \langle A_{\mathfrak{A}}, R_i^{\mathfrak{A}} \rangle_{i \in I}$. Clearly each

$$A_{\mathfrak{A}} \subset \bigcup \{A_{\mathfrak{B}} \mid \mathfrak{B} \in \mathscr{S}\},$$

and if $t(i) > 0$,

$$R_i^{\mathfrak{A}} \subset \bigcup \{R_i^{\mathfrak{B}} \mid \mathfrak{B} \in \mathscr{S}\} \cap A^{t(i)} = T_i \upharpoonright A_{\mathfrak{A}}.$$

However, if

$$\langle a_1, \ldots, a_{t(i)} \rangle \in T_i \upharpoonright A_{\mathfrak{A}},$$

we can find $\mathfrak{B} \in \mathscr{S}$ such that

$$\langle a_1, \ldots, a_{t(i)} \rangle \in R_i^{\mathfrak{B}}.$$

We can also find $\mathfrak{C} \in \mathscr{S}$ such that $\mathfrak{A} \subset \mathfrak{C}$ and $\mathfrak{B} \subset \mathfrak{C}$. Thus $R_i^{\mathfrak{B}} = R_i \upharpoonright$ B, so

$$\langle a_1, \ldots, a_{t(i)} \rangle \in R_i^{\mathfrak{C}}.$$

But $a_1, \ldots, a_{t(i)} \in A_{\mathfrak{A}}$, so

$$\langle a_1, \ldots, a_{t(i)} \rangle \in R_i^{\mathfrak{C}} \upharpoonright A = R_i^{\mathfrak{A}}.$$

Thus

$$R_i^{\mathfrak{A}} = T_i \upharpoonright A_{\mathfrak{A}}.$$

The case $t(i) = 0$ is left for the reader.

Problems

1.1.1 Consider the structure $\langle A, +, \cdot, 0\rangle$, where $\langle A, +, \cdot, 0, 1\rangle$ is a ring with identity. What are the types of these two structures? What are their substructures? Under what conditions is a substructure of $\langle A, +, \cdot, 0\rangle$ a substructure of $\langle A, +, \cdot, 0, 1\rangle$? If $\langle A, +, \cdot, 0\rangle \mid X \subset \langle A, +, \cdot, 0\rangle$, under what conditions is $\langle A, +, \cdot, 0, 1\rangle \mid X \subset \langle A, +, \cdot, 0, 1\rangle$?

1.1.2 Let $\mathscr{G}$ be the class of all groups (considered as structures according to the considerations following Definition 1.1.1). Show that every group with more than two elements has a substructure that is not a subgroup. Check that $\langle B, S, f\rangle$ is a subgroup of $\langle A, R, e\rangle \in \mathscr{G}$ iff $\langle B, S, f\rangle \in \mathscr{G}$ and $\langle B, S, f\rangle \subset \langle A, R, e\rangle$.

1.1.3 The above problem suggests a general definition. Let $\mathfrak{A} \in \mathscr{S}$, $\mathscr{S}$ a class of similar structures. Then $\mathfrak{B}$ is an $\mathscr{S}$-substructure of $\mathfrak{A}$ iff $\mathfrak{B} \subset \mathfrak{A}$ and $\mathfrak{B} \in \mathscr{S}$.

Let $\mathscr{R}$ be the class of rings, $\mathscr{O}$ the class of ordered sets. Show that $\mathfrak{B}$ is a subring of $\mathfrak{A} \in \mathscr{R}$ iff $\mathfrak{B}$ is an $\mathscr{R}$-substructure of $\mathfrak{A}$.

Show that if $\mathfrak{A} \subset \mathfrak{B} \in \mathscr{O}$ then $\mathfrak{A} \in \mathscr{O}$.

1.1.4 Let $\mathfrak{A}$, $\mathfrak{B}$ be structures of type t, and suppose that $f: A \to B$ and that $\mathscr{D}R_i = A^{t(i)-1}$ and S_i is an operation provided that $t(i) > 0$. If f is one–one, show f to be an imbedding iff f is a homomorphism. (Also see Problems 10 and 11.)

1.1.5 Let $\mathfrak{A}$, $\mathfrak{B}$ be similar structures. We define $\mathfrak{A} \times \mathfrak{B} = \mathfrak{C}$ iff $C = A \times B$,

$$T_i = \{\langle\langle a_1, b_1\rangle, \ldots, \langle a_{t_\mathfrak{A}(i)}, b_{t_\mathfrak{A}(i)}\rangle\rangle \mid \langle a_1, \ldots, a_{t_\mathfrak{A}(i)}\rangle \in R_i, \langle b_1, \ldots, b_{t_\mathfrak{A}(i)}\rangle \in S_i\}$$

if $t_\mathfrak{A}(i) > 0$, and $T_i = \langle R_i, S_i\rangle$ if $t_\mathfrak{A}(i) = 0$. Show that if $R_i, S_i \neq \phi$ whenever $t(i) \neq 0$ then $\mathfrak{A}$ and $\mathfrak{B}$ are homomorphic images of $\mathfrak{A} \times \mathfrak{B}$. Also show that $\mathfrak{A}$ can be imbedded in $\mathfrak{A} \times \mathfrak{B}$ iff there is a homomorphism taking $\mathfrak{A}$ into $\mathfrak{B}$.

Let $\mathscr{S}$ be an indexed set of similar structures. Define $\Pi\mathscr{S}$.

1.1.6 In this problem, let $\mathfrak{A}$ H $\mathfrak{B}$ stand for "$\mathfrak{B}$ is a homomorphic image of $\mathfrak{A}$."

(a) If $\mathfrak{A}$ H $\mathfrak{B}$ and $\mathfrak{B}$ H $\mathfrak{C}$, then $\mathfrak{A}$ H $\mathfrak{C}$.

(b) If $\mathfrak{A} \cong \mathfrak{B}$, then $\mathfrak{A}$ H $\mathfrak{B}$ and $\mathfrak{B}$ H $\mathfrak{A}$.

(c) Give an example of $\mathfrak{A}$, $\mathfrak{B}$ such that $\mathfrak{A}$ H $\mathfrak{B}$ and $\mathfrak{B}$ H $\mathfrak{A}$ but not $\mathfrak{A} \cong \mathfrak{B}$.

(d) Provide and solve examples corresponding to (a) to (c) in terms of imbedding rather than homomorphic image.

‡1.1.7 Show that:

(a) $\mathfrak{B} \subset \mathfrak{A}$ iff for some $X \subset A$ containing all distinguished elements of $\mathfrak{A}$, $\mathfrak{B} = \mathfrak{A} \mid X$.

(b) $f: \mathfrak{A} \to \mathfrak{B}$ is an imbedding iff $f: \mathfrak{A} \cong \mathfrak{B} \mid f[A]$ (and $S_i \in f[A]$ whenever $t(i) = 0$).

‡ Indicates that the Problem (or Problem part) is used at some point in the text.

(c) $f: \mathfrak{A} \to \mathfrak{B}$ is a homomorphism of $\mathfrak{A}$ into $\mathfrak{B}$ iff $f: \mathfrak{A} \to \mathfrak{C}$ is a homomorphism of $\mathfrak{A}$ onto $\mathfrak{C}$ for some $\mathfrak{C} \subset \mathfrak{B}$.

1.1.8 If $\mathscr{S}$ is directed, show that for any positive integer n and any $\mathfrak{A}_1, \ldots, \mathfrak{A}_n \in \mathscr{S}$ there is a $\mathfrak{C} \in \mathscr{S}$ such that $\mathfrak{A}_j \subset \mathfrak{C}$ for $1 \leq j \leq n$.

1.1.9 Give an example of a homomorphism that is one–one and onto but not an isomorphism. Now give such an example for finite structures. Show that if $\mathfrak{A}$ is finite, then $\mathfrak{A} \cong \mathfrak{B}$

(i) if $\mathfrak{A}$ H $\mathfrak{B}$ and $\mathfrak{B}$ H $\mathfrak{A}$; or

(ii) if $\mathfrak{A}$ can be imbedded in $\mathfrak{B}$ and $\mathfrak{B}$ in $\mathfrak{A}$.

‡1.1.10 Let $\mathfrak{A} = \langle A, R_i \rangle_{i \in I}$, and let $E \subset A^2$ be an equivalence relation. By $\mathfrak{A}/E$ we mean $\mathfrak{B} = \langle B, S_i \rangle_{i \in I}$, where

$$B = A/E = \{\bar{a} \mid a \in A\}$$

and for each $a \in A$,

$$\bar{a} = \{b \mid \langle a, b \rangle \in E\},$$

$$S_i = \{\langle \overline{a_1}, \ldots, \overline{a_{t(i)}} \rangle \mid \langle a_1, \ldots, a_{t(i)} \rangle \in R_i\} = R_i/E \qquad \text{if } t(i) > 0,$$

$$S_i = \overline{R_i} \qquad \text{if } t(i) = 0.$$

Show that there is a homomorphism from $\mathfrak{A}$ into $\mathfrak{B}$ iff for some equivalence relation E on A there is a one–one homomorphism from $\mathfrak{A}/E$ into $\mathfrak{B}$.

1.1.11 Let $\mathfrak{A}$, $\mathfrak{B}$ be similar structures. A strong homomorphism $f: \mathfrak{A} \to \mathfrak{B}$ is a function $f: A \to B$ such that $f: \mathfrak{A} \to \mathfrak{B} \mid f[A]$ satisfies (i) and (ii) of Definition 1.1.4.

(a) If E is an equivalence relation on A then $\pi: \mathfrak{A} \to \mathfrak{A}/E$ is a strong homomorphism, where $\pi(a) = \bar{a}$.

(b) Let $f: A \to B$. Then $E_f = \{\langle a, a' \rangle \mid f(a) = f(a')\}$ is an equivalence relation on A. Also, $f = \hat{f} \circ \pi$ for a unique $\hat{f}: A/E_f \to B$, and this $\hat{f}$ is one–one. $\hat{f}$ is onto iff f is. In addition, $\hat{f}$ is a homomorphism iff f is one and a strong homomorphism iff f is one (iff $\hat{f}$ is an imbedding).

(c) If for every i such that $t(i) > 0$, $\mathscr{D}R_i = A^{t(i)-1}$, S_i is an operation, then every homomorphism $f: \mathfrak{A} \to \mathfrak{B}$ is a strong homomorphism.

(NOTE: Special cases of the above problem include the isomorphism theorems for groups, rings, etc. Problem 1.1.4 is a special case of (c).)

1.1.12 Let $\varphi: \mathfrak{A} \to \mathfrak{B}$ be a homomorphism. Show that φ is an isomorphism iff there is a homomorphism $\psi: \mathfrak{B} \to \mathfrak{A}$ such that $\psi \circ \varphi = \mathfrak{I}_A$ and $\varphi \circ \psi = \mathfrak{I}_B$ (recall that $\mathfrak{I}_A$ is the identity on A).

1.2 Language and Truth

To discuss our structures formally we need a language. To see what our requirements of such a language should be, we study—informally, of course—the following statement about groups:

$$(\forall x)(\exists y)(xy = e \wedge yx = e).$$

We note that making the statement requires the use of quantifiers (i.e., $\forall$, $\exists$, which discuss the "quantity" of elements satisfying certain statements), symbols to represent the group operation and the distinguished element e, and the conjunction symbol. Parentheses and a symbol for equality are also used, and we can easily imagine other statements that would require the use of the $\vee$ (disjunction) and $\neg$ (negation). Finally, we need variables, that is symbols to represent arbitrary elements of our domain. With this in mind, we write

DEFINITION 1.2.1. Let t be a type. The language L^t is defined as follows. We first take a set of variables, $V = \{v_j \mid j \in \omega\}$, and the set of constants given by t, $C_t = \{c_i \mid t(i) = 0\}$. Let $K_t = V \cup C_t$.

(a) $L^t(0) = \{P_i(x_1, \ldots, x_{t(i)}) \mid t(i) > 0, x_1, \ldots, x_{t(i)} \in K_t\} \cup \{(x_1 = x_2) \mid x_1, x_2 \in K_t\}$.

(b) $L^t(n + 1) = L^t(n) \cup \{(F \vee G) \mid F, G \in L^t(n)\} \cup \{(\neg F) \mid F \in L^t(n)\} \cup \{((\exists v_j)F) \mid F \in L^t(n), v_j \in V\}$.

Then $L^t = \bigcup_{n<\omega} L^t(n)$.

We drop the parentheses in $(x_1 = x_2)$, $(F \vee G)$, $(\neg F)$, and $((\exists v_j)F)$, if this does not cause confusion. The above definition is deceptively simple due to its informality. Since we supposedly work within a model of set theory, all objects under discussion must be sets, and distinct sets must be created for each of the symbols discussed above. Having brought up this problem, we dismiss it with the comment that it can be solved, but its solution is neither enlightening nor essential to our purpose. Note, however, that the fact that all our symbols are distinct implies, for example, that $F \vee (G \vee H) \neq (F \vee G) \vee H$ for any $F, G, H \in L^t$.

DEFINITION 1.2.2. $L^t(0)$ is called the set of atomic formulas of L^t. We also set $F \wedge G = \neg(\neg F \vee \neg G)$, $(\forall v_j)F = \neg(\exists v_j)\neg F$, $F \to G = G \vee \neg F$, $F \leftrightarrow G = (F \to G) \wedge (G \to F)$, and the rank of F,

$$r(F) = \inf\{n \mid F \in L^t(n)\}.$$

L^t is called the set of formulas of type t.

THEOREM 1.2.3. (a) If $F, G \in L^t$, $v_j \in V$, then $\neg F$, $F \vee G$, $F \wedge G$, $(\exists v_j)F$, $(\forall v_j)F \in L^t$.

(b) $r(F \vee G) = \max\{r(F), r(G)\} + 1$, $r(\neg F) = r(F) + 1 = r((\exists v_j)F)$.

(c) If $\neg F = \neg G$, then $F = G$; if $F \vee G = F' \vee G'$, then $F = F'$ and $G = G'$; if $(\exists v_j)F = (\exists v_k)G$, then $j = k$ and $F = G$.

The proofs of (a) and (b) are left to the reader, while (c) is simply a restatement of part of the consequence of the fact that each of the formulas in L^t is represented by a distinct set.

Our language is completely unconnected with our structures in that we have no way as yet to decide whether a formula is true in a given structure. We connect them in such a way as to make the usual instincts of the mathematician hold. For example, let us look at the following formula,

$$(\forall v_0)((0 \leq v_0) \vee (v_1 \leq v_0) \vee \neg(v_2 \leq v_0)),\dagger$$

and the structure $\mathfrak{A} = \langle[-1, 1], \leq, 0\rangle$. We first note that the truth of the above formula depends on the values of v_1 and v_2. For example, if $v_1 = 1$, $v_2 = -1$, then let $v_0 = -1/2$. Thus $0 \nleq v_0$, $v_1 \nleq v_0$, and $v_2 \leq v_0$, so the formula is false (or should be, if our eventual definition is correct). However, it is true if $v_1 = -1, v_2 = 1$, for $v_1 \leq v_0$ is always true in this case.

Instead of discussing truth as a relation between formulas and structures, we must therefore discuss it as a relation between formulas, structures, and sequences of elements in domains of structures. In the above case, it is clear that we must consider at least $a_1, a_2 \in [-1, 1]$ to substitute for the variables v_1, v_2 before we may determine the truth of the formula; its truth might also be influenced by the value of a_0 to be substituted for v_0. Although this formula contains three variables, it is clear that formulas may be written with any finite number of variables, and that any number of elements from the domain may influence the truth of the formula. To state a definition for all formulas, we therefore consider countable sequences of elements in the domain.

Therefore, suppose we have a sequence $\langle a_0, a_1, \ldots\rangle = a \in [-1, 1]^\omega$, and would like to know whether the statement is true in $\mathfrak{A}$ at the sequence a. A mathematician might well first consider the parts of the formula, $0 \leq v_0$, $v_1 \leq v_0$, and $v_2 \leq v_0$ (note that these are atomic formulas), and say that these are true iff $0 \leq a_0$, $a_1 \leq a_0$, and $a_2 \leq a_0$. Then he might consider $(0 \leq v_0) \vee (v_1 \leq v_0) \vee \neg(v_2 \leq v_0)$ to be true iff $0 \leq a_0$ or $a_1 \leq a_0$ or $a_2 \nleq a_0$. Finally, he might in some way run through every possible choice of a_0 and say that our original formula holds on a iff $(0 \leq v_0) \vee (v_1 \leq v_0) \vee \neg(v_2 \leq v_0)$ holds on $\langle b, a_1, a_2, \ldots\rangle$ for every possible choice of $b \in [-1, 1]$.

The above procedure seems to be of an inductive nature, proceeding from the simple atomic formulas to the more complicated formulas, before arriving at the result for the entire formula. Since we have also defined our language in an inductive manner, an inductive definition here turns out to be natural.

† Strictly speaking, instead of $(0 \leq v_0)$, we should have $P(c, v_0)$ or some similar device, etc.

THEOREM 1.2.4. Let $t_{\mathfrak{A}} = t$. There is a unique function $\mathscr{V}^{\mathfrak{A}}: L^t \times A^\omega \to \{0, 1\}$ such that for $a \in A^\omega$:

(a) If $t(i) > 0$,
$\mathscr{V}^{\mathfrak{A}}(P_i(x_1, \ldots, x_{t(i)}), a) = 1$ iff $\langle b_1, \ldots, b_{t(i)} \rangle \in R_i$, where $b_k = a_j$ if $x_k = v_j$ and $b_k = R_m$ $(= e_m)$ if $x_k = c_m$;
$\mathscr{V}^{\mathfrak{A}}(P_i(x_1, \ldots, x_{t(i)}), a) = 0$ otherwise.
$\mathscr{V}^{\mathfrak{A}}(x_1 = x_2, a) = 1$ iff $b_1 = b_2$, where $b_k = a_j$ if $x_k = v_j$ and $b_k = e_m$ if $x_k = c_m$;
$\mathscr{V}^{\mathfrak{A}}(x_1 = x_2, a) = 0$ otherwise.
(b) $\mathscr{V}^{\mathfrak{A}}(\neg F, a) = 1 - \mathscr{V}^{\mathfrak{A}}(F, a)$.
(c) $\mathscr{V}^{\mathfrak{A}}(F \vee G, a) = \mathscr{V}^{\mathfrak{A}}(F, a) + \mathscr{V}^{\mathfrak{A}}(G, a) - \mathscr{V}^{\mathfrak{A}}(F, a)\mathscr{V}^{\mathfrak{A}}(G, a)$.
(d) $\mathscr{V}^{\mathfrak{A}}((\exists v_j)F, a) = \max\{\mathscr{V}^{\mathfrak{A}}(F, a(j \mid d)) \mid d \in A\}$, where

$$a(j \mid d)(n) = \begin{cases} d & \text{if } n = j \\ a_n & \text{if not} \end{cases}.$$

DEFINITION 1.2.5. $\mathscr{V}^{\mathfrak{A}}$ is called the truth function for $\mathfrak{A}$. We say that F holds in $\mathfrak{A}$ at a and write $\mathfrak{A} \models F[a]$ iff $\mathscr{V}^{\mathfrak{A}}(F, a) = 1$. If $\mathscr{V}^{\mathfrak{A}}(F, a) = 0$, then $\mathfrak{A} \not\models F[a]$.

Proof of the theorem: We first show that for every n there is a function $\mathscr{V}_n: L^t(n) \times A^\omega \to \{0, 1\}$ satisfying (a) through (d). For $n = 0$, define $\mathscr{V}_n$ by condition (a) and note that it satisfies (b) through (d) vacuously. Assuming that we have $\mathscr{V}_n$, define $\mathscr{V}_{n+1}$ as follows: $\mathscr{V}_{n+1} \mid L^t(n) \times A^\omega = \mathscr{V}_n$. For $F \in L^t(n + 1) \sim L^t(n)$, we have $F = \neg G$, $F = G \vee H$, or $F = (\exists v_j)G$ for some $G, H \in L^t(n)$. In these cases we define $\mathscr{V}_{n+1}(F, a)$ by the appropriate one of (b) through (d). Since G and H are unique in the above expressions, this may be done and will give us a function if $\mathscr{V}_n$ is one. But this is part of our induction hypothesis.

$\mathscr{V}_n$ is the only function $f: L^t(n) \times A^\omega \to \{0, 1\}$ satisfying (a) through (d), a fact also shown by induction as follows. If f is another such function, then if $n = 0$ (a) implies that $f = \mathscr{V}_0$. Assume now that $\mathscr{V}_n$ is unique, and let $f: L^t(n + 1) \times A^\omega \to \{0, 1\}$ satisfy the four conditions. Then $f \mid L^t(n) \times A^\omega = g$ also satisfies (a) through (d), therefore $g = \mathscr{V}_n$. Now by (b) through (d), $f = \mathscr{V}_{n+1}$.

Let $\mathscr{V}^{\mathfrak{A}} = \bigcup_{n<\omega} \mathscr{V}_n$. $\mathscr{V}^{\mathfrak{A}}$ is a function since if $n \le m$, $\mathscr{V}_n \subset \mathscr{V}_m$. $\mathscr{V}^{\mathfrak{A}}$ satisfies (a) because $\mathscr{V}^{\mathfrak{A}} \mid L^t(0) \times A^\omega = \mathscr{V}_0$. For (b), let $F = \neg G$. Then for some n, $G \in L^t(n)$ and $F \in L^t(n + 1)$. Thus

$$\mathscr{V}^{\mathfrak{A}}(F, a) = \mathscr{V}_{n+1}(F, a) = 1 - \mathscr{V}_{n+1}(G, a) = 1 - \mathscr{V}^{\mathfrak{A}}(G, a).$$

The remaining rules are shown similarly.

It is simple to check that $\mathfrak{A} \models (F \vee G)[a]$ iff $\mathfrak{A} \models F[a]$ or $\mathfrak{A} \models G[a]$; that $\mathfrak{A} \models (F \wedge G)[a]$ iff $\mathfrak{A} \models F[a]$ and $\mathfrak{A} \models G[a]$; that $\mathfrak{A} \models (\forall v_j)F[a]$ iff for every $b \in A$, $\mathfrak{A} \models F[a(j \mid b))]$; and similar well-known facts. A list of some of these facts is given in Problem 1.2.1 following.

The truth value of a formula on a point of A^ω need not depend on the point. For example,

$$(\forall v_0)(\forall v_1)((v_0 \leq v_1) \vee (v_1 \leq v_0))$$

is a formula that is simply satisfied by the structure $\mathfrak{A} = \langle A, \leq \rangle$ independently of our point in A^ω. We note that each of the variables is quantified and none free to affect the truth of the formula, a notion we now formalize.

Definition 1.2.6. Let $F \in L^t$. $FV(F)$ is the set defined inductively as follows:

(a) $FV(P_i(x_1, \ldots, x_{t(i)})) = \{x_1, \ldots, x_{t(i)}\} \cap V$,
$FV(x_1 = x_2) = \{x_1, x_2\} \cap V$.
(b) $FV(\neg F) = FV(F)$.
(c) $FV(F \vee G) = FV(F) \cup FV(G)$.
(d) $FV((\exists v_j)F) = FV(F) \sim \{v_j\}$.

$FV(F)$ is called the set of free variables of F, and if $FV(F) = \phi$, then F is called a sentence. We let Σ^t stand for the set of sentences in L^t, that is,

$$\Sigma^t = \{F \in L^t \mid FV(F) = \phi\}.$$

$BV(F)$, the set of bound variables of F, is defined inductively by

(a′) $BV(x_2 = x_2) = BV(P_i(x_1, \ldots, x_{t(i)})) = \phi$;
(b), (c) analogous to (b), (c) of the definition of $FV(F)$; and
(d′) $BV((\exists v_j)F) = BV(F) \cup \{v_j\}$.

$V(F) = BV(F) \cup FV(F)$, and is called the set of variables of F, while $C(F)$, the set of constants of F is defined inductively by

(a″) $C(P_i(x_1, \ldots, x_{t(i)})) = \{x_1, \ldots, x_{t(i)}\} \cap C_t$,
$C(x_1 = x_2) = \{x_1, x_2\} \cap C_t$;
(b), (c) analogous to (b), (c) of the definition of $FV(F)$; and
(d″) $C((\exists v_j)F) = C(F)$.

Intuitively, a variable is free if it is unquantified somewhere in a formula, bound if it is quantified somewhere in a formula. Note that a variable may be both free and bound, as are v_1 and v_2 in

$$(\exists v_1)(v_1 = v_2) \wedge (\exists v_2)(v_1 = v_2).$$

We now show that the free variables are the only ones "free" to change the truth value of a formula.

THEOREM 1.2.7. Let $a, b \in A^\omega$, $F \in L^t$, and suppose $a_j = b_j$ for $v_j \in FV(F)$. Then $\mathfrak{A} \models F[a]$ iff $\mathfrak{A} \models F[b]$.

Proof: If F is atomic, then for some i, $F = P_i(x_1, \ldots, x_{t(i)})$ or $F = (x_1 = x_2)$. In the first case, $\mathfrak{A} \models F[a]$ iff $\langle d_1, \ldots, d_{t(i)} \rangle \in R_i$, where $d_k = a_j$ if $x_k = v_j$ and $d_k = e_m$ if $x_k = c_m$. Also $\mathfrak{A} \models F[b]$ iff

$$\langle f_1, \ldots, f_{t(i)} \rangle \in R_i,$$

where $f_k = b_j$ if $x_k = v_j$ and $f_k = e_m$ if $x_k = c_m$. But

$$FV(F) = \{x_1, \ldots, x_{t(i)}\} \cap V,$$

so if $x_k = v_j$, then $a_j = b_j$, so $f_k = d_k$. Otherwise $f_k = e_m = d_k$, so

$$\langle d_1, \ldots, d_{t(i)} \rangle = \langle f_1, \ldots, f_{t(i)} \rangle.$$

Thus in this case $\mathfrak{A} \models F[a]$ iff $\mathfrak{A} \models F[b]$. The proof in the case $F = (x_1 = x_2)$ is similar.

If $r(F) = n + 1$, then $F = \neg G$, $G \vee H$, or $(\exists v_j)G$, with $G, H \in L^t(n)$. Assume now that $F = G \vee H$. Then $\mathfrak{A} \models F[a]$ iff $\mathfrak{A} \models G[a]$ or $\mathfrak{A} \models H[a]$. Since $FV(F) = FV(G) \cup FV(H)$, we must have $a_j = b_j$ for $v_j \in FV(G)$ or $v_j \in FV(H)$. Thus by induction, $\mathfrak{A} \models G[a]$ or $\mathfrak{A} \models H[a]$ iff $\mathfrak{A} \models G[b]$ or $\mathfrak{A} \models H[b]$. The case $F = \neg G$ is done similarly. Finally, if $F = (\exists v_j)G$, then $\mathfrak{A} \models F[a]$ iff for some $d \in A$, $\mathfrak{A} \models G[a(j \mid d)]$. Now consider $b(j \mid d)$. We know that

$$a_h = b_h \qquad \text{for } v_h \in FV(F) = FV(G) \sim \{v_j\}.$$

Thus

$$a(j \mid d)_h = b(j \mid d)_h \qquad \text{for} \quad v_h \in FV(G)$$

so $\mathfrak{A} \models G[a(j \mid d)]$ iff $\mathfrak{A} \models G[b(j \mid d)]$, thus $\mathfrak{A} \models F[a]$ iff $\mathfrak{A} \models F[b]$.

The formula $(\forall v_0)((0 \leq v_0) \vee (v_1 \leq v_0) \vee \neg(v_2 \leq v_0))$ studied earlier has free variables v_1, v_2, and thus the choice of a_0 in the sequence $a \in A^\omega$ does not affect its truth.

COROLLARY 1.2.8. If $F \in \Sigma^t$ then for any a, $b \in A^\omega$, $\mathfrak{A} \models F[a]$ iff $\mathfrak{A} \models F[b]$.

DEFINITION 1.2.9. If $F \in L^t$, we say that $\mathfrak{A}$ satisfies F, and we write $\mathfrak{A} \models F$ iff for every $a \in A^\omega$, $\mathfrak{A} \models F[a]$. Otherwise $\mathfrak{A} \not\models F$. If $S \subset L^t$, we write $\mathfrak{A} \models S$ iff for every $F \in S$, $\mathfrak{A} \models F$, and in this case we say $\mathfrak{A}$ satisfies S. For $F \in L^t$, if

$$FV(F) \subset \{v_{j_1}, \ldots, v_{j_n}\} \qquad \text{and} \qquad a \in A^\omega,$$

we may write $\mathfrak{A} \models F[a_{j_1}, \ldots, a_{j_n}]$ in place of $\mathfrak{A} \models F[a]$.

By Corollary 1.2.8 if $F \in \Sigma^t$, $\mathfrak{A}$ of type t, then $\mathfrak{A} \models F$ or $\mathfrak{A} \models \neg F$. This does not hold for arbitrary $F \in L^t$.

DEFINITION 1.2.10. If $S \subset L^t$, $F \in L^t$, we write $S \models F$ and say that S implies F (semantically) iff whenever $\mathfrak{A} \models S$ then $\mathfrak{A} \models F$. If S, $T \subset L^t$, $S \models T$ iff for every $F \in T$, $S \models F$; and in this case we say that S implies T (semantically).

If $S \subset T \subset \Sigma^t$ and $S \models T$, S is called a set of axioms for T.

If for some $\mathfrak{A}$, $\mathfrak{A} \models S$, then S is called (semantically) consistent. Otherwise S is called (semantically) inconsistent.

THEOREM 1.2.11. $f\colon \mathfrak{A} \to \mathfrak{B}$ is an isomorphism iff for every $F \in L^t$, $a \in A^\omega$, $\mathfrak{A} \models F[a]$ iff $\mathfrak{B} \models F[f \circ a]$ (iff for every $F \in L^t(0)$, $a \in A^\omega$, $\mathfrak{A} \models F[a]$ iff $\mathfrak{B} \models F[f \circ a]$), and f is onto.

THEOREM 1.2.12. Let $f\colon A \to B$. Then f is a homomorphism iff for every atomic formula F and every $a \in A^\omega$, if $\mathfrak{A} \models F[a]$, then $\mathfrak{B} \models F[f \circ a]$.

The proofs of the above are left for the reader. We consider below two notions often useful in considerations involving our language. First, the idea of a subformula.

DEFINITION 1.2.13. $SF(F)$, the set of subformulas of F, is defined inductively as follows:

(a) If $r(F) = 0$, then $SF(F) = \{F\}$.
(b) $SF(\neg F) = SF(F) \cup \{\neg F\}$.
(c) $SF(F \vee G) = SF(F) \cup SF(G) \cup \{F \vee G\}$.
(d) $SF((\exists v_j)F) = SF(F) \cup \{(\exists v_j)F\}$.

Next, the idea of substituting for constants and free variables in a formula.

DEFINITION 1.2.14. Let $\varphi\colon K_t \to K_t$. Then $Sb_\varphi F$ is defined inductively as follows:

(a) $Sb_\varphi P_i(x_1, \ldots, x_{t(i)}) = P_i(\varphi(x_1), \ldots, \varphi(x_{t(i)}))$ if $t(i) > 0$,
$Sb_\varphi(x_1 = x_2) = (\varphi(x_1) = \varphi(x_2))$.
(b) $Sb_\varphi(F \vee G) = Sb_\varphi F \vee Sb_\varphi G$.
(c) $Sb_\varphi \neg F = \neg Sb_\varphi F$.
(d) $Sb_\varphi(\exists v_j)F = (\exists v_j)Sb_\psi F$, where $\psi = (\varphi \sim \{\langle v_j, \varphi(v_j)\rangle\}) \cup \{\langle v_j, v_j\rangle\}$.

If ψ is a function and $\mathscr{D}\psi \subset K_t$, $\mathscr{R}\psi \subset K_t$, then

$$Sb_\psi F = Sb_\varphi F, \qquad \text{where} \quad \varphi = \psi \cup \{\langle x, x\rangle \mid x \in K_t \sim \mathscr{D}\psi\}.$$

If $x_1, \ldots, x_n, y_1, \ldots, y_n \in K_t$, then

$$Sb_{y_1,\ldots,y_n}^{x_1,\ldots,x_n} F = Sb_\psi F, \qquad \text{where} \quad \psi = \{\langle x_1, y_1\rangle, \ldots, \langle x_n, y_n\rangle\}.$$

If $\varphi[V] \subset V$ and for $c \in C_t$, $\varphi(c) = c$, then $Rp_\varphi F$ is defined inductively by (a) through (c) above and

(d′) $Rp_\varphi(\exists v_j)F = (\exists\varphi(v_j))Rp_\varphi F.$

The two conventions adopted following (d) above are used for Rp as well.

Note that if $F \in \Sigma^t$ and $\varphi(c) = c$ for every $c \in C(F)$ then $Sb_\varphi F = F$.

THEOREM 1.2.15. Let $\mathfrak{A}$ be of type t, $\varphi: K_t \to K_t$ and define $\varphi^*: A^\omega \to A^\omega$ by

$$\varphi^*(a)(m) = \begin{cases} e_i & \text{if } \varphi(v_m) = c_i \\ a_k & \text{if } \varphi(v_m) = v_k\,. \end{cases}$$

If $\varphi(c) = c$ for every $c \in C(F)$ and $\varphi[FV(F)] \cap BV(F) = \phi$, $F \in L^t$, then $\mathfrak{A} \models Sb_\varphi F[a]$ iff $\mathfrak{A} \models F[\varphi^*(a)]$.

Proof: If $F = P_i(x_1, \ldots, x_{t(i)})$, then $Sb_\varphi F = P_i(\varphi(x_1), \ldots, \varphi(x_{t(i)}))$, so $\mathfrak{A} \models Sb_\varphi F[a]$ iff $\langle b_1, \ldots, b_{t(i)}\rangle \in R_i$, where $b_n = a_k$ if $\varphi(x_n) = v_k$, $b_n = e_i$ if $\varphi(x_n) = c_i$; $\mathfrak{A} \models F[\varphi^*(a)]$ iff $\langle d_1, \ldots, d_{t(i)}\rangle \in R_i$, where $d_n = \varphi^*(a)(m)$ if $x_n = v_m$ and $d_n = e_i$ if $x_n = c_i$. But if $x_n = v_m$, $\varphi(x_n) = v_k$, then $d_n = \varphi^*(a)(m) = a_k = b_n$; if $x_n = v_m$, $\varphi(x_n) = c_i$, then $d_n = \varphi^*(a)(m) = e_i = b_n$; and if $x_n = c_i$, then $\varphi(x_n) = c_i$; so $d_n = e_i = b_n$, thus $\langle b_1, \ldots, b_{t(i)}\rangle = \langle d_1, \ldots, d_{t(i)}\rangle$, so $\mathfrak{A} \models Sb_\varphi F[a]$ iff $\mathfrak{A} \models F[\varphi^*(a)]$, and the case $F = (x_1 = x_2)$ is similar.

If $F = G \vee H$, $\mathfrak{A} \models Sb_\varphi F[a]$ iff $\mathfrak{A} \models (Sb_\varphi G \vee Sb_\varphi H)[a]$ iff $\mathfrak{A} \models Sb_\varphi G[a]$ or $\mathfrak{A} \models Sb_\varphi H[a]$ iff $\mathfrak{A} \models G[\varphi^*(a)]$ or $\mathfrak{A} \models H[\varphi^*(a)]$ iff $\mathfrak{A} \models F[\varphi^*(a)]$, and the case $F = \neg G$ is similar.

For $F = (\exists v_j)H$ we first look at $\psi^*(a(j \mid d))$, $\varphi^*(a)(j \mid d)$, ψ as in Definition 1.2.14 (d). If $m = j$, then

$$\psi^*(a(j \mid d))(m) = d = \varphi^*(a)(j \mid d)(m);$$

if $m \neq j$ and $\varphi(v_m) = c_i$, then

$$\psi^*(a(j \mid d))(m) = e_i = \varphi^*(a)(j \mid d)(m),$$

and if $m \neq j$ and $\varphi(v_m) = v_k$, $k \neq j$ then

$$\psi^*(a(j \mid d))(m) = a_k = \varphi^*(a)(j \mid d)(m).$$

Thus

$$\psi^*(a(j \mid d))(m) = \varphi^*(a)(j \mid d)(m)$$

whenever $m = j$ or $\varphi(v_m) \neq v_j$, so if we never have $\varphi(v_m) = v_j$ for

$$v_m \in FV(H) \sim \{v_j\} = FV(F)$$

then $\mathfrak{A} \models H[\psi^*(a(j \mid d))]$ iff $\mathfrak{A} \models H[\varphi^*(a)(j \mid d)]$. Thus since

$$\varphi[FV(F)] \cap BV(F) = \phi,$$

$\mathfrak{A} \models Sb_\varphi F[a]$ iff $\mathfrak{A} \models (\exists v_j)Sb_\psi H[a]$ iff for some $d \in A$, $\mathfrak{A} \models Sb_\psi H[a(j \mid d)]$ iff for some $d \in A$, $\mathfrak{A} \models H[\psi^*(a(j \mid d))]$ iff for some $d \in A$,

$$\mathfrak{A} \models H[\varphi^*(a)(j \mid d)] \quad \text{iff} \quad \mathfrak{A} \models F[\varphi^*(a)].$$

While the above theorem does not deal with every possible substitution, it discusses those we shall be using. For later work wc also need the following more special results.

Corollary 1.2.16. (a) If $\mathfrak{A}$ is of type t, $F \in L^t$, $a \in A^\omega$, then

$$\mathfrak{A} \models Sb^{v_{j_1},\ldots,v_{j_n}}_{c_{i_1},\ldots,c_{i_n}} F[a] \qquad \text{iff} \quad \mathfrak{A} \models F[a(j_1 \mid e_{i_1}) \cdots (j_n \mid e_{i_n})].$$

(b) If $\mathfrak{A}$ is of type t, $F \in L^t$, $a \in A^\omega$, and, for $p = 1, \ldots, n$, if $v_{j_p} \in FV(F)$, then $v_{k_p} \notin BV(F)$, then

$$\mathfrak{A} \models Sb^{v_{j_1},\ldots,v_{j_n}}_{v_{k_1},\ldots,v_{k_n}} F[a] \qquad \text{iff} \quad \mathfrak{A} \models F[a(j_1 \mid a_{k_1}) \cdots (j_n \mid a_{k_n})].$$

(c) Let $t \subset t'$, $i_1, \ldots, i_n \in \mathscr{D}t' \sim \mathscr{D}t$ all be distinct, $t'(i_k) = 0$ for $k = 1, \ldots, n$, $S \subset \Sigma^t$, and $F \in L^t$. Then

$$S \models F \qquad \text{iff} \quad S \models Sb^{v_{j_1},\ldots,v_{j_n}}_{c_{i_1},\ldots,c_{i_n}} F,$$

and if $G \in \Sigma^t$, then

$$S \models (Sb^{v_{j_1},\ldots,v_{j_n}}_{c_{i_1},\ldots,c_{i_n}} F) \rightarrow G \qquad \text{iff} \quad S \models F \rightarrow G.$$

Proof: (a), (b) are special cases of Theorem 1.2.15. For (c), let

$$\varphi(x) = x \qquad \text{for} \quad x \in K_{t'} \sim \{v_{j_1}, \ldots, v_{j_n}\},$$
$$\varphi(v_{j_p}) = c_{i_p} \qquad \text{for} \quad p = 1, \ldots, n.$$

Let $S \models Sb_\varphi F$, $a \in A^\omega$, $\mathfrak{A} = \langle A, R_i \rangle_{i \in I} \models S$, $\mathfrak{A}' = \langle A, R_i, S_k \rangle_{i \in I, k \in I' \sim I}$, $S_{i_j} = a_{i_j}$ for $1 \leq j \leq n$. $\mathfrak{A}' \models S$ by Problem 1.2.10, thus $\mathfrak{A}' \models Sb_\varphi F[a]$; so by Theorem 1.2.15, $\mathfrak{A}' \models F[\varphi^*(a)] = F[a]$; so by Problem 1.2.10 $\mathfrak{A} \models F[a]$; therefore $S \models F$. Conversely, let $S \models F$, $\mathfrak{B} = \langle B, S_i \rangle_{i \in I'}$ be of type t', $\mathfrak{B} \models S$, $a \in B^\omega$. By Problem 1.2.10, $\mathfrak{B} \models F[\varphi^*(a)]$ so $\mathfrak{B} \models Sb_\varphi F[a]$ by Theorem 1.2.15; therefore $S \models Sb_\varphi F$.

Now $S \models F \to G$ iff $S \models Sb_\varphi(F \to G)$, but

$$Sb_\varphi(F \to G) = Sb_\varphi G \vee Sb_\varphi \neg F = Sb_\varphi G \vee \neg Sb_\varphi F = Sb_\varphi F \to Sb_\varphi G$$

and by comments following Definition 1.2.14, $Sb_\varphi G = G$, thus

$$Sb_\varphi(F \to G) = (Sb_\varphi F) \to G.$$

PROPOSITION 1.2.17. Let φ be one-one and as in the definition of $Rp_\varphi F$. Then for $F \in L^t$, $\mathfrak{A}$ of type t, $a \in A^\omega$,

$$\mathfrak{A} \models Rp_\varphi F[a] \quad \text{iff} \quad \mathfrak{A} \models F[\varphi^*(a)].$$

Proof: We use induction with all parts except that involving $\exists$ identical to corresponding parts of the proof of Theorem 1.2.15. For that part, let $\varphi(v_j) = v_k$. If $m \in \omega$, $\varphi(v_m) = v_p$, then

$$\varphi^*(a)(j \mid d)(m) = \begin{cases} d & \text{if } m = j \\ a_p & \text{if } m \neq j, \end{cases}$$

$$\varphi^*(a(k \mid d))(m) = a(k \mid d)(p) = \begin{cases} d & \text{if } p = k \\ a_p & \text{if } p \neq k. \end{cases}$$

But for φ one-one, $m = j$ iff $p = k$, so

$$\varphi^*(a)(j \mid d) = \varphi^*(a(k \mid d)).$$

Now we have $\mathfrak{A} \models Rp_\varphi(\exists v_j)H[a]$ iff $\mathfrak{A} \models (\exists \varphi(v_j))Rp_\varphi H[a]$ iff $\mathfrak{A} \models (\exists v_k)Rp_\varphi H[a]$ iff for some $d \in A$, $\mathfrak{A} \models Rp_\varphi H[a(k \mid d)]$ iff for some $d \in A$, $\mathfrak{A} \models H[\varphi^*(a(k \mid d))]$ iff for some $d \in A$, $\mathfrak{A} \models H[\varphi^*(a)(j \mid d)]$ iff $\mathfrak{A} \models (\exists v_j)H[\varphi^*(a)]$.

When discussing groups, one often writes the associative law as follows:

$$(\forall v_0)(\forall v_1)(\forall v_2)(v_0(v_1 v_2) = (v_0 v_1)v_2).$$

This is not a formula of the language $L^{\langle 3,0\rangle}$ (or of any of our L^t) but its idea can be expressed within the language (and we suggest that the reader attempt this before proceeding). We now develop an extended language and relate it to the ideas we have presented in this section.

Assume now that we have a type t with domain I and a $J \subset I$ such that if $i \in J$ then $t(i) > 1$. Let $K_t' = \bigcup_{n<\omega} K(n)$, where $K(0) = K_t$ and

$$K(n+1) = K(n) \cup \{f_i(y_1, \ldots, y_{t(i)-1}) \mid y_1, \ldots, y_{t(i)-1} \in K(n), i \in J\}.$$

Then L'^t is defined as L^t is, with K_t' used in place of K_t (note that the $f_i(y_1, \ldots, y_{t(i)-1})$ are simply symbols like the v_n and c_i).

For $y \in K_t'$ we define VAR(y) inductively as follows: VAR(c_i) $= \phi$ for $t(i) = 0$, VAR(v_n) $= \{v_n\}$, and if

$$y = f_i(y_1, \ldots, y_{t(i)-1})$$

with

$$y_1, \ldots, y_{t(i)-1} \in K(n)$$

and VAR defined on $K(n)$, then

$$\mathrm{VAR}(y) = \bigcup_{k=1}^{t(i)-1} \mathrm{VAR}(y_k).$$

Once again by induction we define a mapping $g\colon L'^t \to L^t$ such that $g \mid L^t = \mathfrak{I}_{L^t}$, and

(i) for $y \in K(n + 1) \sim K(n)$, $v_j \notin \mathrm{VAR}(y)$, let

$$m = \max(\{j\} \cup \{n \mid v_n \in \mathrm{VAR}(y)\}).$$

Then

$$g(v_j = y) = (\exists v_{m+1}) \cdots (\exists v_{m+t(i)-1}) \, (g(v_{m+1} = y_1) \wedge \cdots \wedge g(v_{m+t(i)-1} = y_{t(i)-1}) \wedge P_i(v_{m+1}, \ldots, v_{m+t(i)-1}, v_j)),$$

where

$$y = f_i(y_1, \ldots, y_{t(i)-1}).$$

For $y_1, y_2 \in K_t' \sim V$, y_1 or $y_2 \notin K_t$,

$$g(y_1 = y_2) = (\exists v_r)(g(v_r = y_1) \wedge g(v_r = y_2))$$

for the first r such that $v_r \notin \mathrm{VAR}(y_1) \cup \mathrm{VAR}(y_2)$, and if

$$m = \max\left\{n \mid v_n \in \bigcup_{k=1}^{t(i)} \mathrm{VAR}(y_k)\right\},$$

then

$$g(P_i(y_1, \ldots, y_{t(i)})) = (\exists v_{m+1}) \cdots (\exists v_{m+t(i)})(g(v_{m+1} = y_1) \wedge \cdots \wedge g(v_{m+t(i)} = y_{t(i)}) \wedge P_i(v_{m+1}, \ldots, v_{m+t(i)}))$$

(ii) $g(\neg F) = \neg g(F)$.
(iii) $g(F \vee G) = g(F) \vee g(G)$.
(iv) $g((\exists v_j)F) = (\exists v_j)g(F)$.

Now define $\mathfrak{A} \models F[a]$ iff $\mathfrak{A} \models g(F)[a]$ for $\mathfrak{A} \in M^t$, $a \in A^\omega$, $F \in L'^t$.

Assume that for each $i \in J$, R_i is an operation on A, $\mathfrak{A} = \langle A, R_i \rangle_{i \in I}$, and for $i \in J$ denote by $R_i^*(a_1, \ldots, a_{t(i)-1})$ the unique $b \in A$ such that $\langle a_1, \ldots, a_{t(i)-1}, b \rangle \in R_i$. For $a \in A^\omega$, $y \in K_t'$, we define $y(a)$ inductively as follows: $v_n(a) = a_n$; $c_i(a) = e_i$; and, if $y = f_i(y_1, \ldots, y_{t(i)-1})$, $i \in J$, then

$$y(a) = R_i^*(y_1(a), \ldots, y_{t(i)-1}(a)).$$

In Problem 1.2.9 the reader shows for $F \in L'^t$ that

(i′) $\mathfrak{A} \models (y_1 = y_2)[a]$ iff $y_1(a) = y_2(a)$,
$\mathfrak{A} \models P_i(y_1, \ldots, y_{t(i)})[a]$ iff $\langle y_1(a), \ldots, y_{t(i)}(a) \rangle \in R_i$.

(ii′) $\mathfrak{A} \models (\neg F)[a]$ iff not $\mathfrak{A} \models F[a]$.
(iii′) $\mathfrak{A} \models F \vee G[a]$ iff $\mathfrak{A} \models F[a]$ or $\mathfrak{A} \models G[a]$.
(iv′) $\mathfrak{A} \models (\exists v_j)F[a]$ iff for some $b \in A$, $\mathfrak{A} \models F[a(j \mid b)]$.

In the future we shall occasionally write formulas of L'^t; however, we shall always mean their counterparts in L^t. We shall not study L'^t since facts about it are immediate (using g) from facts about L^t.

Problems

‡1.2.1 (a) Check the following facts about $\models$:

(i) $\mathfrak{A} \models (F \vee G)[a]$ iff $\mathfrak{A} \models F[a]$ or $\mathfrak{A} \models G[a]$.
(ii) $\mathfrak{A} \models P_i(v_1, \ldots, v_{t(i)})[a]$ iff $\langle a_1, \ldots, a_{t(i)} \rangle \in R_i$.
(iii) $\mathfrak{A} \models \neg F[a]$ iff $\mathfrak{A} \not\models F[a]$.
(iv) If $\mathfrak{A} \models (F \to G)[a]$ and $\mathfrak{A} \models F[a]$, then $\mathfrak{A} \models G[a]$.
(v) $\mathfrak{A} \models (\forall v_j)F[a]$ iff for every $b \in A$, $\mathfrak{A} \models F[a(j \mid b)]$.

(b) Also formulate and check other properties you would expect to hold.

‡1.2.2 Let $F, G \in L^t$, $S, T, U \subset \Sigma^t$, and check:
(a) $S \models F \wedge G$ iff $S \models F$ and $S \models G$.
(b) $S \models (F \to G)$ iff $S \cup \{F\} \models G$, provided $F \in \Sigma^t$.
(c) If $S \models T$ and $T \models U$, then $S \models U$.
(d) If $S \subset T$ and $S \models F$, then $T \models F$.
(e) If $S \models (G \to F)$ and $v_j \notin FV(F)$, $S \models ((\exists v_j)G \to F)$.

1.2.3 (a) If $S, T \subset \Sigma^t$, T is consistent and $T \models S$, then S is consistent.
(b) T is consistent iff for some $F \in \Sigma^t$, $T \not\models F$.

‡1.2.4 Let $S \subset \Sigma^t$. Show that $\equiv_S$ is an equivalence relation on L^t, where for $F, G \in L^t$, $F \equiv_S G$ iff $S \models (F \leftrightarrow G)$. Let $(F)_S = \{G \mid F \equiv_S G\}$ and show that if $(F)_S = (F')_S$ and $(G)_S = (G')_S$, then

(a) $(F \wedge G)_S = (F' \wedge G')_S$;
(b) $(F \vee G)_S = (F' \vee G')_S$;
(c) $(\neg F)_S = (\neg F')_S$;
(d) $((\exists v_j)F)_S = ((\exists v_j)F')_S$;

and that $L^t/\equiv_S$ is a Boolean algebra with respect to

$$(F)_S \vee (G)_S = (F \vee G)_S;$$
$$(F)_S \wedge (G)_S = (F \wedge G)_S;$$
$$-(F)_S = (\neg F)_S.$$

Show that S is consistent iff for some $F, G \in \Sigma^t$, $F \not\equiv_S G$.

‡1.2.5 Show that if t is finite, $c(L^t) = c(\Sigma^t) = \omega$, and show that if t is infinite, $c(L^t) = c(\Sigma^t) = c(t)$.

‡1.2.6 Show that if $t_{\mathfrak{A}} = t$, and $F \in \Sigma^t$, then $\mathfrak{A} \models F$ or $\mathfrak{A} \models \neg F$, and not both. Now give an example of an $S \subset \Sigma^t$, $F \in \Sigma^t$ such that $S \not\models F$ and $S \not\models \neg F$.

‡1.2.7 If $F \in SF(G)$ and $G \in SF(F)$, show that $F = G$.

‡1.2.8 (a) If $v_j \notin FV(F)$, $F \in L^t$, $S \subset \Sigma^t$, show that $S \models (F <\!\!-\!\!> (\exists v_j)F)$ and $S \models (F <\!\!-\!\!> (\forall v_j)F)$.

(b) If for every $\mathfrak{A}$ such that $\mathfrak{A} \models S$ and every $a \in A^\omega$, $b, c \in A$, $\mathfrak{A} \models F[a(j \mid b)]$ iff $\mathfrak{A} \models F[a(j \mid c)]$, show that there is a $G \in L^t$ such that $v_j \notin FV(G)$ and $F \equiv_S G$.

(c) Let $\mathfrak{A} \models F[a]$ iff $\mathfrak{A} \models F[b]$ for every $\mathfrak{A}$ with $t_{\mathfrak{A}} = t$, $a, b \in A^\omega$. Then for some $G \in \Sigma^t$, $F \equiv_\phi G$. (NOTE: This is generally abbreviated $F \equiv G$.)

‡1.2.9 Prove assertions (i′) to (iv′) at the end of the text of Section 1.2.

‡1.2.10 Let $t \subset t'$, both types, $\mathscr{D}(t) = I$, $\mathscr{D}(t') = I'$, and suppose that $S \subset L^t$ and $\mathfrak{A}$ is of type t. For each $i' \in I' \sim I$, let $R_{i'} \in A$ if $t'(i') = 0$, $R_i \subset A^{t'(i')}$ if $t'(i') > 0$. Show that $\langle A, R_i \rangle_{i \in I'} \models S$ iff $\mathfrak{A} \models S$. Thus for $S \subset \Sigma^t$, $F \in L^t$, show that $S \models F$ iff for each $\mathfrak{A}$ of type t', if $\mathfrak{A} \models S$, then $\mathfrak{A} \models F$.

‡1.2.11 Let $X \subset A$ contain all distinguished elements of $\mathfrak{A} = \langle A, R_i \rangle_{i \in I}$, $t_{\mathfrak{A}} = t$. Let $I' = I \cup \{i'\}$, $i' \notin I$, $t' = t \cup \{\langle i', 1 \rangle\}$, and consider $\mathfrak{A}' = \langle A, R_i \rangle_{i \in I'}$ with $R_{i'} = X$. Show that $\mathfrak{A} \mid X \models F[a]$ for $F \in L^t$, $a \in X^\omega$, iff $\mathfrak{A}' \models F_X[a]$, where

$$(x_1 = x_2)_X = P_{i'}(x_1) \wedge P_{i'}(x_2) \wedge (x_1 = x_2);$$
$$P_i(x_1, \ldots, x_{t(i)})_X = P_{i'}(x_1) \wedge \ldots \wedge P_{i'}(x_{t(i)}) \wedge P_i(x_1, \ldots, x_{t(i)});$$
$$(\neg F)_X = \neg(F_X);$$
$$(F \vee G)_X = (F_X) \vee (G_X); \text{ and}$$
$$((\exists v_j)F)_X = (\exists v_j)(P_{i'}(v_j) \wedge F_X).$$

‡1.2.12 Let $\mathfrak{A}$ be of type t, E an equivalence relation on A, $F \in L^t$, $I' = I \cup \{i'\}$, $i' \notin I$, $t' = t \cup \{\langle i', 2 \rangle\}$, $R_{i'} = E$, $\mathfrak{A}' = \langle A, R_i \rangle_{i \in I'}$. For $a \in A^\omega$ let $a' \in (A/E)^\omega$ be defined by letting a'_k be the equivalence class of a_k mod E. For $F \in L^t$, we define $F_E \in L^{t'}$ by induction:

$$(x_1 = x_2)_E = P_{i'}(x_1, x_2),$$

$$P_i(x_1, \ldots, x_{t(i)}) = (\exists v_{n+1}) \ldots (\exists v_{n+t(i)})(P_{i'}(x_1, v_{n+1}) \wedge \ldots \wedge P_{i'}(x_{t(i)}, v_{n+t(i)}) \wedge P_i(v_{n+1}, \ldots, v_{n+t(i)})),$$

where n is the largest integer such that

$$v_n \in FV(P_i(x_1, \ldots, x_{t(i)})),$$
$$(\neg F)_E = \neg(F_E),$$
$$(F \vee G)_E = (F_E) \vee (G_E),$$

and

$$((\exists v_j)F)_E = (\exists v_j)(F_E).$$

Show that $\mathfrak{A}' \models F_E[a]$ iff $\mathfrak{A}/E \models F[a']$, where $\mathfrak{A}/E$ is as defined in Problem 1.1.10.

1.2.13 Show that Theorem 1.2.15 would be false if the condition $\varphi[FV(F)] \cap BV(F) = \phi$ or the condition $\varphi(c) = c$ for every $c \in C(F)$ were removed, and that Proposition 1.2.17 would be false if the condition "φ is one–one" were removed.

‡1.2.14 Let φ be as in the definition of $Rp_\varphi F$ (thus $Sb_\varphi F$ is also defined). Show that

(a) $FV(Sb_\varphi F) \subset \varphi[FV(F)]$ and $FV(Rp_\varphi F) \subset \varphi[FV(F)]$.

(b) $BV(Rp_\varphi F) = \varphi[BV(F)]$, $BV(Sb_\varphi F) = BV(F)$.

‡1.2.15 If $F \in L^t$, $FV(F) = \{v_{j_1}, \ldots, v_{j_n}\}$, show that $\mathfrak{A} \models F$ iff $\mathfrak{A} \models (\forall v_{j_1}) \ldots (\forall v_{j_n})F$.

1.3 Elementary Classes

In the remainder of the book, $M^t = \{\mathfrak{A} \mid t_\mathfrak{A} = t\}$.

DEFINITION 1.3.1. Let $K \subset M^t$. K is an elementary class iff for some $F \in \Sigma^t$,

$$K = M(F) = \{\mathfrak{A} \in M^t \mid \mathfrak{A} \models F\}.$$

K is an elementary class in the wider sense iff for some $S \subset \Sigma^t$,

$$K = M(S) - \{\mathfrak{A} \in M^t \mid \mathfrak{A} \models S\}.$$

If $K = M(S)$, then S is called a set of axioms for K.

NOTATION. The fact that K is an elementary class is often denoted by $K \in EC$, although this notation is improper since K is usually a proper class, and thus cannot be an element of any class. The fact that K is an elementary class in the wider sense is often denoted by $K \in EC_\Delta$. Sometimes EC^t, EC^t_Δ are used instead to indicate the type under discussion.

Examples: The class of all groups $\mathscr{G}$ is the class of models of the following sentence. (NOTE. If $\mathfrak{A} \in M(S)$, then we call $\mathfrak{A}$ a model of S.)

$$F = (\forall v_0)(\forall v_1)(\forall v_2)((v_0v_1)v_2 = v_0(v_1v_2)) \wedge (\forall v_0)(v_0c = cv_0 = v_0) \wedge (\forall v_0)(\exists v_1)(v_0v_1 = v_1v_0 = c)$$

(this abbreviates a formula of $L^{\langle 3,0\rangle}$, see Problem 1.2.9).

The classes of all fields, all Abelian groups, all rings (with or without identity), integral domains, ordered sets, groups, or fields, the class of all fields of characteristic p ($p > 0$), and many other classes can also be shown to be elementary classes simply by writing down axioms for them.

The class $\mathscr{F}_0$ of all fields of characteristic 0 is an elementary class in the wider sense, which we now check by writing axioms for this class. Our structures will be of the form $\mathfrak{F} = \langle F, +, \cdot, 0, 1\rangle$, of type $\langle 3, 3, 0, 0\rangle$, and our axioms in $L^{\langle 3,3,0,0\rangle}$ are

(f1) $(\forall v_0)(\forall v_1)(\forall v_2)(v_0 + (v_1 + v_2) = (v_0 + v_1) + v_2)$

(f2) $(\forall v_0)(v_0 + 0 = v_0)$

(f3) $(\forall v_0)(\exists v_1)(v_0 + v_1 = 0)$
(f4) $(\forall v_0)(\forall v_1)(v_0 + v_1 = v_1 + v_0)$
(f5) $(\forall v_0)(\forall v_1)(\forall v_2)(v_0(v_1 v_2) = (v_0 v_1)v_2)$
(f6) $(\forall v_0)(v_0 1 = v_0)$
(f7) $(\forall v_0)(\exists v_1)((v_0 = 0) \vee (v_0 v_1 = 1))$
(f8) $(\forall v_0)(\forall v_1)(v_0 v_1 = v_1 v_0)$
(f9) $(\forall v_0)(\forall v_1)(\forall v_2)(v_0(v_1 + v_2) = v_0 v_1 + v_0 v_2)$
($\neg$f10_p) $\neg(1 + \cdots + 1 = 0)$ (where we have p 1's).

Then the class of fields of characteristic 0 is the class of structure of type $\langle 3, 3, 0, 0\rangle$ that satisfy (f1) through (f9) and ($\neg$f10_p) for every prime p. Later we shall show that $\mathscr{F}_0$ is not an elementary class.

The class of all uncountable sets (with no relations), the class of all Archimedean ordered fields, and the class of all well-ordered sets are not elementary classes in the wider sense, although we cannot yet show this.

DEFINITION 1.3.2. Let $\mathfrak{A}$ be a structure of type t.

$$T(\mathfrak{A}) = \{F \in \Sigma^t \mid \mathfrak{A} \models F\}.$$

Let $K \subset M^t$. Then

$$T(K) = \bigcap \{T(\mathfrak{A}) \mid \mathfrak{A} \in K\}.$$

Let $S \subset \Sigma^t$. Then S is a theory iff $S = \{F \in \Sigma^t \mid S \models F\}$.

The following theorem collects many of the basic facts about M and T.

THEOREM 1.3.3. Let $S, T \subset \Sigma^t$, $F, G \in \Sigma^t$, $K, L \subset M^t$, and $\mathfrak{A} \in M^t$.

(a) $M(S \cup T) = M(S) \cap M(T)$.
(b) $M(F \wedge G) = M(F) \cap M(G)$.
(c) $M(F \vee G) = M(F) \cup M(G)$.
(d) $M(\neg F) = M^t \sim M(F)$.
(e) $\mathfrak{A} \in M(S)$ iff $S \subset T(\mathfrak{A})$.
(f) Let $L \in EC_\Delta$. Then $K \subset L$ iff $T(L) \subset T(K)$.
(g) $K \in EC_\Delta$ iff $M(T(K)) = K$.
(h) $S \subset T(M(S))$ and S is a theory iff $S = T(M(S))$.
(i) If S is a theory, then $M(S) \subset M(T)$ iff $T \subset S$.
(j) If T is consistent and $T(\mathfrak{A}) \subset T$ then $T(\mathfrak{A}) = T$.

Proof: Not all parts of the theorem are proven below since some of the proofs are trivial and some are similar to the ones done below.

(a) $\mathfrak{A} \in M(S \cup T)$ iff $\mathfrak{A} \models S \cup T$ iff for every $F \in S$, $\mathfrak{A} \models F$ and for every $F \in T$, $\mathfrak{A} \models F$, iff $\mathfrak{A} \models S$ and $\mathfrak{A} \models T$, iff $\mathfrak{A} \in M(S) \cap M(T)$.

(c) $\mathfrak{A} \in M(F \vee G)$ iff $\mathfrak{A} \models F \vee G$ iff $\mathfrak{A} \models F$ or $\mathfrak{A} \models G$ iff $\mathfrak{A} \in M(F)$ or $\mathfrak{A} \in M(G)$ iff $\mathfrak{A} \in M(F) \cup M(G)$.

(e) Let $\mathfrak{A} \in M(S)$. Then $\mathfrak{A} \models S$, so if $F \in S$, $\mathfrak{A} \models F$. But then

$$F \in \{G \mid \mathfrak{A} \models G\} = T(\mathfrak{A}),$$

thus $S \subset T(\mathfrak{A})$. Conversely, if $S \subset T(\mathfrak{A})$, then $\mathfrak{A} \models S$, so $\mathfrak{A} \in M(S)$.

(f) Let $K \subset L$. Then

$$T(L) = \bigcap \{T(\mathfrak{A}) \mid \mathfrak{A} \in L\} \subset \bigcap \{T(\mathfrak{A}) \mid \mathfrak{A} \in K\} = T(K).$$

Conversely, if $T(L) \subset T(K)$, let $\mathfrak{A} \in K$. Then

$$T(K) \subset \bigcap \{T(\mathfrak{B}) \mid \mathfrak{B} \in K\} \subset T(\mathfrak{A}).$$

Thus $T(L) \subset T(\mathfrak{A})$. Now let $L = M(S)$. Then if $\mathfrak{B} \in L$, by (e) $S \subset T(\mathfrak{B})$. Thus $S \subset \bigcap \{T(\mathfrak{B}) \mid \mathfrak{B} \in L\} = T(L)$. Thus $S \subset T(\mathfrak{A})$, so $\mathfrak{A} \in M(S) = L$. Thus $K \subset L$.

(g) Let $K = M(S)$. Then $S \subset T(K)$ (as in (f)) so $M(T(K)) \subset M(S) = K$. However, if $\mathfrak{A} \in K$, then $T(K) \subset T(\mathfrak{A})$, so $\mathfrak{A} \in M(T(K))$. The converse is clear.

(h) Let $S = T(M(S))$, $S \vdash F$. Then we must have $\mathfrak{A} \models F$ for every $\mathfrak{A} \in M(S)$ (since $\mathfrak{A} \in M(S)$ iff $\mathfrak{A} \models S$), thus

$$F \in \bigcap \{T(\mathfrak{A}) \mid \mathfrak{A} \in M(S)\} = T(M(S)) = S.$$

Conversely, consider any S. We already know that if $K = M(S)$, then $S \subset T(K) - T(M(S))$. If S is a theory and $F \in T(M(S))$, then for every $\mathfrak{A} \in M(S)$, $\mathfrak{A} \models F$, so $S \models F$. Thus $F \in S$.

(i) By (f), $M(S) \subset M(T)$ iff $T(M(T)) \subset T(M(S))$. But by (h),

$$T \subset T(M(T)) \subset T(M(S)) = S.$$

(j) If $F \in T \sim T(\mathfrak{A})$, then $\mathfrak{A} \not\models F$, so $\mathfrak{A} \models \neg F$. Thus $F, \neg F \in T$. But if $\mathfrak{B} \in M(T)$, then $\mathfrak{B} \models F$ and $\mathfrak{B} \models \neg F$, which is impossible.

Problems

1.3.1 For $S \subset T$, show that S is a set of axioms for T iff S is a set of axioms for $M(T)$.

‡1.3.2 (a) Show for $F, G \in \Sigma^t$ that $\phi \models (F \rightarrow G)$ iff $M(F) \subset M(G)$.

(b) Let $T \subset \Sigma^t$ be a theory such that $T \neq \Sigma^t$ and for every $F \in \Sigma^t$, either $F \in T$ or $\neg F \in T$. Show that for some $\mathfrak{A}$ of type t, $T(\mathfrak{A}) = T$. (NOTE: See Problem 1.2.3 (b).)

(c) Show that $T(M(S))$ is the smallest theory containing S for $S \subset \Sigma^t$.

‡1.3.3 (a) Show that if $S \subset \Sigma^t$ is finite, then $M(S) \in EC$.

(b) Show that the following are elementary classes: the class of all rings, not necessarily with identity; the class of rings with identity;

the class of integral domains; the class of ordered sets; the class of ordered fields; the class of fields of characteristic $p(p > 0)$.

(c) Show that the class of algebraically closed fields is elementary in the wider sense.

(d) Show that the class of vector spaces over fields is elementary. (HINT: Consider structures of the form

$$\mathfrak{A} = \langle A, V, +', \cdot', 0', F, +, \cdot, 0, 1 \rangle$$

of type $\langle 1, 3, 3, 0, 1, 3, 3, 0, 0 \rangle$.)

(e) Let $\mathfrak{F}$ be a field. Write a set of axioms for vector spaces over $\mathfrak{F}$.

1.3.4 Show that the theory of fields is not of the form $T(\mathfrak{A})$ for any structure $\mathfrak{A}$. Find a necessary and sufficient condition on $M(T)$ for a theory T to be of the form $T(\mathfrak{A})$.

‡1.3.5 Let $\{S_a \mid a \in A\}$ be a set of subsets of Σ^t. Show that $M(\bigcup_{a \in A} S_a) = \bigcap_{a \in A} M(S_a)$.

1.3.6 An ordered group is a group together with a total ordering such that if $a < a'$ and $b < b'$ then $ab < a'b'$. Show that the class of ordered groups is an elementary class.

‡1.3.7 Let $F, G \in \Sigma^t$. Show that $F \equiv G$ iff $M(F) = M(G)$. (For notation, see Problems 1.2.4 and 1.2.8.)

1.4 The Löwenheim-Skolem Theorem

Probably the first nontrivial fact about EC_Δ classes was shown by Löwenheim in 1915 and extended by Skolem in 1920. It has been further extended since, and now reads:

THEOREM 1.4.1. Let $T \subset \Sigma^t$, $\mathfrak{A} \in M(T)$. Then there is a $\mathfrak{B} \subset \mathfrak{A}$ such that $c(\mathfrak{B}) \leq c(t) + \omega$ and $\mathfrak{B} \in M(T)$.

The preceding is generally called the downward Löwonheim-Skolem theorem (we discuss the upward Löwenheim-Skolem theorem in the next section). Before proving this theorem, we give an example.

Given any countable subset of any group, we can find a countable subgroup containing it.

Proof: We know that a subgroup is simply a subset closed under the two functions $f_1(a, b) = ab$, $f_2(a) = a^{-1}$. Thus let S be any countable nonempty subset of G (where our group is $\mathfrak{A} = \langle G, \cdot, e \rangle$), and consider

$$S_0 = S, \qquad S_{n+1} = S_n \cup f_1[S_n \times S_n] \cup f_2[s_n], \qquad A = \bigcup_{n<\omega} S_n.$$

A is closed under f_1, f_2, for if $a, b \in A$, then $a \in S_n$, $b \in S_m$ for some finite n, m. Thus both are in the larger, say S_n. Then $f_1(a, b) \in S_{n+1}, f_2(a) \in S_{n+1}$, so both are in A. Also, since S is countable, so is S_n for each n. Thus $\bigcup_{n<\omega} S_n$ is countable. Now simply note that $\langle A, \cdot \upharpoonright A, e\rangle$ is a subgroup of $\langle G, \cdot, e\rangle$.

The preceding example suggests the following method of operation: First associate in some manner with each sentence a function or finite set of functions such that the closure of any set under the functions, together with the restrictions of the relations to that closure satisfies that sentence. Then proceed in much the manner described above.

However, "in some manner" is more easily said than done. We show that each formula is equivalent to one with all its quantifiers in front, and then for each formula of this form show how to obtain a finite set of functions, called Skolem functions, with the properties we want. Other proofs of our theorem are possible,† but the discovery of this equivalent form for each formula is important in its own right, and we wish to develop it as well as a proof of our theorem.

DEFINITION 1.4.2. QF^t is the smallest collection of formulas containing the atomic formulas of L^t and closed under $\vee$, $\neg$. Let $P^t(0) = QF^t$,

$$P^t(n+1) = P^t(n) \cup \{(\exists v_{j_{n+1}})F \mid F \in P^t(n), v_{j_{n+1}} \in FV(F)\} \cup \{(\forall v_{j_{n+1}})F \mid F \in P^t(n), v_{j_{n+1}} \in FV(F)\}.$$

$P^t = \bigcup_{n<\omega} P^t(n)$. QF^t is called the set of quantifier-free formulas of L^t, and P^t is called the set of formulas of L^t in prenex form (i.e., the set of all formulas with their quantifiers in front).

THEOREM 1.4.3. If $F \in L^t$, then there is a $G \in P^t$ such that $F \equiv G$ (see Problems 1.2.4, 1.2.8).

Proof:

$$L^t(0) \subset QF^t.$$

Thus let $F \in L^t(n+1)$. We have $F = \neg G$, $F = G \vee H$, or $F = (\exists v_j)G$ for $G, H \in L^t(n)$. If $F = \neg G$, find a $G' \in P^t$ such that $G \equiv G'$. Thus, by Problem 1.2.4, $F \equiv \neg G'$. The reader is left to show (in Problem 1.4.1) that $\neg G' \equiv F'$ for some $F' \in P^t$. If

$$F = (\exists v_j)G,$$

then

$$G \equiv G' \in P^t,$$

† See, for example, Problem 1.7.6.

so (by Problem 1.2.4)

$$F \equiv (\exists v_j)G'.$$

If

$$v_j \notin FV(G'),$$

then

$$(\exists v_j)G' \equiv G' \in P^t$$

(by Problem 1.2.8), so

$$F \equiv G' \in P^t.$$

In the case of $v_j \in FV(G')$, let

$$G' \in P^t(n) \sim P^t(n - 1)$$

(or $P^t(0)$), and let

$$v_j = v_{j_{n+1}}.$$

Thus

$$(\exists v_j)G' = (\exists v_{j_{n+1}})G' \in P^t(n + 1) \subset P^t.$$

The case $F = G \vee H$ is also left for the reader (see Problem 1.4.1).

Our next problem is to associate with each formula of P^t a finite set of functions. Intuitively, if $F \in P^t$, $F = (Q_n v_{j_n}) \cdots (Q_1 v_{j_1})M(v_0, \ldots, v_m)$, where $M(v_0, \ldots, v_m)$ is quantifier-free (and called the matrix of F) $\{v_{j_1}, \ldots, v_{j_n}\} \subset \{v_0, \ldots, v_m\}$, and for each r, k if $1 \leq r < k \leq n$, then $v_{j_r} \neq v_{j_k}$, and where each Q_k is $\forall$ or $\exists$. If we consider the sentence

$$G = (\forall v_0)(\exists v_1)(v_0 < v_1)$$

in $\mathfrak{A} = \langle A, \leq \rangle$ (a totally ordered set) we note that the statement may or may not hold in $\mathfrak{A}$, but if it holds, we can find a function that for each a_0 gives us an a_n with $a_0 < a_1$—in other words, the "value" of the existentially quantified variable depends on the "value" of the universally quantified variable preceding it. With this in mind, we wish to define for a formula $F \in P^t$ the set of existentially quantified variables and for each such variable the set of universally quantified variables preceding it.

Definition 1.4.4. Let $F \in P^t$. Then if $F \in P^t(0)$, $E(F) = \phi$. For

$$F \in P^t(n + 1) \sim P^t(n),$$

if $F = (\exists v_{j_{n+1}})G$, then

$$E(F) = E(G) \cup \{j_{n+1}\},$$

and if

$$F = (\forall v_{j_{n+1}})G,$$

then

$$E(F) = E(G).$$

$e(F) = c(E(F))$.

Now let $j_n \in E(F)$. Then if $F \in P^t(n)$, $A(F, n) = \phi$ (note that F cannot be in $P^t(q)$ for $q < n$). For

$$F \in P^t(m + 1) \sim P^t(m), \qquad m \geq n,$$

if

$$F = (\forall v_{j_{m+1}})G,$$

then

$$A(F, n) = A(G, n) \cup \{j_{m+1}\},$$

and if

$$F = (\exists v_{j_{m+1}})G,$$

then

$$A(F, n) = A(G, n).$$

$a(F, n) = c(A(F, n))$.

LEMMA 1.4.5. If $F \in P^t$, then there is a unique $M_F \in QF^t \cap SF(F)$ such that if $N \in QF^t \cap SF(F)$, then $N \in SF(M_F)$.

This M_F satisfies: If $G \in (SF(F) \cap P^t)$, $M_F \in SF(G)$, then

$$G = M_F$$

or for some $H \in SF(G)$,

$$G = (\exists v_{j_m})H \qquad \text{or} \qquad G = (\forall v_{j_m})H \qquad \text{for some } m.$$

Also, if

$$G \in (SF(F) \cap P^t) \sim P^t(0)$$

then

$$M_G = M_F.$$

M_F is called the matrix of F.

Proof: If $F \in QF^t$, clearly $F = M_F$ satisfies all conditions of the lemma. If

$$F = (\exists v_{j_m})G \qquad \text{or} \qquad F = (\forall v_{j_m})G,$$

then set

$$M_F = M_G.$$

Clearly

$$M_F \in SF(G) \cap QF^t \subset SF(F) \cap QF^t,$$

and if

$$N \in SF(F) \cap QF^t = (SF(G) \cup \{F\}) \cap QF^t = SF(G) \cap QF^t,$$

then

$$N \in SF(M_G) = SF(M_F).$$

M_F is unique by Problem 1.2.7, since if M_F, $M_{F'}$ satisfy the conditions of the lemma, then

$$M_F \in SF(M_{F'}) \qquad \text{and} \qquad M_{F'} \in SF(M_F).$$

Finally, if $G \in SF(F)$, $M_F \in SF(G)$, then either $G \in QF^t$ (in which case $G \in SF(M_F)$, whence follows $G = M_F$) or $G \notin QF^t$, and the rest follows from the fact that $G \in (SF(F) \cap P^t) \subset P^t$.

DEFINITION 1.4.6. Let $F \in P^t$. $\mathscr{S}(\mathfrak{A}, F, a)$ is a complete set of Skolem functions for F at $a \in A^\omega$ on $\mathfrak{A}$ iff $\mathscr{S}(\mathfrak{A}, F, a)$ is indexed by $E(F)$, for each $j_n \in E(F)$, $f_{j_n}: A^{a(F,n)} \to A$, and $\mathfrak{A} \models M_F[b]$ for every $b \in A^\omega$ such that

(i) for $v_j \in FV(F)$, $b_j = a_j$; and

(ii) for $j = j_n \in E(F)$,

$$b_j = f_j(b_{k_1}, \ldots, b_{k_{a(F,n)}}), \qquad \text{where} \quad A(F, n) = \{k_1, \ldots, k_{a(F,n)}\}.$$

For example, if $\langle R, +, \cdot, 0\rangle$ is a ring then $\{\cdot\}$ is the set of Skolem functions for $(\forall v_3)(\forall v_2)(\exists v_1)(\cdot(v_3, v_2, v_1))$ at every $a \in R^\omega$ on $\mathfrak{A} = \langle R, +, \cdot, 0\rangle$. If

$$G = (\forall v_2)(\exists v_1)(\cdot(v_3, v_2, v_1)),$$

then

$$\{f_1\} = \mathscr{S}(\mathfrak{A}, G, a), \qquad \text{where} \quad f_1(x) = a_3 x.$$

Other examples and comments can be found in Problem 1.4.9.

THEOREM 1.4.7. For $F \in P^t$, a complete set of Skolem functions $\mathscr{S}(\mathfrak{A}, F, a)$ exists iff $\mathfrak{A} \models F[a]$.

Proof: Let $F \in QF^t$. Then, our theorem states, $\mathfrak{A} \models F[a]$ iff for every $b \in A^\omega$ such that $b_j = a_j$, for every $v_j \in FV(F)$, $\mathfrak{A} \models F[b]$. Assume now that

$$\mathfrak{A} \models F[a], \qquad F \in P^t(n+1) \sim P^t(n).$$

If $F = (\exists v_{j_{n+1}})G$, we have

$$\mathfrak{A} \models G[a(j_{n+1} \mid d)] \qquad \text{for some } d \in A,$$

thus we have $\mathscr{S}(\mathfrak{A}, G, a(j_{n+1} \mid d))$, a complete set of Skolem functions, so $\mathfrak{A} \models M_G[b]$ if

$$(*) \quad b_k = a(j_{n+1} \mid d)_k \qquad \text{for} \quad v_k \in FV(G)$$

and

$$b_{j_m} = f_{j_m}(b_{k_1}, \ldots, b_{k_{a(G,m)}}) \qquad \text{for} \quad j_m \in E(G),$$

where

$$A(G, m) = \{k_1, \ldots, k_{a(G,m)}\}.$$

However,

$$E(F) = E(G) \cup \{j_{n+1}\},$$

so set

$$\mathscr{S}(\mathfrak{A}, F, a) = \{f_{j_{n+1}}\} \cup \mathscr{S}(\mathfrak{A}, G, a(j_{n+1} \mid d))$$

where $f_{j_{n+1}} \equiv d$ (and has no variables). But $M_F = M_G$ and

$$FV(F) = FV(G) \sim \{v_{j_{n+1}}\}$$

and for each $j_m \in E(G)$, $A(F, m) = A(G, m)$. We therefore have $\mathfrak{A} \models M_F[b]$ for each b such that

$$b_k = a_k \qquad \text{for every} \quad v_k \in FV(F),$$

$$b_{j_m} = f_{j_m}(b_{k_1}, \ldots, b_{k_{a(F,m)}}) \qquad \text{for} \quad j_m \in E(F),$$

since these b are precisely those described by (*). Thus $\mathscr{S}(\mathfrak{A}, F, a)$ is our complete set of Skolem functions.

If $F = (\forall v_{j_{n+1}})G$, we have $\mathfrak{A} \models F[a]$ iff for every $d \in A$,

$$\mathfrak{A} \models G[a(j_{n+1} \mid d)].$$

Thus for each $d \in A$, we have $\mathscr{S}(\mathfrak{A}, G, a(j_{n+1} \mid d))$, a complete set of Skolem functions. $\mathfrak{A} \models M_G[b]$ if

$$(**) \quad b_k = a(j_{n+1} \mid d)_k \qquad \text{for} \quad v_k \in FV(G) = FV(F) \cup \{v_{j_{n+1}}\};$$

$$b_{j_m} = f^d_{j_m}(b_{k_1}, \ldots, b_{k_{a(G,m)}}), \qquad \text{where} \quad A(G, m) = \{k_1, \ldots, k_{a(G,m)}\}.$$

Note:

$$A(F, m) = A(G, m) \cup \{j_{n+1}\} \qquad \text{for} \quad j_m \in E(G).$$

Now set

$$\mathscr{S}(\mathfrak{A}, F, a) = \{f_{j_1}, \ldots, f_{j_{e(F)}}\},$$

where

$$E(F) = \{j_1, \ldots, j_{e(F)}\}$$

and

$$f_{j_m}(b_{k_1}, \ldots, b_{k_{a(G,m)}}, d) = f^d_{j_m}(b_{k_1}, \ldots, b_{k_{a(G,m)}}).$$

The reader may now check that those $b \in A^\omega$ satisfying (**) are precisely those for which

$$b_k = a_k \qquad \text{for} \quad v_k \in FV(F)$$

and

$$b_{j_m} = f_{j_m}(b_{k_1}, \ldots, b_{k_{a(F,m)}}) \qquad \text{for} \quad j_m \in E(F),$$

where

$$\{k_1, \ldots, k_{a(F,m)}\} = A(F, m).$$

Thus $\mathscr{S}(\mathfrak{A}, F, a)$ is our complete set of Skolem functions.

Conversely, for F as above, assume we have $\mathscr{S}(\mathfrak{A}, F, a)$, a complete set of Skolem functions. Then if $F = (\exists v_{j_{n+1}})G$, $f_{j_{n+1}}$ must be a constant since it has no variables. Let $f_{j_{n+1}} \equiv d$. We show that

$$\mathfrak{A} \models G[a(j_{n+1} \mid d)],$$

thus

$$\mathfrak{A} \models F[a]. \qquad \mathscr{S}(\mathfrak{A}, F, a) \sim \{f_{j_{n+1}}\}$$

is a complete set of Skolem functions for G at $a(j_{n+1} \mid d) \in A^\omega$ on $\mathfrak{A}$ because $\mathfrak{A} \models M_G[b]$ if

$$b_k = a(j_{n+1} \mid d)_k \qquad \text{for} \quad v_k \in FV(G),$$
$$b_{j_m} = f_{j_m}(b_{k_1}, \ldots, b_{k_{a(G,m)}}) \qquad \text{for} \quad j_m \in E(G),$$

where

$$\{k_1, \ldots, k_{a(G,m)}\} = A(G, m).$$

Thus, by induction,

$$\mathfrak{A} \models G[a(j_{n+1} \mid d)], \qquad \text{so} \quad \mathfrak{A} \models F[a].$$

If $F = (\forall v_{j_{n+1}})G$, we must show that for every $d \in A$,

$$\mathfrak{A} \models G[a(j_{n+1} \mid d)].$$

Assume that we have

$$\mathscr{S}(\mathfrak{A}, F, a) = \{f_{j_1}, \ldots, f_{j_{e(F)}}\},$$

and set

$$\mathscr{S}(\mathfrak{A}, G, a(j_{n+1} \mid d)) = \{f^d_{j_1}, \ldots, f^d_{j_{e(F)}}\},$$

where

$$f^d_{j_m}(b_{k_1}, \ldots, b_{k_{a(G,m)}}) = f_{j_m}(b_{k_1}, \ldots, d).$$

It is simple to check that for every $d \in A$,

$$\mathscr{S}(\mathfrak{A}, G, a(j_{n+1} \mid d))$$

is a complete set of Skolem functions, thus

$$\mathfrak{A} \models G[a(j_{n+1} \mid d)],$$

and thus

$$\mathfrak{A} \models F[a].$$

Note that if $F \in P^t \cap \Sigma^t$, then a complete set of Skolem functions $\mathscr{S}(\mathfrak{A}, F, a)$ will also be a complete set $\mathscr{S}(\mathfrak{A}, F, b)$. Call such a set $\mathscr{S}(\mathfrak{A}, F)$.

THEOREM 1.4.8. Let $F \in P^t \cap \Sigma^t$, let $\mathfrak{A} \models F$, and let $\mathscr{S}(\mathfrak{A}, F)$ be a complete set of Skolem functions for F in $\mathfrak{A}$. If $B \subset A$ is nonempty and contains all distinguished elements of $\mathfrak{A}$, and if for $f = f_{j_n} \in \mathscr{S}(\mathfrak{A}, F)$, $f[B^{a(F,n)}] \subset B$, then $\mathfrak{B} \models F$, where $\mathfrak{B} = \mathfrak{A} \mid B$.

Proof: The Skolem functions for F in $\mathfrak{B}$ are simply the restrictions of those for F in $\mathfrak{A}$.

THEOREM 1.4.9. Let $\mathfrak{A} \models S$; $S \subset \Sigma^t$, $B'_0 \subset A$ and $c(t) + \omega \leq c(B'_0)$. Then for some B containing all distinguished elements of $\mathfrak{A}$,

$$B'_0 \subset B \subset A, \qquad c(B) = c(B'_0), \qquad \text{and} \qquad \mathfrak{B} = \mathfrak{A} \mid B \models S.$$

Proof: For every $F \in S$, let $F \equiv F' \in P^t$, $F' \equiv F'' \in P^t \cap \Sigma^t$ (this last equivalence by Problem 1.2.8), and $S'' = \{F'' \mid F \in S\}$. Thus for each $F \in S$, we may define $\mathscr{S}(\mathfrak{A}, F) = \mathscr{S}(\mathfrak{A}, F'')$, and we may also set

$$\mathscr{S}(\mathfrak{A}, S) = \bigcup \{\mathscr{S}(\mathfrak{A}, F) \mid F \in S\}.$$

$$c(\mathscr{S}(\mathfrak{A}, S)) \leq \sum_{F \in S} c(\mathscr{S}(\mathfrak{A}, F)) \leq \sum_{F \in S} \omega = c(S)\omega = c(S) + \omega \leq c(t) + \omega.$$

Let

$$B_0 = B'_0 \cup \{R_i \mid t(i) = 0\}$$

and note that $c(B_0) = c(B'_0)$. For $m \geq 0$, let

$$B_{m+1} = B_m \cup (\bigcup \{f_{j_n}[B_m^{a(F'',n)}] \mid F \in S, j_n \in E(F'')\}),$$

and $B = \bigcup_{m \in \omega} B_m$. Let $f \in \mathscr{S}(\mathfrak{A}, S)$, $f\colon B^q \to B$, $b_1, \ldots, b_q \in B$. Then

$$b_1 \in B_{m_1}, \ldots, b_q \in B_{m_q},$$

so for $m = \max\{m_1, \ldots, m_q\}$, $b_1, \ldots, b_q \in B_m$. Thus

$$f(b_1, \ldots, b_q) \in B_{m+1} \subset B.$$

Also

$$c(B_0) \leq c(B) \leq \sum_{m < \omega} c(B_m).$$

But

$$c(f_{j_n}[B_m^{a(F'',n)}]) \leq c(B_m);$$

thus

$$\begin{aligned} c(B_m) \leq c(B_{m+1}) \leq c(B_m) + \sum_{f \in \mathscr{S}(\mathfrak{A}, S)} c(B_m) &\leq c(B_m) + c(S)\omega c(B_m) \\ &= c(B_m) + c(B_m) = c(B_m). \end{aligned}$$

Thus for every m, $c(B_m) = c(B_0)$, so

$$\sum_{m < \omega} c(B_m) = \omega c(B_0) = c(B_0).$$

Thus

$$c(B) = c(B_0) = c(B'_0).$$

Theorem 1.4.1 results directly from Theorem 1.4.9 because if

$$c(t) + \omega \leq c(\mathfrak{A}),$$

we can use the axiom of choice to find $B_0' \subset A$ such that

$$c(B_0') = c(t) + \omega,$$

and then Theorem 1.4.9 gives us a B such that

$$c(B) = c(B_0) = c(t) + \omega,$$

B contains all distinguished elements of $\mathfrak{A}$ and $\mathfrak{A} \mid B \models S$.

Corollary 1.4.10. Let $S \subset \Sigma^t$ be consistent. Then there is a model $\mathfrak{B}'$ of S such that

$$c(\mathfrak{B}') \leq \omega + c(S).$$

If $c(S) \leq \omega$ or $c(t) \leq \omega$, then S has a countable model.

Proof: For $F \in L^t$, let $t_F = t \mid I_F$, I_F the set of i such that c_i or P_i appears in F. An inductive definition, much like Definition 1.2.6 (see Problem 1.4.8), is possible for I_F, and it is clear that I_F is finite. For $S \subset L^t$, let $t_S = \bigcup_{F \in S} t_F$, and note that

$$c(t_S) \leq c(S) + \omega, \qquad S \subset L^{t_S}.$$

Let $\mathfrak{A}' = \langle A, R_i \rangle_{i \in \mathfrak{D} t_S}$, where $\mathfrak{A} = \langle A, R_i \rangle_{i \in I}$ is a model of S, and note that by Problem 1.2.10, $\mathfrak{A}' \models S$. Then by Theorem 1.4.1 for some $\mathfrak{B}' \subset \mathfrak{A}'$,

$$c(\mathfrak{B}') \leq c(t_S) + \omega = c(S) + \omega, \qquad \text{and} \qquad \mathfrak{B}' \models S.$$

Note that the proof of Corollary 1.4.10 actually shows

Corollary 1.4.11. Let $\mathfrak{A} \models S$, $c(S) + \omega \leq \mathfrak{m} \leq c(\mathfrak{A})$. Then there is a $\mathfrak{B}$ of cardinality $\mathfrak{m}$ such that $\mathfrak{B} \models S$.

Problem 1.4.8(b), which uses the result of Problem 1.2.10 in its proof, allows us to refine the statement of 1.4.11 to:

Corollary 1.4.12. Let $\mathfrak{A} \in M(S)$, $c(S) + \omega \leq \mathfrak{m} \leq c(\mathfrak{A})$, S be a set of sentences. Then for some $\mathfrak{B} \in M(S)$, $c(\mathfrak{B}) = \mathfrak{m}$.

The difference between these two corollaries is that the second requires $t_{\mathfrak{A}} = t_{\mathfrak{B}}$.

Löwenheim was interested in showing the existence of a countable model of set theory (assuming that any models at all existed). Since the language of set theory is of type $\langle 2, 0 \rangle$, Corollary 1.4.10 establishes the existence of such a model. If $\mathfrak{A} = \langle A, \varepsilon, \phi \rangle$ is a countable model of set theory, then $\varepsilon \subset A \times A$; thus for any $a \in A$, $\{x \mid x \,\varepsilon\, a\} \subset A$. Thus every element (set) in A must be countable. This was considered a paradox when it first appeared, since a theorem of set theory is that $a < \mathscr{P}a$, thus $\mathscr{P}\omega$ is uncountable. We resolve the paradox, however, by noting that the concepts of countability in the two previous sentences differ. In the first sentence, we mean that some $f\colon \omega \to a$ exists. In the second we mean that such an f exists as an element of A.

Problems

‡1.4.1 (a) Show that

$$\neg(\exists v_j)H \equiv (\forall v_j)\neg H, \qquad \neg(\forall v_j)H \equiv (\exists v_j)\neg H$$

and use this to show by induction on n, where $G' \in P^t(n)$, that if $G' \in P^t$, then for some $F' \in P^t$, $\neg G' \equiv F'$.

(b) If $v_j \notin FV(G')$, show that

$$((\exists v_j)H') \vee G' \equiv (\exists v_j)(H' \vee G'),$$

and

$$((\forall v_j)H') \vee G' \equiv (\forall v_j)(H' \vee G').$$

Use this to show (by induction on $m + n$, where $F' \subset P^t(n)$, $G' \in P^t(m)$) that if

$$BV(F') \cap FV(G') = BV(G') \cap FV(F') = \phi,$$

$F', G' \in P^t$, then for some $H \in P^t$, $F' \vee G' \equiv H$.

(c) If $A, B \subset V$ are finite (or at least $c(\omega \sim A) = c(\omega \sim B) = \omega$), then for some one–one onto $\varphi : V \to V$, $\varphi[A] \cap B = \phi$. Now let $\varphi : V \to V$ be onto and one–one, and such that

$$\varphi[V(F') \cup V(G')] \cap (V(F') \cup V(G')) = \phi.$$

Show that for $H \in L^t$,

$$Sb_{\varphi^{-1}}(Rp_\varphi H) \equiv H, \quad \text{for} \quad H \in P^t,$$
$$Sb_{\varphi^{-1}}(Rp_\varphi H) \in P^t,$$

and finally, by Problem 1.2.14, that

$$FV(Sb_{\varphi^{-1}}(Rp_\varphi F')) \cap BV(Sb_{\varphi^{-1}}(Rp_\varphi G'))$$
$$= \phi = FV(Sb_{\varphi^{-1}}(Rp_\varphi G')) \cap BV(Sb_{\varphi^{-1}}(Rp_\varphi F')).$$

(d) Use the results of (a) through (c) to complete the proof of Theorem 1.4.3.

1.4.2 Let $\mathfrak{A} \in M(T)$, $c(\mathfrak{A}) > \omega + c(T)$. Show that there is a collection $\mathfrak{A}_\eta$, $\eta \in c(\mathfrak{A})$ of models of T such that if $\mu \in \eta \in c(\mathfrak{A})$, then

$$\mathfrak{A}_\mu \subset \mathfrak{A}_\eta, \quad \text{and} \quad c(\mathfrak{A}_\eta) < c(\mathfrak{A}), \quad \text{and} \quad \bigcup_{\eta \in c(\mathfrak{A})} \mathfrak{A}_\eta = \mathfrak{A}.$$

1.4.3 (a) Show that there is no $S \subset \Sigma^\phi$ such that

$$M(S) = \{\mathfrak{A} \mid \mathfrak{A} = \langle A \rangle,$$

A uncountable (and no relations on A)$\}$.

(b) Show that there is no countable t such that for some $S \subset \Sigma^t$, $M(S) = \{\mathbb{R}\}$.

1.4.4 (a) Give an example of a finite consistent S with no finite models.

(b) Give an example of a finite S, $\mathfrak{A} \in M(S)$ (not necessarily finite) such that for no $\mathfrak{B} \in M(S)$ is $\mathfrak{B} \neq \mathfrak{A}$ and $\mathfrak{B} \subset \mathfrak{A}$.

(c) Give an example of a set of sentences T and an uncountable $\mathfrak{A} \in M(T)$ such that if $\mathfrak{B} \in M(T)$ and $\mathfrak{B} \subset \mathfrak{A}$, then $\mathfrak{B} = \mathfrak{A}$.

1.4.5 Which of the following does this section imply?

(a) Every ring has a countable subring.

(b) Every ring has a countable (nontrivial) ideal.

(c) Every field has a countable subfield.

(d) There is a countable algebraically closed field of characteristic 0.

1.4.6 Find where and if the axiom of choice is used in the proof of Theorem 1.4.7.

1.4.7 (a) If T has a model with a nontrivial automorphism, then T has such a model of cardinality at most $c(T) + \omega$.

(b) If $c(T) \leq \omega$ and T has a model $\mathfrak{A}$ such that there is a non-onto imbedding $f: \mathfrak{A} \to \mathfrak{A}$, then T has a model $\mathfrak{B}$ with such an imbedding and such that $c(\mathfrak{B}) = \omega$.

‡1.4.8 (a) Give an inductive definition of the t_F of Corollary 1.4.10.

(b) Show that we may additionally require $\mathfrak{B}'$ to be of type t in Corollary 1.4.10, but that given an $\mathfrak{A} \in M(S)$, we may not be able to insist that $\mathfrak{B}' \subset \mathfrak{A}$.

1.4.9 (a) Let $\mathfrak{A} = \langle \mathbb{R}, +, < \rangle$ and

$$F = (\forall v_0)(\forall v_1)(\exists v_2)(v_0 + v_1 < v_2).$$

Show that a set of Skolem functions exists for F in $\mathfrak{A}$ by finding such a set, but that none exists for F in $\mathfrak{A} \mid [0, 1]$.

(b) Let $\langle A, < \rangle$ be any partially ordered set. Find all possible sets of Skolem functions for

$$G = (\forall v_0)(\exists v_1)(\forall v_2)(v_1 < v_2 \rightarrow v_0 < v_2).$$

1.5 Compactness

The most important theorem in model theory is the compactness theorem.

THEOREM 1.5.1. The following are equivalent:

(a) Let $\{S_m \mid m \in M\}$ be a collection of subsets of Σ^t, $K_m = M(S_m)$. Then $\bigcap_{m \in M} K_m = \phi$ iff for some finite $M' \subset M$, $\bigcap_{m \in M'} K_m = \phi$.

(b) Let $F \in \Sigma^t$, $S \subset \Sigma^t$. Then $S \models F$ iff for some finite $S' \subset S$, $S' \models F$.

(c) Let $S \subset \Sigma^t$. S is consistent iff every finite subset of S is consistent.

Proof: ($a \to b$) Let $T = S \cup \{\neg F\}$, and for $G \in T$, let $K_G = M(G)$. Then $S \models F$ iff $M(T) = \phi$, iff $\bigcap_{G \in T} K_G = \phi$, iff $\bigcap_{G \in T'} K_G = \phi$ for some finite $T' \subset T$ [by (a)], iff $M(T') = \phi$ for some finite $T' \subset T$. For this T',

$$M((T' \sim \{\neg F\}) \cup \{\neg F\}) = \phi,$$

so if $\mathfrak{A} \in M(T' \sim \{\neg F\})$, then

$$\mathfrak{A} \models F, \qquad \text{thus} \quad T' \sim \{\neg F\} \models F,$$

and this is a finite subset of S. "Conversely" it is clear that if some subset of T implies F, then T implies F.

($b \to c$) Let $M(S) = \phi$. Then for some (in fact, for every) $F \in S$, $S \models \neg F$. Thus for some finite $S' \subset S$, $S' \models \neg F$; thus $S' \cup \{F\}$ is a finite inconsistent subset of S. "Conversely," if for some subset S' of S, $M(S') = \phi$ then $M(S) \subset M(S') = \phi$.

($c \to a$) Let $S = \bigcup \{S_m \mid m \subset M\}$, thus $M(S) = \phi$ iff $\bigcap_{m \in M} K_m = \phi$, where $K_m = M(S_m)$. But if $M(S) - \phi$, then $M(S') = \phi$ for some finite $S' \subset S$. Clearly

$$S' \subset S_{m_1} \cup \cdots \cup S_{m_p};$$

thus if $M' = \{m_1, \ldots, m_p\}$,

$$\bigcap_{m \in M'} K_m \subset M(S') = \phi.$$

"Conversely," if $M' \subset M$ and $\bigcap_{m \in M'} K_m = \phi$, then $\bigcap_{m \in M} K_m = \phi$.

Note that (a) asserts that the intersection of a set of elementary classes is empty iff the intersection of some finite subset is empty. The statement that any one (therefore all) of the parts of Theorem 1.5.1 is true is the compactness theorem. The remainder of this section (indeed, of this chapter) is devoted to demonstrating the many uses of the compactness theorem, and its proof is given in Section 2.1.

We now return to the class $\mathscr{F}_0$ of fields of characteristic 0, which we discussed in Section 1.3, and ask whether $\mathscr{F}_0 \in EC$. It is clear that if we take any finite subset S_0 of its axioms S, then S_0 contains only $(\neg f10_{p_1}), \ldots, (\neg f10_{p_n})$, say for $p_1 < \cdots < p_n$. Let $q > p_n$ be a prime. Then $\mathbb{Z}/q\mathbb{Z} = \mathbb{Z}_q$ is a field of characteristic q. Thus $\mathbb{Z}_q \models S_0$, but $\mathbb{Z}_q \notin \mathscr{F}_0$. Thus for no finite $S_0 \subset S$ do we have $M(S_0) = M(S)$. Now consider the following theorem, whose proof depends on compactness.

THEOREM 1.5.2. (a) Let $M(S) = M(T)$ for some finite T. Then for some finite $S' \subset S$, $M(S) = M(S')$. Thus if $M(S) \in EC$, then $M(S) = M(S')$ for some finite $S' \subset S$.

(b) Let $K \subset M^t$, $K' = M^t \sim K$. If $K, K' \in EC_\Delta$, then $K, K' \in EC$.

Proof: (a) Clearly if $S' \subset S$, then

$$M(T) = M(S) \subset M(S').$$

We must therefore find a finite $S' \subset S$ such that $M(S') \subset M(T)$. Since $M(T) \in EC$, let $M(T) = M(F)$. Thus we want $M(S') \subset M(F)$, i.e., $S' \models F$, and $\cdots = M(G_1 \wedge \cdots \wedge G_p)$. But since $S \models F$, compactness gives us S'.

(b) Let $K = M(S)$, $K' = M(T)$. Then $K \cap K' = \phi$, so $M(S \cup T) = \phi$. By compactness we can find a finite $V \subset S \cup T$ such that $M(V) = \phi$. Now let $S' = S \cap V$, $T' = T \cap V$. Clearly $M(S) \subset M(S')$, $M(T) \subset M(T')$. However since $M(S')$, $M(T') \subset M^t$, if either $M(S') \neq K$ or $M(T') \neq K'$, we must have

$$M(S') \cap M(T') \neq \phi,$$

a contradiction

$$(\text{since } M(S') \cap M(T') = M(S' \cup T') = M(V) = \phi).$$

Thus

$$K = M(S') \in EC, \qquad K' = M(T') \in EC \text{ (see Problem 1.3.3.(a))}$$

From now on we assume compactness. This assumption shows that if K is the class of all fields of characteristic 0, then $K \notin EC$.

It also shows that the class L of all fields of characteristic $\neq 0$ is not an EC_Δ class. For let $L = M(S)$, $T = \{(\neg f10_p) \mid p \text{ a prime}\}$, and let $V \subset S \cup T$ be finite. Then

$$V \subset S \cup \{(\neg f10_{p_1}), \ldots, (\neg f10_{p_n})\} \qquad \text{for some} \quad p_1 < \cdots < p_n.$$

If $q > p_n$, then we have a field in L of characteristic q, say C, thus C $\models V$. Thus V is consistent; thus so is $S \cup T$. Therefore

$$\phi \neq M(S \cup T) = M(S) \cap M(T) = L \cap M(T),$$

so there is a field in L of characteristic 0, a contradiction.

Now let $\geq_n$ be the following sentence in Σ^ϕ:

$$(\exists v_1) \cdots (\exists v_n)((v_1 \neq v_2) \wedge \cdots \wedge (v_1 \neq v_n) \wedge (v_2 \neq v_3) \wedge \cdots \wedge (v_{n-1} \neq v_n)).$$

Then $\mathfrak{A} = \langle A \rangle \models \geq_n$ iff $\mathfrak{A}$ has at least n elements. Clearly the class K of infinite sets is $M(S)$, where $S = \{\geq_n \mid n \in \omega\}$. However, it is also true that $M(S) \neq M(S')$ for any finite subset S' of S, for if $S' = \{\geq_{n_1}, \ldots, \geq_{n_p}\}$

and $n > \max\{n_1, \ldots, n_p\}$ a structure $\mathfrak{A} = \langle A \rangle$ with n elements will satisfy S' but not S. Thus the class of infinite sets is in EC_Δ but not in EC. Part (b) of the above theorem now tells us that its complement (in M^ϕ), the collection of finite sets, is not even in EC_Δ. We can go further, however.

THEOREM 1.5.3 (Upward Löwenheim-Skolem). Let $K \in EC_\Delta$ be such that for every finite n there is an $\mathfrak{A} \in K$ with $c(\mathfrak{A}) \geq n$. Then for every cardinality $\mathfrak{m}$ (finite or infinite) there is a $\mathfrak{A} \in K$ with $c(\mathfrak{A}) \geq \mathfrak{m}$.

Proof: Let t be the type of the structures in K, $D = \mathscr{D}(t)$. We construct a new type t' as follows: Let $R = \mathscr{D}(t')$ be the disjoint union of $\mathscr{D}(t)$ and $\mathfrak{m}$; let $t \subset t'$; and for $s \in R \sim D$, let $t'(s) = 0$ (thus $P_s = c_s$, a new constant). Let $K = M(S)$, and let

$$T = \{c_s \neq c_{s'} \mid s, s' \in R \sim D, s \neq s'\}.$$

If we can show that $S \cup T$ is a consistent set, we are through, since any $\mathfrak{A} \in M(S \cup T)$ will have $\mathfrak{A} \models S$, and $c(\mathfrak{A}) \geq \mathfrak{m}$. We must, however, consider the fact that $\mathfrak{A} \notin K$, since $\mathfrak{A} \notin M^t$ ($\mathfrak{A}$ is of type t'). If we let

$$\mathfrak{A} = \langle A, R_i, e_s \rangle_{i \in D, s \in R \sim D},$$

then

$$\mathfrak{A}' = \langle A, R_i \rangle_{i \in D} \in M^t,$$

$\mathfrak{A}' \models S$, (see Problem 1.2.10), and

$$c(\mathfrak{A}') = c(\mathfrak{A}) \geq \mathfrak{m}.$$

Thus $\mathfrak{A}' \in K$ is of cardinality $\geq \mathfrak{m}$.

Now let $V \subset S \cup T$ be finite. Then $V \subset S \cup \{F_1, \ldots, F_n\}$, with $F_1, \ldots, F_n \in T$. Now let $\mathfrak{B} \in K$, $c(\mathfrak{B}) \geq 2n$, and let $\{c_{s_1}, \ldots, c_{s_k}\}$ be the set of all constants that appear in any of $F_1, \ldots, F_n$. Clearly $k \leq 2n$; thus choose distinguished elements e_s for each $s \in R \sim D$ such that $e_{s_1}, \ldots, e_{s_k}$ are all distinct. Thus

$$\mathfrak{B}' \models \{F_1, \ldots, F_n\}, \qquad \mathfrak{B}' \models S,$$

where

$$\mathfrak{B}' = \langle B, S_i, e_s \rangle_{i \in D, s \in R \sim D} \qquad (\mathfrak{B} = \langle B, S_i \rangle_{i \in D})$$

so $\mathfrak{B}' \models V$. Thus $S \cup T$ is consistent.

The preceding proof uses the following method: Relations are added to our structure, studied, and then removed. The original relations are unchanged by this, and those statements (in the original language) that were satisfied by our structure stay satisfied. We use this sort of procedure henceforward and later state some definitions to help clarify it. First, however, we state another version of the Löwenheim-Skolem theorem.

THEOREM 1.5.4. Let $K = M(S)$, and for every finite n assume that there is an $\mathfrak{A} \in K$ with $c(\mathfrak{A}) \geq n$. If $c(S) + \omega \leq \mathfrak{m}$, then there is an $\mathfrak{A} \in K$ such that $c(\mathfrak{A}) = \mathfrak{m}$.

Proof: By Theorem 1.5.3, we can find $\mathfrak{B} \in K$ with $c(\mathfrak{B}) \geq \mathfrak{m}$. Corollary 1.4.12 now assures us that for some $\mathfrak{A} \in M(S)$, $c(\mathfrak{A}) = \mathfrak{m}$.

Any of the results in Theorems 1.4.1, 1.4.9, 1.5.3, and 1.5.4, and in Corollaries 1.4.11 and 1.4.12, and related results, are called Löwenheim-Skolem theorems. We now consider the method of proof used in Theorem 1.5.3.

DEFINITION 1.5.5. Let t be a type. Then t' is a reduct of t iff $t' \subset t$. A structure $\mathfrak{A}$ is a reduct of $\mathfrak{B}$ iff $t_{\mathfrak{A}}$ is a reduct of $t_{\mathfrak{B}}$, $B = A$, and for any $i \in \mathscr{D}(t_{\mathfrak{A}})$, $S_i = R_i$. In this case we also write $\mathfrak{A} = \mathfrak{B}/t_{\mathfrak{A}}$.

In the proof of 1.5.3, $\mathfrak{A}'$ was a reduct of $\mathfrak{A}$, $\mathfrak{B}$ a reduct of $\mathfrak{B}'$. Reducts were also used in the proof of Corollary 1.4.10, and Problem 1.2.10 studied one of their basic properties.

The reader should now note just how Theorem 1.5.3 implies and extends our remarks on finite sets just preceding the statement of that theorem.

Now let $\mathfrak{A} = \langle A, R_i \rangle_{i \in I}$, and let J be the disjoint union of A and I. Consider that $\mathfrak{A}' = \langle A, R_i \rangle_{i \in J}$, with $R_a = a$ for $a \in A$. Our new type t' has the following properties, t is a reduct of t', and for $a \in A$, $t'(a) = 0$.

DEFINITION 1.5.6.

$$\begin{aligned} Dg(\mathfrak{A}) = {} & \{P_i(c_{a_1}, \ldots, c_{a_{t(i)}}) \mid t(i) > 0, \langle a_1, \ldots, a_{t(i)} \rangle \in R_i\} \\ & \cup \{\neg P_i(c_{a_1}, \ldots, c_{a_{t(i)}}) \mid t(i) > 0, \langle a_1, \ldots, a_{t(i)} \rangle \notin R_i\} \\ & \cup \{c_a = c_i \mid t(i) = 0 \quad \text{and} \quad a = R_i\} \\ & \cup \{\neg(c_{a_1} = c_{a_2}) \mid a_1 \neq a_2\}. \end{aligned}$$

$Dg(\mathfrak{A})$ is called the diagram of $\mathfrak{A}$ and is a set of sentences in $L^{t'}$.

THEOREM 1.5.7. Let $\mathfrak{B}$ be of type t' (as defined in the preceding definition, 1.5.6). Then $\mathfrak{B} \models Dg(\mathfrak{A})$ iff

$$f\colon \mathfrak{A} \cong (\mathfrak{B} \mid \{e_a \mid a \in A\})/t,$$

where $f\colon A \to B$ is defined by $f(a) = e_a$, the distinguished element of $\mathfrak{B}$ corresponding to c_a.

Proof: If $\mathfrak{B} \models Dg(\mathfrak{A})$, $\langle a_1, \ldots, a_{t(i)} \rangle \in R_i$, then

$$\mathfrak{B} \models P_i(c_{a_1}, \ldots, c_{a_{t(i)}})$$

so

$$\langle e_{a_1}, \ldots, e_{a_{t(i)}} \rangle \in S_i;$$

and similar reasoning applied to the other types of formulas in $Dg(\mathfrak{A})$ establishes f to be an isomorphism.

Conversely if f is an isomorphism and

$$\langle a_1, \ldots, a_{t(i)} \rangle \in R_i$$

then

$$\langle e_{a_1}, \ldots, e_{a_{t(i)}} \rangle \in S_i, \qquad \text{so} \qquad \mathfrak{B} \models P_i(c_{a_1}, \ldots, c_{a_{t(i)}}), \ldots .$$

THEOREM 1.5.8. Let $\mathfrak{A} \in M(S)$, $S \subset \Sigma^t$, $c(t) + \omega \leq c(\mathfrak{A})$. For every infinite cardinal $\mathfrak{m} \geq c(\mathfrak{A})$, there is a $\mathfrak{B} \in M(S)$ such that $c(\mathfrak{B}) = \mathfrak{m}$ and $\mathfrak{A} \subset \mathfrak{B}$.

Proof: Let $T = Dg(\mathfrak{A}) \cup S$. Then $\mathfrak{A}' \in M(T)$, where $\mathfrak{A}' = \langle A, R_i \rangle_{i \in J}$ where J is the disjoint union of I and A, and for $a \in A$, $R_a = a$, and $\mathfrak{A}'$ is infinite. Thus for each finite number n, we have $\mathfrak{A}' \in M(T)$ with $n \leq c(\mathfrak{A}')$, and we are through, by Theorems 1.5.4 and 1.5.7 (also see Problem 1.5.12).

We now prove two more special results:

PROPOSITION 1.5.9. Let $\mathfrak{A} = \langle A, \leq \rangle$ be a partially ordered set. Then $\leq$ can be extended to a total order on A.

Proof: Consider $\mathfrak{A}' = \langle A, \leq, \leq' \rangle$ of type $\langle 2, 2 \rangle$, let P in our language correspond to $\leq$, P' correspond to $\leq'$, and write $Dg(\mathfrak{A})$ (in terms of P). Let S be the set of axioms for a totally ordered set expressed in terms of P', and let

$$F = (\forall v_0)(\forall v_1)(P(v_0, v_1) \to P'(v_0, v_1)).$$

$\mathfrak{B} \in M(S \cup \{F\})$ iff $\leq'$ is a total ordering and $\leq \subset \leq'$. Let

$$T = Dg(\mathfrak{A}) \cup S \cup \{F\}.$$

If T_1 is a finite subset of T, let

$$D = Dg(\mathfrak{A}) \cap T_1,$$

and let $c_{a_1}, \ldots, c_{a_n}$ be all the constants mentioned in D,

$$\mathfrak{A}_0 = \langle A_0, \leq \mid A_0 \rangle, \qquad \text{where} \quad A_0 = \{a_1, \ldots, a_n\}.$$

It can be shown that every partial ordering on a finite set can be extended to a total ordering (see Problem 1.5.2). So for some $\mathfrak{C}$,

$$\mathfrak{C} \models S \cup \{F\} \cup D,$$

and since $T_1 \subset S \cup \{F\} \cup D$,

$$\mathfrak{C} \models T_1.$$

By compactness, T is consistent, so let

$$\mathfrak{B} \in M(T), \qquad \mathfrak{B} = \langle B, \leq, \leq', e_a \rangle_{a \in A} \qquad \text{with} \quad \leq \subset \leq',$$

the latter a total ordering of B. By Theorem 1.5.7, we have

$$\mathfrak{B}' \subset \mathfrak{B}, \qquad f: \mathfrak{A} \cong \mathfrak{B}'/\langle 2 \rangle.$$

But $\leq' \restriction B'$ is a total ordering of B', so if

$$\mathfrak{A}' = \langle A, \leq, \leq^* \rangle,$$

where

$$\leq^* = \{\langle f^{-1}(x), f^{-1}(y) \rangle \mid \langle x, y \rangle \in \leq' \restriction B'\},$$

where f is our isomorphism, then $\leq^*$ is a total order extending $\leq$.

Corollary 1.5.10. Every set can be totally ordered.

Proof: $\mathfrak{A} = \langle A, = \rangle$ is a partially ordered set, and thus $=$ can be extended to a total order.

Proposition 1.5.11. Every field

$$\mathfrak{F} = \langle F, +, \cdot, 0, 1 \rangle$$

has an algebraic closure (i.e., a field containing $\mathfrak{F}$ together with a root for each polynomial over $\mathfrak{F}$ and such that each of its elements is a root for a polynomial over $\mathfrak{F}$).

Proof: By Problem 1.5.2, it suffices to show the existence of a field

$$\mathfrak{G} = \langle G, +, \cdot, 0, 1 \rangle$$

with $\mathfrak{F} \subset \mathfrak{G}$ and such that G contains a root for each polynomial with coefficients in F. Let T be the field axioms (see beginning of Section 1.3), and extend our language to that of the diagram $Dg(\mathfrak{F})$, and for a polynomial f over $\mathfrak{F}$, let

$$F_f = (\exists v_0)(c_{a_n} v_0^n + \cdots + c_{a_0} = 0),$$

where $f = a_n X^n + \cdots + a_0$ and is of positive degree. Then let

$$S = T \cup Dg(\mathfrak{F}) \cup \{F_f \mid f \text{ a polynomial over } \mathfrak{F} \text{ of degree at least } 1\},$$

and let $S' \subset S$ be finite. Then

$$S \subset T \cup Dg(\mathfrak{F}) \cup \{F_{f_1}, \ldots, F_{f_n}\}.$$

Most algebra texts contain the proof that given a field $\mathfrak{F}$ and a polynomial f over $\mathfrak{F}$, we can extend $\mathfrak{F}$ to a field $\mathfrak{G}$ containing a root for f (for example, see Fraleigh). Thus we may construct fields $\mathfrak{F}_1, \ldots, \mathfrak{F}_n$ such that

$$\mathfrak{F} \subset \mathfrak{F}_1 \subset \cdots \subset \mathfrak{F}_n$$

and f_i has a root in $\mathfrak{F}_i$. Clearly $\mathfrak{F} \subset \mathfrak{F}_n$ and $\mathfrak{F}_n$ contains roots for $f_1, \ldots, f_n$. Thus

$$\mathfrak{F}_n \models Dg(\mathfrak{F}) \cup T \cup \{F_{f_1}, \ldots, F_{f_n}\}.$$

By compactness, S is consistent, so we have $\mathfrak{G} \models S$ for some $\mathfrak{G}$. But then $\mathfrak{G}/\langle 3, 3, 0, 0\rangle$ is a field, $\mathfrak{F} \subset \mathfrak{G}'$, and for every polynomial over $\mathfrak{F}$ we have a root in $\mathfrak{G}'$.

Problems

1.5.1 (a) Give an example of a well-known axiom that cannot be replaced by an equivalent set of axioms in any Σ^t (what should *equivalent* mean here).

‡(b) Let t be a reduct of t', $S \subset \Sigma^t$, $F \in \Sigma^t$. Show that $S \models F$ (in Σ^t) iff $S \models F$ (in $\Sigma^{t'}$).

‡1.5.2 (a) Show that if $\langle A, \leq \rangle$ is a finite partially ordered set, then $\leq \subset \leq'$ for some total ordering $\leq'$ of A.

(b) Let $\mathfrak{F}$, $\mathfrak{G}$ be fields, $\mathfrak{F} \subset \mathfrak{G}$, and $\mathfrak{G}$ contain a root for every polynomial of positive degree over $\mathfrak{F}$. Show that $G \mid \{x \in G \mid$ for some $f \in \mathfrak{F}[X], f(x) = 0\}$ is a field that is an algebraic closure for $\mathfrak{F}$.

(Neither of these problems involves model theory. Each is placed here to complete a proof done in this section.)

1.5.3 (a) Let BA be the class of all Boolean algebras. Show that $BA \in EC$. $a \in \mathfrak{B} \in BA$ is called an *atom* iff $a \neq 0$ and for each $b \in \mathfrak{B}$, $ba = a$ or $ba = 0$. A Boolean algebra $\mathfrak{B}$ is called *atomistic* iff for each $a \in \mathfrak{B}$ there is an atom $b \in \mathfrak{B}$ such that $ab = b$. Show that $AB \in EC$, AB the class of atomistic Boolean algebras.

(b) Show that every Boolean algebra can be imbedded in an atomistic Boolean algebra.

(c) If $\mathfrak{B} = \langle B, +, \cdot, 0, 1\rangle$ is an atomistic Boolean algebra and $a \in B$, let

$$S_a = \{b \mid ba = b \neq 0 \text{ and for every } c \in B, bc = b \text{ or } bc = 0\}.$$

Show that

$$f : \mathfrak{B} \to \mathscr{P}\{b \in B \mid b \text{ an atom}\},$$

where $f(a) = S_a$ is an imbedding, thus that every atomistic Boolean algebra [and by (b) every Boolean algebra] can be imbedded in a Boolean algebra of sets.

‡1.5.4 $$Pd(\mathfrak{A}) = \{P_i(c_{a_1}, \ldots, c_{a_{t_i}}) \mid t(i) > 0, \langle a_1, \ldots, a_{t(i)} \rangle \in R_i\}$$
$$\cup \{c_a = c_i \mid t(i) = 0 \text{ and } a = R_i\} \subset \Sigma^{t'}$$

is called the positive diagram of $\mathfrak{A}$, where t' is the type of the diagram of $\mathfrak{A}$, as defined in remarks preceding Definition 1.5.6. Show that the f of Theorem 1.5.7 is a homomorphism iff the $\mathfrak{B}$ of 1.5.7 satisfies $Pd(\mathfrak{A})$.

1.5.5 An ordered group is a structure $\mathfrak{A} = \langle A, \cdot, e, \leq \rangle$ such that $\langle A, \cdot, e \rangle$ is a group, $\langle A, \leq \rangle$ a totally ordered set, and

$$\mathfrak{A} \models (\forall v_0)(\forall v_1)(\forall v_2)(v_0 \leq v_1 \to (v_0v_2 \leq v_1v_2 \wedge v_2v_0 \leq v_2v_1)).$$

A group $\mathfrak{B}$ is defined to be orderable iff $\mathfrak{B} = \mathfrak{A}/\langle 3, 0 \rangle$ for some ordered group $\mathfrak{A}$.

Let P be a set of sentences. $\mathfrak{A}$ is said to have P locally iff every finitely generated subgroup of $\mathfrak{A}$ satisfies P. Prove that a group which is locally orderable is orderable (first find P here).

Show that an Abelian group, all elements of which are infinite in order, is orderable.

Is it true that for every P that if $\mathfrak{A}$ has P locally then $\mathfrak{A}$ has P?

1.5.6 (a) Show that the class of Archimedean ordered fields is not in EC_Δ.
(b) Show that there is a non-Archimedean ordered field.

1.5.7 Show that the class of well-ordered sets is not an EC_Δ class.

1.5.8 Use an argument similar to that used to prove Theorem 1.4.9 to show that the condition "$c(t) + \omega \leq c(\mathfrak{A})$" of Theorem 1.5.8 can be weakened to "$c(S) + \omega \leq c(\mathfrak{A})$."

1.5.9 Show that the class K of algebraically closed fields is in EC_Δ but not in EC.

1.5.10 Let $S \subset \Sigma^t$ be such that if $F, G \in S$ then $F \vee G \in S$. If for some $K \in EC_\Delta$, $\mathfrak{A} \in M^t$,

$$T(K) \cap S \subset T(\mathfrak{A}) \cap S,$$

then for some $\mathfrak{B} \in K$,

$$T(\mathfrak{B}) \cap S \subset T(\mathfrak{A}) \cap S.$$

1.5.11 (a) Let $F \in \Sigma^{\langle 3,3,0,0 \rangle}$. Show that if $\mathfrak{F} \models F$ for every field of characteristic 0, then for some prime p_0, $\mathfrak{G} \models F$ for every field $\mathfrak{G}$ of characteristic $p > p_0$.
(b) Let $\mathfrak{F}$ be a field; $\mathfrak{F}[X_1, \ldots, X_n]$ will denote the set of polynomials in the n indeterminates $X_1, \ldots, X_n$ with coefficients in $\mathfrak{F}$, and the same notation will be used for rings. A polynomial in $\mathfrak{F}[X_1, \ldots, X_n]$ is called absolutely irreducible over $\mathfrak{F}$ iff it is not factorable in $\mathfrak{G}[X_1, \ldots, X_n]$ for any extension field $\mathfrak{G}$ of the field $\mathfrak{F}$. Show that $q \in \mathbb{Z}[X_1, \ldots, X_n]$ is absolutely irreducible over $\mathbb{Q}$ iff for some p_0 it is absolutely irreducible over every field of characteristic $p > p_0$.

‡1.5.12 The careful reader might note that in the proof of Theorem 1.5.8 we did not produce a $\mathfrak{B}$ with $\mathfrak{A} \subset \mathfrak{B}$, but rather one in which $\mathfrak{A}$ can be

imbedded. However, any reader this conscientious will be conscientious enough to check the following: Let

$$\mathfrak{B} = \langle B, S_i \rangle_{i \in I} \in M(S),$$

$f : \mathfrak{A} \to \mathfrak{B}$ an imbedding (such a $\mathfrak{B}$ exists by the proof of Theorem 1.5.8). Now let $h : (B \sim f[A]) \to D$ be a one–one onto map, $D \cap A = \phi$, and let $g : B \to C = A \cup D$ be defined by $g(b) = f^{-1}(b)$ if $b \in f[A]$, $g(b) = h(b)$ otherwise. For $t(i) > 0$, let

$$T_i = \{\langle g(b_1), \ldots, g(b_{t(i)}) \rangle \mid \langle b_1, \ldots, b_{t(i)} \rangle \in S_i\},$$

and for $t(i) = 0$, let $T_i = g(S_i)$. If $\mathfrak{C} = \langle C, T_i \rangle_{i \in I}$, then $g : \mathfrak{B} \cong \mathfrak{C}$ and $\mathfrak{A} \subset \mathfrak{C}$ (also $\mathfrak{C} \in M(S)$).

‡1.5.13 Use Problem 2.15 to show that if $S \subset L^t$ then $M(S) = M(T)$, where $T = \{(\forall v_{j_1}) \ldots (\forall v_{j_n})F \mid F \in S, FV(F) = \{v_{j_1}, \ldots, v_{j_n}\}\}$. Now show that compactness implies (thus is equivalent to) any of the statements in Theorem 5.1 with L^t substituted for Σ^t throughout.

1.6 Elementary Equivalence and Complete Theories

DEFINITION 1.6.1. Let $\mathfrak{A}, \mathfrak{B} \in M^t$. Then $\mathfrak{A}$ and $\mathfrak{B}$ are elementarily equivalent (written $\mathfrak{A} \equiv \mathfrak{B}$) iff $T(\mathfrak{A}) = T(\mathfrak{B})$.

It is obvious that $\equiv$ is an equivalence relation.

THEOREM 1.6.2. (a) If $\mathfrak{A}$ is finite and $\mathfrak{A} \equiv \mathfrak{B}$, then $\mathfrak{A} \cong \mathfrak{B}$.

(b) If $\mathfrak{A}$ is infinite and $c(t_{\mathfrak{A}}) + \omega \leq \mathfrak{m}$, then there is a $\mathfrak{B} \in M^{t_{\mathfrak{A}}}$ such that $c(\mathfrak{B}) = \mathfrak{m}$ and $\mathfrak{A} \equiv \mathfrak{B}$.

Proof: (a) is left to the reader in Problem 1.6.4.

(b) Let $T = T(\mathfrak{A})$. Then $c(T) + \omega \leq \mathfrak{m}$, and the rest follows from Löwenheim-Skolem and Theorem 1.3.3(j).

DEFINITION 1.6.3. A theory T is complete iff $T \neq \Sigma^t$ and for every $F \in \Sigma^t$, $F \in T$ or $\neg F \in T$.

THEOREM 1.6.4. Let $T \subset \Sigma^t$ be a theory. The following are equivalent:

(a) T is complete.

(b) For some $\mathfrak{A} \in M^t$, $T = T(\mathfrak{A})$.

(c) For every $\mathfrak{A}, \mathfrak{B} \in M(T)$, $\mathfrak{A} \equiv \mathfrak{B}$, and $M(T) \neq \phi$.

Proof: (a $\rightarrow$ b) was shown in Problem 1.3.2(b).

($b \rightarrow c$) Let $\mathfrak{A}$ be such that $T = T(\mathfrak{A})$. If $\mathfrak{B} \in M(T)$,

$$\mathfrak{B} \models T, \qquad \text{so} \quad T(\mathfrak{A}) = T \subset T(\mathfrak{B}).$$

Thus by Theorem 1.3.3(j), $T(\mathfrak{A}) = T(\mathfrak{B})$.

($c \rightarrow a$) Assume (c) and assume that T is not complete. Then we have an $F \in \Sigma^t$ such that $T \not\models F$ and $T \not\models \neg F$. Thus we have $\mathfrak{A} \in M(T)$ such that $\mathfrak{A} \models F$, $\mathfrak{B} \in M(T)$ such that $\mathfrak{B} \models \neg F$. Thus $T(\mathfrak{A}) \neq T(\mathfrak{B})$, a contradiction.

THEOREM 1.6.5 (Vaught's Condition). Let $c(t) \leq \omega$, $T \subset \Sigma^t$ with no finite models. If for some infinite $\mathfrak{m}$, T is categorical in cardinality $\mathfrak{m}$, then T is complete, where:

DEFINITION 1.6.6. T is categorical in cardinality $\mathfrak{m}$ iff for every $\mathfrak{A}$, $\mathfrak{B} \in M(T)$ such that $c(\mathfrak{A}) = c(\mathfrak{B}) = \mathfrak{m}$, $\mathfrak{A} \cong \mathfrak{B}$, and for some $\mathfrak{A} \in M(T)$, $c(\mathfrak{A}) = \mathfrak{m}$.

Proof of Theorem 1.6.5: Let $\mathfrak{A}$, $\mathfrak{B} \in M(T)$. Then $\mathfrak{A}$, $\mathfrak{B}$ are infinite, so we can find $\mathfrak{C}$, $\mathfrak{D}$ such that $\mathfrak{C} \equiv \mathfrak{A}$, $\mathfrak{D} \equiv \mathfrak{B}$ and $c(\mathfrak{C}) = c(\mathfrak{D}) = \mathfrak{m}$. Thus $\mathfrak{C} \cong \mathfrak{D}$, so by Theorem 1.2.11, $\mathfrak{C} \equiv \mathfrak{D}$. Thus $\mathfrak{A} \equiv \mathfrak{B}$.

Despite the simplicity of its proof, Vaught's condition is one of the most useful methods for proving a theory to be complete. More general theorems (with essentially the same proof—see Problem 1.6.1) are possible, but the particular importance of this version is demonstrated in the examples below.

DEFINITION 1.6.7. $\mathfrak{A} = \langle A, +, 0 \rangle$ is called a torsion-free divisible Abelian group iff $\mathfrak{A}$ is an Abelian group with at least two elements, and for every positive integer n:

(1n) $(\forall v_0)(v_0 \neq 0 \rightarrow v_0 + \cdots + v_0 \neq 0)$ (here we have n v_0's)

(2n) $(\forall v_0)(\exists v_1)(v_1 + \cdots + v_1 = v_0)$ (here we have n v_1's)

LEMMA 1.6.8. Let $\mathfrak{A}$ be a torsion-free divisible Abelian group. Then there is a $\cdot : \mathbb{Q} \times A \rightarrow A$ such that $\mathfrak{A}$ together with this multiplication forms a vector space over $\mathbb{Q}$.

Proof: Let $a \in A$, $m/n \in \mathbb{Q}$. Define $(m/n)a = mb$, where b is an element of A such that $nb = a$ (i.e., $b + \cdots + b = a$, with n b's). We first show our $\cdot$ to be well-defined: Let $m/n = m'/n'$. Then

$$\frac{m}{n}\,a = mb, \qquad \frac{m'}{n'}\,a = m'c, \qquad \text{where} \quad nb = a = n'c.$$

Thus

$$nn'(mb - m'c) = (mn')(nb) - (nm')(n'c) = (mn' - nm')a = 0,$$

so $mb = m'c$. The rules

$$\left(\frac{m}{n} + \frac{m'}{n'}\right) a = \frac{m}{n}\,a + \frac{m'}{n'}\,a,$$

$$\frac{m}{n}\,(a + b) = \frac{m}{n}\,a + \frac{m}{n}\,b,$$

$$1a = a,$$

$$\frac{m}{n}\left(\frac{m'}{n'}\,a\right) = \left(\frac{m}{n}\frac{m'}{n'}\right) a$$

must also be shown. We do the last here and leave the rest to the reader.

$$nn'\left[\frac{m}{n}\left(\frac{m'}{n'}\,a\right) - \left(\frac{m}{n}\frac{m'}{n'}\right) a\right]$$

$$= (mn')\left(\frac{m'}{n'}\,a\right) - mm'a = m\left(n'\left(\frac{m'}{n'}\,a\right)\right) - mm'a$$

$$= mm'a - mm'a = 0.$$

We note without proof that every vector space has a basis, and that every one–one correspondence between the bases of two vector spaces over the same field extends uniquely to an isomorphism between those spaces.

LEMMA 1.6.9. Let V be a vector space over $\mathfrak{F}$, $c(V) > c(\mathfrak{F}) + \omega$. If B is a basis for V, then $c(B) = c(V)$.

Proof: Let

$$R_n = \{a_1 b_1 + \cdots + a_n b_n \mid a_1, \ldots, a_n \in \mathfrak{F},\, b_1, \ldots, b_n \in B\}.$$

Then $V = \bigcup_{n<\omega} R_n$ and $c(R_n) \leq (c(\mathfrak{F})c(B))^n = c(\mathfrak{F})c(B)$ if $\mathfrak{F}$ or B is infinite and is finite otherwise. Thus in every case,

$$c(V) \leq \omega c(\mathfrak{F})c(B),$$

so if

$$c(V) > \omega + c(\mathfrak{F})(= \omega c(\mathfrak{F}))$$

we must have $c(V) = c(B)$.

PROPOSITION 1.6.10. The theory of torsion-free divisible Abelian groups ($\bigcap \{T(\mathfrak{A}) \mid \mathfrak{A}$ a torsion-free divisible Abelian group$\}$) is complete.

Proof: Let K be the class of torsion-free divisible Abelian groups. Then $K = M(T)$, where T is the theory with axioms

$$S = A \cup \{(1n) \mid n \in \omega\} \cup \{(2n) \mid n \in \omega\},$$

A the set of axioms for Abelian groups. All models of T by $(1n)$ of Definition 1.6.7 are infinite, and if $\mathfrak{A}$, $\mathfrak{B}$ are models of T with $c(\mathfrak{A}) = c(\mathfrak{B}) > \omega$, then we can find bases for $\mathfrak{A}$, $\mathfrak{B}$ as vector spaces over $\mathbb{Q}$. These bases are in one–one correspondence (since the cardinality of each is $c(\mathfrak{A})$ by Lemma 1.6.9), so $\mathfrak{A} \cong \mathfrak{B}$: i.e., K is categorical in every uncountable cardinality.

We now proceed to show that the class K_p of algebraically closed fields of characteristic p ($p = 0$ or p a prime), which is already known to be in EC_Δ, is the class of models of a complete theory. Let $\mathfrak{F} \subset \mathfrak{G}$, $\mathfrak{F}$, $\mathfrak{G}$ fields, and let $S = \{x_j \mid j \in J\} \subset G$. Then $\mathfrak{F}(S)$ (the smallest subfield of $\mathfrak{G}$ containing $\mathfrak{F}$ and S) is called a transcendental extension of $\mathfrak{F}$ iff $f\colon \mathfrak{F}[X] \to \mathfrak{F}(S)$ defined by

$$f(\textstyle\sum a(j_1, \ldots, j_n, k_1, \ldots, k_n)X_{j_1}^{k_1} \cdots X_{j_n}^{k_n}) = \textstyle\sum a(j_1, \ldots, j_n, k_1, \ldots, k_n)x_{j_1}^{k_1} \cdots x_{j_n}^{k_n}$$

is a one–one mapping, where

$$X = \{X_j \mid j \in J\}$$

and $\mathfrak{F}[X]$ is the ring of polynomials in all the variables X_j. In this case S is called a transcendence base for $\mathfrak{F}(S)$.

Let $\mathfrak{F}$, $\mathfrak{G}$ be fields, $\mathfrak{F} \subset \mathfrak{G}$. Then $\mathfrak{G}$ is called an algebraic extension of $\mathfrak{F}$ iff every element of $\mathfrak{G}$ is a root of some polynomial over $\mathfrak{F}$.

LEMMA 1.6.11. Let $\mathfrak{F}$, $\mathfrak{G}$ be fields, $\mathfrak{F} \subset \mathfrak{G}$. Then there is a maximal subfield $\mathfrak{H} \subset \mathfrak{G}$ which is a transcendental extension of $\mathfrak{F}$. Also, $\mathfrak{G}$ is an algebraic extension of $\mathfrak{H}$. Let S be a transcendence basis for $\mathfrak{H}$. Then if $c(\mathfrak{G}) > c(\mathfrak{F}) + \omega$,

$$c(S) = c(\mathfrak{H}) = c(\mathfrak{G}).$$

Finally, if $\mathfrak{F} \cong \mathfrak{F}'$ and S is in one–one correspondence with S', then $\mathfrak{F}(S) \cong \mathfrak{F}(S')$ for transcendence bases S, S'.

Proof: The proof is left to the reader with these comments: The existence of such a maximal $\mathfrak{H}$ is shown by Zorn's lemma. The fact that $\mathfrak{G}$ is an algebraicextension of $\mathfrak{H}$ is shown by otherwise contradicting the maximality of $\mathfrak{H}$. The fact that $c(\mathfrak{G}) = c(\mathfrak{H})$ can be shown by downward Löwenheim-Skolem.

The prime field of a field $\mathfrak{F}$ is defined to be the intersection of all subfields of $\mathfrak{F}$. It can be shown that if $\mathfrak{F}$ is of characteristic $p \neq 0$, then the prime field of $\mathfrak{F}$ is isomorphic to $\mathbb{Z}_p$, and if $p = 0$, then its prime field is isomorphic to $\mathbb{Q}$, thus it is always countable. By Lemma 1.6.11, every field is an algebraic extension of a transcendental extension of its prime field, and if its cardinality is uncountable, then the cardinality of the transcendence basis is its cardinality.

LEMMA 1.6.12. Let $\mathfrak{F}$, $\mathfrak{G}$ be algebraically closed fields of the same characteristic and same uncountable cardinality. Then $\mathfrak{F} \cong \mathfrak{G}$.

Proof: Let $\mathfrak{F}_p$, $\mathfrak{G}_p$ be the prime fields of $\mathfrak{F}$, $\mathfrak{G}$ respectively, and $\mathfrak{F}'$, $\mathfrak{G}'$ be maximal transcendental extensions of $\mathfrak{F}_p$, $\mathfrak{G}_p$ in $\mathfrak{F}$, $\mathfrak{G}$. Then by Lemma 1.6.11, $\mathfrak{F}' \simeq \mathfrak{G}'$. Thus let $f: \mathfrak{F}' \to \mathfrak{G}'$ be our isomorphism.

We now show that f can be extended to an isomorphism between $\mathfrak{F}$ and $\mathfrak{G}$. Zorn's lemma can be used to show that

$$f \subset g : \mathfrak{F}'' \cong \mathfrak{G}''$$

for some maximal field isomorphism g and fields $\mathfrak{F}''$, $\mathfrak{G}''$ such that

$$\mathfrak{F}' \subset \mathfrak{F}'' \subset \mathfrak{F}, \qquad \mathfrak{G}' \subset \mathfrak{G}'' \subset \mathfrak{G}.$$

If $\mathfrak{F} \neq \mathfrak{F}''$, then $\mathfrak{F}''$ is not algebraically closed (why?), so we may let $a_0 + \cdots + a_n X^n$ be a polynomial of degree > 1 over $\mathfrak{F}''$ irreducible over $\mathfrak{F}''$. Then $g(a_0) + \cdots + g(a_n)X^n$ is such a polynomial over $\mathfrak{G}''$. Let $b \in \mathfrak{F}$, $c \in \mathfrak{G}$ be roots for these. We leave the reader to check (or see in Dean, p. 210) that

$$h: \mathfrak{F}''(b) \cong \mathfrak{G}''(c),$$

where

$$h(d_0 + \cdots + d_{n-1}b^{n-1}) = g(d_0) + \cdots + g(d_{n-1})c^{n-1},$$

a contradiction to the maximality of g, thus $\mathfrak{F}'' = \mathfrak{F}$; but since the domain of g is algebraically closed, so is its range, thus it is $\mathfrak{G}$.

PROPOSITION 1.6.13. $T(K_p)$ is complete. (K_p is defined following the proof of Proposition 1.6.10.)

Proof: We have shown it to be categorical in every uncountable cardinality (in Lemma 1.6.12).

As a final example we consider the theory of dense linear ordering with no first or last element. Axioms for this theory in $\Sigma^{\langle 2\rangle}$ follow:

(01) $(\forall v_0)(\forall v_1)\neg(v_0 < v_1 \wedge v_1 < v_0)$.
(02) $(\forall v_0)(\forall v_1)(\forall v_2)(v_0 < v_1 \wedge v_1 < v_2 \rightarrow v_0 < v_2)$.
(03) $(\forall v_0)(\forall v_1)(v_0 < v_1 \vee v_0 = v_1 \vee v_1 < v_0)$

(These first three axioms say that we have a strict total order.)

(04) $(\forall v_0)(\exists v_1)(v_0 < v_1)$
(05) $(\forall v_0)(\exists v_1)(v_1 < v_0)$
(06) $(\forall v_0)(\forall v_1)(v_0 < v_1 \rightarrow (\exists v_2)(v_0 < v_2 \wedge v_2 < v_1))$

(Axioms (04) and (05) say that no first nor last element exists, while axiom (06) says that between any two elements there lies a third.)

THEOREM 1.6.14 (Cantor). Every two countable dense linearly ordered structures with no first or last element are isomorphic.

Proof: Let $\mathfrak{A} = \langle A, <\rangle$, $\mathfrak{B} = \langle B, <'\rangle$ be countable dense linearly ordered sets, and write

$$A = \{a_n \mid n \in \omega\}, \qquad B = \{b_n \mid n \in \omega\}.$$

We define f_n, a map from part of A into part of B by induction as follows: $f_0 = \{\langle a_0, b_0\rangle\}$. f_0 is clearly an isomorphism from its domain to its range. If n is even, define

$$f_{n+1} = f_n \cup \{\langle a, b\rangle\}$$

where $b = b_m$ for the first m such that $b_m \notin \mathscr{R}f_n$, and a is defined as follows: Let

$$\mathscr{R}f_n = \{b_{j_1}, \ldots, b_{j_n}\}, \qquad \text{where} \quad b_{j_1} < \cdots < b_{j_n}.$$

Either $b < b_{j_1}$ or for some $r \in n$,

$$b_{j_r} < b < b_{j_{r+1}}, \qquad \text{or} \qquad b_{j_n} < b.$$

Now let $a = a_{m'}$ for the first m' such that $a_{m'} \notin \mathscr{D}f_n$; and

$$\text{if} \quad b < b_{j_1}, \qquad \text{then} \quad a_{m.} < f_n^{-1}(b_{j_1});$$

$$\text{if} \quad b_{j_r} < b < b_{j_{r+1}}, \qquad \text{then} \quad f_n^{-1}(b_{j_r}) < a_{m'} < f_n^{-1}(b_{j_{r+1}});$$

$$\text{if} \quad b_{j_n} < b, \qquad \text{then} \quad f_n^{-1}(b_{j_n}) < a_{m'}.$$

On the assumption that f_n is an isomorphism (i.e., order-preserving) from its domain to its range, f_{n+1} is also clearly an isomorphism from its domain to its range. If n is odd, we reverse the roles of a and b. That is, we set $a = a_m$ for the first m, with $a_m \notin \mathscr{D}f_n$, and b is defined as follows: Let

$$\mathscr{D}f_n = \{a_{j_1}, \ldots, a_{j_n}\}, \qquad \text{where} \quad a_{j_1} < \cdots < a_{j_n}.$$

$a < a_{j_1}$, $a_{j_r} < a < a_{j_{r+1}}$, or $a_{j_n} < a$, and we set $b = b_{m'}$ for the first m' such that $b_{m'} \notin \mathscr{R}f_n$, and $b_{m'}$ falls in the same order among the $f_n(a_{j_r})$ as a_m falls among the a_{j_r}. The choice in any of these cases is possible by axioms (04) through (06), and the reader can show that our new map once again is an isomorphism from its domain to its range. If $n < n'$, $f_n \subset f_{n'}$ thus $f = \bigcup_{n \in \omega} f_n$ is a function. Also, if $a, a' \in \mathscr{D}f$, then $a, a' \in \mathscr{D}f_n$ for some n; thus since f_n is order-preserving, so is f. Since f is order-preserving, f is also one–one. To show that f is an isomorphism from $\mathfrak{A}$ onto $\mathfrak{B}$, it remains to be seen that $\mathscr{D}f = A$, $\mathscr{R}f = B$. Assume, then, that $\mathscr{D}f \neq A$. Then we can find a first m such that $a_m \notin \mathscr{D}f$. Thus for each $p < m$, $a_p \in \mathscr{D}f$. Therefore we can find a single n such that for $p < m$, $a_p \in \mathscr{D}f_n$. If n is odd, then by definition of f_{n+1}, $a_m \in \mathscr{D}f_{n+1}$. If n is even, then $a_m \in \mathscr{D}f_{n+1}$ or, by its definition, $a_m \in \mathscr{D}f_{n+2}$. The proof that $\mathscr{R}f = B$ is similar. Thus $f\colon \mathfrak{A} \to \mathfrak{B}$ is an isomorphism.

THEOREM 1.6.14 was proved in greater detail than the corresponding lemmas (1.6.8, 1.6.9, 1.6.11, and 1.6.12) were, and it was called a theorem to emphasize its importance. The reason for this importance is that its technique has proven useful in model theory. We shall refer to this theorem and its proof in the future and the reader would be well advised to understand it thoroughly (see Problem 1.6.5).

PROPOSITION 1.6.15. Let T be the theory of dense linear orderings with no first or last element. Then T is complete.

Proof: All models of T are infinite, since any finite totally ordered set must have a last element. Thus, since T is categorical in cardinality ω, T is complete.

DEFINITION 1.6.16. Let T be a theory. T' is a completion of T iff T' is a complete theory and $T \subset T'$.

DEFINITION 1.6.17. Let $S \subset L^t$. Then $B(S)$ is the smallest set R such that $S \subset R \subset L^t$, for every

$$F, G \in R, \qquad \neg F, F \vee G \in R, \qquad \text{and} \qquad \mathbb{T} = (\forall v_1)(v_1 = v_1) \in R.$$

$B(S)$ is called the set of Boolean combinations of S.

THEOREM 1.6.18. Let S be a consistent theory, and D a set of sentences such that for every completion T of S, there exists a set $B \subset D$ with

$$T(M(S \cup B)) = T.$$

Then for every $F \in \Sigma^t$, there is a $G \in B(D)$ such that $F \equiv_S G$.

Proof: Let

$$A = \{G \in B(D) \mid S \models (F \to G)\},$$

and assume that for no $G \in A$ do we have $S \models (G \to F)$. We assert that $S \cup A \cup \{\neg F\}$ is consistent—otherwise $S \cup A \models F$; so by compactness we have $G_1, \ldots, G_n \in A$ such that $S \models (G_1 \wedge \cdots \wedge G_n) \to F$. But $G_1 \wedge \cdots \wedge G_n \in A$ (why?), contradicting our assumption. Let $S \cup A \cup \{\neg F\} \subset T$ for some complete theory T. Then

$$T = T(M(S \cup B)) \qquad \text{for some } B \subset D.$$

Since $\neg F \in T$, $S \cup B \models \neg F$, thus we can find $H_1, \ldots, H_m \in B$ by compactness such that

$$S \cup \{H_1, \ldots, H_m\} \models \neg F;$$

thus by Problem 1.2.2(b),

$$S \models (H_1 \wedge \cdots \wedge H_m \to \neg F), \qquad \text{so} \quad S \models (F \to \neg(H_1 \wedge \cdots \wedge H_m));$$

thus

$$\neg(H_1 \wedge \cdots \wedge H_m) \in A \subset T.$$

Thus $H_1, \ldots, H_m, \neg(H_1 \wedge \cdots \wedge H_m) \in T$, a contradiction establishing our theorem.

We apply the above theorem in Problem 1.6.10.

Problems

‡1.6.1 (a) Let $c(t) \leq \omega$, $T \subset \Sigma^t$ with no finite models, T consistent. T is complete iff for some infinite $\mathfrak{m}$, when $\mathfrak{A}, \mathfrak{B} \in M(T)$ and $c(\mathfrak{A}) = c(\mathfrak{B}) = \mathfrak{m}$, then $\mathfrak{A} \equiv \mathfrak{B}$.

(b) Show that a theory T is complete if it has no finite models and for some $\mathfrak{m} \geq c(T)$, T is categorical in cardinality $\mathfrak{m}$.

1.6.2 (a) Find two countable nonisomorphic algebraically closed fields of characteristic p (for p prime or 0).

(b) Find two countable nonisomorphic torsion-free divisible Abelian groups.

(c) If (a, b) here denotes the open interval of real numbers between a and b, show that $(0, 1) \cup (1, 2)$ and $(0, 2)$ under the usual order form nonisomorphic dense linearly ordered sets of the same uncountable cardinality.

1.6.3 (a) Let T be the theory of infinite Abelian groups $\langle A, +, 0\rangle$ such that for every element $a \in A$, $a + a = 0$. Write a set of axioms for T and show that T is complete.

(b) Let $T \subset \Sigma^{\phi}$ be the theory of infinite sets. Show that T is complete.

(c) Let $\mathfrak{F}$ be a finite field, K the class of infinite vector spaces over $\mathfrak{F}$. Show that K is an EC_{Δ} class (see Problem 1.3.3 (d)), and that $T(K)$ is complete.

1.6.4 Let $\mathfrak{A}$, $\mathfrak{B}$ be finite. Show that $T(\mathfrak{A}) = T(\mathfrak{B})$ iff $\mathfrak{A} \cong \mathfrak{B}$.

1.6.5 Let $\mathfrak{A} \in M(T)$ be countable. We call $\mathfrak{A}$ ω-homogeneous-universal iff

(i) if $\mathfrak{C} \in M(T)$ is finite, then for some $\mathfrak{D} \subset \mathfrak{A}$, $\mathfrak{C} \cong \mathfrak{D}$, and

(ii) if $f : \mathfrak{C} \cong \mathfrak{D}$ and $\mathfrak{C}, \mathfrak{D} \in M(T)$ are finite substructures of $\mathfrak{A}$, then there is an automorphism g of $\mathfrak{A}$ such that $f \subset g$.

Note that $\langle \mathbb{Q}, \leq\rangle$ has these properties for the theory T of totally ordered sets.

If $\mathfrak{A}, \mathfrak{B} \in M(T)$ are countable ω-homogeneous-universal structures and each finite model of T is contained in a larger finite model, show that $\mathfrak{A} \cong \mathfrak{B}$.

1.6.6 Let $f_i(X_1, \ldots, X_{n_i})$, $i = 1, 2, \ldots$ be a sequence of polynomials with integer coefficients such that any finite number of the equations $f_i = 0$ have a common solution in $\mathbb{C}$. Prove that there is a common solution $a \in \mathbb{C}^{\omega}$ for all these equations (i.e., an a such that $f_i(a_1, \ldots, a_{n_i}) = 0$ for each $i \in \omega$). Is this result still true if $\mathbb{C}$ is replaced by the algebraic closure of $\mathbb{Q}$?

‡1.6.7 For $\mathfrak{A}_n = \langle[-n, n], \leq\rangle$, $n = 1, 2, \ldots$, $[-n, n]$, the closed interval in the reals, $<$ the usual order, show that $\mathfrak{A}_n \equiv \mathfrak{A}_m$ for any m, n. Also show that $\mathfrak{A}_n \not\equiv \bigcup_{n\in\omega} \mathfrak{A}_n$.

1.6.8 (a) Show that $\{T(\mathfrak{A}) \mid \mathfrak{A} \in M(T)\}$ is the set of completions of T.

(b) Find the set of completions of the theory of equality in Σ^{ϕ}.

1.6.9 Show that the class of non–well-ordered totally ordered sets is not in EC_{Δ}.

1.6.10 (a) Show that any two countable dense totally ordered structures are isomorphic if

(i) Both have first elements and neither has a last element;

(ii) Both have last elements, but neither has a first element;

(iii) Both have first and last elements, and these elements are distinct.

(b) Let $D = \{(04), (05)\}$. Show that for every $F \in \Sigma^{\langle 2\rangle}$, there is a $G \in B(D)$ such that

$$\{(01), (02), (03), (06), (\exists v_1)(\exists v_2)\neg(v_1 = v_2)\} \models (F \leftrightarrow G).$$

‡1.6.11 If $\mathfrak{m}$ is an infinite cardinal show that the theory $T_{\mathfrak{m}}$ with axioms $\{\geq_n \mid n < \omega\} \cup \{c_\alpha \neq c_\beta \rightarrow c_\gamma \neq c_\delta \mid \alpha < \beta < \mathfrak{m}, \gamma < \delta < \mathfrak{m}\}$ is categorical in each infinite cardinality $\mathfrak{p} < \mathfrak{m}$ and has only infinite models, but is not complete.

1.7 Elementary Extensions and Model-Completeness

It is often difficult to decide whether a theory is complete. The following concepts often prove useful for this purpose and many others.

DEFINITION 1.7.1. Let $\mathfrak{A} \subset \mathfrak{B}$, $\mathfrak{A}$, $\mathfrak{B} \in M^t$. Then $\mathfrak{A} < \mathfrak{B}$ ($\mathfrak{B}$ is an elementary extension of $\mathfrak{A}$ or $\mathfrak{A}$ an elementary substructure of $\mathfrak{B}$) iff for every $F \in L^t$, $a \in A^\omega$, $\mathfrak{A} \models F[a]$ iff $\mathfrak{B} \models F[a]$.

$\mathfrak{A} <' \mathfrak{B}$ iff there is a $\mathfrak{C} < \mathfrak{B}$ such that $\mathfrak{A} \cong \mathfrak{C}$. If f is this isomorphism, then we write $f\colon \mathfrak{A} <' \mathfrak{B}$.

Clearly if $\mathfrak{A} < \mathfrak{B}$, then $\mathfrak{A} \equiv \mathfrak{B}$. However, we can go further.

THEOREM 1.7.2. (a) $\mathfrak{A} <' \mathfrak{B}$ iff $\mathfrak{A}' \equiv \mathfrak{B}'$ in $L^{t'}$, where t' is the type of $Dg(\mathfrak{A})$, for some $\mathfrak{B}' \in M^{t'}$ such that $\mathfrak{B}'/t = \mathfrak{B}$, where

$$\mathfrak{A}' = \langle A, R_i, a\rangle_{i \in I, a \in A}.$$

(b) $\mathfrak{A} < \mathfrak{B}$ iff

$$\langle A, R_i, a\rangle_{i \in I, a \in A} \equiv \langle B, S_i, a\rangle_{i \in I, a \in A}.$$

Proof: We leave (a) to the reader in Problem 1.7.7. For (b) let $\mathfrak{B}'' = \langle B, S_i, a\rangle_{i \in I, a \in A}$, $\mathfrak{A}' \equiv \mathfrak{B}''$, $F \in L^t$, $a \in A^\omega$, and $FV(F) = \{v_{j_1}, \ldots, v_{j_n}\}$. Let

$$\varphi = \{\langle v_{j_1}, c_{a_{j_1}}\rangle, \ldots, \langle v_{j_n}, c_{a_{j_1}}\rangle\}, \qquad G = Sb_\varphi F \in \Sigma^{t'}.$$

Then $\mathfrak{A} \models F[a]$ iff $\mathfrak{A}' \models F[a]$ (by Problem 1.2.10) iff $\mathfrak{A}' \models G[a]$ (by Corollary 1.2.16(a), since $\varphi^*(a) = a$) iff $\mathfrak{A}' \models G$ (since G is a sentence) iff $\mathfrak{B}'' \models G$ (by elementary equivalence) iff $\mathfrak{B}'' \models G[a]$ iff $\mathfrak{B}'' \models F[a]$ iff $\mathfrak{B} \models F[a]$. Conversely, if $\mathfrak{A} < \mathfrak{B}$, $G \in \Sigma^{t'}$, let

$$\{c_{a_1}, \ldots, c_{a_n}\} = C(G) \sim C_t,$$

$$\{v_{k_1}, \ldots, v_{k_n}\} \notin V(G),$$

$$\psi = \{\langle c_{a_1}, v_{k_1}\rangle, \ldots, \langle c_{a_n}, v_{k_n}\rangle\}.$$

Then

$$F = Sb_\psi G \in L^t \qquad \text{and} \qquad G = Sb_{\psi^{-1}} F,$$

so $\mathfrak{A}' \models G$ iff $\mathfrak{A}' \models G\,[a]$ iff $\mathfrak{A} \models F[a(k_1 \mid a_1) \cdots (k_n \mid a_n)]$ iff

$$\mathfrak{B} \models F[a(k_1 \mid a_1) \cdots (k_n \mid a_n)]$$

iff $\mathfrak{B}'' \models G$.

THEOREM 1.7.3. $\mathfrak{A} \equiv \mathfrak{B}$ iff for some $\mathfrak{C}$,

$$\mathfrak{A} <' \mathfrak{C} \qquad \text{and} \qquad \mathfrak{B} <' \mathfrak{C}.$$

Proof: If $\mathfrak{A} <' \mathfrak{C}$ and $\mathfrak{B} <' \mathfrak{C}$, then

$$\mathfrak{A} \equiv \mathfrak{C} \equiv \mathfrak{B}, \qquad \text{so} \quad \mathfrak{A} \equiv \mathfrak{B}.$$

Conversely, let

$$t' = t \cup \{\langle a, 0\rangle \mid a \in A\}, \qquad t'' = \{\langle b, 0\rangle \mid b \in B\} \cup t,$$
$$t^* = t' \cup t''$$

(where we assume that A, B, $\mathscr{D}t$ are pairwise disjoint). By Theorem 1.7.2 it will do to show that $T(\mathfrak{A}') \cup T(\mathfrak{B}'')$ is consistent, where

$$\mathfrak{A}' = \langle A, R_i, a\rangle_{i \in I, a \in A}, \qquad \mathfrak{B}'' = \langle B, S_i, b\rangle_{i \in I, b \in B},$$

$T(\mathfrak{A}')$ is the theory of $\mathfrak{A}'$ (in $L^{t'}$), and $T(\mathfrak{B}'')$ is the theory of $\mathfrak{B}''$ (in $L^{t''}$). For if

$$\mathfrak{C} \in M^{t^*}, \mathfrak{C} \in M(T(\mathfrak{A}') \cup T(\mathfrak{B}''))$$

then

$$\mathfrak{C}/t' \equiv \mathfrak{A}' \qquad \text{and} \qquad \mathfrak{C}/t'' \equiv \mathfrak{B}'',$$

so

$$\mathfrak{A} <' \mathfrak{C}/t \qquad \text{and} \qquad \mathfrak{B} <' \mathfrak{C}/t.$$

Now let $S \subset T(\mathfrak{A}') \cup T(\mathfrak{B}'')$ be finite, $S = \{F_1, \ldots, F_n\} \cup \{G_1, \ldots, G_m\}$, with

$$F_1, \ldots, F_n \in T(\mathfrak{A}'), \qquad G_1, \ldots, G_m \in T(\mathfrak{B}'').$$

Set

$$F = F_1 \wedge \cdots \wedge F_n \subset T(\mathfrak{A}') \qquad \text{and} \qquad G = G_1 \wedge \cdots \wedge G_m \in T(\mathfrak{B}''),$$

and note that $\mathfrak{C} \models S$ iff $\mathfrak{C} \models F \wedge G$. Let $\{c_{a_1}, \ldots, c_{a_r}\} = C(F) \sim C_t$, $v_{j_1}, \ldots, v_{j_r} \notin V(F)$, then as in the proof of Theorem 1.7.2(b), since $\mathfrak{A}' \models F$,

$$\mathfrak{A} \models Sb_\varphi F[a(j_1 \mid a_1) \cdots (j_r \mid a_r)]$$

where

$$\varphi = \{\langle c_{a_k}, v_{j_k}\rangle \mid 1 \leq k \leq r\},$$

so $\mathfrak{B} \models (\exists v_{j_1}) \cdots (\exists v_{j_r}) Sb_\varphi F$, thus we can find $b_1, \ldots, b_r \in B$ such that if $b \in B^\omega$,

$$\mathfrak{B} \models Sb_\varphi F[b(j_1 \mid b_1) \cdots (j_r \mid b_r)].$$

Now let

$$\mathfrak{B}^* = \langle B, S_i, e_a, b\rangle_{i \in I, a \in A, b \in B}$$

with $e_{a_1} = b_1, \ldots, e_{a_r} = b_r$, the remainder of the e_a arbitrary. Now

$$\mathfrak{B}^* \models Sb_\varphi F[b(j_1 \mid b_1) \cdots (j_r \mid b_r)],$$

thus $\mathfrak{B}^* \models F$. Also $\mathfrak{B}^* \models G$ (since $\mathfrak{B}^*/t'' = \mathfrak{B}''$). Thus by compactness,

$$T(\mathfrak{A}') \cup T(\mathfrak{B}'')$$

is consistent.

COROLLARY 1.7.4. T is a complete theory iff for every $\mathfrak{A}, \mathfrak{B} \in M(T)$ there is a $\mathfrak{C}$ such that

$$\mathfrak{A} <' \mathfrak{C} \qquad \text{and} \qquad \mathfrak{B} <' \mathfrak{C}.$$

COROLLARY 1.7.5 (to Theorem 1.7.2). If $\mathfrak{m} \geq c(\mathfrak{A}) + c(t)$ and $\mathfrak{A}$ is infinite, then there is a $\mathfrak{B}$ such that

$$c(\mathfrak{B}) = \mathfrak{m} \qquad \text{and} \qquad \mathfrak{A} < \mathfrak{B}.$$

Proof: Apply Theorem 1.7.2 to Theorem 1.6.2(b).

The following is a useful criterion for determining whether $\mathfrak{A} < \mathfrak{B}$.

THEOREM 1.7.6. $\mathfrak{A} < \mathfrak{B}$ iff $\mathfrak{A} \subset \mathfrak{B}$ and for every $j \in \omega$, every $F \in L^t$, and every $a \in A^\omega$, if for some $b \in B$ $\mathfrak{B} \models F[a(j \mid b)]$, then there is a $c \in A$ such that $\mathfrak{B} \models F[a(j \mid c)]$.

Proof: Assume that our condition holds. We show that for every $F \in L^t$

$$(*) \qquad \text{if} \quad a \in A^\omega; \qquad \mathfrak{A} \models F[a] \qquad \text{iff} \quad \mathfrak{B} \models F[a]$$

by induction. If $F \in L^t(0)$, then (*) is implied by $\mathfrak{A} \subset \mathfrak{B}$. Assume that (*) holds for all $F \in L^t(k)$, and let

$$F \in L^t(k + 1) \sim L^t(k).$$

Then

$$F = \neg G, \qquad G \vee H, \qquad \text{or} \qquad (\exists v_j)G \qquad \text{for} \quad G, H \in L^t(k).$$

Since G, H satisfy (*), so do $\neg G$, $G \vee H$, so let $F = (\exists v_j)G$ and suppose that $\mathfrak{A} \models F[a]$. Then we may pick $c \in A$ such that

$$\mathfrak{A} \models G[a(j \mid c)].$$

By induction,

$$\mathfrak{B} \models G[a(j \mid c)], \qquad \text{so} \quad \mathfrak{B} \models (\exists v_j)G[a] = F[a].$$

"Conversely," let $\mathfrak{B} \models (\exists v_j)G[a]$. Then for some $b \in B$, $\mathfrak{B} \models G[a(j \mid b)]$. Thus for some $c \in A$,

$$\mathfrak{B} \models G[a(j \mid c)], \qquad \text{so} \qquad \mathfrak{A} \models G[a(j \mid c)]$$

by induction. Thus $\mathfrak{A} \models F[a]$. This establishes (*), so $\mathfrak{A} < \mathfrak{B}$.

Conversely, suppose

$$\mathfrak{A} < \mathfrak{B}, \qquad \mathfrak{B} \models F[a(j \mid b)],$$

with $a \in A^\omega$. Then

$$\mathfrak{A} \models (\exists v_j)F[a],$$

so we can find $c \in A$ such that

$$\mathfrak{A} \models F[a(j \mid c)].$$

Thus

$$\mathfrak{B} \models F[a(j \mid c)].$$

THEOREM 1.7.7. If

$$c(t) + \omega \leq \mathfrak{m} \leq c(\mathfrak{A}),$$

then there is a $\mathfrak{B} < \mathfrak{A}$, with $c(\mathfrak{B}) = \mathfrak{m}$.

Proof: As in the proof of downward Löwenheim-Skolem, let

$$B_0 \subset A, \qquad c(B_0) = \mathfrak{m}.$$

Assume now that we have constructed $B_j \supset B_0$. Let

$$S_j = \{b \in B_j^\omega \mid \text{for some } n \in \omega, \text{ if } k \geq n \text{ then } b_k = b_n\}.$$

S_j then is the set of eventually constant sequences in B_j. Note that

$$S_j = \bigcup_{n<\omega} S_j^{(n)},$$

where

$$S_j^{(n)} = \{b \in B_j^\omega \mid \text{if } k \geq n,\ b_k = b_n\}.$$

Thus

$$c(S_j) \geq c(B_j),$$

but

$$c(S_j) \leq \sum_{n<\omega} c(S_j^{(n)}) = \sum_{n<\omega} c(B_j)^{n+1} = \sum_{n<\omega} c(B_j) = c(B_j),$$

so $c(S_j) = c(B_j)$. We now define $f\colon S_j \times \omega \times L^t \to A$ as follows: If for some $a \in A$,

$$\mathfrak{A} \models F[b(k \mid a)] \qquad (b \in S_j, k \in \omega, F \in L^t),$$

then by the axiom of choice pick such an a and let $f(b, k, F) = a$. If for no $a \in A$ does this occur, then let $f(b, k, F) = b_k$. Now let $B_{j+1} = B_j \cup \mathscr{R}f$.

$$c(\mathscr{R}f) \leq c(\mathscr{D}f) = c(B_j) \cdot \omega \cdot c(t) = c(B_j).$$

Thus

$$c(B_j) \leq c(B_{j+1}) \leq c(B_j) + c(B_j) = c(B_j).$$

Thus by induction, $c(B_j) = c(B_0)$. Let $B = \bigcup_{j<\omega} B_j$, and note that $c(B) = c(B_0)$. Let

$$F \in L^t, \qquad a \in A, \qquad \{v_{k_1}, \ldots, v_{k_n}\} = FV(F),$$

and assume that

$$\mathfrak{A} \models F[b(j \mid a)], \qquad \text{where} \quad b \in B^{\omega}.$$

Then let $k \geq k_1, \ldots, k_n$, and let $c \in B^{\omega}$ be such that

$$c_r = b_r \qquad \text{for} \quad r \leq k, \qquad c_r = c_k \qquad \text{for} \quad r > k.$$

By Theorem 1.2.7,

$$\mathfrak{A} \models F[b(j \mid a)] \qquad \text{iff} \quad \mathfrak{A} \models F[c(j \mid a)].$$

Since $c \in B^{\omega}$, $c_1 \in B_{j_1}, \ldots, c_k \in B_{j_k}$, so let $j' = \max\{j_1, \ldots, j_k\}$. Thus $c \in B^{\omega}_{j'}$; in fact, $c \in S_{j'}$; and since $\mathfrak{A} \models F[c(j \mid a)]$,

$$F(c, j, F) \in B_{j'+1}, \qquad \text{and} \qquad \mathfrak{A} \models F[c(j \mid f(c, j, F))]$$

by definition of f. But we have now found $d = f(c, j, F) \in B$ such that $\mathfrak{A} \models F[b(j \mid d)]$. Thus if $\mathfrak{B} = \mathfrak{A} \mid B$, then $\mathfrak{B} \subset \mathfrak{A}$ and the condition of Theorem 1.7.6 is met, so

$$\mathfrak{B} < \mathfrak{A}, \qquad c(\mathfrak{B}) = c(B_0) = \mathfrak{m}.$$

Note that Theorem 1.7.7 implies downward Löwenheim-Skolem, and its proof is independent of the proof of that theorem.

In Problem 1.6.7, an example of structures $\mathfrak{A}_n$ with

$$\mathfrak{A}_n \subset \mathfrak{A}_m, \qquad \mathfrak{A}_n \equiv \mathfrak{A}_m \qquad \text{for} \quad n < m$$

was developed such that

$$\mathfrak{A}_n \not\equiv \bigcup_{n<\omega} \mathfrak{A}_n.$$

However, $<$ is better behaved.

THEOREM 1.7.8. Let $\mathscr{A}$ be a set of structures directed by $<$ (i.e., such that if $\mathfrak{A}, \mathfrak{B} \in \mathscr{S}$, then for some $\mathfrak{C} \in \mathscr{A}$, $\mathfrak{A} < \mathfrak{C}$ and $\mathfrak{B} < \mathfrak{C}$). Then for every $\mathfrak{A} \in \mathscr{S}$, $\mathfrak{A} < \bigcup \mathscr{S}$.

Proof: We already know that every $\mathfrak{A} \subset \bigcup \mathscr{S}$. Now we show by induction that for $F \in L^t$, $a \in A^{\omega}$,

$$\mathfrak{A} \models F[a] \qquad \text{iff} \quad \bigcup \mathscr{S} \models F[a].$$

For $F \in L^t(0)$, this is precisely the statement that $\mathfrak{A} \subset \bigcup \mathscr{S}$. For $F = \neg G$ or $G \vee H$, the induction step is trivial, thus let $F = (\exists v_j)G$. Clearly if

$\mathfrak{A} \models (\exists v_j)G[a]$, then for some $c \in A$, $\mathfrak{A} \models G[a(j \mid c)]$, thus by induction $\bigcup \mathscr{S} \models G[a(j \mid c)]$, so $\bigcup \mathscr{S} \models F[a]$. If

$$\bigcup \mathscr{S} \models (\exists v_j)G[a] \qquad (\text{with } a \in A^\omega)$$

then we have

$$\bigcup \mathscr{S} \models G[a(j \mid b)] \qquad \text{for some } b.$$

Now since $b \in \bigcup \{A_\mathfrak{B} \mid \mathfrak{B} \in \mathscr{S}\}$, for some $\mathfrak{B} \in \mathscr{S}$, $b \in A_\mathfrak{B} = B$. Thus let $\mathfrak{C} \in \mathscr{S}$ be such that $\mathfrak{A} < \mathfrak{C}$, $\mathfrak{B} < \mathfrak{C}$. By induction,

$$\mathfrak{C} \models G[a(j \mid b)], \qquad \text{thus} \quad \mathfrak{C} \models (\exists v_j)G[a], \qquad \text{thus} \quad \mathfrak{A} \models (\exists v_j)G[a].$$

THEOREM 1.7.9. Let $\mathfrak{A} \subset \mathfrak{B}$. If for every $n \in \omega$, $a_1, \ldots, a_n \in A$, $b \in B$, there is an automorphism f of $\mathfrak{B}$ such that for $j = 1, \ldots, n$, $f(a_j) = a_j$ and $f(b) \in A$, then $\mathfrak{A} < \mathfrak{B}$.

Proof: Suppose that $\mathfrak{B} \models F[a(j \mid b)]$ with $a \in A^\omega$, and let

$$\{v_{j_1}, \ldots, v_{j_n}\} = FV(F) \sim \{v_j\},$$

and let f be an automorphism of $\mathfrak{B}$ such that

$$f(a_{j_1}) = a_{j_1}, \ldots, f(a_{j_n}) = a_{j_n}, f(b) \in A.$$

Thus

$$\mathfrak{B} \models F[f \circ a(j \mid b)].$$

But

$$\text{for} \quad v_k \in FV(F) \sim \{v_j\}, \qquad f(a_k) = a_k,$$

so $f(a(j \mid b)_k) = a(j \mid b)_k$, so $\mathfrak{B} \models F[f \circ a(j \mid b)]$ iff $\mathfrak{B} \models F[a(j \mid f(b))]$. Thus there is a $c \in A$ such that $\mathfrak{B} \models F[a(j \mid c)]$.

DEFINITION 1.7.10. Let T be a theory. T is model-complete iff for every $\mathfrak{A}, \mathfrak{B} \in M(T)$, if $\mathfrak{A} \subset \mathfrak{B}$ then $\mathfrak{A} < \mathfrak{B}$.

Theorem 1.7.2 now yields A. Robinson's original definition of model-completeness (see his [1]). Much of what follows in this and the next section originated (in somewhat different form) in that book.

PROPOSITION 1.7.11. T is model-complete iff for every $\mathfrak{A} \in M(T)$, $T \cup Dg(\mathfrak{A})$ is a complete theory.

Completeness does not imply model-completeness, nor does model-completeness imply completeness. For example, the theory of algebraically closed fields is model-complete, but not complete, since we have not decided the characteristic of our field. The theory of dense linear orderings with distinct first and last elements is complete (see Problem 1.6.10) but not model-complete, since if

$$\mathfrak{A}_1 = \langle[-1, 1], < \rangle, \qquad \mathfrak{A}_2 = \langle[-2, 2], < \rangle,$$

then $\mathfrak{A}_1, \mathfrak{A}_2$ are models of this theory and $\mathfrak{A}_1 \subset \mathfrak{A}_2$. However, $\mathfrak{A}_1 \nprec \mathfrak{A}_2$ for if $F = (\exists v_0)(v_0 < v_1)$, then $\mathfrak{A}_2 \models F[-1]$, but $\mathfrak{A}_1 \not\models F[-1]$. Other examples will be given in the problems. However, the two notions are closely connected, and completeness can often be deduced from model-completeness in the presence of other properties. For example:

PROPOSITION 1.7.12. Let T be model-complete, and
(a) let $\mathfrak{A} \in M(T)$ be such that if $\mathfrak{B} \in M(T)$, then $\mathfrak{A}' \subset \mathfrak{B}$ for some $\mathfrak{A}' \cong \mathfrak{A}$; or
(b) for every $\mathfrak{A}, \mathfrak{B} \in M(T)$, let there be a $\mathfrak{C} \in M(T)$ such that $\mathfrak{A} \subset \mathfrak{C}$ and $\mathfrak{B} \cong \mathfrak{D}$ for some $\mathfrak{D} \subset \mathfrak{C}$.
Then T is complete.

(The proof is clear and left for the reader in Problem 1.7.6.)

DEFINITION 1.7.13. F is existential iff $F \in P^t$ and for every $G \in SF(F) \sim QF^t$, $G = (\exists v_j)H$ for some H, j. F is universal iff $F \in P^t$ and for every $G \in P^t \cap (SF(F) \sim QF^t)$, $G = (\forall v_j)H$ for some H, j. (Thus existential formulas are those in prenex form using only existential quantifiers, etc.)

The reason for the introduction of the above definition at this point is that we shall show a theory to be model-complete iff it implies that every universal formula is equivalent to an existential formula. We need the following:

DEFINITION 1.7.14. Let $S \subset \Sigma^t$. $F \in L^t$ persists with respect to S iff for every $\mathfrak{A}, \mathfrak{B} \in M(S)$, $a \in A^\omega$, if $\mathfrak{A} \models F[a]$ and $\mathfrak{A} \subset \mathfrak{B}$, then $\mathfrak{B} \models F[a]$.

It can be shown by induction (on P^t) that if F is existential then F persists with respect to any S. Also note that if $F_1, \ldots, F_n$ are existential (or universal), then $F_1 \wedge \cdots \wedge F_n$, $F_1 \vee \cdots \vee F_n$ are equivalent to existential (universal) formulas (see Problem 1.4.1(b) through (d) for an indication of the proof for this).

THEOREM 1.7.15. $F \in \Sigma^t$ is persistent relative to $S \subset \Sigma^t$ iff for some existential sentence $G \in \Sigma^t$, $F \equiv_S G$.

Proof: The proof that if $F \equiv_S G$ for some existential G, then F persists with respect to S, is left to the reader (Problem 1.7.1).

Conversely, suppose F persists with respect to S. Let

$$T = \{G \in \Sigma^t \mid G \text{ existential and } S \models (G \rightarrow F)\}.$$

$$(\exists v_0)\neg(v_0 = v_0) \in T, \qquad \text{so} \quad T \neq \phi.$$

Assume by way of contradiction that for no $G \in T$ do we have $S \models (F \rightarrow G)$. Thus $S \cup \{F\} \cup \{\neg G \mid G \in T\}$ is consistent: any finite subset $V \subset S \cup \{F\} \cup \{\neg G \mid G \in T\}$ is a subset of $S \cup \{F\} \cup \{\neg G_1, \ldots, \neg G_n\}$, $n \geq 1$, but $S \cup \{F\} \not\models G_1 \vee \cdots \vee G_n$ (since $G_1 \vee \cdots \vee G_n$ is equivalent to an element of T) and

$$\mathfrak{A} \models S \cup \{F\} \cup \{\neg(G_1 \vee \cdots \vee G_n)\}$$

iff

$$\mathfrak{A} \models S \cup \{F\} \cup \{\neg G_1, \ldots, \neg G_n\},$$

so $\mathfrak{A} \models V$. Thus let

$$\mathfrak{A} \models S \cup \{F\} \cup \{\neg G \mid G \in T\}.$$

Then $\mathfrak{A} \models S \cup \{F\}$, so $Dg(\mathfrak{A}) \cup S \cup \{\neg F\}$ is not consistent, since any $\mathfrak{B} \in M(Dg(\mathfrak{A}) \cup S)$ must contain (up to isomorphism and reducts) $\mathfrak{A}$, and since F is persistent with respect to S, $\mathfrak{B} \models F$. Therefore, for some finite $D \subset Dg(\mathfrak{A})$, $S \cup D \models F$; so

$$S \vdash (D_1 \wedge \cdots \wedge D_r) \rightarrow F, \qquad \text{where} \quad D = \{D_1, \ldots, D_r\}.$$

Since $D_j \in Dg(\mathfrak{A})$,

$$D_j = P_i(c_{a_1}, \ldots, c_{a_{t(i)}}) \qquad \text{or} \qquad D_j = (c_i = c_a), \text{ etc.}$$

Thus

$$D_1 \wedge \cdots \wedge D_r = Sb^{v_1, \ldots, v_n}_{c_{a_1}, \ldots, c_{a_n}} G \qquad \text{for some} \quad G \in QF^t$$

with $FV(G) = \{v_1, \ldots, v_n\}$. Since $c_{a_1}, \ldots, c_{a_n}$ do not occur in S nor in F, we have $S \models G \rightarrow F$ (by Corollary 1.2.16(c)). Thus by Problem 1.2.2(e), $S \models (\exists v_1) \cdots (\exists v_n)G \rightarrow F$. So $(\exists v_1) \cdots (\exists v_n)G \in T$, and this contradicts the assumption that for no $H \in T$ do we have $\mathfrak{A} \models H$.

COROLLARY 1.7.16. $F \in L^t$ is persistent relative to S iff there is an existential G such that $S \models (F \leftrightarrow G)$.

Proof: Proceed as above with appropriate constants added to the language.

The above are examples of preservation theorems, i.e., theorems of the form "F is preserved under ____________ iff F is of the following form: - - - - - - - - - - - - -." In this case, preservation under extensions is equivalent to being equivalent to an existential formula. We shall see other preservation theorems.

THEOREM 1.7.17 (Robinson's Test for Model-Completeness). S is model-complete iff for every $\mathfrak{A}, \mathfrak{B} \in M(S)$ with $\mathfrak{A} \subset \mathfrak{B}$, every universal formula F and every $a \in A^\omega$, if $\mathfrak{A} \models F[a]$, then $\mathfrak{B} \models F[a]$. (In other words: If and only if every universal formula persists with respect to S.)
Proof: Model-completeness trivially implies our condition. Conversely, assume the condition to hold. Thus for every universal F there is an existential E such that $F \equiv_S E$. We contend that every formula is equivalent to an existential formula. Thus for $F \in L^t$, let $F \equiv_S G$, $G \in P^t$. If $G \in P^t(0)$, then G is existential. Thus let $G \in P^t(n + 1)$. The case $G = (\exists v_{j_{n+1}})H$ is trivial, so assume that $G = (\forall v_{j_{n+1}})H$. Thus, $\neg G \equiv (\exists v_{j_{n+1}})\neg H$. But $\neg H \equiv_S H'$ for some existential H'. Thus

$$G \equiv_S (\forall v_{j_{n+1}})\neg H' \equiv_S U$$

for some universal formula U (see Problem 1.7.1). However, by hypothesis, $U \equiv_S E$ for some existential formula E, and our induction is completed.

Thus every formula $F \in L^t$ is equivalent to an existential formula with respect to S. Now let $\mathfrak{A}, \mathfrak{B} \in M(S)$, $\mathfrak{A} \subset \mathfrak{B}$, and $\mathfrak{A} \models F[a]$. Since $F \equiv_S G$ for some existential G, $\mathfrak{A} \models G[a]$, so $\mathfrak{B} \models G[a]$, thus $\mathfrak{B} \models F[a]$. If $\mathfrak{B} \models F[a]$, $\mathfrak{A} \not\models F[a]$, then $\mathfrak{A} \models \neg F[a]$, thus $\mathfrak{B} \models \neg F[a]$, a contradiction.

We now show that the theory of torsion-free divisible Abelian groups (see Definition 1.6.7) is model-complete. Let T be this theory, and let

$$\mathfrak{A} \in M(T), \qquad \mathfrak{B}, \mathfrak{C} \in M(T \cup Dg(\mathfrak{A})).$$

Let

$$\mathfrak{A} \cong \mathfrak{A}' \subset \mathfrak{B}/t, \qquad \mathfrak{A} \cong \mathfrak{A}'' \subset \mathfrak{C}/t.$$

If

$$c(\mathfrak{B}) = c(\mathfrak{C}) > c(\mathfrak{A}),$$

then we extend the bases of $\mathfrak{A}'$, $\mathfrak{A}''$ to bases for $\mathfrak{B}$, $\mathfrak{C}$ (as vector spaces over $\mathbb{Q}$). A one-one correspondence between these bases can be found, giving rise to an isomorphism from $\mathfrak{B}$ to $\mathfrak{C}$ such that for the distinguished elements R_a, S_a in $\mathfrak{A}'$, $\mathfrak{A}''$, $f(R_a) = S_a$. Thus f is an isomorphism in the type of $Dg(\mathfrak{A})$; so $T \cup Dg(\mathfrak{A})$ is categorical in any cardinality $> c(\mathfrak{A})$ and has no models of cardinality $< c(\mathfrak{A})$. Thus by the extension of Vaught's condition given in Problem 1.6.1(b), the theory for which $T \cup Dg(\mathfrak{A})$ forms axioms is complete. Thus by Proposition 1.7.11, T is model-complete.

Problems

‡1.7.1 (a) Show that an existential formula persists with respect to any S. Also show that for any two existential formulas F, G, $F \vee G$ and $F \wedge G$ are equivalent to existential formulas.

(b) Show that the negation of any existential formula is equivalent to a universal formula, and the negation of a universal formula is equivalent to an existential formula.

(c) Show that every universal formula is equivalent with respect to S to an existential formula iff every existential formula is equivalent with respect to S to a universal formula.

1.7.2 Give an example of $\mathfrak{A}$, $\mathfrak{B} \in M(T)$, T complete, such that $A \cap B = \phi$ but there is no $\mathfrak{C} \in M(T)$ such that

$$\mathfrak{A} \cong \mathfrak{A}' < \mathfrak{C}, \qquad \mathfrak{B} \cong \mathfrak{B}' < \mathfrak{C}, \qquad \text{and} \qquad A' \cap B' = \phi.$$

1.7.3 (a) Show that the theories mentioned in Problem 1.6.3 are all model-complete.

(b) (A. Robinson) Show that the theory of algebraically closed fields is model-complete.

(c) (A. Robinson) Let $\mathfrak{F}$ be an algebraically closed field,

$$f \in \mathfrak{F}[X_1, \ldots, X_n]$$

(a polynomial in n variables over $\mathfrak{F}$). If for some extension $\mathfrak{G}$ of $\mathfrak{F}$, f has a root $\langle x_1, \ldots, x_n \rangle \in G^n$, show that it has a root in F^n.

1.7.4 Give a definition for $<'$ not involving $<$, and a theorem corresponding to 7.6 for $<'$.

1.7.5 Let $c(t) \leq \omega$.

(a) Show that if $\mathfrak{m}$ is an infinite cardinal, then there are at most $2^{\mathfrak{m}}$ nonisomorphic $\mathfrak{A} \in M^t$ such that $c(\mathfrak{A}) \leq \mathfrak{m}$. (Hint: Choose an A such that $c(A) = \mathfrak{m}$, and find out how many different structures exist with universe A.)

(b) If $T \subset \Sigma^t$ is complete, show that for every infinite cardinal $\mathfrak{m}$, there is an $\mathfrak{A} \in M(T)$ such that $c(\mathfrak{A}) \leq 2^{\mathfrak{m}}$, and that for every $\mathfrak{B} \in M(T)$, if $c(\mathfrak{B}) \leq \mathfrak{m}$, then $\mathfrak{B} <' \mathfrak{A}$.

‡1.7.6 (a) Show that Theorem 1.7.7 implies downward Lôwenheim-Skolem.

(b) Prove Proposition 1.7.12.

‡1.7.7 (a) Prove Theorem 1.7.2 (a).

(b) Prove Corollary 1.7.4.

1.7.8 (a) Let $\mathfrak{A}$ be a countable, dense, totally ordered structure with no first or last elements, and f be a one–one order-preserving correspondence between two subsets of A, each with n elements. Show that f can be extended to an automorphism of $\mathfrak{A}$. Need this be true if $\mathfrak{A}$ is uncountable?

(b) Show that there are two countable subsets of A and an isomorphism between them that cannot be extended to an automorphism of $\mathfrak{A}$.

(c) Use Part (a) and Theorem 1.6.18 to show that for every positive integer n, if $F \in \Sigma^{\langle 2,0,\cdots,0\rangle}$ (n 0's), then $F \equiv_S G$ for some

$$G \in B(\{c_r < c_s \mid r \neq s, 1 \leq r, s \leq n\}),$$

where S is the set of axioms for dense, totally ordered structures with no first or last element.

(d) Now show that the theory of dense totally ordered structures with no first or last element is model-complete, but the theories with first or last element (or both) are not.

1.7.9 Show that if $\mathfrak{A} < \mathfrak{B}$ and $\mathfrak{B} < \mathfrak{C}$, then $\mathfrak{A} < \mathfrak{C}$; and that if $f : \mathfrak{A} <' \mathfrak{B}$ and $g : \mathfrak{B} <' \mathfrak{C}$, then $g \circ f : \mathfrak{A} <' \mathfrak{C}$. Also show that if $\mathfrak{A} \subset \mathfrak{B} < \mathfrak{C}$ and $\mathfrak{A} < \mathfrak{C}$, then $\mathfrak{A} < \mathfrak{B}$.

‡1.7.10 Let $S \subset L^t$. $\mathfrak{A} <_S \mathfrak{B}$ iff $\mathfrak{A} \subset \mathfrak{B}$ and for each $a \in A^\omega$, $F \in S$, $\mathfrak{A} \models F[a]$ iff $\mathfrak{B} \models F[a]$.

(a) Establish the following generalization of Theorem 1.7.8: If $\mathscr{A}$ is directed by $<_S$ and S is closed under subformulas (i.e., if $F \in S$ then $SF(F) \subset S$) then for each $\mathfrak{A} \in \mathscr{A}$, $\mathfrak{A} <_S \cup \mathscr{A}$.

(b) Also extend Theorem 1.7.6 to this situation.

1.8 Real-Closed Fields

Definition 1.8.1. (a) A field $\mathfrak{F}$ is formally real iff for no $x_1, \ldots, x_n \in F$ is $x_1^2 + \cdots + x_n^2 = -1$.

(b) A field $\mathfrak{F}$ is real-closed iff $\mathfrak{F}$ is formally real and has no proper formally real algebraic extensions.

Theorem 1.8.2. (a) $\mathfrak{F}$ is real-closed iff $\mathfrak{F}$ is formally real and:

(i) every polynomial of odd degree has a root in F;

(ii) if $a \in F$, then for some $b \in F$, $b^2 = a$ or $b^2 = -a$.

(b) If $\mathfrak{F}$ is real-closed then every polynomial in $\mathfrak{F}[X]$ is the product of polynomials of degree at most 2.

(c) If $\mathfrak{F}$ is real-closed and $i^2 = -1$, then $\mathfrak{F}(i)$ is algebraically closed.

For the proofs of the above the reader is referred to *Modern Algebra*, Vol. I, by Van der Waerden (pp. 225–234). We also use comments we made following Proposition 1.6.10.

Theorem 8.2 implies that the class of real-closed fields is in EC_Δ. In fact, our axioms for real-closed fields are the field axioms together with:

($r1$) $(\forall v_0)(\exists v_1)(v_0 = v_1^2 \vee v_0 + v_1^2 = 0)$;

($r2_p$) $(\forall v_0)\cdots(\forall v_p)(\exists v_{p+1})(v_0 + \cdots + v_p v_{p+1}^p = 0)$ for every odd p;

($r3_n$) $(\forall v_0)\cdots(\forall v_n)(v_0^2 + \cdots + v_n^2 + 1 \neq 0)$ for every positive n.

DEFINITION 1.8.3. (a) $\mathfrak{A} = \langle F, +, \cdot, 0, 1, < \rangle$ of type $\langle 3, 3, 0, 0, 2 \rangle$ is an ordered field iff $\langle F, +, \cdot, 0, 1 \rangle$ is a field, $\langle F, +, 0, < \rangle$ an ordered group (see Problem 1.5.5 for definition), and

$$(\forall v_0)(\forall v_1)(0 < v_0 \wedge 0 < v_1 \rightarrow 0 < v_0 v_1)$$

is satisfied by $\mathfrak{A}$.

(b) A field $\mathfrak{F}$ is orderable iff $\mathfrak{F} = \mathfrak{A}/\langle 3, 3, 0, 0 \rangle$ for some ordered field $\mathfrak{A}$. (Note that every orderable field is formally real.)

THEOREM 1.8.4. If $\mathfrak{F}$ is formally real, then there is a real-closed field $\mathfrak{G}$ such that $\mathfrak{F} \subset \mathfrak{G}$.

Proof: Let $\mathfrak{H}$ be the algebraic closure of $\mathfrak{F}$ ($\mathfrak{H}$ is not formally real because $x^2 + 1 = 0$ has a solution). The set of fields

$$\mathcal{S} = \{\mathfrak{E} \mid \mathfrak{F} \subset \mathfrak{E} \subset \mathfrak{H}, \mathfrak{E} \text{ formally real}\}$$

satisfies Zorn's condition; thus by Zorn's lemma there is a maximal such $\mathfrak{E}$, say $\mathfrak{G}$. Clearly $\mathfrak{F} \subset \mathfrak{G} \subset \mathfrak{H}$, and if $\mathfrak{K}$ is formally real and is an algebraic extension of $\mathfrak{H}$ then there is an isomorphism

$$f: \mathfrak{K} \cong \mathfrak{K}' \subset \mathfrak{H}$$

such that $f \mid \mathfrak{G}$ is the identity (see proof of Lemma 1.6.12 or Dean, p. 210), so $\mathfrak{G} \subset \mathfrak{K}'$ and $\mathfrak{K}'$ is formally real, contradicting the maximality of $\mathfrak{G}$. Thus $\mathfrak{G}$ has no proper formally real extensions that are algebraic, so $\mathfrak{G}$ is real-closed.

COROLLARY 1.8.5. Any real-closed field is orderable (uniquely), thus every formally real field is orderable.

Proof: For $\mathfrak{F}$ real-closed, set $0 < a$ iff $a \neq 0$ is a perfect square. It is simple to check that $\langle F, +, \cdot, 0, 1, < \rangle$ is an ordered field, where the definition of $<$ is completed by setting $a < b$ iff $b - a > 0$. Finally, if $\mathfrak{G}$ is a formally real field, then let $\mathfrak{F}$ be a real-closed extension of $\mathfrak{G}$. Then $< \restriction G$, $<$ as defined above, provides an order making $\langle G, +, \cdot, 0, 1, < \rangle$ an ordered field. We leave it to the reader to check details as well as the uniqueness of the order in the real-closed case.

This ordering, however, is extremely nonunique for most formally real fields.

LEMMA 1.8.6. If $\mathfrak{F}$ is formally real and $x \in F$ is not a sum of squares, then $\mathfrak{F}(\sqrt{-x})$ is formally real (thus $\mathfrak{F}(\sqrt{-x})$ can be extended to a real-closed field, whose unique order will require $0 < -x$).

Proof: Assume that $\mathfrak{F}(\sqrt{-x}) = \mathfrak{G}$ is not formally real. Then we have $y_1^2 + \cdots + y_n^2 = -1$ for some $y_1, \ldots, y_n \in G$. Thus

$$y_1 = r_1 + s_1\sqrt{-x}, \ldots, y_n = r_n + s_n\sqrt{-x},$$

so

$$r_1^2 + 2r_1s_1\sqrt{-x} - s_1^2x + \cdots - s_n^2x = -1,$$

so

$$(r_1^2 + \cdots + r_n^2) - x(s_1^2 + \cdots + s_n^2) = -1$$

(since if $a + b\sqrt{-x} \in F$, then $b = 0$ since $\sqrt{-x} \notin F$). But then

$$\frac{r_1^2 + \cdots + r_n^2 + 1}{s_1^2 + \cdots + s_n^2} = x,$$

so

$$x = \frac{(r_1^2 + \cdots + r_n^2 + 1)(s_1^2 + \cdots + s_n^2)}{(s_1^2 + \cdots + s_n^2)^2},$$

a sum of squares, of the form

$$\left(\frac{r_is_j}{s_2^1 + \cdots + s_n^2}\right)^2 \quad \text{or} \quad \left(\frac{s_j}{s_1^2 + \cdots + s_n^2}\right)^2,$$

a contradiction.

If $\mathfrak{F}$ is formally real and x is positive in every possible ordering of $\mathfrak{F}$, then the above shows that x is a sum of squares in $\mathfrak{F}$.

THEOREM 1.8.7. If $\mathfrak{A}$ is on ordered field, then there is, up to isomorphism, one ordered field $\mathfrak{B}$ such that $\mathfrak{B}/\langle 3, 3, 0, 0\rangle$ is real-closed and an algebraic extension of $\mathfrak{A}/\langle 3, 3, 0, 0\rangle$, and $\mathfrak{A} \subset \mathfrak{B}$.

Proof: Let $\mathfrak{B}$, $\mathfrak{C}$ be ordered fields with real-closed reducts of type $\langle 3, 3, 0, 0\rangle$ which are algebraic extensions of $\mathfrak{A}/\langle 3, 3, 0, 0\rangle$. By a proof similar to that of 1.6.12, we find that

$$\mathfrak{B}/\langle 3, 3, 0, 0\rangle \cong \mathfrak{C}/\langle 3, 3, 0, 0\rangle.$$

Furthermore, for $a, b \in B$, $a < b$ iff $b - a = c^2$ for some $c \in B$. Thus if f is our field isomorphism,

$$f(b) - f(a) = f(b - a) = f(c^2) = f(c)^2,$$

so $f(a) < f(b)$. Using f^{-1} as well, we find that an element of B is less than another in our order iff its image under f is less than that of the other. Thus f must be an ordered field isomorphism.

THEOREM 1.8.8. Let $\mathfrak{F}$ be real-closed. Then there is at most one order on $\mathfrak{F}(x)$ (x transcendental over $\mathfrak{F}$) satisfying a given set of relations $a < x$, $x < a$, where each $a \in F$ appears once in such a relation.

Proof: Consider $r(x) \in \mathfrak{F}[x]$. Once we know which elements of $\mathfrak{F}[x]$ are positive, we note that $r(x)/s(x)$ must be positive iff both $r(x)$ and $s(x)$ are positive or neither is positive. But

$$\begin{aligned} r(x) &= a(x - a_1)\cdots(x - a_n)(x^2 + b_1x + c_1)\cdots(x^2 + b_mx + c_m) \\ &= a(x - a_1)\cdots(x - a_n)\left(\left(x + \frac{b_1}{2}\right)^2 + \left(c_1 - \frac{b_1^2}{4}\right)\right) + \cdots \\ &\quad + \left(\left(x + \frac{b_m}{2}\right)^2 + \left(c_m - \frac{b_m^2}{4}\right)\right). \end{aligned}$$

Furthermore, assuming that $x^2 + b_jx + c_j$ is irreducible, we find that $c_j - (b_j^2/4)$ is positive, thus so must be $[x + (b_j/2)]^2 + [c_j - (b_j^2/4)]$ as a sum of squares. Thus the relation $0 < r(x)$ depends on (and only on) whether

$$0 < x - a_1, \ldots, 0 < x - a_n, 0 < a.$$

THEOREM 1.8.9. The theory of real-closed ordered fields is model-complete (where by a real-closed ordered field, we mean an ordered field $\mathfrak{A}$ such that $\mathfrak{A}/\langle 3, 3, 0, 0\rangle$ is real-closed).

Proof: Let T be the theory of real-closed ordered fields. If T were not model-complete, by Theorem 1.7.17 and Problem 1.7.1(b) we would have an existential $D \in L^t$ and a pair $\mathfrak{A}$, $\mathfrak{B} \in M(T)$ such that $\mathfrak{A} \subset \mathfrak{B}$ and a sequence $a \in A^\omega$ such that $\mathfrak{B} \models D[a]$ but $\mathfrak{A} \models \neg D[a]$. The set of ordered fields $\mathfrak{B}'$ such that $\mathfrak{A} \subset \mathfrak{B}' \subset \mathfrak{B}$, $\mathfrak{B}'/\langle 3, 3, 0, 0\rangle$ is real-closed, and $\mathfrak{B}' \models \neg D[a]$ is a nonempty set because $\mathfrak{A}$ will be in this set. This set also satisfies Zorn's condition, thus it contains a maximal element, say $\mathfrak{A}_1$. Thus $\mathfrak{A}_1/\langle 3, 3, 0, 0\rangle$ is real-closed, and if $\mathfrak{A}_1 \subsetneq \mathfrak{B}_1 \subset \mathfrak{B}$, $\mathfrak{B}_1$ a real-closed ordered field, then $\mathfrak{B}_1 \models D[a]$. Now let $x \in B \sim A_1$. x is transcendental over $\mathfrak{A}_1$, and the smallest real-closed ordered field in $\mathfrak{B}$ containing $A_1 \cup \{x\}$ is the real-closure of the rational functions in x over $\mathfrak{A}_1$. Thus we see that we can find a real-closed field $\mathfrak{A}_1$ such that $\mathfrak{A}_1 \models \neg D[a]$, and the real-closure $\mathfrak{B}_1$ of $\mathfrak{A}_1(x)$ has the property $\mathfrak{B}_1 \models D[a]$.

Let c be a new constant added to our language, and also add all the constants of $Dg(\mathfrak{A}_1)$. Let

$$E = \{c < c_a \mid x < a \text{ (in } \mathfrak{B}_1)\} \cup \{c_a < c \mid a < x \text{ (in } \mathfrak{B}_1)\},$$

$$H = E \cup Dg(\mathfrak{A}_1) \cup T.$$

H is consistent since $\mathfrak{B}_1$ is a reduct of a model of H. Let $\mathfrak{C}' \in M(H)$. We may assume that

$$\mathfrak{A}_1 \subset \mathfrak{C} = \mathfrak{C}'/\langle 3, 3, 0, 0, 2\rangle.$$

Let $x' \in C$ correspond to c. Then $\mathfrak{A}_1(x') \subset \mathfrak{C}$. Let $\mathfrak{C}_1$ be the real-closure of $\mathfrak{A}_1(x')$ in $\mathfrak{C}$. x' has the same ordering relations with respect to elements of A_1 as x does, since $\mathfrak{C} \models E$. Thus by Theorem 1.8.8, $\mathfrak{A}_1(x) \cong \mathfrak{A}_1(x')$ (as ordered fields), so Theorem 1.8.7 $\mathfrak{B}_1 \cong \mathfrak{C}_1$. Hence $\mathfrak{C}_1 \models D[a]$, so $\mathfrak{C} \models D[a]$, since D is existential. $\mathfrak{C}$ was an arbitrary model of H, so

$$H \models Sb^{v_0,\ldots,v_n}_{c_{a_0},\ldots,c_{a_n}} D = D^*, \qquad \text{where} \quad a = \langle a_0, a_1, \ldots\rangle,$$

and for the sake of simplicity we take $FV(D) = \{v_0, \ldots, v_n\}$. Since $a \in A^\omega \subset A_1^\omega$, we can find $J_1 \subset Dg(\mathfrak{A}_1)$, $E_1 \subset E$ (both finite) such that

$$J_1 \cup E_1 \cup T \models D^*.$$

Let

$$J_1 = \{F_1, \ldots, F_k\} \qquad \text{and} \qquad E_1 = \{G_1, \ldots, G_m\}.$$

Thus

$$J_1 \cup T \cup \{G_1 \wedge \cdots \wedge G_m\} \models D^*,$$

so

$$J_1 \cup T \models G_1 \wedge \cdots \wedge G_m \mathrel{->} D^*.$$

Since the constant c does not occur in $J_1 \cup T$ or D^*, by Corollary 1.2.16(c),

$$J_1 \cup T \models Sb^c_{v_0}(G_1 \wedge \cdots \wedge G_m) \mathrel{->} D^*,$$

thus by Problem 1.2.2(e) (since D^* is a sentence),

$$J_1 \cup T \models (\exists v_0)[Sb^c_{v_0}(G_1 \wedge \cdots \wedge G_m)] \mathrel{->} D^*.$$

$G_1, \ldots, G_m$ are all of the form $c_b < c$ or $c < c_b$ for some $b \in A_1$, so let c, $c_{b_1}, \ldots, c_{b_q}$ be all the constants mentioned in $G_1, \ldots, G_m$, with $b_1, \ldots, b_q \in A_1$ indexed in such a way that

$$b_1 < \cdots < b_p < x < b_{p+1} < \cdots < b_q,$$

and let

$$y = \frac{b_p + b_{p+1}}{2}.$$

Then

$$\mathfrak{A}_1 \models Sb^c_{v_0}(G_1 \wedge \cdots \wedge G_m)[y],$$

so

$$\mathfrak{A}_1 \models (\exists v_0)[Sb^c_{v_0}(G_1 \wedge \cdots \wedge G_m)],$$

and, since $\mathfrak{A}_1 \in M(J_1 \cup T)$, $\mathfrak{A}_1 \models D^*$. Thus by Corollary 1.2.16(a), $\mathfrak{A}_1 \models D[a]$, a contradiction proving our theorem.

Let $\mathfrak{A}$ be any ordered real-closed field. Since the characteristic of $\mathfrak{A}$ is 0, $\mathbb{Q} \subset \mathfrak{A}$, thus $\mathfrak{B} \subset \mathfrak{A}$ for the ordered real-closure of the rationals, that real-closure being unique up to isomorphism. Thus:

THEOREM 1.8.10 (Tarski). The theory of real-closed ordered fields is complete.

Proof: Apply Proposition 1.7.12 to Theorem 1.8.9 and our preceding comments.

One of the main reasons for the study of real-closed ordered fields was Hilbert's 17th problem, stated in 1900 and solved by Artin in 1927. Robinson, using his result on the model-completeness of the theory of real-closed ordered fields, was able to solve this problem (later) by model-theoretic means, and was able to obtain a sharper result.

THEOREM 1.8.11 (Hilbert's 17th problem as solved by Artin). If $\mathfrak{A}$ is a real-closed ordered field and $P \in \mathfrak{A}[X_1, \ldots, X_n]$ satisfies

$$(*) \qquad \text{for all} \quad a_1, \ldots, a_n \in A, \qquad 0 \leq P(a_1, \ldots, a_n),$$

then there are rational functions

$$r_1, \ldots, r_k \in \mathfrak{A}(X_1, \ldots, X_n)$$

such that

$$r_1^2 + \cdots + r_k^2 = P.$$

NOTE: A polynomial satisfying (*) is called definite. The converse of our theorem is obvious: If a polynomial in n variables is a sum of squares, then it is definite, so we are really asked to show that the two conditions are equivalent.

Proof: P is an element of the rational functions in n variables over $\mathfrak{A}$, $\mathfrak{A}(X_1, \ldots, X_n) = \mathfrak{B}$. $\mathfrak{B}$ is formally real (check!). Thus $x \in B$ is a sum of squares iff it is positive in all possible orderings of $\mathfrak{B}$. Thus if P is not a sum of squares of rational functions, then there is an ordering $<$ of $\mathfrak{B}$ such that $P < 0$. Let $\mathfrak{B}' = \langle B, +, \cdot, 0, 1, < \rangle$. Then $\mathfrak{A} \subset \mathfrak{B}'$ (since $\mathfrak{A}$ is real-closed and its order is unique). Let $\mathfrak{C}$ be a real-closed ordered extension of $\mathfrak{B}'$, thus $\mathfrak{A} \subset \mathfrak{B}' \subset \mathfrak{C}$, $\mathfrak{A}$, $\mathfrak{C}$ real-closed ordered. Clearly,

$$X_1, \ldots, X_n \in B \subset C \qquad \text{and} \qquad P = P(X_1, \ldots, X_n) < 0.$$

Thus

$$P(t_1, \ldots, t_n) \in \mathfrak{C}[t_1, \ldots, t_n]$$

has the property that it becomes negative upon the substitution of

$$X_1, \ldots, X_n \in C \qquad \text{for} \quad t_1, \ldots, t_n.$$

Thus

$$\mathfrak{C} \models (\exists v_1) \cdots (\exists v_n)(P(v_1, \ldots, v_n) < 0),$$

and since $\mathfrak{A} < \mathfrak{C}$,

$$\mathfrak{A} \models (\exists v_1) \cdots (\exists v_n)(P(v_1, \ldots, v_n) < 0),$$

therefore P cannot be definite.

Artin left open the question of how many r_j's are required and what their degrees might be, or indeed if there was a bound on these numbers. We give a partial answer. Note that if

$$P = \sum a_{i_1,\ldots,i_n} X_1^{\,i_1} \cdots X_n^{\,i_n}$$

is a polynomial in n variables, then

$$\deg(P) = \max\left\{ \sum_{=1}^{n} i_j \right\}.$$

THEOREM 1.8.12. There is a function $f\colon \omega \times \omega \to \omega$ such that if $\mathfrak{A}$ is a real-closed ordered field, $P \in \mathfrak{A}[X_1, \ldots, X_n]$, a definite polynomial of degree $\leq m$, there are at most $f(n, m)$ rational functions

$$r_1, \ldots, r_k \in \mathfrak{A}(X_1, \ldots, X_n), \qquad k \leq f(n, m)$$

such that the degrees of their numerators and denominators are also at most $f(n, m)$ and

$$r_1^2 + \cdots + r_k^2 = P.$$

Proof: If our theorem does not hold, then there is an n and an m such that for each k there is a real-closed field $\mathfrak{A}$ and a polynomial P satisfying (*) such that $P \in \mathfrak{A}[X_1, \ldots, X_n]$, $\deg(P) \leq m$, and P cannot be represented as a sum of squares of fewer than k rational functions, each of degree $\leq k$ in numerator and denominator. Now let

$$P = \sum a_{i_1,\ldots,i_n} X_1^{\,i_1} \cdots X_n^{\,i_n},$$

and for each $a_{i_1,\ldots,i_n}$ introduce a constant $c_{i_1,\ldots,i_n}$ into our language. Let F_k be the sentence in our new language that says that the polynomial with coefficients $a_{i_1,\ldots,i_n}$ (the distinguished elements corresponding to $c_{i_1,\ldots,i_n}$) is definite and not a sum of k rational functions with degrees $\leq k$ in the numerator and denominator. We leave it to the reader to write the F_k, thereby verifying that they are first-order sentences. Now by compactness applied to our assumption at the beginning of the proof, $T \cup$

$\{F_1, F_2, \ldots\}$ has a model, where T is the set of axioms for real-closed fields. Let

$$\mathfrak{B} = \langle F, +, \cdot, 0, 1, <, \ldots, a'_{i_1,\ldots,i_n}, \ldots\rangle$$

be such a model. Since $\mathfrak{B}/\langle 3, 3, 0, 0, 2\rangle$ is real-closed ordered, it is a model of T. Also we can find a P, determined by the $a'_{i_1,\ldots,i_n}$, which is definite, yet not the sum of k rational functions each with numerator and denominator of degree at most k for any positive integer k, contradicting Theorem 1.8.11.

Problems

‡1.8.1 Verify that the $<$ introduced in the proof of Corollary 1.8.5 is indeed an order for our field, and that it is the only such order.

‡1.8.2 Fill in any gaps in the proof of Theorem 1.8.7 in the manner of the proof of Lemma 1.6.12.

1.8.3 (a) Attempt by a proof similar to that for Theorem 1.8.9 to establish again the model-completeness of the theory of dense total ordering with no first or last element.

(b) Why is it essential to the success of the attempt made in (a) that there be no first or last element?

1.8.4 (a) Show that the theory of real-closed fields is not categorical in any cardinality, and that our effort in the proof of Theorem 1.8.9 was therefore justified.

(b) Let S be the theory of dense totally ordered structures with no first or last element, and let $\mathfrak{A} \in M(S)$, $\mathfrak{A}$ uncountable. Show that $S \cup Dg(\mathfrak{A})$ is complete but not categorical in any cardinality.

‡1.8.5 The proof of Theorem 1.8.11 is incomplete in that the formulas used are never mentioned, and therefore the application of model-completeness is not clear. The reader should write out the formulas and clarify the use of model-completeness. Will completeness do in this proof in place of model-completeness?

2

Ultraproducts

2.1 Definition of Ultraproducts

In the mid 1950s, a new construction was developed that incorporated many algebraic techniques into model theory.

NOTE: In this chapter $\Gamma = \mathscr{D}t$, so that we may use $\mathbf{I}$ to denote an index set.

DEFINITION 2.1.1. Let $\{\mathfrak{A}_{\mathbf{i}} \mid \mathbf{i} \in \mathbf{I}\} \subset M^t$ for some set $\mathbf{I}$, $\mathfrak{A}_{\mathbf{i}} = \langle A_{\mathbf{i}}, R_\gamma^{(\mathbf{i})}\rangle_{\gamma \in \Gamma}$. The direct product

$$\prod_{\mathbf{I}} \mathfrak{A}_{\mathbf{i}} = \langle A, R_\gamma\rangle_{\gamma \in \Gamma},$$

where

$$A = \prod_{\mathbf{I}} A_{\mathbf{i}} = \{f\colon \mathbf{I} \to \bigcup_{\mathbf{i} \in \mathbf{I}} A_{\mathbf{i}} \mid \text{for every } \mathbf{i} \in \mathbf{I}, f(\mathbf{i}) \in A_{\mathbf{i}}\},$$

$$R_\gamma = \{\langle f_1, \ldots, f_{t(\gamma)}\rangle \mid \text{for all } \mathbf{i} \in \mathbf{I}, \langle f_1(\mathbf{i}), \ldots, f_{t(\gamma)}(\mathbf{i})\rangle \in R_\gamma^{(\mathbf{i})}\} \quad \text{for} \quad t(\gamma) > 0,$$

if $t(\gamma) = 0$, $R_\gamma \in A$ is defined by

$$R_\gamma(\mathbf{i}) = R_\gamma^{(\mathbf{i})}.$$

DEFINITION 2.1.2. Let $\mathbf{I}$ be any set, $D \subset \mathscr{P}\mathbf{I}$. D is called a filter on $\mathbf{I}$ iff:

(i) $\phi \notin D$, $\phi \neq D$;
(ii) if $a \in D$ and $b \in D$, then $a \cap b \in D$;
(iii) if $a \in D$ and $a \subset b \subset \mathbf{I}$, then $b \in D$.

The intuitive content of the above is that a set in D contains "almost all" elements of $\mathbf{I}$. For example, the subsets of $[0, 1]$ of measure 1 form a filter on $[0, 1]$. Another example is the following: Let $\mathbf{I}$ be any infinite set, $\mathfrak{m} = c(\mathbf{I})$, and $\mathfrak{n} \leq \mathfrak{m}$ another infinite cardinal. Then

$$\mathscr{P}_{\mathfrak{n}}(\mathbf{I}) = \{a \subset \mathbf{I} \mid c(\mathbf{I} \sim a) < \mathfrak{n}\}$$

is a filter on $\mathbf{I}$.

From now on we shall also use the notation

$$\mathscr{P}^{\mathfrak{n}}(\mathbf{I}) = \{a \subset \mathbf{I} \mid c(a) < \mathfrak{n}\}.$$

Definition 2.1.3. Let D be a filter on $\mathbf{I}$, $f, g \in \prod_{\mathbf{I}} A_{\mathbf{i}}$. We say that

$$f \sim_D g \qquad \text{iff} \quad \{\mathbf{i} \mid f(\mathbf{i}) = g(\mathbf{i})\} \in D.$$

In other words, $f \sim_D g$ iff $f = g$ "almost everywhere." The reader can easily show (see Problem 2.1.1) that $\sim_D$ is an equivalence relation.

Definition 2.1.4.

$$f/D = \{g \mid f \sim_D g\}, \qquad \prod_{\mathbf{I}} A_{\mathbf{i}}/D = \{f/D \mid f \in \prod_{\mathbf{I}} A_{\mathbf{i}}\}.$$

Definition 2.1.5. Let D be a filter on $\mathbf{I}$.

$$\prod_{\mathbf{I}} \mathfrak{A}_{\mathbf{i}}/D = \langle \prod_{\mathbf{I}} A_{\mathbf{i}}/D, S_\gamma \rangle_{\gamma \in \Gamma},$$

where

$$S_\gamma = \{\langle f_1/D, \ldots, f_{t(\gamma)}/D \rangle \mid \{\mathbf{i} \mid \langle f_1(\mathbf{i}), \ldots, f_{t(\gamma)}(\mathbf{i})\rangle \in R_\gamma^{(\mathbf{I})}\} \in D\} \qquad \text{for} \quad t(\gamma) > 0,$$

if

$$t(\gamma) = 0, \; S_\gamma = R_\gamma/D \qquad (R_\gamma \text{ from } 1.1.1),$$

and is called the reduced product of $\{\mathfrak{A}_{\mathbf{i}} \mid \mathbf{i} \in \mathbf{I}\}$ by D.

Definition 2.1.6. Let D be a filter on $\mathbf{I}$. Then D is an ultrafilter on $\mathbf{I}$ iff there is no filter E on $\mathbf{I}$ such that $D \subsetneqq E$.

Example: Let $\mathbf{i} \in \mathbf{I}$, $D_{\mathbf{i}} = \{a \subset \mathbf{I} \mid \mathbf{i} \in a\}$. Then $D_{\mathbf{i}}$ is clearly a filter and is maximal, since if $D_{\mathbf{i}} \subsetneqq D$, then we have $b \in D \sim D_{\mathbf{i}}$, so $\mathbf{i} \notin b$. Thus $\mathbf{i} \in \mathbf{I} \sim b$, so $\mathbf{I} \sim b \in D_{\mathbf{i}} \subset D$, so $b, \mathbf{I} \sim b \in D$, thus $\phi = b \cap (\mathbf{I} \sim b) \in D$, contradicting the assertion that D is a filter. An ultrafilter of the form $D_{\mathbf{i}}$ for some $\mathbf{i}$ is called principal.

THEOREM 2.1.7. Every filter D on $\mathbf{I}$ can be extended to an ultrafilter E on $\mathbf{I}$.

Proof: An ascending union of filters is a filter. Thus the set of filters E on $\mathbf{I}$ such that $D \subset E$ satisfies Zorn's condition, thus it contains maximal elements.

COROLLARY 2.1.8. Let $E \subset \mathscr{P}\mathbf{I}$ be such that for any finite $E' \subset E$, $\bigcap E' \neq \phi$. Then $E \subset D$ for some ultrafilter D on $\mathbf{I}$.

Proof: Let

$$D' = \{a \in \mathscr{P}\mathbf{I} \mid \text{for some finite } E' \subset E, \bigcap E' \subset a\}.$$

It is simple to check that $E \subset D'$, and that D' is a filter on $\mathbf{I}$. Thus $D' \subset D$ for some ultrafilter D on $\mathbf{I}$, so $E \subset D$.

THEOREM 2.1.9. Let D be a filter on $\mathbf{I}$. Then D is an ultrafilter on $\mathbf{I}$ iff for every $a \subset \mathbf{I}$, $a \in D$ or $\mathbf{I} \sim a \in D$.

Proof: Let D be an ultrafilter, $a \notin D$. If

$$E = \{x \subset \mathbf{I} \mid a \cap d \subset x \quad \text{for some } d \in D\},$$

then $D \subset E$ and $D \neq E$, so E is not a filter. However, $E \neq \phi$ and is clearly closed under intersections and supersets, thus by Definition 1.1.2, E can fail to be a filter only if $\phi \in E$. Therefore $a \cap d = \phi$ for some $d \in D$. For this d we have

$$d \subset \mathbf{I} \sim a, \qquad \text{so} \qquad \mathbf{I} \sim a \in D.$$

Conversely, let D be a filter such that for every $a \subset \mathbf{I}$, $a \in D$ or $\mathbf{I} \sim a \in D$, and let $D \subset E$, E a filter on $\mathbf{I}$. If for some b, $b \in E \sim D$, then

$$\mathbf{I} \sim b \in D \subset E,$$

so

$$\phi = b \cap (\mathbf{I} \sim b) \in E,$$

contradicting the fact that E is a filter. Thus D is maximal.

LEMMA 2.1.10. (a) If D is an ultrafilter on $\mathbf{I}$ and $a, b \subset \mathbf{I}$, $a \cup b \in D$, then $a \in D$ or $b \in D$.

(b) If D is an ultrafilter on $\mathbf{I}$, $a_1, \ldots, a_k \subset \mathbf{I}$, and $a_1 \cup \cdots \cup a_k \in D$, then one of the $a_j \in D$.

Proof: (a) Assume that $a \notin D$. Then $\mathbf{I} \sim a \in D$, so

$$(\mathbf{I} \sim a) \cap (a \cup b) \in D.$$

But

$$(\mathbf{I} \sim a) \cap (a \cup b) = [(\mathbf{I} \sim a) \cap a] \cup [(\mathbf{I} \sim a) \cap b] = (\mathbf{I} \sim a) \cap b \subset b,$$

thus $b \in D$.

(b) follows from (a) by induction.

Note that if in the above lemma one of the $a_j \in D$, then their union must be in D. Thus the conditions are actually necessary and sufficient.

THEOREM 2.1.11. If $\mathbf{I}$ is infinite, then there are nonprincipal ultrafilters on $\mathbf{I}$.

Proof: Extend $\mathscr{P}_\omega(\mathbf{I})$ to an ultrafilter. It cannot be principal, since for every $\mathbf{i} \in \mathbf{I}$, $\mathbf{I} \sim \{\mathbf{i}\} \in D$, thus $\{\mathbf{i}\} \notin D$.

DEFINITION 2.1.12. A reduced product $\prod_\mathbf{I} \mathfrak{A}_\mathbf{i}/D$ is called an ultraproduct iff D is an ultrafilter. ($\prod_\mathbf{I} = \prod\limits_\mathbf{I}$.)

NOTATION. In future theorems we shall deal with elements of $(\prod_\mathbf{I} A_\mathbf{i}/D)^\omega$, i.e., elements of the form

$$f/D = \langle f_0/D, f_1/D, \ldots \rangle.$$

By $f(\mathbf{i})$ we mean

$$\langle f_0(\mathbf{i}), \ldots \rangle \in A_\mathbf{i}^\omega,$$

and by f_n, we mean a representative of f_n/D in $\prod_\mathbf{I} A_\mathbf{i}$.

We now state our basic result.

THEOREM 2.1.13 (Łos). Let $\mathfrak{A} = \prod_\mathbf{I} \mathfrak{A}_\mathbf{i}/D$ be an ultraproduct, $f/D \in (\prod_\mathbf{I} A_\mathbf{i}/D)^\omega$. Then for every $F \in L^t$,

$$\mathfrak{A} \models F[f/D] \quad \text{iff} \quad \{\mathbf{i} \mid \mathfrak{A}_\mathbf{i} \models F[f(\mathbf{i})]\} \in D.$$

Proof: If $F \in L^t(0)$, then $F = (x_1 = x_2)$ or $P_\gamma(x_1, \ldots, x_{t(\gamma)})$. In this case, the theorem holds, by Definitions 2.1.3 and 2.1.5. Assume now that the result holds for $F \in L^t(n)$, and let

$$F \in L^t(n+1) \sim L^t(n).$$

If $F = \neg G$, $\mathfrak{A} \models F[f/D]$

$$\text{iff not} \quad \mathfrak{A} \models G[f/D]$$

iff (by induction) $\{\mathbf{i} \mid \mathfrak{A}_\mathbf{i} \models G[f(\mathbf{i})]\} \notin D$,

iff $\mathbf{I} \sim \{\mathbf{i} \mid \mathfrak{A}_\mathbf{i} \models G[f(\mathbf{i})]\} \in D$,

iff $\{\mathbf{i} \mid \mathfrak{A}_\mathbf{i} \models \neg G[f(\mathbf{i})]\} \in D$,
iff $\{\mathbf{i} \mid \mathfrak{A}_\mathbf{i} \models F[f(\mathbf{i})]\} \in D$.
If $F = G \vee H$, $\mathfrak{A} \models F[f/D]$
iff $\mathfrak{A} \models G[f/D]$ or $\mathfrak{A} \models H[f/D]$,
iff $\{\mathbf{i} \mid \mathfrak{A}_\mathbf{i} \models G[f(\mathbf{i})]\} \in D$ or $\{\mathbf{i} \mid \mathfrak{A}_\mathbf{i} \models H[f(\mathbf{i})]\} \in D$
iff $\{\mathbf{i} \mid \mathfrak{A}_\mathbf{i} \models G[f(\mathbf{i})]\} \cup \{\mathbf{i} \mid \mathfrak{A}_\mathbf{i} \models H[f(\mathbf{i})]\} \in D$,
iff $\{\mathbf{i} \mid \mathfrak{A}_\mathbf{i} \models G[f(\mathbf{i})]$ or $\mathfrak{A}_\mathbf{i} \models H[f(\mathbf{i})]\} \in D$
iff $\{\mathbf{i} \mid \mathfrak{A}_\mathbf{i} \models F[f(\mathbf{i})]\} \in D$.
Finally, let $F = (\exists v_j)G$. If $\mathfrak{A} \models F[f/D]$, then for some $g \in \prod_\mathbf{I} A_\mathbf{i}$,

$$\mathfrak{A} \models G[f(j \mid g)/D]$$

so

$$\{\mathbf{i} \mid \mathfrak{A}_\mathbf{i} \models G[f(j \mid g)(\mathbf{i})]\} \in D,$$

so

$$\{\mathbf{i} \mid \mathfrak{A}_\mathbf{i} \models (\exists v_j)G[f(\mathbf{i})]\} \in D.$$

Conversely, if

$$\{\mathbf{i} \mid \mathfrak{A}_\mathbf{i} \models F[f(\mathbf{i})]\} \in D,$$

then

$$S = \{\mathbf{i} \mid \text{for some } g_\mathbf{i} \in A_\mathbf{i}, \mathfrak{A}_\mathbf{i} \models G[f(\mathbf{i})(j \mid g_\mathbf{i})]\} \in D.$$

Now let $g \in \prod_\mathbf{I} A_\mathbf{i}$ be defined by $g(\mathbf{i}) = g_\mathbf{i}$ for $\mathbf{i} \in S$, $g(\mathbf{i})$ arbitrary for $\mathbf{i} \in \mathbf{I} \sim S$. Thus

$$\{\mathbf{i} \mid \mathfrak{A}_\mathbf{i} \models G[f(j \mid g)(\mathbf{i})]\}$$
$$= \{\mathbf{i} \mid \text{for some } g_\mathbf{i} \in A_\mathbf{i}, \mathfrak{A}_\mathbf{i} \models G[f(\mathbf{i})(j \mid g_\mathbf{i})]\} = S \in D.$$

Thus

$$\mathfrak{A} \models G[f(j \mid g)/D] \quad \text{so} \quad \mathfrak{A} \models F[f/D],$$

completing our induction.

Corollary 2.1.14. If $F \in \Sigma^t$, then $\mathfrak{A} \models F$ iff $\{\mathbf{i} \mid \mathfrak{A}_\mathbf{i} \models F\} \in D$.

Corollary 2.1.15. If for every $\mathbf{i}, \mathbf{j} \in \mathbf{I}$, $\mathfrak{A}_\mathbf{i} \equiv \mathfrak{A}_\mathbf{j}$, then for each $\mathbf{i} \in \mathbf{I}$,

$$\mathfrak{A}_\mathbf{i} \equiv \prod_\mathbf{I} \mathfrak{A}_\mathbf{i}/D.$$

If for each $\mathbf{i} \in \mathbf{I}$, $\mathfrak{A}_\mathbf{i} = \mathfrak{A}$, then $\prod_\mathbf{I} \mathfrak{A}_\mathbf{i}/D$ is called an ultrapower and denoted $\mathfrak{A}^\mathbf{I}/D$. Thus

$$\mathfrak{A} \equiv \mathfrak{A}^\mathbf{I}/D.$$

THEOREM 2.1.16 (Compactness). If for every finite subset $S' \subset S$, $M(S') \neq \phi$, then $M(S) \neq \phi$.

Proof: For each finite subset $S' \subset S$, let $\mathfrak{A}_{S'} \in M(S')$. Let $\mathbf{I} = \mathscr{P}^{\omega}(S)$ and for each $F \in S$ set

$$S_F = \{S' \in \mathbf{I} \mid F \in S'\}, \qquad E = \{S_F \mid F \in S\}.$$

Then E has the finite intersection property, for if $S_{F_1}, \ldots, S_{F_k} \in E$, then

$$\{F_1, \ldots, F_k\} \in S_{F_1} \cap \cdots \cap S_{F_k}.$$

Thus let $E \subset D$ for some ultrafilter D on $\mathbf{I}$, and consider

$$\mathfrak{A} = \prod_{\mathbf{I}} \mathfrak{A}_{S'}/D.$$

We show $\mathfrak{A} \in M(S)$. Let $F \in S$. Then

$$\{S' \mid \mathfrak{A}_{S'} \models F\} \supset \{S' \mid F \in S'\} = S_F \in D.$$

Thus

$$\mathfrak{A} \models F.$$

It is important to note that none of the results leading to this proof of the compactness theorem depend on results in Chapter 1 that depended on compactness. It is simple to check that only the definitions and results of this section and the definitions of structure, language, and truth, as well as some trivial results following them in Sections 1.1 and 1.2 were used here. The proof of Theorem 2.1.16, however, indicates that more than the compactness theorem could be proved in this manner. It shows a way, given a set $\mathbf{I}$ of similar structures, to construct an ultrafilter D on $\mathbf{I}$ and the new structure $\prod_{\mathbf{I}} \mathfrak{A}_{\mathbf{i}}/D$ in such a way as to satisfy certain statements that interest us. Some future proofs involving ultraproducts will be similar to the one above, though generally more difficult.

DEFINITION 2.1.17. Let $\mathfrak{A}, \mathfrak{B} \in M^t$. $\mathfrak{A} \ll' \mathfrak{B}$ iff whenever $\mathfrak{A}'/t = \mathfrak{A}$, there is a $\mathfrak{B}'$ such that

$$\mathfrak{B}'/t = \mathfrak{B} \quad \text{and} \quad \mathfrak{A}' \equiv \mathfrak{B}'.$$

$\mathfrak{A} \ll \mathfrak{B}$ iff whenever $\mathfrak{A}'/t = \mathfrak{A}$ there is a $\mathfrak{B}'$ such that

$$\mathfrak{B}'/t = \mathfrak{B}, \quad \mathfrak{A}' \subset \mathfrak{B}', \quad \text{and} \quad \mathfrak{A}' \equiv \mathfrak{B}'.$$

$f\colon \mathfrak{A} \ll' \mathfrak{B}$ iff $f\colon \mathfrak{A} \cong \mathfrak{C}$ for some $\mathfrak{C} \ll \mathfrak{B}$.

THEOREM 2.1.18. (a) $\mathfrak{A} \ll' \mathfrak{B}$ iff for every $\mathfrak{A}'$, if $\mathfrak{A}'/t = \mathfrak{A}$, there is a $\mathfrak{B}'$ such that

$$\mathfrak{B}'/t = \mathfrak{B} \quad \text{and} \quad \mathfrak{A}' <' \mathfrak{B}'.$$

$\mathfrak{A} \ll \mathfrak{B}$ iff for every $\mathfrak{A}'$, if $\mathfrak{A}'/t = \mathfrak{A}$, there is a $\mathfrak{B}'$ such that

$$\mathfrak{B}'/t = \mathfrak{B} \qquad \text{and} \qquad \mathfrak{A}' < \mathfrak{B}'.$$

(b) If $\mathfrak{A} \ll' \mathfrak{B}$, then $\mathfrak{A} <' \mathfrak{B}$; if $\mathfrak{A} \ll \mathfrak{B}$, then $\mathfrak{A} < \mathfrak{B}$.
(c) $\mathfrak{A} \ll' \mathfrak{B}$ iff for some f, $f\colon \mathfrak{A} \ll' \mathfrak{B}$.

Proof: (a) Let $\mathfrak{A} \ll' \mathfrak{B}$ and $\mathfrak{A}'/t = \mathfrak{A}$, thus we may let $\mathfrak{A}' = \langle A, R_\gamma\rangle_{\gamma\in\Gamma}$. Let $\mathfrak{A}'' = \langle A, R_\gamma, a\rangle_{\gamma\in\Gamma, a\in A}$. Then we can find $\mathfrak{B}''$ with

$$\mathfrak{B}''/t = \mathfrak{B}, \qquad \mathfrak{A}'' \equiv \mathfrak{B}''.$$

However, this elementary equivalence is in the language of $Dg(\mathfrak{A}')$, and by Theorem 1.7.2,

$$\mathfrak{A}' <' \mathfrak{B}''/t' \qquad (t' \text{ the type of } \mathfrak{A}').$$

The converse is clear.

We leave the case of $\ll$ for the reader.

(b) is immediate from (a).

For (c) let

$$\Gamma = \mathscr{D}t \cup A \cup \left(\bigcup \{\mathscr{P}(A^n) \mid n < \omega\}\right),$$

considered as a disjoint union, and let t' be the type with domain Γ such that

$$t \subset t', \quad t'(a) = 0 \quad \text{for} \quad a \in A, \quad \text{and if} \quad \gamma \in \mathscr{P}(A^n), \quad \text{then} \quad t'(\gamma) = n.$$

Define $\mathfrak{A}' = \langle A, R'_\gamma\rangle_{\gamma\in\Gamma}$ by $\mathfrak{A}'/t = \mathfrak{A}$ and for $\gamma \in \Gamma \sim \mathscr{D}t$, $R'_\gamma = \gamma$. $\mathfrak{A}'$ is a structure in which every possible relation on A is mentioned at least once. Since $\mathfrak{A} \ll' \mathfrak{B}$, let

$$\mathfrak{B}' = \langle B, S'_\gamma\rangle_{\gamma\in\Gamma} \equiv \mathfrak{A}', \qquad \mathfrak{B}'/t = \mathfrak{B}.$$

We can now define $f\colon A \to B$ by $f(a) = S'_a \in B$.

To see that $f\colon \mathfrak{A} \ll' \mathfrak{B}$, let

$$\mathfrak{A} = \mathfrak{A}''/t, \qquad \mathfrak{A}'' = \langle A, R''_\delta\rangle_{\delta\in\Delta}.$$

For every $\delta \in \Delta \sim \mathscr{D}t$, there is a $\gamma \in \Gamma \sim \mathscr{D}t$ such that $R''_\delta = R'_\gamma$. Thus there is a map $\varphi\colon \Delta \to \Gamma$ such that

$$\varphi(r) = r \qquad \text{for} \quad r \in \mathscr{D}t$$

and

$$R'_{\varphi(\delta)} = R''_\delta.$$

Using this φ, we define a map $\psi: L^{t''} \to L^{t'}$ by $\psi(v_n) = v_n$, $\psi(c_\delta) = c_{\varphi(\delta)}$ for $c_\delta \in C_{t''}$,

$$\psi(x_1 = x_2) = (\psi(x_1) = \psi(x_2)),$$

$$\psi(P_\delta(x_1, \ldots, x_{t''(\delta)})) = P_{\varphi(\delta)}(\psi(x_1), \ldots, \psi(x_{t''(\delta)})),$$

$$\psi(\neg F) = \neg\psi(F),$$

$$\psi(F \vee G) = \psi(F) \vee \psi(G),$$

and

$$\psi((\exists v_n)F) = (\exists v_n)\psi(F).$$

It is clear that for $F \in L^{t''}$, $a \in A^\omega$,

$$\mathfrak{A}'' \models F[a] \quad \text{iff} \quad \mathfrak{A}' \models \psi(F)[a].$$

Define $\mathfrak{B}'' = \langle B, S''_\delta \rangle_{\delta \in \Delta}$ by $S''_\delta = S'_{\varphi(\delta)}$ and note that $\mathfrak{B}'' \models F[b]$ iff $\mathfrak{B}' \models \psi(F)[b]$ for $F \in L^{t''}$, $b \in B^\omega$. Also note that for $G \in L^{t'}$, $a \in A^\omega$,

$$\mathfrak{A}' \models G[a] \quad \text{iff} \quad \mathfrak{B}' \models G[f \circ a]$$

(since

$$\mathfrak{A}' = \langle A, R'_\gamma \rangle_{\gamma \in \Gamma} \equiv \langle B, S'_\gamma \rangle_{\gamma \in \Gamma} = \mathfrak{B}'$$

and

$$f(b) = S'_b \quad \text{for} \quad b = R'_b \in A).$$

Thus for $F \in L^{t''}$, $a \in A^\omega$, $\mathfrak{A}'' \models F[a]$
iff $\mathfrak{A}' \models \psi(F)[a]$
iff $\mathfrak{B}' \models \psi(F)[f \circ a]$
iff $\mathfrak{B}'' \models F[f \circ a]$,

so $f: \mathfrak{A}'' <' \mathfrak{B}''$, but since $\mathfrak{A}''$ is arbitrary

$$f: \mathfrak{A} \cong \mathfrak{C} \ll \mathfrak{B}.$$

Conversely, if $f: \mathfrak{A} \cong \mathfrak{C} \ll \mathfrak{B}$, then $f: \mathfrak{A} \ll' \mathfrak{C} \ll' \mathfrak{B}$, so $\mathfrak{A} \ll' \mathfrak{B}$.

Note that part of the proof of (c) is simply the formalization of the assertion that if $\mathfrak{A}''/t = \mathfrak{A}$, then $\mathfrak{A}''$ is essentially a reduct of $\mathfrak{A}'$, and thus elementarily imbeddable in the corresponding reduct of $\mathfrak{B}'$.

Corollary 2.1.19. $\mathfrak{A} \ll' \mathfrak{A}^{\mathbf{I}}/D$, thus $\mathfrak{A} <' \mathfrak{A}^{\mathbf{I}}/D$. In fact,

$$j_{\mathfrak{A}}: \mathfrak{A} \ll' \mathfrak{A}^{\mathbf{I}}/D, \qquad \text{where} \quad j_{\mathfrak{A}}(a) = f_a/D,$$

$f_a \in A^{\mathbf{I}}$ the function such that for every $\mathbf{i} \in \mathbf{I}$, $f_a(\mathbf{i}) = a$.

The proof is straightforward from Theorem 2.1.13 and Definition 2.1.17. The purpose of this corollary is to point out that $j_{\mathfrak{A}}\colon \mathfrak{A} <' \mathfrak{A}^{\mathbf{I}}/D$ and that further relations may be added to $\mathfrak{A}$ with this relation still holding (indeed, this is the main objective of 2.1.17 and what has followed).

Problems

‡2.1.1 Let D be a filter.

(a) Show that $\sim_D$ is an equivalence relation.

(b) Let $R_\gamma^{(\mathbf{i})} \neq \phi$ for each $\mathbf{i} \in \mathbf{I}$. Then show

$$\langle f_1, \ldots, f_{t(\gamma)} \rangle \in S_\gamma$$

iff for some $g_1, \ldots, g_{t(\gamma)}$,

$$f_1 \sim_D g_1, \ldots, \qquad f_{t(\gamma)} \sim_D g_{t(\gamma)},$$

and

$$\langle g_1(\mathbf{i}), \ldots, g_{t(\gamma)}(\mathbf{i}) \rangle \in R_\gamma^{(\mathbf{i})} \qquad \text{for every} \quad \mathbf{i} \in \mathbf{I}.$$

(c) If $\phi \neq a \subset \mathbf{I}$, show that $D_a = \{b \mid a \subset b\}$ is always a filter. Give necessary and sufficient conditions for it to be an ultrafilter.

(d) Show that

$$\prod_{\mathbf{I}} c(A_{\mathbf{i}}) \geq c(\prod_{\mathbf{I}} \mathfrak{A}_{\mathbf{i}}/D).$$

‡2.1.2 (a) Let $n \in \omega$, and suppose that for every $\mathbf{i} \in \mathbf{I}$, $c(\mathfrak{A}_{\mathbf{i}}) \leq n$. Show that

$$c(\prod_{\mathbf{I}} \mathfrak{A}_{\mathbf{i}}/D) \leq n$$

for any ultrafilter D on $\mathbf{I}$.

(b) If $\mathfrak{A}$ is finite, D an ultrafilter on $\mathbf{I}$, and $\mathbf{I}$ any nonempty set, show that

$$\mathfrak{A}^{\mathbf{I}}/D \cong \mathfrak{A}.$$

‡2.1.3 (a) Let $D = D_{\mathbf{i}}$ be a principal ultrafilter on $\mathbf{I}$. Show that the map given by $f/D \to f(\mathbf{i})$ is an isomorphism from $\prod_{\mathbf{I}} \mathfrak{A}_{\mathbf{i}}/D$ onto $\mathfrak{A}_{\mathbf{i}}$.

(b) If $\mathbf{I}$ is finite, show that for every ultrafilter D on $\mathbf{I}$,

$$\prod_{\mathbf{I}} \mathfrak{A}_{\mathbf{i}}/D \cong \mathfrak{A}_{\mathbf{i}} \qquad \text{for some} \quad \mathbf{i} \in \mathbf{I}.$$

2.1.4 ‡(a) Show that for $\mathbf{I}$ infinite, D an ultrafilter on $\mathbf{I}$, D is nonprincipal iff $\mathscr{P}_\omega(\mathbf{I}) \subset D$.

(b) Let D be a nonprincipal ultrafilter on ω and set $\omega^\omega/D = A$. Show that $c(A) = 2^\omega$. (HINT: For every decimal $.a_1a_2a_3\ldots \in [0, 1)$, define

$$f(.a_1a_2a_3\ldots) = \langle a_1, 10a_1 + a_2, 100a_1 + 10a_2 + a_3, \ldots \rangle/D.$$

Then show that f is one–one.)

2.1.5 Let D be a filter.

(a) For each $\mathbf{i} \in \mathbf{I}$, let $f_\mathbf{i} : \mathfrak{A}_\mathbf{i} \to \mathfrak{B}_\mathbf{i}$ be an injection. Show that

$$f : \prod_\mathbf{I} \mathfrak{A}_\mathbf{i}/D \to \prod_\mathbf{I} \mathfrak{B}_\mathbf{i}/D$$

is well-defined, where

$$f(g/D) = h/D, \qquad h(\mathbf{i}) = f_\mathbf{i}(g(\mathbf{i})),$$

and show that f is an injection.

(b) State and prove corresponding facts for homomorphisms and isomorphisms, showing, among other things, that if each $\mathfrak{B}_\mathbf{i}$ is the homomorphic image of $\mathfrak{A}_\mathbf{i}$, then $\prod_\mathbf{I}\mathfrak{B}_\mathbf{i}/D$ is a homomorphic image of $\prod_\mathbf{I}\mathfrak{A}_\mathbf{i}/D$.

(c) If for each $\mathbf{i} \in \mathbf{I}$, the map $f_\mathbf{i}$ of (a) is an elementary imbedding, show that f is also, provided that D is an ultrafilter.

2.1.6 Let $\mathfrak{A}$ be a countable ordered field, D an ultrafilter. Show that if $j_\mathfrak{A} : \mathfrak{A} \not\cong \mathfrak{A}^\mathbf{I}/D$ then $\mathfrak{A}^\mathbf{I}/D$ is a non-Archimedean ordered field.

‡2.1.7 Show that $\mathfrak{A} \ll' \mathfrak{B}$ iff $\mathfrak{A}' \equiv \mathfrak{B}'$ for some $\mathfrak{B}'$ such that $\mathfrak{B}'/t = \mathfrak{B}$ (here $\mathfrak{A}'$ is as in the proof of Theorem 1.18 (c)).

2.1.8 (a) Let $\{\mathfrak{R}_\mathbf{i} \mid \mathbf{i} \in \mathbf{I}\}$ be a set of similar structures. Show that

$$f : \prod_\mathbf{I} \mathfrak{R}_\mathbf{i} \to \prod_\mathbf{I} \mathfrak{R}_\mathbf{i}/D$$

is a strong homomorphism for any filter D on $\mathbf{I}$, where for $a \in \prod_\mathbf{I} R_\mathbf{i}$, $f(a) = a/D$. (See Problem 1.1.11.)

By the first isomorphism theorem for rings (see Fraleigh, for example), we know that

$$\prod_\mathbf{I} \mathfrak{R}_\mathbf{i}/D \cong \Big(\prod_\mathbf{I} \mathfrak{R}_\mathbf{i}\Big)/K$$

for some ideal $K \subset \prod_\mathbf{I}\mathfrak{R}_\mathbf{i}$ if each $\mathfrak{R}_\mathbf{i}$ is a ring with identity. The remainder of this problem is devoted to finding such a K.

For every element $a \in \prod_\mathbf{I} R_\mathbf{i}$, let

$$Z(a) = \{\mathbf{i} \mid a(\mathbf{i}) = 0_\mathbf{i}\},$$

1_a be the function on $\mathbf{I}$ such that

$$1_a(\mathbf{i}) = \begin{cases} 0_\mathbf{i} & \text{if } a(\mathbf{i}) = 0_\mathbf{i} \\ 1_\mathbf{i} & \text{otherwise} \end{cases},$$

and for every ideal $K \subset \prod_\mathbf{I}\mathfrak{R}_\mathbf{i}$ set

$$D(K) = \{Z(a) \mid a \in K\}.$$

K is special iff for every $a \in K$, $1_a \in K$.

(b) Show that $D(K)$ is a filter on $\mathbf{I}$ or $D(K) = \mathscr{P}\mathbf{I}$.

Now for every filter D, set

$$K_D = \{a \mid Z(a) \in D\}.$$

(c) K_D is a special ideal and for every ideal K in our product, $K_{D(K)}$ is the smallest special ideal containing K.
(d) $K_D \subset K_E$ iff $D \subset E$, thus those special ideals maximal in the set of special ideals correspond to ultrafilters.
(e) $\prod_{\mathbf{I}} \mathfrak{R}_{\mathbf{i}}/D \cong (\prod_{\mathbf{I}} \mathfrak{R}_{\mathbf{i}})/K_D$.
(f) If for every $\mathbf{i} \in \mathbf{I}$, $\mathfrak{R}_{\mathbf{i}}$ is a division ring (skew field) then every ideal in the product is special. Thus if $\mathfrak{R}$ is a division ring, K a maximal ideal in $\mathfrak{R}^{\mathbf{I}}$, then $\mathfrak{R} \ll' (\mathfrak{R}^{\mathbf{I}})/K$.
(g) The reasoning in part (a) holds for groups and compels us to attempt to follow the rest of the problem through for groups in general. What parts of the problem fail for groups? Can the major conclusions be salvaged?

‡2.1.9 (a) For any structure $\mathfrak{A}$, any type $t \subset t_{\mathfrak{A}}$ and any filter, D, show that

$$\mathfrak{A}^{\mathbf{I}}/D/t = (\mathfrak{A}/t)^{\mathbf{I}}/D,$$

and extend this to reduced products of sets of similar structures.
(b) Prove Corollary 2.1.19.

2.1.10 Let $\{\mathfrak{A}_{\mathbf{i}} \mid \mathbf{i} \in \mathbf{I}\}$ be a set of structures, each with n elements, D an ultrafilter on $\mathbf{I}$. Must

$$\prod_{\mathbf{I}} \mathfrak{A}_{\mathbf{i}}/D \cong \mathfrak{A}_{\mathbf{i}} \qquad \text{for some} \qquad \mathbf{i} \in \mathbf{I}?$$

Provide a proof or counterexample to justify your answer.

2.2 Further Properties and Examples

An ultrafilter D is called countably incomplete iff there is a countable $X \subset D$ such that $\bigcap X \notin D$ (a short discussion of similar situations is in Problem 2.3.2).

If $\mathbf{I}$ is countable, D nonprincipal on $\mathbf{I}$, then D is countably incomplete, for by Problem 2.1.4(a),

$$\mathscr{P}_\omega(\mathbf{I}) \subset D \qquad \text{and} \qquad c(\mathscr{P}_\omega(\mathbf{I})) = \omega, \qquad \bigcap \mathscr{P}_\omega(\mathbf{I}) = \phi.$$

Also if D is countably incomplete on $\mathbf{I}$, we can find $y_0, y_1, \ldots$ such that

$$y_0 = \mathbf{I},\ y_{n+1} \subset y_n \qquad \text{for each} \quad n \in \omega,$$

and

$$\bigcap_{n \in \omega} y_n = \phi.$$

Let $y_0 = \mathbf{I}$, $X = \{x_0, x_1, \ldots\} \subset D$, $\bigcap X \notin D$, $y_1 = \mathbf{I} \sim \bigcap X \in D$, $y_{n+1} = y_n \cap x_{n-1}$ for $n \geq 1$. The facts that

$$y_0 = \mathbf{I},\ y_{n+1} \subset y_n \qquad \text{for each} \quad n \in \omega$$

are then clear, and

$$\bigcap_{n\in\omega} y_n \subset (\mathbf{I} \sim \bigcap X) \cap \bigcap_{n\geq 2} y_n \subset (\mathbf{I} \sim \bigcap X) \cap \bigcap_{n\in\omega} x_n$$
$$= (\mathbf{I} \sim \bigcap X) \cap \bigcap X = \phi.$$

The converse, that if such a collection of y's exists then D is countably incomplete, is also clear.

THEOREM 2.2.1. Let D be a countably incomplete ultrafilter on $\mathbf{I}$, $\{A_{\mathbf{i}} \mid \mathbf{i} \in \mathbf{I}\}$ such that for no $n \in \omega$ is

$$\{\mathbf{i} \mid c(A_{\mathbf{i}}) \leq n\} \in D.$$

Then

$$2^{\omega} \leq c\left(\prod_{\mathbf{I}} A_{\mathbf{i}}/D\right).$$

Proof: Assume that we have $y_0, y_1, \ldots$ as above, and for $\mathbf{i} \in \mathbf{I}$ let

$$q(\mathbf{i}) = \min\{k, n\},$$

where

$$\mathbf{i} \in y_k \sim y_{k+1} \qquad \text{and} \qquad 2^n \leq c(A_{\mathbf{i}}) < 2^{n+1}$$

(or $n = \omega$, $c(A_{\mathbf{i}}) \geq \omega$). Note that if $p \in \omega$,

$$\{\mathbf{i} \mid q(\mathbf{i}) \leq p\} = \{\mathbf{i} \mid \mathbf{i} \notin y_{p+1}\} \cup \{\mathbf{i} \mid c(A_{\mathbf{i}}) < 2^{p+1}\} \notin D$$

since neither of the last two sets is in D. Also, for each $\mathbf{i} \in \mathbf{I}$, there is an $F_{\mathbf{i}}$: $2^{q(\mathbf{i})} \rightarrow A_{\mathbf{i}}$ one-one (recall that

$$2^{q(\mathbf{i})} = \{f \mid f\colon \{0, \ldots, q(\mathbf{i}) - 1\} \rightarrow \{0, 1\}\}).$$

Now define F: $2^{\omega} \rightarrow \prod_{\mathbf{I}} A_{\mathbf{i}}$ by

$$F(s)(\mathbf{i}) = F_{\mathbf{i}}(s \mid q(\mathbf{i})) \qquad \text{for} \quad s \in 2^{\omega}$$

and G: $2^{\omega} \rightarrow \prod_{\mathbf{I}} A_{\mathbf{i}}/D$ by

$$G(s) = F(s)/D.$$

We now show G one-one (completing the proof). Suppose that $s, t \in 2^{\omega}$, $s \neq t$. Then for some $n \in \omega$, $s(n) \neq t(n)$ so if $n < m$, $s \mid m \neq t \mid m$, thus if $n < q(\mathbf{i})$,

$$F(s)(\mathbf{i}) = F_{\mathbf{i}}(s \mid q(\mathbf{i})) \neq F_{\mathbf{i}}(t \mid q(\mathbf{i})) = F(t)(\mathbf{i});$$

thus

$$\{\mathbf{i} \mid F(s)(\mathbf{i}) = F(t)(\mathbf{i})\} \subset \{\mathbf{i} \mid q(\mathbf{i}) \leq n\} \notin D,$$

so

$$G(s) \neq G(t).$$

COROLLARY 2.2.2. (a) Let D be any nonprincipal ultrafilter over ω, $\{\mathfrak{A}_n \mid n \in \omega\}$ a set of structures such that for each $m \in \omega$, $\{n \mid c(\mathfrak{A}_n) \leq m\}$ is finite. Then $c(\prod_\omega \mathfrak{A}_n/D) = 2^\omega$ if each $\mathfrak{A}_n$ is of cardinality $\leq 2^\omega$.

(b) Let D be a nonprincipal ultrafilter on $\mathbf{I}$, $c(\mathbf{I}) = \omega$, $\{\mathfrak{A}_\mathbf{i} \mid \mathbf{i} \in \mathbf{I}\}$ a set of structures, each of cardinality $\leq 2^\omega$. Then either:

(i) for some $n \in \omega$, $\{\mathbf{i} \mid c(\mathfrak{A}_\mathbf{i}) = n\} \in D$, in which case

$$c\left(\prod_\mathbf{I} \mathfrak{A}_\mathbf{i}/D\right) = n;$$

or

(ii) for no $n \in \omega$ is $\{\mathbf{i} \mid c(\mathfrak{A}_\mathbf{i}) = n\} \in D$, in which case

$$c\left(\prod_\mathbf{I} \mathfrak{A}_\mathbf{i}/D\right) = 2^\omega.$$

Proof: (a) is immediate from (b). For (b), by Theorem 2.2.1, if for no $n \in \omega$ is $\{\mathbf{i} \mid c(\mathfrak{A}_\mathbf{i}) = n\} \in D$, if $n \in \omega$,

$$\{\mathbf{i} \mid c(\mathfrak{A}_\mathbf{i}) \leq n\} = \{\mathbf{i} \mid c(\mathfrak{A}_\mathbf{i}) = 1\} \cup \cdots \cup \{\mathbf{i} \mid c(\mathfrak{A}_\mathbf{i}) = n\} \notin D,$$

so the cardinality of our ultraproduct is at least 2^ω. If we combine this fact with the result of Problem 2.1.1(d), we complete the proof of case (ii). In case (i),

$$\{\mathbf{i} \mid \mathfrak{A}_\mathbf{i} \models (\geq_n) \wedge \neg(\geq_{n+1})\} \in D,$$

where $\geq_n$ is the sentence introduced after Theorem 1.5.2 to state that there were at least n elements. Thus the ultraproduct also satisfies this sentence, and must therefore have n elements.

Further results on the cardinality and structure of ultraproducts will be given in the next section. We now consider several examples.

Example 1: For each $n \in \omega$, let $\mathfrak{A}_n = \langle \mathbb{Z}_{p_n}, +, 0\rangle$, where p_n is a prime and for $n \neq m$, $p_n \neq p_m$. Consider $\prod_\omega \mathfrak{A}_n/D$, D any nonprincipal ultrafilter on ω. $c(\prod_\omega \mathfrak{A}_n/D) = 2^\omega$, and we also note the following:

(a) $\mathfrak{A} = \prod_\omega \mathfrak{A}_n/D$ is torsion-free. Consider

$$F_n = (\forall v_0)(c_0 \neq v_0 \rightarrow c_0 \neq nv_0).$$

Clearly if $p_m > n$, then $\mathfrak{A}_m \models F_n$. But $\{m \mid p_m \leq n\}$ is finite, thus $\{m \mid \mathfrak{A}_m \models F_n\} \in D$, so $\mathfrak{A} \models F_n$. But this holds for every n.

(b) $\mathfrak{A}$ is divisible. Let

$$G_n = (\forall v_0)(\exists v_1)(nv_1 = v_0), \qquad n < p_m.$$

If $x \in \mathbb{Z}_{p_m}$ and $nx = 0$, the order of x (least integer $k > 0$ such that $kx = 0$) divides n, but it also divides p_m, and p_m, n have no common divisors greater than 1. Thus x is of order 1, so $x = 0$. Thus

$$x \to nx\colon \mathfrak{A}_m \to \mathfrak{A}_m$$

is one-one, thus onto. Thus for each $n \in \omega$,

$$\{m \mid n < p_m\} \subset \{m \mid \mathfrak{A}_m \models G_n\} \in D, \qquad \text{so} \qquad \mathfrak{A} \models G_n.$$

Since every $\mathfrak{A}_n$ is Abelian, so is $\mathfrak{A}$. As mentioned in Section 1.6, $\mathfrak{A}$ may therefore be "made" a vector space over $\mathbb{Q}$ of dimension 2^ω.

Example 2: Let $\mathfrak{C} = \langle \mathbb{Q}, +, 0 \rangle$, $\mathfrak{B} = \mathfrak{C}^\omega/D$ for any nonprincipal ultrafilter D. Then $\mathfrak{C} \equiv \mathfrak{B}$, so $\mathfrak{B}$ is also a torsion-free divisible Abelian group, 2^ω also its cardinality. Thus $\mathfrak{B}$ is isomorphic to the $\mathfrak{A}$ of Example 1, so $\mathfrak{B} \equiv \mathfrak{A}$.

THEOREM 2.2.3. Let $F \in \Sigma^{\langle 3,0 \rangle}$. Then $\mathfrak{C} \models F$ iff $\{n \mid \mathfrak{A}_n \not\models F\}$ is finite (where $\mathfrak{A}_n$, $\mathfrak{C}$ are from Examples 1 and 2).

Proof: If $\{n \mid \mathfrak{A}_n \not\models F\}$ is finite, then for every nonprincipal ultrafilter D, $\{n \mid \mathfrak{A}_n \models F\} \in D$. Thus $\mathfrak{A} \models F$, so $\mathfrak{C} \models F$.

Conversely, let $\{n \mid \mathfrak{A}_n \not\models F\}$ be infinite, and call this set X. Let $E = \mathscr{P}_\omega(\omega) \cup \{X\}$. E has the finite intersection property, since

$$(\omega \sim a_1) \cap \cdots \cap (\omega \sim a_k) \cap X = X \sim (a_1 \cup \cdots \cup a_k),$$

and $a_1 \cup \cdots \cup a_k$ is finite, so

$$X \sim (a_1 \cup \cdots \cup a_k) \neq \phi.$$

Thus $E \subset D$ for some ultrafilter D, $\mathscr{P}_\omega(\omega) \subset D$ so D is nonprincipal, and

$$\prod_\omega \mathfrak{A}_n/D \models \neg F.$$

Thus

$$\mathfrak{C} \models \neg F.$$

COROLLARY 2.2.4. For every $F \in \Sigma^{\langle 3,0 \rangle}$, either $\{n \mid \mathfrak{A}_n \models F\}$ is finite, or $\{n \mid \mathfrak{A}_n \models \neg F\}$ is finite.

Proof: If both are infinite, then by Theorem 2.2.3, $\mathfrak{C} \not\models F$ and $\mathfrak{C} \not\models \neg F$.

Example 3: For each prime n, let $\mathfrak{F}_n = \langle F_n, +, \cdot, 0, 1 \rangle$, the algebraic closure of $\langle \mathbb{Z}_n, +, \cdot, 0, 1 \rangle$, the integers modulo n, and let D be nonprincipal on the set P of primes. Then $\prod_P \mathfrak{F}_n/D$ is an algebraically closed field of cardinality 2^ω, and this ultraproduct is of characteristic 0, since each of the axioms $(\neg 10 f_p)$ is implied by all but one of the $\mathfrak{F}_n$. Thus $\prod_P \mathfrak{F}_n/D \cong \mathbb{C}$ (the complex field).

THEOREM 2.2.5. Let $F \in \Sigma^{\langle 3,3,0,0\rangle}$.
(a) $\{n \mid \mathfrak{F}_n \not\models F\}$ is finite iff $\mathbb{C} \models F$.
(b) $\{n \mid \mathfrak{F}_n \models F\}$ is finite or $\{n \mid \mathfrak{F}_n \models \neg F\}$ is finite.

Proof: Similar to those of Theorem 2.2.3 and Corollary 2.2.4.

Example 4: Let $\mathbb{R}$ be the real numbers considered as a real-closed ordered field, D a nonprincipal ultrafilter on ω, and let $\mathbb{R}^* = \mathbb{R}^\omega/D$. Clearly $\mathbb{R}^*$ is a real-closed ordered field. It is non-Archimedean, for let $f: \omega \to \mathbb{R}$ by $f(n) = n$. Then

$$1_{\mathbb{R}^*} = \langle 1, 1, 1, \ldots\rangle/D,$$

so

$$\{m \mid n < f(m)\} = \{n+1, n+2, \ldots\} \in D \qquad \text{for every } n,$$

so $n1_{\mathbb{R}^*} < f/D$.

$$2^\omega = c(\mathbb{R}) \leq c(\mathbb{R}^\omega) = (2^\omega)^\omega = 2^\omega,$$

thus $c(\mathbb{R}) = c(\mathbb{R}^*)$. Clearly since $\mathbb{R} \neq \mathbb{R}^*$, there are nonempty bounded sets in $\mathbb{R}^*$ with no least upper bounds. However, let F be a formula of our language with one free variable v_0, and let

$$S_F = \{a \in \mathbb{R}^* \mid \mathbb{R}^* \models F[a]\}.$$

Then if S_F is bounded,

$$\mathbb{R}^* \models (\exists v_1)(\forall v_0)(F \rightarrow v_0 \leq v_1).$$

If $S_F \neq \phi$, $\mathbb{R}^* \models (\exists v_0)F$. Thus $\mathbb{R}$ satisfies both these sentences, so $\{b \in \mathbb{R} \mid \mathbb{R} \models F[b]\}$ is nonempty and bounded. By the least upper bound axiom, $\mathbb{R} \models G$, where

$$G = (\exists v_1)(\forall v_0)((F \rightarrow v_0 \leq v_1) \wedge (\forall v_2)((F \rightarrow v_0 \leq v_2) \rightarrow (v_1 \leq v_2)).$$

Thus $\mathbb{R}^* \models G$, so S_F has a least upper bound.

Example 5: Let $\mathfrak{A} = \langle M, \in, \phi, \mathbb{R}, \omega\rangle$, where $\langle M, \in, \phi\rangle$ is a model of set theory, and ω, $\mathbb{R}$ are the natural numbers and the real numbers our model gives rise to (as we know, the axioms of set theory imply the existence of structures of natural and real numbers and their uniqueness, up to isomorphism, with respect to certain properties; see the introduction for a reference in set theory). Let $\mathfrak{A}^* = \mathfrak{A}^\omega/D$ for some nonprincipal ultrafilter

D. $\mathfrak{A}^*$ is clearly a model of set theory, with $\mathbb{R}^*$, ω^* corresponding to $\mathbb{R}$, ω. Clearly $a/D \in^* \omega^*$ iff $\{n \mid a(n) \in \omega\} \in D$. Thus ω^* is uncountable (in fact of cardinality 2^ω). However, if we consider a formula characterizing ω in the language of set theory (we leave it to the reader to find such a formula) since ω satisfies it in $\mathfrak{A}$, ω^* does so in $\mathfrak{A}^*$. It can also be checked that in $\mathfrak{A}^*$, $\mathbb{R}^*$ can be given the structure of an ordered field in which each nonempty bounded set has a least upper bound. However, $\omega^* \not\cong \omega$ (in $\mathfrak{A}$, where they are both sets), and $\mathbb{R}^* = \mathbb{R}^\omega/D \not\cong \mathbb{R}$. The set-theoretical categoricity results generally discussed, which state that ω and $\mathbb{R}$ are unique up to isomorphism, are relative to the model of set theory within which one works.

Examples 4 and 5 will be used in Chapter 5.

Problems

‡2.2.1 Let $\{\mathfrak{A}_\mathbf{i} \mid \mathbf{i} \in \mathbf{I}\}$ be a set of finite structures, D an ultrafilter on $\mathbf{I}$ such that for every $n \in \omega$, $\{\mathbf{i} \mid c(\mathfrak{A}_\mathbf{i}) \leq n\} \notin D$. Then

$$2^\omega \leq c(\prod_{\mathbf{I}} \mathfrak{A}_\mathbf{i}/D).$$

(Hint: Under these conditions show D countably incomplete.)

2.2.2 Let $\{F_1, \ldots\}$ be a countable set of formulas of L^t with $FV(F_n) \subset \{v_0\}$ for each n. Show that if for each m we can find an $a_m \in A$ such that $\mathfrak{A} \models F_n[a_m]$ for $n \leq m$, then there is an $a \in A^\omega/D$ (for nonprincipal ultrafilter D on ω) such that

$$\mathfrak{A}^{(\omega)}/D \models F_n[a] \qquad \text{for every } n.$$

2.2.3 Let $\{\mathfrak{A}_\mathbf{i} \mid \mathbf{i} \in \mathbf{I}\}$ be a set of structures, D an ultrafilter on $\mathbf{I}$, $d \in D$. Show that $D \mid d = \{d \cap e \mid e \in D\}$ is an ultrafilter on d and that

$$\prod_{\mathbf{i} \in d} \mathfrak{A}_\mathbf{i}/(D \mid d) \cong \prod_{\mathbf{I}} \mathfrak{A}_\mathbf{i}/D.$$

Note that the above can be used in an alternative proof of Problem 2.1.3.

2.2.4 Verify that there is no formula of any L^t with free variable v_0 such that $\{a \mid \mathbb{R}^* \models F[a]\} = \mathbb{R}$ (or more appropriately $j_\mathbb{R}[\mathbb{R}]$—see Corollary 2.1.19).

2.2.5 For each prime p, let T_p be the theory of algebraically closed fields of characteristic p, S_p the theory of infinite Abelian groups, each element of which, other than the identity, is of order p.

(a) For every $F \in \Sigma^{\langle 3,3,0,0 \rangle}$, either $\{p \mid T_p \models F\}$ is finite, or $\{p \mid T_p \models \neg F\}$ is finite.

(b) For every $F \in \Sigma^{\langle 3,0 \rangle}$, either $\{p \mid S_p \models F\}$ is finite, or its complement in the set of primes is finite.

(c) After showing (a) and (b) by the methods introduced in this section, do them by methods from Chapter 1 (particularly Theorem 1.6.18).

‡2.2.6 Let $\mathfrak{m}$ be an infinite cardinal, D an ultrafilter, and

$$Y = \{y_\beta \mid \beta < \mathfrak{m}\} \subset D$$

be such that if $\alpha < \beta < \mathfrak{m}$ then $y_\beta \subset y_\alpha$ and $\bigcap Y = \phi$. If $c(A)^{\mathfrak{p}} = c(A)$ for $\mathfrak{p} < \mathfrak{m}$ then $c(A^{\mathbf{I}}/D) \geq c(A)^{\mathfrak{m}}$.

2.3 Set-Theoretic Relations; Regular Ultraproducts

DEFINITION 2.3.1. Let $\mathbf{I}$, $\mathbf{J}$ be sets: D a filter on $\mathbf{I}$; E one on $\mathbf{J}$. Then

$$D \dot{\times} E = \{K \mid K \subset \mathbf{I} \times \mathbf{J} \quad \text{and} \quad \{\mathbf{j} \mid \{\mathbf{i} \mid \langle \mathbf{i}, \mathbf{j} \rangle \in K\} \in D\} \in E\}.$$

We leave it to the reader to check that $D \dot{\times} E$ is a filter on $\mathbf{I} \times \mathbf{J}$, and if D, E are ultrafilters then so is $D \dot{\times} E$.

THEOREM 2.3.2.

$$\prod_{\mathbf{J}} (\prod_{\mathbf{I}} \mathfrak{A}_{\langle \mathbf{i},\mathbf{j} \rangle}/D)/E \cong \prod_{\mathbf{I} \times \mathbf{J}} \mathfrak{A}_{\langle \mathbf{i},\mathbf{j} \rangle}/D \dot{\times} E.$$

Proof: Let

$$h/D \dot{\times} E \in \prod_{\mathbf{I} \times \mathbf{J}} A_{\langle \mathbf{i},\mathbf{j} \rangle}/D \dot{\times} E,$$

and set

$$\varphi(h) = f/E,$$

where

$$f \in \prod_{\mathbf{J}} (\prod_{\mathbf{I}} A_{\langle \mathbf{i},\mathbf{j} \rangle}/D)$$

is defined by

$$f(\mathbf{j}) = h(\langle \mathbf{i}, \mathbf{j} \rangle)/D \in \prod_{\mathbf{I}} A_{\langle \mathbf{i},\mathbf{j} \rangle}/D.$$

It is simple to check that φ is an isomorphism, particularly if we leave it to the reader.

The above corresponds to the exponential law $(a^b)^c = a^{bc}$, well-known for the Cartesian product. In particular, it involves

$$(\mathfrak{A}^{\mathbf{I}}/D)^{\mathbf{J}}/E \cong \mathfrak{A}^{\mathbf{I} \times \mathbf{J}}/D \dot{\times} E.$$

We now have a theorem corresponding to

$$a^b a^c = a^{b+c}.$$

THEOREM 2.3.3. Let $\{\mathbf{I_j} \mid \mathbf{j} \in \mathbf{J}\}$ be a family of pairwise disjoint sets. Let E be a filter on $\mathbf{J}$, and for each $\mathbf{I_j}$, $D_\mathbf{j}$ a filter on $\mathbf{I_j}$. Let

$$\mathbf{I} = \bigcup_{\mathbf{j} \in \mathbf{J}} \mathbf{I_j},$$

and define D by the condition

$$s \in D \quad \text{iff} \quad \{\mathbf{j} \mid s \cap \mathbf{I_j} \in D_\mathbf{j}\} \in E.$$

Then D is a filter on $\mathbf{I}$. If E, $D_\mathbf{j}$ are all ultrafilters, then so is D. Also,

$$\mathfrak{A}^\mathbf{I}/D \cong \prod_\mathbf{J} (\mathfrak{A}^{\mathbf{I_j}}/D_\mathbf{j})/E.$$

Proof: The proof that D is a filter or an ultrafilter and that the following is an isomorphism are left to the reader:

$$\psi(f/D) = g/E,$$

where for $\mathbf{j} \in \mathbf{J}$,

$$g(\mathbf{j}) = h_\mathbf{j}/D_\mathbf{j}, \qquad h_\mathbf{j}(\mathbf{i}) = f(\mathbf{i}) \qquad \text{for} \quad \mathbf{i} \in \mathbf{I_j}.$$

DEFINITION 2.3.4. An ultrafilter D on $\mathbf{I}$ is regular iff for some infinite $\mathbf{J}$, $\mathbf{I} = \mathscr{P}^\omega(\mathbf{J})$ and for every $\mathbf{j} \in \mathbf{J}$,

$$\hat{\mathbf{j}} = \{\mathbf{i} \in \mathbf{I} \mid \mathbf{j} \in \mathbf{i}\} \subset D.$$

LEMMA 2.3.5. If $\mathbf{J}$ is infinite, there is a regular ultrafilter over $\mathbf{I} = \mathscr{P}^\omega(\mathbf{J})$, and every such ultrafilter is countably incomplete.

Proof:

$$\{\mathbf{j}_1, \ldots, \mathbf{j}_k\} \in \hat{\mathbf{j}}_1 \cap \cdots \cap \mathbf{j}_k,$$

so $\{\mathbf{j} \mid \mathbf{j} \in \mathbf{J}\}$ has the finite intersection property. However, for any countable subset

$$\{\mathbf{j}_1, \mathbf{j}_2, \ldots\} \subset \mathbf{J}, \quad \hat{\mathbf{j}}_1 \cap \hat{\mathbf{j}}_2 \cap \cdots = \phi,$$

showing countable incompleteness.

THEOREM 2.3.6. For any regular ultrafilter D on $\mathbf{I} = \mathscr{P}^\omega(\mathbf{J})$ and any infinite set A,

$$c(A^\mathbf{I}/D) = c(A^\mathbf{I}).$$

Proof: We know that

$$c(A^\mathbf{I}/D) \leq c(A^\mathbf{I}),$$

and must find a map $\psi\colon A^{\mathbf{I}} \to A^{\mathbf{I}}/D$ one-one. It will do to find

$$\psi\colon A^{\mathbf{J}} \to A^{\mathbf{I}}/D$$

one-one, since $c(\mathbf{J}) = c(\mathbf{I})$. Since A is infinite, there is a one-one map from A' onto A, where A' is the set of finite ordered subsets of A (formally,

$$A' = \{x \mid \text{for some } n \in \omega,\ x\colon n \to A\}).$$

Let ρ be this map, and let $<$ well-order $\mathbf{J}$. For $f\colon \mathbf{J} \to A$, define $f^*\colon \mathbf{I} \to A$ by

$$f^*(\mathbf{i}) = \rho(x), \qquad \text{where} \quad x = \langle f(\mathbf{j}_1), \ldots, f(\mathbf{j}_n)\rangle,$$

with

$$\mathbf{j}_1 < \cdots < \mathbf{j}_n, \qquad \mathbf{i} = \{\mathbf{j}_1, \ldots, \mathbf{j}_n\}.$$

We now define ψ by $\psi(f) = f^*/D$. If $f \neq g$, $f, g \in A^{\mathbf{J}}$, then for some $\mathbf{j}$, $f(\mathbf{j}) \neq g(\mathbf{j})$. If $\mathbf{j} = \mathbf{j}_m \in \mathbf{i}$, then clearly

$$\langle f(\mathbf{j}_1), \ldots, f(\mathbf{j}_m), \ldots, f(\mathbf{j}_n)\rangle \neq \langle g(\mathbf{j}_1), \ldots, g(\mathbf{j}_m), \ldots, g(\mathbf{j}_n)\rangle,$$

thus $f^*(\mathbf{i}) \neq g^*(\mathbf{i})$. Therefore,

$$\hat{\mathbf{j}} \subset \{\mathbf{i} \mid f^*(\mathbf{i}) \neq g^*(\mathbf{i})\}, \qquad \text{so} \qquad \psi(f) \neq \psi(g).$$

From now on, let $V_0^t = \{F \in L^t \mid FV(F) \subset \{v_0\}\}$.

DEFINITION 2.3.7. Let $X \subset A$. Then $\mathfrak{A}$ has the finite satisfaction property for X iff whenever $S \subset V_0^t$ and for every finite $S' \subset S$ there is a $c \in X$ such that if $F \in S'$ then $\mathfrak{A} \models F[c]$, then there is a $b \in A$ such that for every $F \in S$, $\mathfrak{A} \models F[b]$ (i.e., any such S finitely satisfiable in X is satisfiable in $\mathfrak{A}$).

$\mathfrak{A}$ has the finite satisfaction property iff $\mathfrak{A}$ has the finite satisfaction property for A. (For examples of these properties see Problem 2.3.6.)

THEOREM 2.3.8. Let $c(t) \leq c(\mathbf{I})$, $\mathbf{I} = \mathscr{P}^{\omega}(\mathbf{J})$, $\mathfrak{B} = \mathfrak{A}^{\mathbf{I}}/D$, D a regular ultrafilter on $\mathbf{I}$, $\mathfrak{A} \in M^t$. Then $\mathfrak{B}$ has the finite satisfaction property for $j_{\mathfrak{A}}[A]$.

Proof:

$$c(S) \leq c(V_0^t) \leq c(L^t) = c(t) + \omega \leq c(\mathbf{I}) = c(\mathbf{J}).$$

Thus we may consider $S \subset \mathbf{J}$ by way of some imbedding. For $\mathbf{i} \in \mathbf{I}$, let $c_{\mathbf{i}} \in j_{\mathfrak{A}}[A]$ be such that

$$\mathfrak{B} \models F[c_{\mathbf{i}}] \qquad \text{for every} \quad F \in \mathbf{i} \cap S.$$

Let $F \in S$, $j_{\mathfrak{A}}(c(\mathbf{i})) = c_{\mathbf{i}}$, and consider c/D.

$$\mathfrak{B} \models F[c/D] \quad \text{iff} \quad \{\mathbf{i} \mid \mathfrak{A} \models F[c(\mathbf{i})]\} = \{\mathbf{i} \mid \mathfrak{B} \models F[c_{\mathbf{i}}]\} \in D,$$

but since $F \in \mathbf{J}$,

$$\hat{F} = \{\mathbf{i} \mid F \in \mathbf{i}\} \subset \{\mathbf{i} \mid \mathfrak{B} \models F[c_{\mathbf{i}}]\}.$$

The following is a simple application of the finite satisfaction property mentioned above. Let $\mathfrak{A}$ be totally ordered with no last element, D a regular ultrafilter on $\mathbf{I}$. Then $j_{\mathfrak{A}}[A]$ is bounded above in $\mathfrak{A}^{\mathbf{I}}/D$, provided that there is a cofinal set $B \subset A$ with $c(B) \leq c(\mathbf{I})$. For consider $\mathfrak{A}' = \langle A, <, b\rangle_{b \in B}$, of type t', with $c(t') \leq c(\mathbf{I})$, and let

$$S \subset V_0^{t'}, \qquad S = \{c_b < v_0 \mid b \in B\}.$$

Since $\mathfrak{A}$ has no last element, any finite subset is satisfiable in $\mathfrak{B}'$ by an element of $j_{\mathfrak{A}}[A]$. Thus the whole set must be satisfiable in $\mathfrak{B}'$, and an element satisfying the whole set bounds $\mathfrak{A}$.

In certain cases we can show ultraproducts to have the finite satisfaction property (for their domains as a whole).

LEMMA 2.3.9. Let S be countable, $G\colon \mathscr{P}_\omega(S) \to D$ such that if $S_1 \subset S_2$ then $G(S_1) \subset G(S_2)$, D an ultrafilter on $\mathbf{I}$. Then there is an $H\colon \mathscr{P}_\omega(S) \to D$ such that

$$\text{if} \quad S_1 \in \mathscr{P}_\omega(S), \qquad H(S_1) \subset G(S_1)$$

and

$$\text{for} \quad S_1, S_2 \in \mathscr{P}_\omega(S), \qquad H(S_1 \cap S_2) = H(S_1) \cap H(S_2).$$

Proof: Let $S = \{s_1, s_2, \ldots\}$, and define

$$J\colon S \to D \quad \text{by} \quad J(s_n) = G(S \sim \{s_1, \ldots, s_n\}),$$

$$H\colon \mathscr{P}_\omega(S) \to D \quad \text{by} \quad H(S \sim \{s_{m_1}, \ldots, s_{m_r}\}) = J(s_{m_1}) \cap \cdots \cap J(s_{m_r}).$$

If $S_1, S_2 \in \mathscr{P}_\omega(S)$, let

$$S_1 = S \sim \{s_{m_1}, \ldots, s_{m_r}\}, \qquad S_2 = S \sim \{s_{n_1}, \ldots, s_{n_q}\}.$$

Thus

$$\begin{aligned} H(S_1 \cap S_2) &= H(S \sim \{s_{m_1}, \ldots, s_{n_q}\}) \\ &= J(s_{m_1}) \cap \cdots \cap J(s_{n_q}) \\ &= H(S_1) \cap H(S_2). \end{aligned}$$

Also $H(S_1) \subset G(S_1)$, for $H(S_1) \subset J(s_{m_k})$ for each $k = 1, \ldots, r$, and for the largest m_k,

$$S \sim \{s_1, \ldots, s_{m_k}\} \subset S_1, \qquad \text{so} \qquad J(s_{m_k}) \subset G(S_1).$$

THEOREM 2.3.10. Let $\mathfrak{A} = \prod_{\mathbf{I}} \mathfrak{A}_{\mathbf{i}}/D$, D countably incomplete on $\mathbf{I}$, $\mathfrak{A} \in M^t$, t countable. Then $\mathfrak{A}$ has the finite satisfaction property.

Proof: Let $S \subset V_0^t$, S finitely satisfiable in $\mathfrak{A}$. Since t is countable,

$$c(S) \leq c(V_0^t) \leq c(L^t) = \omega,$$

and if $c(S) < \omega$, the theorem is trivial, so let $c(S) = \omega$. Define

$$G\colon \mathscr{P}_\omega(S) \to \mathscr{P}(\mathbf{I}) \qquad \text{by} \quad G(S_1) = \{\mathbf{i} \mid S \sim S_1 \text{ is satisfiable in } \mathfrak{A}_{\mathbf{i}}\}$$

(note that $S \sim S_1$ is finite). Clearly if $S_1 \subset S_2$, then $S \sim S_2 \subset S \sim S_1$, so $G(S_1) \subset G(S_2)$. For $S_1 \in \mathscr{P}_\omega(S)$, let

$$F_{S_1} = (\exists v_0)(F_1 \wedge \cdots \wedge F_n), \qquad \text{where} \quad S \sim S_1 = \{F_1, \ldots, F_n\}.$$

Since $S \sim S_1$ is satisfiable in $\mathfrak{A}$ for every $S_1 \in \mathscr{P}_\omega(S)$, $\mathfrak{A} \models F_{S_1}$ for each such S_1, thus $\{\mathbf{i} \mid \mathfrak{A}_{\mathbf{i}} \models F_{S_1}\} \in D$ for each S_1, but $\{\mathbf{i} \mid \mathfrak{A}_{\mathbf{i}} \models F_{S_1}\} = G(S_1)$, so $G\colon \mathscr{P}_\omega(S) \to D$. Since D is countably incomplete, let

$$\mathbf{I} = X_0 \supset X_1 \supset \cdots$$

such that

$$\bigcap_{n<\omega} X_n = \phi \qquad \text{and} \qquad X_n \in D.$$

Now let $G'\colon \mathscr{P}_\omega(S) \to D$ be defined by

$$G'(S_1) = G(S_1) \cap X_{c(S \sim S_1)}.$$

Once again, if $S_1 \subset S_2$,

$$G'(S_1) = G(S_1) \cap X_{c(S \sim S_1)} \subset G(S_2) \cap X_{c(S \sim S_2)} = G'(S_2).$$

Thus by Lemma 2.3.9 there is an $H\colon \mathscr{P}_\omega(S) \to D$ such that if $S_1, S_2 \in \mathscr{P}_\omega(S)$ then

$$H(S_1) \subset G'(S_1) \qquad \text{and} \qquad H(S_1 \cap S_2) = H(S_1) \cap H(S_2).$$

For $\mathbf{i} \in \mathbf{I}$, let

$$r(\mathbf{i}) = \max\{m \mid \mathbf{i} \in X_m\}$$

and let

$$S(\mathbf{i}) = \{F \in S \mid \mathbf{i} \in H(S \sim \{F\})\}.$$

$c(S(\mathbf{i})) \leq r(\mathbf{i})$, for otherwise we can find a finite $S_0 \subset S(\mathbf{i})$ with $r(\mathbf{i}) < c(S_0)$. But then

$$\mathbf{i} \in \bigcap_{F \in S_0} H(S \sim \{F\}) = H(S \sim S_0) \subset X_{c(S_0)}$$

contradicting the definition of $r(\mathbf{i})$. Thus $S(\mathbf{i})$ is finite and

$$\mathbf{i} \in H(S \sim S(\mathbf{i})) \qquad \text{for every} \quad \mathbf{i} \in \mathbf{I}.$$

Thus

$$\mathbf{i} \in G(S \sim S(\mathbf{i}))$$

so $S(\mathbf{i})$ is satisfiable in $\mathfrak{A}_{\mathbf{i}}$.

Now, let $g \in \prod_{\mathbf{I}} A_{\mathbf{i}}$ be such that if $\mathbf{i} \in \mathbf{I}$ then $\mathfrak{A}_{\mathbf{i}} \models F[g(\mathbf{i})]$ for every $F \in S(\mathbf{i})$. Thus if $F \in S$,

$$H(S \sim \{F\}) = \{\mathbf{i} \mid F \in S(\mathbf{i})\} \subset \{\mathbf{i} \mid \mathfrak{A}_{\mathbf{i}} \models F[g(\mathbf{i})]\},$$

but $H(S \sim \{F\}) \in D$. Thus for every $F \in S$, $\mathfrak{A} \models F[g/D]$.

THEOREM 2.3.11. Let D, E be nonprincipal ultrafilters on ω,

$$c(t) \leq \omega, \qquad \{\mathfrak{A}_n \mid n \in \omega\}, \{\mathfrak{B}_n \mid n \in \omega\} \subset M^t,$$

and for each $n \in \omega$, let

$$\omega \leq c(\mathfrak{A}_n) \leq 2^{\omega}, \qquad \omega \leq c(\mathfrak{B}_n) \leq 2^{\omega}.$$

Assume the continuum hypothesis $\omega^+ = 2^{\omega}$, and let

$$\mathfrak{A} = \prod_{\omega} \mathfrak{A}_n/D, \qquad \mathfrak{B} = \prod_{\omega} \mathfrak{B}_n/E.$$

Then $\mathfrak{A} \equiv \mathfrak{B}$ iff $\mathfrak{A} \cong \mathfrak{B}$.

Clearly if $\mathfrak{A} \cong \mathfrak{B}$, $\mathfrak{A} \equiv \mathfrak{B}$, by Theorem 1.2.11, for example. It is the converse that is intriguing and difficult to show. The proof that follows is based on Cantor's proof (the proof of Theorem 1.6.14).

Proof: Let $\mathfrak{A} = \langle A, R_\gamma\rangle_{\gamma \in \Gamma}$, $\mathfrak{B} = \langle B, S_\gamma\rangle_{\gamma \in \Gamma}$, $A = \{a_\eta \mid \eta \in \omega^+\}$, $B = \{b_\eta \mid \eta \in \omega^+\}$, possible since by Corollary 2.2.2 $c(A) = c(B) = 2^{\omega}$ and we have assumed the continuum hypothesis. We now construct a set of maps $\{\varphi_\mu \mid \mu \leq \omega^+\}$ such that:

(a) If $\mu \leq \omega^+$, $\{a_\eta \mid \eta < \mu\} \subset \mathscr{D}\varphi_\mu$ and $\{b_\eta \mid \eta < \mu\} \subset \mathscr{R}\varphi_\mu$.
(b) If $\mu \leq \mu' \leq \omega^+$, then $\varphi_\mu \subset \varphi_{\mu'}$.
(c) If $\mu \leq \omega^+$ and $\varphi_\mu = \{\langle a_x, b_x\rangle \mid x \in X\}$, then

$$\langle A, R_\gamma, a_x\rangle_{\gamma \in \Gamma, x \in X} \equiv \langle B, S_\gamma, b_x\rangle_{\gamma \in \Gamma, x \in X}.$$

(d) If $\eta < \omega^+$, then $c(\varphi_\eta) \leq \omega$.

Once we have this collection, $\mathscr{D}\varphi_{\omega^+} = A$, $\mathscr{R}\varphi_{\omega^+} = B$ [by (a)], and thus by (c) $\varphi_{\omega^+}: \mathfrak{A} \cong \mathfrak{B}$ (also see Theorem 1.2.11).

Our maps are defined by transfinite induction. Let $\varphi_0 = \phi$, then (a) through (d) clearly hold. Assume now that we have φ_μ for $\mu \leq \alpha < \omega^+$. We then define

$$\varphi_{\alpha+1} = \varphi_\alpha \cup \{\langle a_\alpha, b_\beta\rangle\} \cup \{\langle a_\delta, b_\alpha\rangle\},$$

where β, δ are as found below. Whatever β, δ might be it is clear that (a), (b), (d) are still satisfied. To find β, let $\varphi_\alpha = \{\langle a_x, b_x\rangle \mid x \in X\}$, $t \oplus X$ be the type of $\langle A, R_\gamma, a_x\rangle_{\gamma \in \Gamma, x \in X}$, and

$$T = \{F \in V_0^{t \oplus X} \mid \langle A, R_\gamma, a_x\rangle_{\gamma \in \Gamma, x \in X} \models F[a_\alpha]\}.$$

T is finitely satisfiable in $\langle B, S_\gamma, b_x\rangle_{\gamma \in \Gamma, x \in X}$: Let $\{F_1, \ldots, F_n\} \subset T$ and consider $G = (\exists v_0)(F_1 \wedge \cdots \wedge F_n)$. Then

$$\langle A, R_\gamma, a_x\rangle_{\gamma \in \Gamma, x \in X} \models F_1 \wedge \cdots \wedge F_n[a_\alpha]$$

so

$$\langle A, R_\gamma, a_x\rangle_{\gamma \in \Gamma, x \in X} \models G,$$

thus by (c)

$$\langle B, S_\gamma, b_x\rangle_{\gamma \in \Gamma, x \in X} \models G.$$

Thus for some $b \in B$,

$$\langle B, S_\gamma, b_x\rangle_{\gamma \in \Gamma, x \in X} \models F_j[b] \qquad \text{for} \quad j = 1, \ldots, n.$$

Thus T is satisfiable in B, so let β be the first ordinal such that

$$\langle B, S_\gamma, b_x\rangle_{\gamma \in \Gamma, x \in X} \models F[b_\beta] \qquad \text{for every} \quad F \in T.$$

We now assert that

$$\langle A, R_\gamma, a_x, a_\alpha\rangle_{\gamma \in \Gamma, x \in X} \equiv \langle B, S_\gamma, b_x, b_\beta\rangle_{\gamma \in \Gamma, x \in X}.$$

If

$$F \in T(\langle A, R_\gamma, a_x, a_\alpha\rangle_{\gamma \in \Gamma, x \in X})$$

then

$$\langle A, R_\gamma, a_x\rangle_{\gamma \in \Gamma, x \in X} \models Sb_{v_0}^{c_{a_\alpha}} F[a_\alpha];$$

thus

$$Sb_{v_0}^{c_{a_\alpha}} F \in T;$$

thus

$$\langle B, S_\gamma, b_x\rangle_{\gamma \in \Gamma, x \in X} \models Sb_{v_0}^{c_{a_\alpha}} F[b_\beta],$$

so

$$\langle B, S_\gamma, b_x, b_\beta\rangle_{\gamma \in \Gamma, x \in X} \models F.$$

Thus by Theorem 1.3.3(j)

$$T(\langle A, R_\gamma, a_x, a_\alpha\rangle_{\gamma \in \Gamma, x \in X}) = T(\langle B, S_\gamma, b_x, b_\beta\rangle_{\gamma \in \Gamma, x \in X}).$$

Let

$$\psi = \varphi_\alpha \cup \{\langle a_\alpha, b_\beta\rangle\}.$$

δ is found similarly by the fact that if

$$\psi^{-1} = \{\langle b_y, a_y\rangle \mid y \in Y\},$$

then

$$\langle B, S_\gamma, b_y\rangle_{\gamma \in \Gamma, y \in Y} \equiv \langle A, R_\gamma, a_y\rangle_{\gamma \in \Gamma, y \in Y}.$$

If α is a limit ordinal, $\alpha \leq \omega^+$, let $\varphi_\alpha = \bigcup_{\mu<\alpha} \varphi_\mu$. (a) through (d) are easy to check in this case (we note for the proof of (c) that if

$$\varphi_\alpha = \{\langle a_x, b_x\rangle \mid x \in X\}, \qquad F \in L^{t\oplus X},$$

then for some $\mu < \alpha$,

$$Y \subset X, \qquad \varphi_\mu = \{\langle a_y, b_y\rangle \mid y \in Y\}, \qquad \text{and} \qquad F \in L^{t\oplus Y}).$$

Problems

‡2.3.1 (a) Show that $D \dot{\times} E$ is a filter and an ultrafilter if D, E are. Also show that $(D \dot{\times} E) \dot{\times} F = D \dot{\times} (E \dot{\times} F)$, and that the map of Theorem 2.3.2 is an isomorphism.

(b) Show that the D defined in Theorem 2.3.3 is a filter, and an ultrafilter if each of the $D_{\mathbf{j}}$, E are. Also show that the map ψ of Theorem 2.3.3 is an isomorphism.

‡2.3.2 A filter D on $\mathbf{I}$ is called $\mathfrak{m}$-complete (for $\mathfrak{m}$ an infinite cardinal) iff for every $S \subset D$ with $c(S) < \mathfrak{m}$, $\bigcap S \in D$.

(a) Show that the following are equivalent and that each is equivalent to the condition that D is $\mathfrak{m}$-complete:

(i) There is no $S \subset \mathscr{P}\mathbf{I}$ such that $c(S) < \mathfrak{m}$, $\bigcup S \in D$, and $S \cap D = \phi$.

(ii) There is no $S \subset \mathscr{P}\mathbf{I}$ such that $c(S) < \mathfrak{m}$, $\bigcup S = \mathbf{I}$, and $S \cap D = \phi$.

(b) Every filter is ω-complete.

For the remainder of this problem, let D be an ultrafilter.

(c) If D is $\mathfrak{m}$-complete, $\mathfrak{n} < \mathfrak{m}$, and for every $\mathbf{i} \in \mathbf{I}$, $c(\mathfrak{A}_\mathbf{i}) \leq \mathfrak{n}$, then

$$c\prod_{\mathbf{I}} \mathfrak{A}_\mathbf{i}/D \leq \mathfrak{n}.$$

(d) If D is $\mathfrak{m}$-complete, $c(\mathfrak{A}) < \mathfrak{m}$, then $j_\mathfrak{A}$ is an isomorphism.

(e) If D is not $\mathfrak{m}$-complete, we can find an $\mathfrak{A}$ with $c(\mathfrak{A}) < \mathfrak{m}$ such that $j_\mathfrak{A}$ is not an isomorphism.

(f) D is $\mathfrak{m}$-complete for every $\mathfrak{m}$ iff D is principal.

2.3.3 Show by the methods of Chapter 1 the existence of an elementary extension of $\mathfrak{A}$ that has the finite satisfaction property for A.

2.3.4 Let $\mathfrak{A}$ be an infinite structure with second-order axioms (i.e., axioms like the least-upper-bound axiom that refer to subsets of $\mathfrak{A}$ as well as elements of $\mathfrak{A}$). If $\mathfrak{B} = \langle B, \in, \phi\rangle$ is a model of set theory with respect to which $\mathfrak{A}$ satisfies these second-order axioms and $\mathfrak{m}$ is an infinite cardinal, then we can find a $\mathfrak{C}$ such that $\mathfrak{B} <' \mathfrak{C}$, and $\mathfrak{C}$ contains a structure $\mathfrak{A}^*$ satisfying the same axioms as $\mathfrak{A}$ (with respect, now, to $\mathfrak{C}$) such that $\mathfrak{m} \leq c(\mathfrak{A}^*)$.

‡2.3.5 (a) If $c(t) \leq \omega$, then $\prod_{\mathbf{I}} \mathfrak{A}_i/D$ has the finite satisfaction property whenever D is regular.

(b) Let $j : \mathbb{Z} \not\cong \mathbb{Z}^{\mathbf{I}}/D$. Then $\mathbb{Z}^{\mathbf{I}}/D$ is ω^+-saturated, where $\mathbb{Z}$ denotes the integer ring with usual operations and order (see Definition 2.7.1 and the comment following it).

2.3.6 (a) If each $a \in A$ is a distinguished element of $\mathfrak{A}$, then $\mathfrak{A}$ does not have the finite satisfaction property.

(b) $\langle \mathbb{Q}, <, x \rangle_{x \in X}$ has the finite satisfaction property for each finite X.

(c) $\langle \mathbb{R}, <, n \rangle_{n \in \omega}$ does not have the finite satisfaction property for ω.

2.4 Ultralimits

Results in this section, except as noted, are found in Kochen. They provide a generalization of the ultrapower construction with applications which include a characterization of elementary classes to be developed in Section 2.5. From now on by an ultrafilter pair we mean $\langle \mathbf{I}, D \rangle$, where $\mathbf{I}$ is an infinite set, D an ultrafilter on $\mathbf{I}$.

THEOREM 2.4.1 (Frayne): For $\mathfrak{A}, \mathfrak{B} \in M^t$, $\mathfrak{A} \equiv \mathfrak{B}$ iff for some ultrafilter pair $\langle \mathbf{I}, D \rangle$, $\mathfrak{B} <' \mathfrak{A}^{\mathbf{I}}/D$.

Proof: Let $\mathfrak{B}' = \langle B, S_\gamma, b \rangle_{\gamma \in \Gamma, b \in B} \in M^{t'}$, where

$$\mathfrak{B} = \langle B, S_\gamma \rangle_{\gamma \in \Gamma}, \qquad \mathbf{I} = \{F \in \Sigma^{t'} \mid \mathfrak{B}' \models F\}.$$

Let

$$C(F) \sim C_t = \{c_{b_1}, \ldots, c_{b_n}\}, \qquad \{v_{j_1}, \ldots, v_{j_n}\} \cap V(F) = \phi,$$

and

$$\rho = \{\langle c_{b_1}, v_{j_1} \rangle, \ldots, \langle c_{b_n}, v_{j_n} \rangle\}$$

be a one-one map. Then $\mathfrak{B}' \models F$ thus by Theorem 1.2.15,

$$\mathfrak{B}' \models Sb_\rho F[b_1, \ldots, b_n]$$

(since $F = Sb_{\rho-1}(Sb_\rho F)$ here) so

$$\mathfrak{B} \models Sb_\rho F[b_1, \ldots, b_n]$$

thus

$$\mathfrak{B} \models (\exists v_{j_1}) \cdots (\exists v_{j_n}) Sb_\rho F$$

so

$$\mathfrak{A} \models (\exists v_{j_1}) \cdots (\exists v_{j_n}) Sb_\rho F.$$

Thus for some $a_1, \ldots, a_n \in A$,

$$\mathfrak{A} \models Sb_\rho F[a_1, \ldots, a_n].$$

Now let $\mathfrak{A}_F = \langle A, R_\gamma, a_b^F\rangle_{\gamma\in\Gamma, b\in B}$ where $\mathfrak{A} = \langle A, R_\gamma\rangle_{\gamma\in\Gamma}$, and $a_{b_j}^F = a_j$ for $j = 1, \ldots, n$, $a_b^F \in A$ arbitrary otherwise. Then

$$\mathfrak{A}_F \models Sb_\rho F[a_{b_1}^F, \ldots, a_{b_n}^F] \qquad \text{so} \quad \mathfrak{A}_F \models F.$$

For $F \in \mathbf{I}$ let $J_F = \{F' \in \mathbf{I} \mid \mathfrak{A}_{F'} \models F\}$, $E = \{J_F \mid F \in \mathbf{I}\}$, and suppose $J_{F_1}, \ldots, J_{Fm} \in E$. Then $F_1, \ldots, F_m \in \mathbf{I}$ thus $\mathfrak{A}_{F_1\wedge\cdots\wedge F_m} \models F_1, \ldots, F_m$, so $F_1 \wedge \cdots \wedge F_m \in J_{F_1} \cap \cdots \cap J_{F_m}$. Thus E has the finite intersection property so let $E \subset D$, D an ultrafilter on $\mathbf{I}$. If $\mathfrak{B}' \models F$ then

$$\{F' \in \mathbf{I} \mid \mathfrak{A}_{F'} \models F\} = J_F \in D \qquad \text{so} \quad \textstyle\prod_{\mathbf{I}} \mathfrak{A}_{F'}/D \models F,$$

thus

$$T(\mathfrak{B}') \subset T(\textstyle\prod_{\mathbf{I}} \mathfrak{A}_{F'}/D), \qquad \text{so} \quad \mathfrak{B}' \equiv \textstyle\prod_{\mathbf{I}} \mathfrak{A}_{F'}/D,$$

thus by Theorem 1.7.2, $\mathfrak{B} <' \prod_{\mathbf{I}} \mathfrak{A}_{F'}/D$. (Also see Problem 2.4.2.)

The above constitutes a direct construction to show that if $\mathfrak{A} \equiv \mathfrak{B}$, then for some $\mathfrak{C}$, $\mathfrak{A} <' \mathfrak{C}$ and $\mathfrak{B} <' \mathfrak{C}$.

LEMMA 2.4.2. A map $\varphi: \mathfrak{A} \to \mathfrak{B}$ is an elementary imbedding iff for some ultrafilter pair $\langle \mathbf{I}, D\rangle$, and map $\psi: \mathfrak{B} <' \mathfrak{A}^{\mathbf{I}}/D$,

$$j_{\mathfrak{A}} = \psi \circ \varphi.$$

Proof: φ is an elementary imbedding iff $\mathfrak{A}' \equiv \mathfrak{B}'$, where

$$\mathfrak{A}' = \langle A, R_\gamma, a\rangle_{\gamma\in\Gamma, a\in A}, \qquad \mathfrak{B}' = \langle B, S_\gamma, \varphi(a)\rangle_{\gamma\in\Gamma, a\in A}.$$

Thus by Theorem 2.4.1, there is an elementary imbedding of $\mathfrak{B}'$ into $\mathfrak{A}'^{\mathbf{I}}/D$, which we call ψ.

But then $\psi(\varphi(a)) = j_{\mathfrak{A}}(a)$, since $\varphi(a)$ and $j_{\mathfrak{A}}(a)$ are corresponding distinguished elements. The converse is clear.

Suppose now that we have $\mathfrak{A} \equiv \mathfrak{B}$. By Theorem 2.4.1, we have

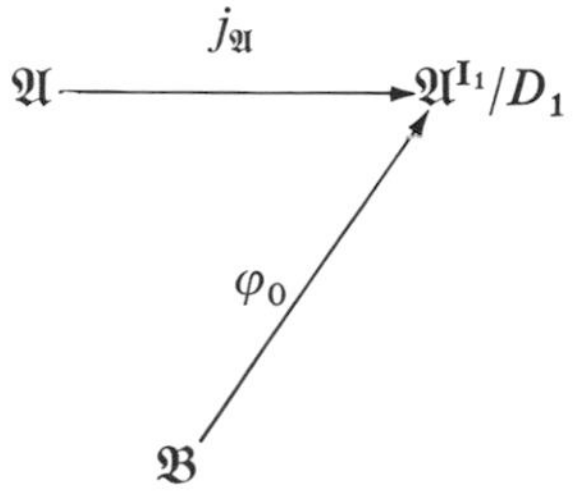

but since φ_0 is elementary, by Lemma 2.4.2 we must have $\langle \mathbf{J}_1, E_1 \rangle$ an ultrafilter pair, and a map ψ_1 such that

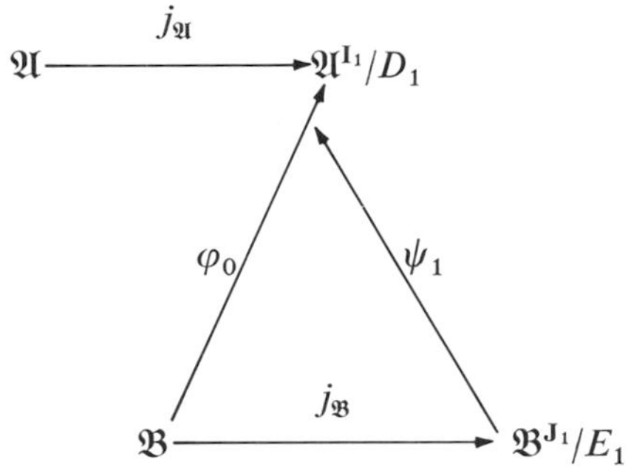

with ψ_1 elementary and $\psi_1 \circ \varphi_0 = j_{\mathfrak{B}}$.

But since ψ_1 is elementary we must also have

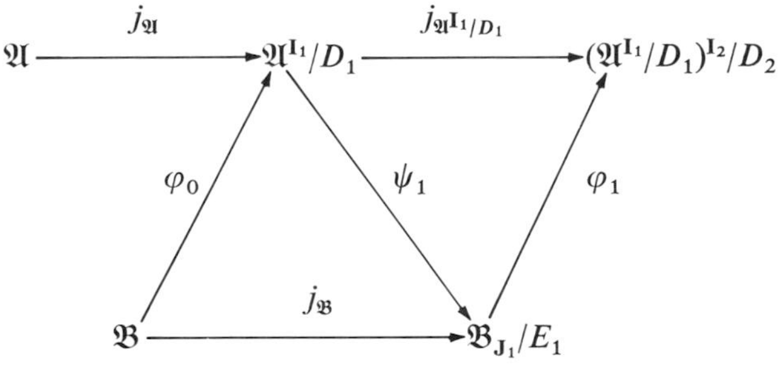

It appears that we can continue indefinitely in this manner, and we soon shall for the following reason. If our relation were $<$ rather than $<'$ and we were to look at the preceding diagrams, we should see

$$\begin{matrix} \mathfrak{A} < \\ \mathfrak{B} < \end{matrix} \mathfrak{A}^{\mathbf{I}_1}/D_1 < \mathfrak{B}^{\mathbf{J}_1}/E_1 < (\mathfrak{A}^{\mathbf{I}_1}/D_1)^{\mathbf{I}_2}/D_2 <$$

therefore $\mathfrak{A}$ and $\mathfrak{B}$ would have identical unions for their ascending chains of ultrapowers. Since we have $<'$ rather than $<$, certain changes are necessary, although the above remains the motivation. First, our definition of union must be changed, since the structures we wish to take the union of are being shifted about by functions.

DEFINITION 2.4.3. Let $\langle X, \leq \rangle$ be a directed set,

$$\mathscr{A} = \{\mathfrak{A}_r \mid r \in X\} \cup \{\varphi_{rs} \mid r \leq s,\ r, s \in X\},$$

such that $\{\mathfrak{A}_r \mid r \in X\} \subset M^t$ and

(i) $\varphi_{rr} = \mathfrak{I}_r$, the identity function on $\mathfrak{A}_r$;
(ii) for $r \le s$, $\varphi_{rs}: \mathfrak{A}_r \to \mathfrak{A}_s$ is a homomorphism;
(iii) for $r \le s \le t$, $\varphi_{rt} = \varphi_{st} \circ \varphi_{rs}$.

Then $\mathscr{A}$ is called a directed system of structures.

DEFINITION 2.4.4. Let $\mathscr{A}$ be a directed system of structures. Then $\mathscr{B} = \{\mathfrak{A}\} \cup \{\varphi_r \mid r \in X\}$ is called a direct limit for $\mathscr{A}$ iff $\mathfrak{A} \in M^t$ and

(i) for each $r \in X$, $\varphi_r: \mathfrak{A}_r \to \mathfrak{A}$ is a homomorphism;
(ii) for $r \le s$, $r, s \in X$, $\varphi_r = \varphi_s \circ \varphi_{rs}$;
(iii) if for each $r \in X$, $\psi_r: \mathfrak{A}_r \to \mathfrak{B}$ is a homomorphism and whenever $r \le s$, $r, s \in X$, $\psi_s \circ \varphi_{rs} = \psi_r$, then there is a unique homomorphism $\psi: \mathfrak{A} \to \mathfrak{B}$ such that for each $r \in X$, $\psi_r = \psi \circ \varphi_r$. Here $\mathfrak{A}$ is called the object limit of $\mathscr{A}$.

In the comments following Lemma 2.4.2, we were "generating" a directed system and were interested in its object limit.

LEMMA 2.4.5. Every directed system $\mathscr{A}$ has a direct limit

$$\{\mathfrak{A}\} \cup \{\varphi_r \mid r \in X\}$$

and if $\{\mathfrak{B}\} \cup \{\psi_r \mid r \in X\}$ is a second direct limit there is an isomorphism $f: \mathfrak{A} \cong \mathfrak{B}$ such that for each r, $\psi_r = f \circ \varphi_r$. If each φ_{rs} is an elementary imbedding, then so is each φ_r.

Proof: (Existence) Let A' be the disjoint union of the A_r, $A = A'/\sim$, where for $a \in A_r$, $b \in A_s$, $a \sim b$ iff for some q,

$$r \le q, \qquad s \le q, \qquad \text{and} \qquad \varphi_{rq}(a) = \varphi_{sq}(b).$$

For $a \in A'$, set

$$[a] = \{b \mid a \sim b\}.$$

For $[a_1], \ldots, [a_{t(\gamma)}] \in A$, set

$$\langle [a_1], \ldots, [a_{t(\gamma)}] \rangle \in R_\gamma$$

iff for some $b_1 \in [a_1], \ldots, b_{t(\gamma)} \in [a_{t(\gamma)}]$, $r \in X$,

$$\langle b_1, \ldots, b_{t(\gamma)} \rangle \in R^r_\gamma,$$

and if $t(\gamma) = 0$,

$$R_\gamma = [R^r_\gamma].$$

Finally, we define

$$\varphi_r: \mathfrak{A}_r \to \mathfrak{A} = \langle A, R_\gamma \rangle_{\gamma \in \Gamma}$$

by $\varphi_r(a) = [a]$ for $a \in A_r$. We leave for the reader the proof that $\sim$ is in fact an equivalence relation, $\{\mathfrak{A}\} \cup \{\varphi_r \mid r \in X\}$ a direct limit, and that the φ_r are elementary if the φ_{rs} are.

(Uniqueness) Let $\{\mathfrak{C}\} \cup \{\rho_r \mid r \in X\}$ be another direct limit. By (iii) of Definition 2.4.4, we have $\rho: \mathfrak{A} \to \mathfrak{C}$ and another use of (iii) gives us $\varphi: \mathfrak{C} \to \mathfrak{A}$, both homomorphisms, such that if $r \in X$ then $\rho_r = \rho \circ \varphi_r$ and $\varphi_r = \varphi \circ \rho_r$. Thus $\varphi_r = \varphi \circ \rho_r = \varphi \circ \rho \circ \varphi_r$ for $r \in X$ (also $\rho_r = \rho \circ \varphi \circ \rho_r$ for $r \in X$). However, then $\varphi \circ \rho: \mathfrak{A} \to \mathfrak{A}$ is such that for each $r \in X$, $\varphi \circ \rho \circ \varphi_r = \mathfrak{I}_A \circ \varphi_r$, and by the uniqueness asserted in (iii) of Definition 2.4.4 applied to $\mathfrak{B} = \mathfrak{A}$, $\psi_r = \varphi_r$, $\mathfrak{I}_A = \varphi \circ \rho$; similarly $\mathfrak{I}_B = \rho \circ \varphi$, so by Problem 1.1.12, φ is an isomorphism.

LEMMA 2.4.6. Let Y be a cofinal subset of X,

$$\mathscr{A} = \{\mathfrak{A}_r \mid r \in X\} \cup \{\varphi_{rs} \mid r \leq s,\ r, s \in X\},$$

a directed system. We denote by $\mathscr{A} \mid Y$ the directed system

$$\{\mathfrak{A}_r \mid r \in Y\} \cup \{\varphi_{rs} \mid r \leq s,\ r, s \in Y\}.$$

Then the object limit $\mathfrak{A}$ of $\mathscr{A}$ is isomorphic to the object limit $\mathfrak{B}$ of $\mathscr{A} \mid Y$.

Before proceeding with the proof, we note that object limit is our generalization of union, and that in this context. Lemma 2.4.6 says that the union of a subset that happens to contain an extension for each element of the full set, is identical to the entire union. We choose to give this proof in greater detail than that of Lemma 2.4.5 to show techniques having to do with the direct limit concept that can be used to complete the proof of 2.4.5 and others.

Proof: For $a \in A_r$, $r \in Y$, set $[a]$ to bc the class of a in A, $[a]'$ that of a in B. Now set $f: \mathfrak{B} \to \mathfrak{A}$ by $f([a]') = [a]$. f is well-defined, for if $[a]' = [b]'$, we have

$$\varphi_{rq}(a) = \varphi_{sq}(b) \qquad \text{for some} \quad r, s, q \in Y,$$

thus

$$\varphi_{rq}(a) = \varphi_{sq}(b) \qquad \text{for some} \quad r, s, q \in X,$$

so $[a] = [b]$. f is one-one, for if $[a] = [b]$, with $[a]', [b]' \in B$, then

$$\varphi_{rq}(a) = \varphi_{sq}(b) \qquad \text{for some} \quad q \in X.$$

(Note that since $[a]', [b]' \in B$, $r, s \in Y$.) Thus for some $u \in Y$, $t \leq u$, so

$$\varphi_{ru}(a) = \varphi_{qu} \circ \varphi_{rq}(a) = \varphi_{qu} \circ \varphi_{sq}(b) = \varphi_{su}(b),$$

thus

$$[a]' = [b]'.$$

f is onto, since if $[b] \in A$, then for some $r \in X$, $b \in A_r$, thus for some $s \in Y$,

$$r \leq s \qquad \text{and} \qquad [b] = [\varphi_{rs}(b)] = f([\varphi_{rs}(b)]').$$

Finally,

$$\langle [a_1]', \ldots, [a_{t(\gamma)}]' \rangle \in S_\gamma$$

iff for some $r \in Y$,

$$b_1 \in [a_1]', \ldots, b_{t(\gamma)} \in [a_{t(\gamma)}]' \qquad \text{and} \qquad \langle b_1, \ldots, b_{t(\gamma)} \rangle \in R_\gamma^r.$$

This clearly implies that

$$\langle [a_1], \ldots, [a_{t(\gamma)}] \rangle \in R_\gamma.$$

On the other hand, if

$$\langle [a_1], \ldots, [a_{t(\gamma)}] \rangle \in R_\gamma,$$

pick $s \in X$ with

$$b_1 \in [a_1], \ldots, b_{t(\gamma)} \in [a_{t(\gamma)}] \qquad \text{and} \qquad \langle b_1, \ldots, b_{t(\gamma)} \rangle \in R_\gamma^s.$$

But then for some $r \geq s$, $r \in Y$; thus

$$\langle \varphi_{rs}(b_1), \ldots, \varphi_{rs}(b_{t(\gamma)}) \rangle \in R_\gamma^s,$$

and since $b \sim \varphi_{rs}(b)$,

$$\langle [a_1]', \ldots, [a_{t(\gamma)}]' \rangle \in S_\gamma.$$

A similar argument works for distinguished elements, so f is an isomorphism.

DEFINITION 2.4.7. $\mathfrak{A}_\omega$ is an ultralimit of $\mathfrak{A}$ (also called a strong limit ultrapower of $\mathfrak{A}$) iff for some set

$$\mathscr{S} = \{\langle \mathbf{I}_n, D_n \rangle \mid n \in \omega\}$$

of ultrafilter pairs, $\mathfrak{A}_\omega$ is the object limit of

$$\{\mathfrak{A}_n \mid n < \omega\} \cup \{\varphi_{mn} \mid m \leq n < \omega\},$$

where

$$\mathfrak{A}_0 = \mathfrak{A}, \qquad \mathfrak{A}_{n+1} = \mathfrak{A}_n^{\mathbf{I}_n}/D_n, \qquad \varphi_{mm} = \mathfrak{I}_m,$$

and for $n \leq m$,

$$\varphi_{nm+1} = j_{\mathfrak{A}_m} \circ \varphi_{nm}.$$

$\mathfrak{A} \cong_\omega \mathfrak{B}$ iff for some ultralimits $\mathfrak{A}_\omega$ of $\mathfrak{A}$, $\mathfrak{B}_\omega$ of $\mathfrak{B}$,

$$\mathfrak{A}_\omega \cong \mathfrak{B}_\omega.$$

THEOREM 2.4.8. $\mathfrak{A} \equiv \mathfrak{B}$ iff $\mathfrak{A} \cong_\omega \mathfrak{B}$.

Proof: If $\mathfrak{A} \cong_\omega \mathfrak{B}$, then

$$\mathfrak{A} \equiv \mathfrak{A}_\omega \cong \mathfrak{B}_\omega \equiv \mathfrak{B},$$

thus $\mathfrak{A} \equiv \mathfrak{B}$.

Conversely, let $\mathfrak{A} \equiv \mathfrak{B}$ and set $\mathfrak{C}_0 = \mathfrak{B} = \mathfrak{B}_0$.

Theorem 4.1 gives us

$$\mathfrak{C}_1 = \mathfrak{A}_1 = \mathfrak{A}^{\mathbf{I}_0}/D_0,$$

and $\varphi_{01}\colon \mathfrak{C}_0 <' \mathfrak{C}_1$. By Lemma 2.4.2, we can now find a $\langle \mathbf{J}_0, E_0\rangle$, φ_{12} such that

$$\mathfrak{C}_2 = \mathfrak{B}_0^{\mathbf{J}_0}/E_0 = \mathfrak{B}_1, \qquad \varphi_{12}\colon \mathfrak{C}_1 <' \mathfrak{C}_2, \qquad \text{and} \qquad \varphi_{12} \circ \varphi_{01} = j_{\mathfrak{B}_0}.$$

Assume now that we have

$$\mathfrak{C}_0 = \mathfrak{B}_0, \qquad \mathfrak{C}_1 = \mathfrak{A}_1, \ldots, \mathfrak{C}_{2n} = \mathfrak{B}_n,$$

$$\mathfrak{C}_{2n+1} = \mathfrak{A}_{n+1}, \qquad \varphi_{kr} \qquad \text{for} \quad 0 \le k \le r \le 2n+1$$

such that for $k \le 2n - 1$,

$$\text{if} \quad k = 2p, \qquad \text{then} \quad \varphi_{k(k+2)} = j_{\mathfrak{B}_p},$$

$$\text{if} \quad k = 2p+1, \qquad \varphi_{k(k+2)} = j_{\mathfrak{A}_{p+1}}.$$

By Lemma 2.4.2 we can find $\langle \mathbf{J}_n, E_n\rangle$, $\varphi_{(2n+1)(2n+2)}$ such that

$$\mathfrak{C}_{2n+2} = \mathfrak{B}_{n+1} = \mathfrak{B}_n^{\mathbf{J}_n}/E_n,$$

$$\varphi_{(2n+1)(2n+2)}\colon \mathfrak{C}_{2n+1} <' \mathfrak{C}_{2n+2}, \quad \text{and} \quad \varphi_{(2n+1)(2n+2)} \circ \varphi_{2n(2n+1)} = j_{\mathfrak{B}_n}.$$

We also define $\varphi_{(2n+2)(2n+2)} = \mathfrak{I}_{2n+2}$, and for $m < 2n+1$,

$$\varphi_{m(2n+2)} = \varphi_{(2n+1)(2n+2)} \circ \varphi_{m(2n+1)}.$$

A second use of Lemma 2.4.2 gives us

$$\langle \mathbf{I}_{n+1}, D_{n+1}\rangle, \qquad \varphi_{(2n+2)(2n+3)}\colon \mathfrak{C}_{2n+2} <' \mathfrak{C}_{2n+3} = \mathfrak{A}_{n+2} = \mathfrak{A}_{n+1}^{\mathbf{I}_{n+1}}/D_{n+1}$$

such that

$$\varphi_{(2n+2)(2n+3)} \circ \varphi_{(2n+1)(2n+2)} = j_{\mathfrak{A}_{n+1}}.$$

Once again we define

$$\varphi_{(2n+3)(2n+3)} = \mathfrak{I}_{2n+3},$$

and for $m < 2n + 2$,

$$\varphi_{m(2n+3)} = \varphi_{(2n+2)(2n+3)} \circ \varphi_{m(2n+2)}.$$

Thus by induction, we produce a directed system

$$\mathscr{A} = \{\mathfrak{C}_n \mid n < \omega\} \cup \{\varphi_{mn} \mid m \le n < \omega\}.$$

Let $\mathfrak{C}$ be the object limit of this system. By Lemma 2.4.6, $\mathfrak{C}$ is isomorphic to the object limits of $\mathscr{A} \mid \{0, 2, 4, \ldots\}$ and $\mathscr{A} \mid \{1, 3, 5, \ldots\}$.

Since we have taken care to set $\varphi_{2n(2n+2)} = j_{\mathfrak{B}_n}$, $\mathscr{A} \mid \{0, 2, 4, \dots\}$ satisfies the conditions of Definition 2.4.7; thus its object limit is $\mathfrak{B}_\omega$, an ultralimit of $\mathfrak{B}$.

Now consider that $\mathfrak{C}_{-1} = \mathfrak{A}_0 = \mathfrak{A}$, $\varphi_{-1m} = \varphi_{1m} \circ j_{\mathfrak{A}}$, and let

$$\mathscr{B} = \mathscr{A} \mid \{1, 3, 5, \dots\} \cup \{\mathfrak{C}_{-1}\} \cup \{\varphi_{-1m} \mid m < \omega, m \text{ odd}\}.$$

Then the object limit of $\mathscr{B}$ is an ultralimit $\mathfrak{A}_\omega$ of $\mathfrak{A}$ by reasoning similar to that in the previous paragraph. However, since $\{1, 3, 5, \dots\}$ is cofinal in $\{-1, 1, 3, \dots\}$, the object limit $\mathfrak{D}$ of $\mathscr{A} \mid \{1, 3, 5, \dots\}$ is isomorphic to $\mathfrak{A}_\omega$.

Thus

$$\mathfrak{A}_\omega \cong \mathfrak{D} \cong \mathfrak{C} \cong \mathfrak{B}_\omega, \qquad \text{so} \qquad \mathfrak{A} \equiv_\omega \mathfrak{B}.$$

The above is a strictly algebraic characterization of elementary equivalence. A similar proof shows the following.

THEOREM 2.4.9. $k: \mathfrak{A} <' \mathfrak{B}$ iff there are ultralimits $\mathfrak{A}_\omega$ of $\mathfrak{A}$ and $\mathfrak{B}_\omega$ of $\mathfrak{B}$ and an isomorphism $f: \mathfrak{A}_\omega \cong \mathfrak{B}_\omega$ such that $f \circ \varphi_0 = \psi_0 \circ k$, where $\varphi_0: \mathfrak{A} <' \mathfrak{A}_\omega$ corresponds to the φ_r of Definition 2.4.4, $\psi_0: \mathfrak{B} <' \mathfrak{B}_\omega$ the analogous map for $\mathfrak{B}$.

We now consider the cardinalities of the $\mathfrak{A}_\omega$, $\mathfrak{B}_\omega$ constructed above. We note that if

$$\mathfrak{m} = \max\{c(t), c(\mathfrak{A}), c(\mathfrak{B})\},$$

then

$$c(\mathfrak{A}_1) \leq \mathfrak{m}^{\mathfrak{m}} = 2^{\mathfrak{m}}, \qquad c(\mathfrak{B}_1) \leq \mathfrak{m}^{2^{\mathfrak{m}}} = 2^{2^{\mathfrak{m}}}.$$

Assume now that we define inductively $\mathfrak{m}_0 = \mathfrak{m}$, $\mathfrak{m}_{n+1} = 2^{\mathfrak{m}_n}$. Then it can be shown by induction that

$$c(\mathfrak{A}_n) \leq \mathfrak{m}_{2n+1}, \qquad c(\mathfrak{B}_n) \leq \mathfrak{m}_{2n+2}.$$

Thus

$$c(\mathfrak{A}_\omega) = c(\mathfrak{B}_\omega) \leq \sum_{n<\omega} \mathfrak{m}_n.$$

It may be asked whether one must actually take the limits in Theorem 2.4.8, or whether, in fact, one can arrange matters in such a way that at some point, $\mathfrak{A}_n \cong \mathfrak{B}_n$. By Theorem 2.3.2, however, we know that if ultrafilter pairs can be found so that $\mathfrak{A}_n \cong \mathfrak{B}_n$, then they can be found so that $\mathfrak{A}_1 \cong \mathfrak{B}_1$, in other words, so that for some ultrafilter pairs, $\langle \mathbf{I}, D\rangle$, $\langle \mathbf{J}, E\rangle$,

$$\mathfrak{A}^{\mathbf{I}}/D \cong \mathfrak{B}^{\mathbf{J}}/E.$$

Thus we may ask whether $\mathfrak{A}$ and $\mathfrak{B}$ are elementarily equivalent iff they have isomorphic ultrapowers. Keisler [6] has shown that the answer is affirmative if we assume the generalized continuum hypothesis (Theorem 2.3.11 is a special case of this result; also see Sections 2.7 and 2.8 and

Problem 2.8.7). Shelah [1] has recently shown this without assuming the generalized continuum hypothesis, using some results due to Kunen.

We now wish to state some results related to Theorem 2.4.1 and Lemma 2.4.2 and important in their own right. Our approach and results now begin to differ from Kochen's.

DEFINITION 2.4.10. $Q \subset L^t$ is called well-closed iff it is closed under $\vee$, $\wedge$, $\equiv$ (as defined in Problem 1.2.4) and one-one replacement of variables (i.e., if $F \in Q$, $\rho: V \to V$ is one-one and onto, then $Rp_\rho F \in Q$).

If $Q \subset L^t$, $K \subset M^t$, $\mathfrak{A}$, $\mathfrak{B} \in M^t$, then $T_Q(K) = T(K) \cap Q$, $T_Q(\mathfrak{A}) = T_Q(\{\mathfrak{A}\})$, and $\mathfrak{A}\ Q\ \mathfrak{B}$ iff $T_Q(\mathfrak{A}) \subset T_Q(\mathfrak{B})$.

Let $\varphi \subset A \times B$, $Y \subset \omega$. By $\varphi^{(Y)}$ we mean

$$\{\langle a, b\rangle \mid a \in A^\omega, b \in B^\omega, \text{ and if } y \in Y \text{ then } \langle a_y, b_y\rangle \in \varphi\}$$

(if $X \subset V$, $\varphi^{(X)} = \varphi^{(\{y \mid v_y \in X\})}$).

Given $Q \subset L^t$, φ is a Q-relation from $\mathfrak{A}$ into $\mathfrak{B}$ (denoted $\varphi: \mathfrak{A}\ Q\ \mathfrak{B}$) iff $\varphi \subset A \times B$ and for each $F \in Q$, $\langle a, b\rangle \in \varphi^{(FV(F))}$, if $\mathfrak{A} \models F[a]$ then $\mathfrak{B} \models F[b]$. A Q-relation φ is called total iff $\mathscr{D}\varphi = A$, onto iff $\mathscr{R}\varphi = B$, and a Q-map iff it is a function on its domain.

Again for arbitrary $Q \subset L^t$ we define,

$$\overline{Q} = \{G \mid \text{for some } F \in Q,\ G \equiv \neg F\},$$

$$\forall Q = \{G \mid \text{for some } F \in Q,\ n, j_1, \ldots, j_n \in \omega,\ (\forall v_{j_1}) \cdots (\forall v_{j_n})F \equiv G\}$$

and $\exists Q$ is defined in a similar manner. $\forall_n Q$, $\exists_n Q$ are defined inductively by

$$\forall_0 Q = \exists_0 Q = \{G \mid \text{for some } F \in Q,\ G \equiv F\},$$

$$\forall_{n+1} Q = \forall(\exists_n Q), \qquad \exists_{n+1} Q = \exists(\forall_n Q).$$

We also define

$$Q_\omega = \textstyle\bigcup_{n \in \omega} \forall_n Q = \bigcup_{n \in \omega} \exists_n Q.$$

Thus $\forall_n Q$ is the set of formulas equivalent to those beginning with $\forall$ and having $n - 1$ alternations of quantifier before ending in a formula in Q. Also note that

$$\overline{\forall Q} = \exists \overline{Q}, \qquad \overline{\exists Q} = \forall \overline{Q},$$

and if $1 \leq n < \omega$,

$$\overline{\forall_n Q} = \exists_n \overline{Q}, \qquad \overline{\exists_n Q} = \forall_n \overline{Q}.$$

A Q-relation is simply a relation which preserves Q. We have had several examples of Q-relations in earlier sections: isomorphisms are QF-relations (Theorem 1.2.11) homomorphisms are $L^t(0)$-relations (Theorem 1.2.12), elementary imbeddings are L^t-relations. Some sets Q in which we are particularly interested and some useful notations are introduced below.

DEFINITION 2.4.11. POS_0 is the set of formulas built from atomic formulas by use of $\wedge$, and $\vee$ (i.e.,

$$POS_0 = \bigcup_{n<\omega} A_n, \qquad \text{where} \quad A_0 = L^t(0),$$

the set of atomic formulas in L^t, and

$$A_{n+1} = A_n \cup \{F \vee G \mid F, G \in A_n\} \cup \{F \wedge G \mid F, G \in A_n\})$$

and is called the set of positive atomic formulas. $\exists POS_0$ ($\forall POS_0$) is the set of existential (universal) positive formulas, and $POS = POS_{0\omega}$ the set of positive formulas.

$\exists_n = \exists_n QF$, $\forall_n = \forall_n QF$ (QF is the set of quantifier-free formulas).

Let t be a type, Δ a set. Then $t \oplus \Delta$ is defined to be the disjoint union of t and $\{\langle \delta, 0\rangle \mid \delta \in \Delta\}$ (see the proof of Theorem 2.3.11).

Let $Q \subset L^t$, $C = \{c_\delta \mid \delta \in \Delta\}$. Then

$$Sb_C^V Q = \{Sb_\rho F \mid F \in Q, \rho \subset V \times C \text{ a function}\} \subset L^{t \oplus \Delta}.$$

The reader might be interested in knowing why we study the concept of Q-relation. A clue is found in Theorem 2.4.8, which may be restated: $\mathfrak{A}\ L^t\ \mathfrak{B}$ iff there are ultralimits $\mathfrak{A}_\omega$, $\mathfrak{B}_\omega$ of $\mathfrak{A}$, $\mathfrak{B}$ and a total, onto φ: $\mathfrak{A}_\omega\ QF^t\ \mathfrak{B}_\omega$. This restatement is possible since isomorphisms are precisely total, onto QF^t-relations: also homomorphisms are precisely total POS_0-relations (the reader is left to check these facts in Problem 2.4.6), so we can imagine a theorem corresponding to 2.4.8 and stating $\mathfrak{A}\ POS\ \mathfrak{B}$ iff there are ultralimits $\mathfrak{A}_\omega$, $\mathfrak{B}_\omega$ and a total, onto $\varphi: \mathfrak{A}_\omega\ POS_0\ \mathfrak{B}_\omega$. This may also be stated: Every positive sentence true in $\mathfrak{A}$ holds in $\mathfrak{B}$ iff there are ultralimits $\mathfrak{A}_\omega$, $\mathfrak{B}_\omega$ of $\mathfrak{A}$, $\mathfrak{B}$ such that $\mathfrak{B}_\omega$ is a homomorphic image of $\mathfrak{A}_\omega$. These and other facts shown below lead to preservation theorems (see comments following Section 1.7.16) to be shown in Section 2.5.

The following lemma collects some useful facts about the concepts defined above.

LEMMA 2.4.12. (a) If Q is well-closed, C as in Definition 2.4.11, then $\overline{Q}$, $\exists_n Q$ and $\forall_n Q$ (if $n \in \omega$), Q_ω and $Sb_C^V Q$ are well-closed, and also

$$Sb_C^V \overline{Q} = \overline{Sb_C^V Q},$$

$$\exists_n Sb_C^V Q = Sb_C^V \exists_n Q,$$

$$\forall_n Sb_C^V Q = Sb_C^V \forall_n Q,$$

and

$$Sb_C^V(Q_\omega) = (Sb_C^V Q)_\omega.$$

(b) $Q = Q_\omega$ iff Q is closed under $\forall$, $\exists$, and $\equiv$.

(c) Let $\mathfrak{A} = \langle A, R_\gamma \rangle_{\gamma \in \Gamma}$, $\mathfrak{B} = \langle B, S_\gamma \rangle_{\gamma \in \Gamma}$, $\eta \subset \varphi \subset A \times B$, $\eta \subset \{\langle a_\delta, b_\delta \rangle \mid \delta \in \Delta\}$. Then

$$\varphi\colon \mathfrak{A}\ Q\ \mathfrak{B} \quad \text{iff} \quad \varphi \sim \eta\colon \mathfrak{A}'\ Sb^V_C Q\ \mathfrak{B}',$$

where C is as in Definition 2.4.11,

$$\mathfrak{A}' = \langle A, R_\gamma, a_\delta \rangle_{\gamma \in \Gamma, \delta \in \Delta} \qquad \text{and} \qquad \mathfrak{B}' = \langle B, S_\gamma, b_\delta \rangle_{\gamma \in \Gamma, \delta \in \Delta}.$$

(d) If $\varphi \subset \psi$, $Q' \subset Q$ and $\psi\colon \mathfrak{A}\ Q\ \mathfrak{B}$, then $\varphi\colon \mathfrak{A}\ Q'\ \mathfrak{B}$.

(e) $\varphi\colon \mathfrak{A}\ Q\ \mathfrak{B}$ iff $\varphi^{-1}\colon \mathfrak{B}\ \bar{Q}\ \mathfrak{A}$. If $\varphi\colon \mathfrak{A}\ Q\ \mathfrak{B}$ and $\psi\colon \mathfrak{B}\ Q\ \mathfrak{C}$, then $\psi \circ \varphi\colon \mathfrak{A}\ Q\ \mathfrak{C}$.

(f) A nonempty function $\varphi \subset A \times B$ is a Q-map iff for every $a \in (\mathscr{D}\varphi)^\omega$ and every $F \in Q$ such that $\mathfrak{A} \models F[a]$ we have $\mathfrak{B} \models F[\varphi \circ a]$.

(g) $\phi\colon \mathfrak{A}\ Q\ \mathfrak{B}$ iff $\mathfrak{A}\ Q\ \mathfrak{B}$ [thus by (d) if for some φ, $\varphi\colon \mathfrak{A}\ Q\ \mathfrak{B}$, $\mathfrak{A}\ Q\ \mathfrak{B}$] and if $\varphi \neq \phi$, $\varphi\colon \mathfrak{A}\ Q\ \mathfrak{B}$ *iff* whenever $F \in Q$, $\langle a, b \rangle \in \varphi^{(\omega)}$, and $\mathfrak{A} \models F[a]$ then $\mathfrak{B} \models F[b]$.

(h) Every total Q-relation is an $\exists Q$-relation and every total, onto Q-relation a Q_ω-relation.

Proof: (a) Consider first $\exists Q$. It is closed by definition under $\equiv$ and is closed under one-one replacement of variables, for if $F \equiv G$ then by Proposition 1.2.17 $Rp_\rho F \equiv Rp_\rho G$ for $\rho\colon K_t \to K_t$ one-one such that

$$\rho\,[V] \subset V \qquad \text{and} \qquad \rho(c) = c \qquad \text{for each} \quad c \in C_t;$$

thus if

$$F \equiv (\exists v_{j_1}) \cdots (\exists v_{j_n})H, \qquad H \in Q$$

then

$$Rp_\rho F \equiv (\exists \rho(v_{j_1})) \cdots (\exists \rho(v_{j_n}))Rp_\rho H \in \exists Q,$$

so

$$Rp_\rho F \in \exists Q.$$

Slight alterations of Problem 1.4.1(b), (c) show $\exists Q$ closed under $\vee$, $\wedge$ if Q is.

The proof that $\bar{Q}$ is well-closed is left for the reader. $\forall Q = \overline{\exists \bar{Q}}$ establishes the well-closure of $\forall Q$ and induction completes the proofs for $\exists_n Q$, $\forall_n Q$. We leave the rest of (a) and the proof of (b) for the reader.

(c) If $\varphi \sim \eta\colon \mathfrak{A}'\ Sb^V_C Q\ \mathfrak{B}'$, $F \in Q$, $\langle a, b \rangle \in \varphi^{(FV(F))}$, and $\mathfrak{A} \models F[a]$ then define

$$\rho = \{\langle v_x, c_\delta \rangle \mid \langle a_x, b_x \rangle = \langle a_\delta, b_\delta \rangle \in \eta\}.$$

Then $Sb_\rho F \in Sb^V_C Q$, and by Theorem 1.2.15, since $a = \rho^*(a)$, $\mathfrak{A}' \models Sb_\rho F[a]$ so $\mathfrak{B}' \models Sb_\rho F[b]$ thus

$$\mathfrak{B} \models F[\rho^*(b)] = F[b].$$

Conversely if $\varphi: \mathfrak{A}\ Q\ \mathfrak{B}$, $G \in Sb_C^V Q$, $\langle a, b\rangle \in (\varphi \sim \eta)^{(FV(G))}$ and $\mathfrak{A}' \models G[a]$, then let $G = Sb_\rho F$,

$$\text{thus} \quad \mathfrak{A}' \models Sb_\rho F[a] \qquad \text{so} \quad \mathfrak{A} \models F[\rho^*(a)],$$

and since $\langle \rho^*(a), \rho^*(b)\rangle \in \varphi^{(FV(F))}$,

$$\mathfrak{B} \models F[\rho^*(b)] \qquad \text{so} \quad \mathfrak{B}' \models Sb_\rho F[b], \qquad \text{thus} \quad \mathfrak{B}' \models G[b].$$

We leave (d) and (e) for the reader, while (g) has (f) as a special case.

For (g) let $\varphi \neq \phi$, $\varphi: \mathfrak{A}\ Q\ \mathfrak{B}$, $\langle a, b\rangle \in \varphi^{(\omega)}$, $F \in Q$, $\mathfrak{A} \models F[a]$. Then $\langle a, b\rangle \in \varphi^{(FV(F))}$ so $\mathfrak{B} \models F[b]$, establishing our condition. Conversely, let φ be such that if $\langle a, b\rangle \in \varphi^{(\omega)}$, $F \in Q$ and $\mathfrak{A} \models F[a]$, then $\mathfrak{B} \models F[b]$, and suppose $\langle a', b'\rangle \in \varphi^{(FV(F))}$, $\mathfrak{A} \models F[a']$. Since $\varphi \neq \phi$, let $\langle c, d\rangle \in \varphi$, and define a, b by

$$a_x = \begin{cases} c & \text{if } v_x \notin FV(F), \\ a'_x & \text{if } v_x \in FV(F) \end{cases} \qquad b_x = \begin{cases} d & \text{if } v_x \notin FV(F) \\ b'_x & \text{if } v_x \in FV(F) \end{cases}.$$

Then $\langle a, b\rangle \in \varphi^{(\omega)}$, and since

$$\mathfrak{A} \models F[a'] \qquad \text{and} \qquad a_x = a'_x \qquad \text{for} \quad v_x \in FV(F),$$

we have $\mathfrak{A} \models F[a]$, thus $\mathfrak{B} \models F[b]$, and therefore $\mathfrak{B} \models F[b']$, so φ is a Q-relation.

(h) Let φ be a total Q-relation, $F \equiv (\exists v_{z_1}) \cdots (\exists v_{z_n})G$, $G \in Q$, $\langle a, b\rangle \in \varphi^{(\omega)}$, $\mathfrak{A} \models F[a]$. Then for some $c_{z_1}, \ldots, c_{z_n} \in A$,

$$\mathfrak{A} \models G[a(z_1 \mid c_{z_1}) \cdots (z_n \mid c_{z_n})],$$

and since $c_{z_1}, \ldots, c_{z_n} \in \mathscr{D}\varphi$, we have $d_{z_1}, \ldots, d_{z_n} \in B$ such that

$$\langle c_{z_j}, d_{z_j}\rangle \in \varphi \qquad \text{for} \quad j = 1, \ldots, n.$$

Thus

$$\langle a(z_1 \mid c_{z_1}) \cdots (z_n \mid c_{z_n}), b(z_1 \mid d_{z_1}) \cdots (z_n \mid d_{z_n})\rangle \in \varphi^{(\omega)},$$

so

$$\mathfrak{B} \models G[b(z_1 \mid d_{z_1}) \cdots (z_n \mid d_{z_n})],$$

thus

$$\mathfrak{B} \models F[b].$$

If φ is also onto, we show by induction that φ is a $\forall_n Q$- and $\exists_n Q$-relation for each n. We know φ to be a $\exists_0 Q$- $= Q = \forall_0 Q$-relation, and assume it to be a $\forall_n Q$- and $\exists_n Q$-relation. Then $\varphi^{-1}: \mathfrak{B}\ \forall_n \overline{Q}\ \mathfrak{A}$, thus by the first part of (h) a $\exists(\forall_n \overline{Q}) = \exists_{n+1}\overline{Q}$-relation, so φ is a $\overline{\exists_{n+1}\overline{Q}} = \forall_{n+1} Q$-relation, and an application of the first part of (h) to the fact that $\varphi: \mathfrak{A}\ \forall_n Q\ \mathfrak{B}$ shows φ must also be a $\exists(\forall_n Q) = \exists_{n+1} Q$-relation. Thus φ is a $\bigcup_{n<\omega} \exists_n Q = Q_\omega$-relation.

THEOREM 2.4.13. Let $\varphi \subset B \times A$, $Q \subset L^t$ well-closed. Then

$$\varphi: \mathfrak{B}\ \exists Q\ \mathfrak{A}$$

iff for some ultrafilter pair $\langle \mathbf{I}, D\rangle$ and total $\psi: \mathfrak{B}\ Q\ \mathfrak{A}^{\mathbf{I}}/D$,

$$j_{\mathfrak{A}} \circ \varphi \subset \psi.$$

Proof: If ψ exists, then by 2.4.12(h),

$$\psi: \mathfrak{B}\ \exists Q\ \mathfrak{A}^{\mathbf{I}}/D,$$

so by 2.4.12(d),

$$j_{\mathfrak{A}} \circ \varphi: \mathfrak{B}\ \exists Q\ \mathfrak{A}^{\mathbf{I}}/D,$$

by 2.4.12(e),

$$j_{\mathfrak{A}}^{-1}: (\mathfrak{A}^{\mathbf{I}}/D)\ L^t\ \mathfrak{A},$$

and since $\exists Q \subset L^t = \overline{L^t}$, 2.4.12(d) assures us that

$$j_{\mathfrak{A}}^{-1}: (\mathfrak{A}^{\mathbf{I}}/D)\ \exists Q\ \mathfrak{A},$$

thus by 2.4.12(e),

$$j_{\mathfrak{A}}^{-1} \circ j_{\mathfrak{A}} \circ \varphi: \mathfrak{B}\ \exists Q\ \mathfrak{A}$$

however

$$\varphi = \mathfrak{I}_A \circ \varphi = j_{\mathfrak{A}}^{-1} \circ j_{\mathfrak{A}} \circ \varphi.$$

The proof of the converse in the case $\varphi = \phi$ is identical to that of Theorem 2.4.1 except that now

$$\mathbf{I} = \{F \in Sb^v{}_{C_t' \sim C_t} Q \mid \mathfrak{B}' \models F\},$$

ψ is used in place of φ, and ψ is only a Q-relation because of this changed definition of $\mathbf{I}$.

In general, by Lemma 2.4.12(c),

$$\varphi: \mathfrak{B}\ \exists Q\ \mathfrak{A} \qquad \text{iff} \quad \phi: \mathfrak{B}'\ Sb^V_C(\exists Q)\ \mathfrak{A}'$$

(by using $\eta = \varphi$), and since $Sb^V_C(\exists Q) = \exists Sb^V_C Q$, and by the preceding paragraph there is a total ψ',

$$\psi': \mathfrak{B}'\ Sb^V_C Q\ \mathfrak{A}'^{\mathbf{I}}/D.$$

Let $\psi = (j_{\mathfrak{A}} \circ \varphi) \cup \psi'$; then

$$\psi \sim (j_{\mathfrak{A}} \circ \varphi) \subset \psi', \qquad \text{so} \quad \psi \sim (j_{\mathfrak{A}} \circ \varphi): \mathfrak{B}'\ Sb^V_C Q\ \mathfrak{A}'^{\mathbf{I}}/D,$$

$$\text{thus} \quad \psi: \mathfrak{B}\ Q\ \mathfrak{A}^{\mathbf{I}}/D, \qquad \text{and} \qquad B = \mathscr{D}\psi' \subset \mathscr{D}\psi, \qquad j_{\mathfrak{A}} \circ \varphi \subset \psi.$$

The roles of $\mathfrak{A}$ and $\mathfrak{B}$ are apparently reversed in Theorem 2.4.13 (as compared with Theorem 2.4.1), but the reader should check that this is not really the case. These roles will, however, often be reversed in the work to follow.

Since $L^t = \exists L^t$, Theorem 2.4.1 and Lemma 2.4.2 are special cases of Theorem 2.4.13, if we use also the fact that L^t is well-closed. Theorem 2.4.1

is the case in which $\varphi = \phi$, $Q = L^t$; and Lemma 2.4.2 is that in which $\varphi = \varphi^{-1}$ (of that lemma), $Q = L^t$. Some other special cases follow.

COROLLARY 2.4.14. Below, let $Q \subset L^t$ be well-closed.

(a) Let $\varphi \subset A \times B$. Then $\varphi: \mathfrak{A}\ \exists Q\ \mathfrak{B}$ iff there is a total Q-relation $\psi: \mathfrak{A}\ Q\ \mathfrak{B}^{\mathbf{I}}/D$ for some ultrafilter pair $\langle \mathbf{I}, D\rangle$ such that $j_{\mathfrak{B}} \circ \varphi = \psi \mid \mathscr{D}\varphi$.

(b) Let $\varphi \subset A \times B$ be a function. Then $\varphi: \mathfrak{A}\ \exists Q\ \mathfrak{B}$ iff there are an ultrafilter pair $\langle \mathbf{I}, D\rangle$ and total Q-map $\psi: \mathfrak{A}\ Q\ \mathfrak{B}^{\mathbf{I}}/D$ such that $j_{\mathfrak{B}} \circ \varphi = \psi \mid \mathscr{D}\varphi$.

(c) $\mathfrak{A}\ \exists Q\ \mathfrak{B}$ iff there are an ultrafilter pair $\langle \mathbf{I}, D\rangle$ and a total Q-map $\varphi: \mathfrak{A}\ Q\ \mathfrak{B}^{\mathbf{I}}/D$.

(d) $\mathfrak{A}\ \forall_1\ \mathfrak{B}$ iff for some $\langle \mathbf{I}, D\rangle$, $\mathfrak{C} \subset \mathfrak{A}^{\mathbf{I}}/D$, $\mathfrak{B} \cong \mathfrak{C}$.

(e) $\mathfrak{A}\ \exists_1\ \mathfrak{B}$ iff for some $\langle \mathbf{I}, D\rangle$, $\mathfrak{C} \subset \mathfrak{B}^{\mathbf{I}}/D$, $\mathfrak{A} \cong \mathfrak{C}$.

(f) $\mathfrak{A}\ \forall POS_0\ \mathfrak{B}$ iff for some $\langle \mathbf{I}, D\rangle$ and homomorphism ψ, $\psi: \mathfrak{C} \to \mathfrak{B}$ onto for some $\mathfrak{C} \subset \mathfrak{A}^{\mathbf{I}}/D$.

(g) $\mathfrak{A}\ \exists POS_0\ \mathfrak{B}$ iff for some $\langle \mathbf{I}, D\rangle$ and homomorphism ψ,

$$\psi: \mathfrak{A} \to \mathfrak{B}^{\mathbf{I}}/D.$$

Proof: (a) Assume that $\varphi: \mathfrak{A}\ \exists Q\ \mathfrak{B}$, and that ψ_1 has been given us by Theorem 2.4.13. Then set

$$\psi = \psi_1 \sim \{\langle a, c\rangle \mid a \in \mathscr{D}\varphi \text{ and } \langle a, c\rangle \notin j \circ \varphi\}.$$

We leave the proof that ψ works and the converse for the reader. Part (b) is shown similarly and (c) is a special case of (b).

(e) Is the special case of (c) in which Q is the well-closure of QF. In Problem 2.4.6, the well-closure of a set is defined and it is shown that for $P \subset L^t$, φ is a P-relation iff φ is a W-relation, where W is the well-closure of P. By Theorem 1.2.11 QF-relations are precisely those that are isomorphisms to their images, thus Q-relations are the same, and $\exists_1 = \exists_1 Q$ (see Problem 2.4.6), completing the proof. (d) results from (e) and the fact that $\mathfrak{A}\ \forall_1\ \mathfrak{B}$ iff $\mathfrak{B}\ \exists_1\ \mathfrak{A}$.

(g) and (f) fall out from Theorem 1.2.12 in much the way (e) and (d) arose from Theorem 1.2.11, once we note that a simple check reveals that if $\varphi: \mathfrak{A}\ Q'\ \mathfrak{B}$ and Q is the set of formulas produced from Q' by repeated use of $\wedge$ and $\vee$, then $\varphi: \mathfrak{A}\ Q\ \mathfrak{B}$.

THEOREM 2.4.15. (a) Let Q be well-closed, $\varphi \subset A \times B$. Then $\varphi: \mathfrak{A}\ Q_\omega\ \mathfrak{B}$ iff there are ultralimits $\mathfrak{A}_\omega$, $\mathfrak{B}_\omega$ of $\mathfrak{A}$, $\mathfrak{B}$ respectively, and an onto total Q-relation $\varphi_\omega: \mathfrak{A}_\omega\ Q\ \mathfrak{B}_\omega$ such that $k_\omega \circ \varphi \circ j_\omega^{-1} \subset \varphi_\omega$, where

$$j_\omega: \mathfrak{A} \to \mathfrak{A}_\omega, \qquad k_\omega: \mathfrak{B} \to \mathfrak{B}_\omega$$

are the maps whose existence is guaranteed by Definition 2.4.4.

(b) Let Q be well-closed. Then $\mathfrak{A}\ Q_\omega\ \mathfrak{B}$ iff there are ultralimits $\mathfrak{A}_\omega$, $\mathfrak{B}_\omega$ of $\mathfrak{A}$, $\mathfrak{B}$ respectively, and an onto total Q-relation $\varphi\colon \mathfrak{A}_\omega\ Q\ \mathfrak{B}_\omega$.

(c) $\mathfrak{A}\ POS\ \mathfrak{B}$ iff there are ultralimits $\mathfrak{A}_\omega$, $\mathfrak{B}_\omega$ of $\mathfrak{A}$, $\mathfrak{B}$ respectively, and an onto homomorphism $\varphi\colon \mathfrak{A}_\omega \to \mathfrak{B}_\omega$.

Proof: (a) By induction we produce a system of the following sort:

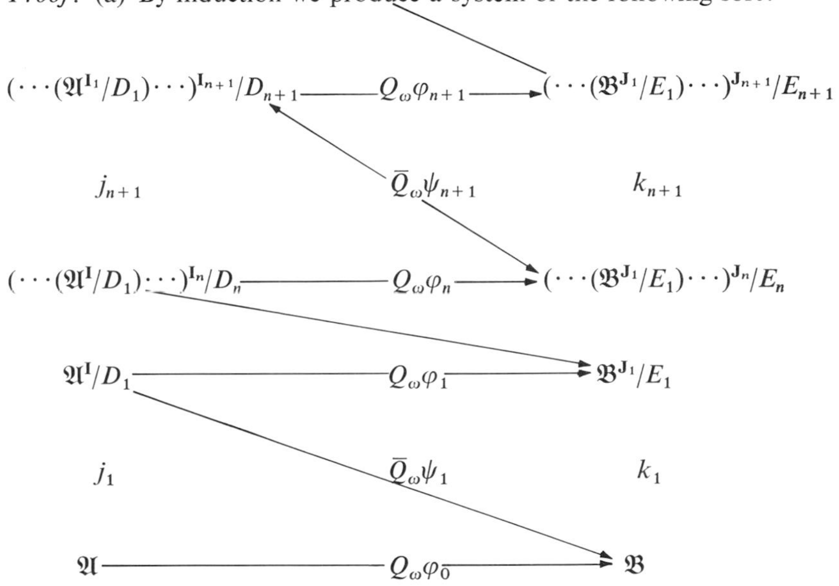

such that

$$k_i = j_{(\ldots(\mathfrak{B}^{\mathbf{J}_1}/E_1)\ldots)^{\mathbf{J}_{i-1}}/E_{i-1}},$$

$$j_i = j_{(\ldots(\mathfrak{B}^{\mathbf{I}_1}/D_1)\ldots)^{\mathbf{I}_{i-1}}/D_{i-1}}$$

and for each $i \geq 1$,

$$k_i \circ \psi_i^{-1} = \varphi_i \mid \mathscr{R}\psi_i, \qquad j_i \circ \varphi_{i-1}^{-1} = \psi_i \mid \mathscr{R}\varphi_{i-1},$$

where $\varphi_0 = \varphi$ and φ_i is a total Q_ω-relation, ψ_i a total $\bar{Q}_\omega$-relation.

Assume we have

$$\mathfrak{A}_0, \ldots, \mathfrak{A}_n, \qquad \mathfrak{B}_0, \ldots, \mathfrak{B}_n, \qquad \varphi_0, \ldots, \varphi_n,$$

$$\psi_0, \ldots, \psi_n, \qquad j_1, \ldots, j_n, \qquad k_1, \ldots, k_n$$

such that

$$\mathfrak{A}_0 = \mathfrak{A}, \qquad \mathfrak{B}_0 = \mathfrak{B}, \qquad \varphi_0 = \varphi,$$

and if $1 \leq i \leq n$ then

$$\mathfrak{A}_i = \mathfrak{A}_{i-1}^{\mathbf{I}_i}/D_i, \qquad j_i = j_{\mathfrak{A}_{i-1}},$$

$$\mathfrak{B}_i = \mathfrak{B}_{i-1}^{\mathbf{J}_i}/E_i, \qquad k_i = j_{\mathfrak{A}_{i-1}},$$

$\psi_i\colon \mathfrak{B}_{i-1}\ \bar{Q}_\omega\ \mathfrak{A}_i$ is a total $\bar{Q}_\omega$-relation, $\varphi_i\colon \mathfrak{A}_i\ Q_\omega\ \mathfrak{B}_i$ also total, and

$$k_i \circ \psi_i^{-1} = \varphi_i \mid \mathscr{R}\psi_i, \qquad j_i \circ \varphi_{i-1}^{-1} = \psi_i \mid \mathscr{R}\varphi_{i-1}.$$

Note that by hypothesis, we have the above for $n = 0$; we now complete the induction by showing that we must have it for $n + 1$ if we have it for n. By Corollary 2.4.14(a), we have

$$\langle \mathbf{I}_{n+1}, D_{n+1}\rangle, \qquad \psi_{n+1}\colon \mathfrak{B}_n\ \bar{Q}_\omega\ \mathfrak{A}_{n+1} = \mathfrak{A}_n^{\mathbf{I}_{n+1}}/D_{n+1}$$

with domain B_n such that

$$j_{n+1} \circ \varphi_n^{-1} = \psi_{n+1} \mid \mathscr{R}\varphi_n,$$

and a second application gives us

$$\langle \mathbf{J}_{n+1}, E_{n+1}\rangle, \qquad k_{n+1}, \qquad \varphi_{n+1}\colon \mathfrak{A}_{n+1}\ Q_\omega\ \mathfrak{B}_{n+1} = \mathfrak{B}_n^{\mathbf{J}_{n+1}}/E_{n+1},$$

a total Q_ω-relation such that

$$k_{n+1} \circ \psi_{n+1}^{-1} = \varphi_{n+1} \mid \mathscr{R}\psi_{n+1},$$

completing our induction step [note that by Lemma 2.4.12(b), $\exists Q_\omega = \forall Q_\omega = Q_\omega$, thus $\exists\bar{Q}_\omega = \bar{Q}_\omega$, allowing us to apply Corollary 2.4.14(a)].

Now let $\mathfrak{A}_\omega, \mathfrak{B}_\omega$ be our ultralimits, for $n < \omega$,

$$j_{n,\omega}\colon \mathfrak{A}_n \to \mathfrak{A}_\omega, \qquad k_{n,\omega}\colon \mathfrak{B}_n \to \mathfrak{B}_\omega$$

the maps given in Definition 2.4.4,

$$j_\omega = j_{0,\omega}, \qquad k_\omega = k_{0,\omega}, \qquad \varphi_\omega = \bigcup_{n<\omega} k_{n,\omega} \circ \varphi_n \circ j_{n,\omega}^{-1}.$$

Then clearly

$$k_\omega \circ \varphi \circ j_\omega^{-1} \subset \varphi_\omega.$$

Also

$$\mathscr{D}\varphi_\omega = \bigcup_{n<\omega} \mathscr{D}(k_{n,\omega} \circ \varphi_n \circ j_{n,\omega}^{-1}),$$

and if $x \in \mathscr{R}_{j_{n,\omega}}$ then

$$j_{n,\omega}^{-1}(x) \in A_n = \mathscr{D}\varphi_n,$$

so

$$\langle x, y\rangle \in \varphi_n \circ j_{n,\omega}^{-1} \qquad \text{for some} \quad y \in B_n,$$

thus

$$\langle x, k_{n,\omega}(y)\rangle \in k_{n,\omega} \circ \varphi_n \circ j_{n,\omega}^{-1},$$

so

$$\mathscr{D}\varphi_\omega = \bigcup_{n<\omega} \mathscr{D}j_{n,\omega} = A_\omega.$$

$$\begin{aligned}\mathscr{R}\varphi_\omega &= \bigcup_{n<\omega} \mathscr{R}(k_{n,\omega} \circ \varphi_n \circ j_{n,\omega}^{-1}) \supset \bigcup_{n<\omega}^{0<n} \mathscr{R}(k_{n,\omega} \circ (k_n \circ \psi_n^{-1}) \circ j_{n,\omega}^{-1}) \\ &= \bigcup_{n<\omega}^{0<n} \mathscr{R}(k_{n-1,\omega} \circ \psi_n^{-1} \circ j_{n,\omega}^{-1}),\end{aligned}$$

which is $B_\omega \cdot \bigcup_{n<\omega} k_{n,\omega} \circ \varphi_n \circ j_{n,\omega}^{-1}$ is an ascending union since

$$\begin{aligned} k_{n,\omega} \circ \varphi_n \circ (j_{n+1,\omega} \circ j_{n+1})^{-1} &= k_{n+1,\omega} \circ (k_{n+1} \circ \varphi_n \circ j_{n+1}^{-1}) \circ j_{n+1,\omega}^{-1} \\ &= k_{n+1,\omega} \circ (k_{n+1} \circ (j_{n+1} \circ \varphi_n^{-1})^{-1}) \circ j_{n+1,\omega}^{-1} \\ &\subset k_{n+1,\omega} \circ k_{n+1} \circ \psi_{n+1}^{-1} \circ j_{n+1,\omega}^{-1} \\ &\subset k_{n+1,\omega} \circ \varphi_{n+1} \circ j_{n+1,\omega}^{-1}. \end{aligned}$$

However, an ascending union of Q-relations is a Q-relation, a fact we leave for the reader to show in Problem 2.4.5(b) which completes (a) except for a trivial converse we leave for the reader as well.

(b) is a special case of (a) and (c) is a special case of (b).

Note also that Theorem 2.4.8 is a special case of (b), while Theorem 2.4.9 is a special case of (a). We now return to Kochen's presentation.

THEOREM 2.4.16. Let K be a class of similar structures closed under isomorphism and the formation of ultrapowers. Then for every $\mathfrak{A}, \mathfrak{B} \in K$, $\mathfrak{A} \subset \mathfrak{B}$ iff $\mathfrak{A} < \mathfrak{B}$ holds iff:

(*) for every $\mathfrak{A}, \mathfrak{B} \in K$, $\mathfrak{A} \subset \mathfrak{B}$ implies that there is an ultrafilter pair $\langle \mathbf{I}, D\rangle$ and an imbedding $\psi: \mathfrak{B} \to \mathfrak{A}^{\mathbf{I}}/D$ such that $\psi \mid \mathfrak{A} = j_{\mathfrak{A}}$.

Proof: By Lemma 2.4.2, we know that if $\mathfrak{A} < \mathfrak{B}$ then we can find such an $\langle \mathbf{I}, D\rangle$ and ψ. Thus if $\mathfrak{A} \subset \mathfrak{B}$ implies that $\mathfrak{A} < \mathfrak{B}$, we must have that $\mathfrak{A} \subset \mathfrak{B}$ implies the existence of $\langle \mathbf{I}, D\rangle$ and ψ.

Conversely, assume (*), and note that this implies that for any imbedding $k: \mathfrak{A} \to \mathfrak{B}$, there is an imbedding $\varphi: \mathfrak{B} \to \mathfrak{A}^{\mathbf{I}}/D$ such that $\varphi \circ k = j_{\mathfrak{A}}$. As in the proof of Theorem 2.4.8, we may continue this process and obtain ultralimits $\mathfrak{A}_\omega$ and $\mathfrak{B}_\omega$ (not necessarily in K) and an isomorphism $f: \mathfrak{A}_\omega \cong \mathfrak{B}_\omega$ such that $f \circ \varphi_0 = \psi_0 \circ k$. But by Theorem 2.4.9, $k: \mathfrak{A} <' \mathfrak{B}$, and allowing k to be the identity on A, we obtain our desired result.

Since every EC_Δ-class is closed under isomorphisms and ultrapowers, we have

COROLLARY 2.4.17. A theory T is model-complete iff for every $\mathfrak{A}, \mathfrak{B} \in M(T)$ with $\mathfrak{A} \subset \mathfrak{B}$ there is an ultrafilter pair $\langle \mathbf{I}, D\rangle$ and an imbedding $\varphi: \mathfrak{B} \to \mathfrak{A}^{\mathbf{I}}/D$ such that $\varphi \mid \mathfrak{A} = j_{\mathfrak{A}}$.

Clearly $\mathfrak{I}_A: \mathfrak{A}\ QF\ \mathfrak{B}$ iff $\mathfrak{A} \subset \mathfrak{B}$. Applying Corollary 2.4.14, we have that $\mathfrak{I}_A: \mathfrak{A}\ \forall_1\ \mathfrak{B}$ iff for some ultrafilter pair $\langle \mathbf{I}, D\rangle$ and map ψ we have

$\psi: \mathfrak{B} \to \mathfrak{A}^I/D$ an imbedding with $\psi \mid \mathfrak{A} = j_{\mathfrak{A}}$. But by Corollary 2.4.17 a theory T is model-complete iff whenever $\mathfrak{A} \subset \mathfrak{B}$ this holds, i.e. iff whenever $\mathfrak{A} \subset \mathfrak{B}$ then $\mathfrak{J}_A: \mathfrak{A}\ \forall_1\ \mathfrak{B}$. Thus:

COROLLARY 2.4.18 (Robinson's Test). T is model-complete iff for every $\mathfrak{A}, \mathfrak{B} \in M(T)$, if $\mathfrak{A} \subset \mathfrak{B}$ then $\mathfrak{J}_A: \mathfrak{A}\ \forall_1\ \mathfrak{B}$, i.e. iff for every $\mathfrak{A} \subset \mathfrak{B}$, $\mathfrak{A}, \mathfrak{B} \in M(T)$, $F \in L^t$ universal, $a \in A^\omega$, if $\mathfrak{A} \models F[a]$ then $\mathfrak{B} \models F[a]$.

The above says that T is model-complete iff every universal formula persists with respect to T, also the statement of Theorem 1.7.17.

Problems

2.4.1 ‡(a) Complete the proof of Lemma 2.4.5.

(b) Devise a proof of Lemma 2.4.2 independent of the results of Theorems 2.4.1 and 2.4.13.

2.4.2 (a) Use a proof similar to that of Theorem 1.7.2(b) to show that if $\mathfrak{A} = \langle A, R_\gamma \rangle_{\gamma \in \Gamma}$, $\mathfrak{B} = \langle B, S_\gamma \rangle_{\gamma \in \Gamma}$, then $\varphi: \mathfrak{A} <' \mathfrak{B}$ iff

$$\langle A, R_\gamma, a \rangle_{\gamma \in \Gamma, a \in A} \equiv \langle B, S_\gamma, \varphi(a) \rangle_{\gamma \in \Gamma, a \in A}.$$

(b) Use this to show that $\varphi: \mathfrak{B} <' \mathfrak{A}^I/D$, where $\varphi(b) = a_b/D$; here $a_b^F = a_b(F)$, and $\mathfrak{A}, \mathfrak{B}$ and our notation are as in Theorem 2.4.1 and its proof.

2.4.3 (a) Let

$$\mathscr{A} = \{\mathfrak{A}_n \mid n < \omega\} \cup \{\varphi_{mn} \mid m \leq < \omega\},$$

$$\mathscr{B} = \{\mathfrak{B}_n \mid n < \omega \cup \{\psi_{mn} \mid m \leq n < \omega\}$$

be directed systems of structures, and for each n let

$$\mu_n : \mathfrak{B}_n \to \mathfrak{A}_n, \qquad \rho_n : \mathfrak{A}_n \to \mathfrak{B}_{n+1}$$

be elementary imbeddings such that

$$\rho_n \circ \mu_n = \psi_{nn+1} \qquad \text{and} \qquad \mu_{n+1} \circ \rho_n = \varphi_{nn+1}.$$

If the direct limits of $\mathscr{A}$ and $\mathscr{B}$ are respectively

$$\{\mathfrak{A}\} \cup \{\varphi_n \mid n < \omega\} \qquad \text{and} \qquad \{\mathfrak{B}\} \cup \{\psi_n \mid n < \omega\},$$

then there is an isomorphism $\rho : \mathfrak{A} \cong \mathfrak{B}$ such that for every n,

$$\rho \circ \varphi_n = \psi_{n+1} \circ \rho_n \qquad \text{and} \qquad \mu \circ \psi_n = \varphi_n \circ \mu_n,$$

where $\mu = \rho^{-1}$. Now attempt to generalize the above to two directed systems indexed by the same directed set.

(b) Use the above to give an alternative proof of Theorem 2.4.8, as in Theorem 2.4.15 (a).

2.4.4 (a) Show the following result due to Kochen: $\mathfrak{I}_A : \mathfrak{A}\forall_n\mathfrak{B}$ iff there is a collection $\langle \mathbf{I}_1, D_1 \rangle, \ldots, \langle \mathbf{I}_n, D_n \rangle$ of ultrafilter pairs and injections $\varphi_{-1}, \varphi_0, \varphi_1, \ldots, \varphi_{n-1}$, such that

$$\varphi_m : \mathfrak{C}_m \to \mathfrak{C}_{m+1}, \qquad \mathfrak{C}_{-1} = \mathfrak{A}, \qquad \mathfrak{C}_0 = \mathfrak{B},$$

and for $m > 0$,

$$\mathfrak{C}_m = \mathfrak{C}_{m-2}{}^{\mathbf{I}_m}/D_m,$$

φ_{-1} is the identity on A considered as an injection from $\mathfrak{A}$ into $\mathfrak{B}$, and for $m = 0, \ldots, n - 1$,

$$j_{\mathfrak{C}_m} = \varphi_{m+1} \circ \varphi_m.$$

(b) Keisler and then Kochen showed the following: $\mathfrak{I}_A : \mathfrak{A} \forall_n \mathfrak{B}$ iff there is a sequence $\mathfrak{C}_0, \ldots, \mathfrak{C}_{n+1}$ of structures such that $\mathfrak{C}_0 = \mathfrak{A}$, $\mathfrak{C}_1 = \mathfrak{B}$, $\mathfrak{C}_m \subset \mathfrak{C}_{m+1}$ for $m \leq n$, and $\mathfrak{C}_{m-1} < \mathfrak{C}_{m+1}$ for $1 \leq m \leq n$. Now it's your turn.

‡2.4.5 (a) (The relationship between object limits and unions) Let $\mathscr{A}$ be directed by $\subset$, $\bigcup \mathscr{A} = \mathfrak{A}$, and suppose that for some set $\mathscr{T} = \{\langle \mathfrak{C}, \varphi_{\mathfrak{C}} \rangle\}$ of ordered pairs, the first element of which is a structure and the second an isomorphism $\rho_{\mathfrak{C}} : \mathfrak{C} \to \mathfrak{B} \in \mathscr{A}$, it is true that for every $\mathfrak{B}', \mathfrak{B}'' \in \mathscr{A}$ there is a

$$\mathfrak{B} \in \mathscr{A} \qquad \text{and a} \qquad \varphi_{\mathfrak{C}} : \mathfrak{C} \cong \mathfrak{B}, \qquad \langle \mathfrak{C}, \varphi_{\mathfrak{C}} \rangle \in \mathscr{T}$$

such that $\mathfrak{B}', \mathfrak{B}'' \subset \mathfrak{B}$. Now consider the directed set

$$\mathscr{T}' = \mathscr{D}(\mathscr{T}) \cup \{\psi_{\mathfrak{C}\mathfrak{C}'} \mid \mathfrak{C}, \mathfrak{C}' \in \mathscr{D}\mathscr{T}, \varphi_{\mathfrak{C}}(\mathfrak{C}) \subset \varphi_{\mathfrak{C}'}(\mathfrak{C}'),$$
$$\text{and } \psi_{\mathfrak{C}\mathfrak{C}'} = \varphi_{\mathfrak{C}'}{}^{-1} \cdot \varphi_{\mathfrak{C}}\}.$$

Show that the object limit of $\mathscr{T}'$ is isomorphic to $\mathfrak{A}$, and that every directed system $\mathscr{T}'$ in which the maps are imbeddings can be considered to have been constructed in the manner considered above.

(b) Show that an ascending union of Q-relations is a Q-relation to complete the proof of Theorem 2.4.15.

2.4.6 (a) If $(v_0 = v_1) \in Q$ then every Q-relation is a Q-map.

(b) Let

$$\varphi \subset A \times B, \qquad \varphi' = \{\langle R_\gamma, S_\gamma \rangle \mid t(\gamma) = 0\} \cup \varphi.$$

Then

$$\varphi : \mathfrak{A}\ QF\ \mathfrak{B} \qquad \text{iff} \quad \varphi' : \mathfrak{A}|\mathscr{D}\varphi' \cong \mathfrak{B}|\mathscr{R}\varphi'$$

and

$$\varphi : \mathfrak{A}\ POS_0\ \mathfrak{B}$$

iff $\varphi' : \mathfrak{A}|\mathscr{D}\varphi' \to \mathfrak{B}|\mathscr{R}\varphi'$ is a homorphism (see Theorems 1.2.11 and 1.2.12). Also show that

$$\mathfrak{A} \equiv \mathfrak{B} \qquad \text{iff} \quad \phi : \mathfrak{A}\ L^t\ \mathfrak{B},$$

$$\varphi : \mathfrak{A} <' \mathfrak{B} \qquad \text{iff} \quad \varphi : \mathfrak{A}\ L^t\ \mathfrak{B} \quad \text{and} \quad \mathscr{D}\varphi = A.$$

For $Q \subset L^t$, let WQ be the smallest well-closed set containing Q; also call Q almost well-closed iff Q is closed under $\wedge$, $\vee$ and one–one replacement.

(c) Show that WQ always exists, and that Q-relations are precisely WQ-relations. If Q is almost well-closed then

$$WQ = \{F \mid \text{for some } G \in Q,\ F \equiv G\}.$$

(d) If Q is almost well-closed, then

$$\overline{WQ} = \bar{Q},$$

$$W\exists_n Q = \exists_n Q = \exists_n WQ \qquad \text{and} \qquad W\forall_n Q = \forall_n Q = \forall_n WQ$$

for each positive integer n, and

$$WQ_\omega = Q_\omega = W(Q_\omega).$$

(e) Find Q such that $\exists WQ \neq W\exists Q$.

(f) Show that "well-closed" can be replaced by "almost well-closed" in Theorem 2.4.13. Note that QF and POS_0 are both almost well-closed but not well-closed.

2.4.7 (A. Robinson) Let T, T', T'', be consistent theories such that $T \subset \Sigma^t$, $T' \subset \Sigma^{t'}$, $T'' \subset \Sigma^{t''}$, $T = T' \cap T''$, and T is complete. Then $T' \cup T''$ is consistent. Give a counterexample in the case that T is not complete. (HINT: If $\mathfrak{A} \in M(T')$, $\mathfrak{B} \in M(T'')$, then $\mathfrak{A}/t \equiv \mathfrak{B}/t$; now use Theorem 2.4.8.)

2.4.8 (Craig's Interpolation Theorem) Let $F \in \Sigma^t$, $G \in \Sigma^{t'}$, $F \models G$. Then there is an $H \in \Sigma^{t \cap t'}$ such that $F \models H$ and $H \models G$. (HINT: Let

$$S = \{H' \in \Sigma^{t \cap t'} \mid F \models H'\}.$$

If $S \cup \{\neg G\}$ is consistent, find a complete $T \subset \Sigma^{t \cap t'}$ with $S \subset T$, $T \cup \{\neg G\}$ consistent; use Problem 2.4.7.)

2.4.9 (Beth's Theorem on Definition) Let $t(\gamma) = t(\delta)$, $F(P_\gamma) \in \Sigma^{t \sim \{\langle \delta, t(\delta) \rangle\}}$, $F(P_\delta)$ the result of substituting P_δ for every occurrence of P_γ. Then show the following to be equivalent:

(i)

$$F(P_\gamma) \wedge F(P_\delta) \to (\forall v_1) \ldots (\forall v_{t(\gamma)})(P_\gamma(v_1, \ldots, v_{t(\gamma)}) \leftrightarrow P_\delta(v_1, \ldots, v_{t(\gamma)})).$$

(ii) For some

$$G \in L^{t|(I \sim \{\gamma, \delta\})},\ F(P_\gamma) \to (\forall v_1) \ldots (\forall v_{t(\gamma)})(G \leftrightarrow P_\gamma(v_1, \ldots, v_{t(\gamma)})),$$

and $FV(G) \subset \{v_1, \ldots, v_{t(\gamma)}\}$.

Interpretation: Implicit and explicit definitions are equivalent. (HINT: Introduce new constants $c_1, \ldots, c'_{t(\gamma)}$, rewrite (i) as

$$F(P_\gamma) \wedge F(P_\delta) \to (P_\gamma(c'_1, \ldots, c'_{t(\gamma)})) \leftrightarrow P_\delta(c'_1, \ldots, c'_{t(\gamma)})),$$

juggle to obtain

$$F(P_\gamma) \wedge P_\gamma(c'_1, \ldots, c'_{t(\gamma)}) \rightarrow (F(P_\delta) \rightarrow P_\delta(c'_1, \ldots, c'_{t(\gamma)})),$$

use Problem 2.4.8 to obtain H, guaranteed by Problem 2.4.8 possibly involving $c'_1, \ldots, c'_{t(\gamma)}$ but not P_γ or P_δ, and continue to juggle using the fact that if $G(P_\gamma)$ does not involve P_δ and $G(P_\delta)$ is the result of substituting P_δ for P_γ in G then $H \models G(P_\gamma)$ iff $H \models G(P_\delta)$. This extended sort of substitution has not been defined nor this result yet proved, but definition and proof are both routine in the spirit of 1.2.14–1.2.17.)

2.4.10 (a) Establish (d) through (f) of Lemma 2.4.12 and complete the proof of 2.4.12 (g).

(b) Establish the comment made in the proof of (f) of Corollary 2.4.14, and its connection with that proof.

(c) Show 2.4.12 (b) and the rest of 2.4.12 (a). (HINT: For the well-closedness of $Sb_C^V Q$ show and use: $Rp_\rho Sb_\psi F = Sb_{\rho\psi\rho^{-1}} Rp_\rho F$.)

2.4.11 (a) If $\varphi : \mathfrak{A}\ Q\ \mathfrak{B}$ and $\varphi^{-1} : \mathfrak{B}\ Q\ \mathfrak{A}$, prove $\varphi : \mathfrak{A}\ B(Q)\ \mathfrak{B}$ ($B(Q)$ denotes the Boolean combinations of elements of Q as defined in 1.6.17).

(b) Let $\mathfrak{A} = \langle \omega, \{0\}, \omega \sim \{0\} \rangle$, $\mathfrak{B} = \langle \omega, \omega \sim \{0\}, \{0\} \rangle$, $Q = \{P_i(v_j) \mid i \in \{0, 1\}, j \in \omega\}$. Show that $\mathfrak{A}\ B(Q)\ _\omega\mathfrak{B}$, but there are no ultralimits $\mathfrak{A}_\omega$, $\mathfrak{B}_\omega$ and total, onto $B(Q)$-maps $\varphi : \mathfrak{A}_\omega \to \mathfrak{B}_\omega$, so our theorem on the existence of a total, onto Q-relation cannot assert the existence of a total, onto Q-map. (Note that in this situation $B(Q)_\omega$ can be treated as the set of all formulas in $L^{\langle 1,1 \rangle}$ not using $=$.)

2.4.12 Prove the following theorems related to Theorem 2.3.11:

Let D, E be nonprincipal ultrafilters on ω, $\{\mathfrak{A}_n \mid n \in \omega\}$, $\{\mathfrak{B}_n \mid n \in \omega\} \subset M^t$, $c(t) \leq \omega$, and if $n \in \omega$, $\omega \leq c(\mathfrak{A}_n) \leq 2^\omega$, $\omega \leq c(\mathfrak{B}_n) \leq 2^\omega$. Assume the continuum hypothesis and let $\mathfrak{A} = \prod_\omega \mathfrak{A}_n/D$, $\mathfrak{B} = \prod_\omega \mathfrak{B}_n/E$, $Q \subset L^t$ be well-closed, and $\varphi \subset A \times B$ be countable.

(a) If φ: $\mathfrak{A}\ \exists Q\ \mathfrak{B}$, then for some total ψ: $\mathfrak{A}\ Q\ \mathfrak{B}$, $\varphi \subset \psi$.

(b) If φ: $\mathfrak{A}\ Q_\omega\ \mathfrak{B}$, then for some total, onto ψ: $\mathfrak{A}\ Q\ \mathfrak{B}$, $\varphi \subset \psi$. As special cases of (a) and (b), we have Theorem 2.3.11 and:

(c) If $\mathfrak{A}\ POS\ \mathfrak{B}$, then $\mathfrak{B}$ is a homomorphic image of $\mathfrak{A}$.

(d) If $\mathfrak{A}\ \exists_1\ \mathfrak{B}$, then for some $\mathfrak{C} \subset \mathfrak{B}$, $\mathfrak{A} \cong \mathfrak{C}$.

(e) If $\mathfrak{A}\ \forall_1\ \mathfrak{B}$, then for some $\mathfrak{C} \subset \mathfrak{A}$, $\mathfrak{C} \cong \mathfrak{B}$.

(f) If $\mathfrak{A}\ \exists_1 POS_0\ \mathfrak{B}$, then there is a homomorphism f: $\mathfrak{A} \to \mathfrak{B}$.

(g) If $\mathfrak{A}\ \forall_1 POS_0\ \mathfrak{B}$, then for some $\mathfrak{C} \subset \mathfrak{A}$, $\mathfrak{B}$ is a homomorphic image of $\mathfrak{C}$.

Assume in addition that for each $n \in \omega$, $\mathfrak{A}_n = \mathfrak{A}_0$ and $\mathfrak{B}_n = \mathfrak{B}_0$, and that $\mu \subset A_0 \times B_0$ is countable. Then $\mathfrak{A} = \mathfrak{A}_0^\omega/D$, $\mathfrak{B} = \mathfrak{B}_0^\omega/E$, so let $j = j_{\mathfrak{A}_0}$, $k = j_{\mathfrak{B}_0}$.

(h) If μ: $\mathfrak{A}_0\ \exists Q\ \mathfrak{B}_0$, then for some total η: $\mathfrak{A}\ Q\ \mathfrak{B}$, $k \circ \mu \subset \eta \circ j$, and if μ: $\mathfrak{A}_0\ Q_\omega\ \mathfrak{B}_0$ then for some total, onto η: $\mathfrak{A}\ Q\ \mathfrak{B}$, $k \circ \mu \subset \eta \circ j$. As a special case of (h), derive results corresponding to (c) through (g) and

(i) If μ: $\mathfrak{A}_0 <'\ \mathfrak{B}_0$, then for some η: $\mathfrak{A} \cong \mathfrak{B}$, $k \circ \mu = \eta \circ j$.

2.4.13 Show that $\mathfrak{A} \ll' \mathfrak{A}_\omega$.

2.4.14 If D is a regular ultrafilter on $\mathbf{I}$, $c(\mathfrak{B}) \leq c(\mathbf{I})$ and $\mathfrak{A} \equiv \mathfrak{B}$, show that $\mathfrak{B} <' \mathfrak{A}^{\mathbf{I}}/D$. (This uses Theorem 2.3.8 in an alternative proof of Theorem 2.4.1.)

2.5 Algebraic Characterization of Elementary Classes

Using his results as described in the previous section (up to Theorem 2.4.9), Kochen was able to give an algebraic characterization of elementary classes, and we follow him to it, and go further. For the remainder of this section, unless otherwise indicated (see comments following Corollary 2.5.6), Q will denote a collection of formulas in L^t closed under $\wedge$, $\vee$.

DEFINITION 2.5.1.

$$K \in QC \quad \text{iff} \quad K = M(F) \quad \text{for some} \quad F \in Q \cap \Sigma^t;$$

$$K \in QC_\Delta \quad \text{iff} \quad K = \bigcap X \quad \text{for some} \quad X \subset QC;$$

$$K \in QC_\Sigma \quad \text{iff} \quad K = \bigcup X \quad \text{for some} \quad X \subset QC.$$

LEMMA 2.5.2. $QC = QC_\Delta \cap QC_\Sigma$.

Proof: Compactness (left for the reader in Problem 2.5.1).

LEMMA 2.5.3. $K \in QC_\Delta$ iff $K = M(T_Q(K))$ iff $K = \{\mathfrak{A} \mid T_Q(K) \subset T_Q(\mathfrak{A})\}$.

Proof: If $K \in QC_\Delta$, then $K = M(S)$ for some $S \subset Q$; thus

$$K = M(S) = M(S \cap Q) \supset M(T(K) \cap Q) \supset M(T(K)) = K,$$

so

$$K = M(T_Q(K)).$$

If $K = M(T_Q(K))$, then $\mathfrak{A} \in K$ iff $T(K) \subset T(\mathfrak{A})$ (by Theorem 1.3.3) iff $T_Q(K) \subset T(\mathfrak{A}) \cap Q = T_Q(\mathfrak{A})$.

If $K = \{\mathfrak{A} \mid T_Q(K) \subset T_Q(\mathfrak{A})\}$ then $K = \{\mathfrak{A} \mid T_Q(K) \subset T(\mathfrak{A})\}$, so $K = M(T_Q(K))$ thus $K = M(S)$ for $S = T_Q(K) \subset Q$.

LEMMA 2.5.4. Let $K \subset M^t$ be closed under ultraproducts. Then $T_Q(K) \subset T_Q(\mathfrak{B})$ iff for some $\mathfrak{A} \in K$, $T_Q(\mathfrak{A}) \subset T_Q(\mathfrak{B})$.

Proof: Assume that $T_Q(K) \subset T_Q(\mathfrak{B})$ and note that if $F \in Q \sim T_Q(\mathfrak{B})$ and $F \in \Sigma^t$, since $Q \sim T_Q(\mathfrak{B}) \subset Q \sim T_Q(K)$, $F \notin T_Q(K)$, so we can find $\mathfrak{A}_F \in K$ such that $\mathfrak{A}_F \models \neg F$. Since Q is closed under $\vee$, for each finite

$$Q' = \{F_1, \ldots, F_n\} \subset (Q \sim T_Q(\mathfrak{B})) \cap \Sigma^t$$

we can find $\mathfrak{A}_{Q'} \in K$ such that

$$\mathfrak{A}_{Q'} \models \{\neg F_1, \ldots, \neg F_n\} = \{\neg F \mid F \in Q'\},$$

for let

$$\mathfrak{A}_{Q'} = \mathfrak{A}_{F_1 \vee \dots \vee F_n} \models \neg(F_1 \vee \cdots \vee F_n) = \neg F_1 \wedge \cdots \wedge \neg F_n.$$

It may be shown as in the proof of compactness (Theorem 2.1.16) that there is an ultrafilter D on

$$\mathbf{I} = \{Q' \subset \Sigma^t \cap (Q \sim T_Q(\mathfrak{B})) \mid Q' \text{ finite}\}$$

such that

$$\mathfrak{A} = \prod_{\mathbf{I}} \mathfrak{A}_{Q'}/D \models \{\neg F \mid F \in \Sigma^t \cap (Q \sim T_Q(\mathfrak{B}))\}.$$

Thus $\mathfrak{A} \in K$ and $T_Q(\mathfrak{A}) \subset T_Q(\mathfrak{B})$. The converse is obvious.

THEOREM 2.5.5 (A generalization of earlier results by D. Scott, S. Kochen). $K \in QC_\Delta$ iff both these statements hold:

(i) K is closed under the formation of ultraproducts, and
(ii) if $\mathfrak{A} \in K$ and $\mathfrak{A}\ Q\ \mathfrak{B}$, then $\mathfrak{B} \in K$.

Proof: We know that $K \in QC_\Delta$ iff

$$K = \{\mathfrak{B} \mid T_Q(K) \subset T_Q(\mathfrak{B})\}$$

and that for every K,

$$\begin{aligned}\{\mathfrak{B} \mid T_Q(K) \subset T_Q(\mathfrak{B})\} &= \{\mathfrak{B} \mid T_Q(K) \subset T(\mathfrak{B})\} \\ &= \{\mathfrak{B} \mid \mathfrak{B} \models T_Q(K)\} \supset \{\mathfrak{B} \mid \mathfrak{B} \models T(K)\} \supset K\end{aligned}$$

(for the last inclusion see Theorem 1.3.3(f)). Thus it suffices to show that K satisfies (i) and (ii) iff

$$\{\mathfrak{B} \mid T_Q(K) \subset T_Q(\mathfrak{B})\} \subset K.$$

But if K satisfies (i) and $T_Q(K) \subset T_Q(\mathfrak{B})$, we can find $\mathfrak{A} \in K$ such that $T_Q(\mathfrak{A}) \subset T_Q(\mathfrak{B})$, i.e., $\mathfrak{A}\ Q\ \mathfrak{B}$; and if K satisfies (ii) as well, $\mathfrak{B} \in K$.

Conversely, if $K \in QC_\Delta$, then K satisfies (i) by Łos' theorem (2.1.13) and (ii) because if $\mathfrak{A} \in K$ and $\mathfrak{A}\ Q\ \mathfrak{B}$, then

$$T_Q(K) \subset T_Q(\mathfrak{A}) \subset T_Q(\mathfrak{B}),$$

so by our assumption, $\mathfrak{B} \in K$.

COROLLARY 2.5.6. $K \in QC$ iff both these hold:

(i) K, $M^t \sim K$ are both closed under the formation of ultraproducts; and
(ii) if $\mathfrak{A} \in K$ and $\mathfrak{A}\ Q\ \mathfrak{B}$, then $\mathfrak{B} \in K$.

Proof: If we can show that $M^t \sim K \in \bar{Q}C_\Delta$, we are through (by 2.5.5 and the fact that then $K \in QC_\Sigma$). But $M^t \sim K$ satisfies (i) of Theorem 2.5.5 and for (ii) note that if $\mathfrak{A} \in M^t \sim K$, $\mathfrak{A}\ \bar{Q}\ \mathfrak{B}$, then $\mathfrak{B}\ Q\ \mathfrak{A}$ so $\mathfrak{B} \in K$ would yield $\mathfrak{A} \in K$, a contradiction. Thus $\mathfrak{B} \in M^t \sim K$, establishing (ii) and our Corollary.

Note that until the proof of the above corollary we did not actually use the fact that Q is closed under $\wedge$. Henceforth, however, we shall assume Q to be well-closed, in order to use the results of Section 2.4.

COROLLARY 2.5.7. (a) $K \in \forall QC_\Delta$ iff K is closed under ultraproducts and images of onto Q-relations.

(b) $K \in \exists QC_\Delta$ iff K is closed under ultraproducts, $M^t \sim K$ closed under ultrapowers; and if $\mathfrak{A} \in K$, $\varphi: \mathfrak{A}\ Q\ \mathfrak{B}$ is total, then $\mathfrak{B} \in K$.

(c) $K \in Q_\omega C_\Delta$ iff K is closed under ultraproducts, K and $M^t \sim K$ closed under ultralimits, and K closed under the images of total onto Q-relations.

Proof: In (a) through (c) we have assumed (i) of Theorem 2.5.5, so it will suffice to show that in each case the remaining conditions are equivalent to (ii).

For (a) if $\mathfrak{A}\ \forall Q\ \mathfrak{B}$, then for some $\langle \mathbf{I}, D\rangle$, φ, $\varphi: \mathfrak{B}\ \bar{Q}\ \mathfrak{A}^{\mathbf{I}}/D$ is a total $\bar{Q}$-relation, thus $\varphi^{-1}: \mathfrak{A}^{\mathbf{I}}/D\ Q\ \mathfrak{B}$ is onto. Thus, if our remaining conditions hold and $\mathfrak{A} \in K$, then $\mathfrak{B} \in K$ so (ii) holds. Conversely, if (ii) is satisfied, $\mathfrak{A} \in K$, $\varphi: \mathfrak{B}\ Q\ \mathfrak{B}$ is onto, then $\varphi^{-1}: \mathfrak{B}\ \bar{Q}\ \mathfrak{A}$ is total, thus an $\exists\bar{Q}$-relation, thus $\mathfrak{B}\ \exists\bar{Q}\ \mathfrak{A}$, so $\mathfrak{A}\ \forall Q\ \mathfrak{B}$, so $\mathfrak{B} \in K$, and our remaining conditions hold.

For (b), $\mathfrak{A}\ \exists Q\ \mathfrak{B}$ iff for some $\langle \mathbf{I}, D\rangle$, φ, $\varphi: \mathfrak{A}\ Q\ \mathfrak{B}^{\mathbf{I}}/D$ is total. Thus, if our remaining conditions hold and $\mathfrak{A} \in K$, then $\mathfrak{B}^{\mathbf{I}}/D \in K$, and since $M^t \sim K$ is closed under ultrapowers, $\mathfrak{B} \in K$, establishing (ii). Conversely, if (ii) holds and $\varphi: \mathfrak{A}\ Q\ \mathfrak{B}$ is total, then φ is an $\exists Q$-relation, so $\mathfrak{A}\ \exists Q\ \mathfrak{B}$, thus $\mathfrak{B} \in K$ so K satisfies our remaining conditions.

For (c), $\mathfrak{A}\ Q_\omega\ \mathfrak{B}$ iff we have ultralimits $\mathfrak{A}_\omega$, $\mathfrak{B}_\omega$ and $\varphi: \mathfrak{A}_\omega\ Q\ \mathfrak{B}_\omega$ a total, onto Q-relation. Thus, if the remaining conditions in (c) hold and $\mathfrak{A} \in K$, then $\mathfrak{A}_\omega \in K$ thus $\mathfrak{B}_\omega \in K$ so $\mathfrak{B} \in K$, thus (ii) holds. Conversely, if (ii) holds and $\varphi: \mathfrak{A}\ Q\ \mathfrak{B}$ is a total, onto Q-relation, then by 2.4.12 (h), φ is a Q_ω-relation, so $\mathfrak{A}\ Q_\omega\ \mathfrak{B}$, thus $\mathfrak{B} \in K$. Also, since $K \in EC_\Delta$, both K and $M^t \sim K$ are closed under ultralimits (why?), so our remaining conditions are again equivalent to (ii).

We leave (in Problem 2.5.4) for the reader the proof of a corollary like 2.5.7 dealing with $\forall QC$, $\exists QC$, and $Q_\omega C$ classes. The following special case of 2.5.7(c) is of exceptional importance (with $Q = L^t$).

COROLLARY 2.5.8. $K \in EC_\Delta$ iff K is closed under ultraproducts, ultralimits and isomorphic images, and $M^t \sim K$ closed under ultralimits.

A simple application of compactness to the above assures us that $K \in EC$ iff K, $M^t \sim K$ are both closed under ultraproducts, ultralimits, and isomorphic images.

Here are some other uses of Corollary 2.5.7.

COROLLARY 2.5.9. (a) $K \in POSC_\Delta$ iff K is closed under ultraproducts and homomorphic images, and K, $M^t \sim K$ are both closed under ultralimits.

(b) $K \in \forall_1 C_\Delta$ iff K is closed under ultraproducts, isomorphic images, and substructures.

(c) $K \in \exists_1 C_\Delta$ iff K is closed under ultraproducts, isomorphic images, and extensions (i.e., if $\mathfrak{A} \in K$, $\mathfrak{A} \subset \mathfrak{B}$, then $\mathfrak{B} \in K$), and $M^t \sim K$ is closed under ultrapowers.

(d) $K \in \forall POS_0 C_\Delta$ iff K is closed under ultraproducts, homomorphic images, and substructures.

(e) $K \in \exists POS_0 C_\Delta$ iff K is closed under ultraproducts, homomorphic images, and extensions, and $M^t \sim K$ closed under ultrapowers.

Proof: (a) is a special case of 2.5.7(c). We leave (b) through (e) for the reader (see Problem 2.5.2).

COROLLARY 2.5.10. (a) Let $Q \subset QF$ be closed under substitution of constants for variables and almost well-closed (see Problem 2.4.6). Then $K \in \forall_2\ Q\ C_\Delta$ iff K is closed under ultraproducts, images of total, onto Q-relations and unions of chains, and $M^t \sim K$ closed under ultralimits.

(b) $K \in \forall_2 C_\Delta$ iff K is closed under ultraproducts, isomorphic images and unions of ascending chains, and $M^t \sim K$ closed under ultralimits.

(c) $K \in \forall_2 POS_0 C_\Delta$ iff K is closed under ultraproducts, homomorphic images, and unions of ascending chains, and $M^t \sim K$ closed under ultralimits.

Proof: (a) By two applications of Theorem 2.4.13 we see that if $\mathfrak{A}\ \forall_2 Q\ \mathfrak{B}$ then we have:

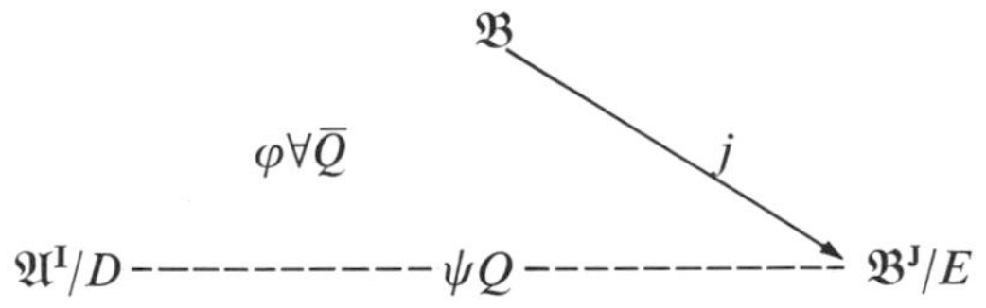

with φ, ψ total and $\psi \mid \mathscr{R}\varphi = j \circ \varphi^{-1}$.

In Problem 2.5.2 the reader shows that there is a total, onto Q-relation

$$\psi' \supset \psi, \qquad \psi' \colon \mathfrak{A}^{\mathbf{I}}/D \; Q \; \mathfrak{C} \subset \mathfrak{B}^{\mathbf{J}}/E.$$

Since

$$j = j \circ \mathfrak{I}_B \subset j \circ \varphi^{-1} \circ \varphi \subset \psi \circ \varphi \subset \psi' \circ \varphi,$$

we have

$$j[B] \subset \psi' \circ \varphi[B] = \psi'[\varphi[B]] \subset \psi'[A^{\mathbf{I}}/D] = C.$$

Also

$$(\mathfrak{A}^{\mathbf{I}}/D) \; \forall_2 Q \; (\mathfrak{B}^{\mathbf{J}}/E),$$

thus we may continue in this manner (formally by induction) obtaining $\mathfrak{B}_0 = \mathfrak{B}$,

$$\mathfrak{C}_1 \subset \mathfrak{B}_1 = \mathfrak{B}^{\mathbf{J}_1}/E_1, \ldots, \mathfrak{C}_n \subset \mathfrak{B}_n = \mathfrak{B}_{n-1}{}^{\mathbf{J}_n}/E_n, \ldots,$$

with

$$j_n = j_{\mathfrak{B}_{n-1}}, \qquad j_n[B_{n-1}] \subset C_n \subset B_n \qquad \text{for each} \quad n \geq 1$$

and each $\mathfrak{C}_n$ the image under a total, onto Q-relation of an ultrapower of $\mathfrak{A}$. Note that since K is closed under the image of total, onto Q-relations, each $\mathfrak{C}_n \in K$. Taking the ultralimit $\mathfrak{B}_\omega$ and imbeddings $j_{n,\omega} \colon \mathfrak{B}_n \to \mathfrak{B}_\omega$ and defining

$$\mathfrak{B}'_n = j_{n,\omega}[\mathfrak{B}_n], \qquad \mathfrak{C}'_n = j_{n,\omega}[\mathfrak{C}_n]$$

we obtain

$$\mathfrak{B}'_0 \subset \mathfrak{C}'_1 \subset \mathfrak{B}'_1 \subset \mathfrak{C}'_2, \ldots, \mathfrak{C}'_n \in K$$

(since K is closed under images of onto Q relations, and every isomorphism is an onto Q-relation), and

$$\bigcup_{n<\omega} \mathfrak{C}'_n = \mathfrak{B}_\omega.$$

Thus if K is closed under ascending chains $\mathfrak{B}_\omega \in K$, and if $M^t \sim K$ is closed under ultralimits, $\mathfrak{B} \in K$. Thus if our conditions hold, $K \in \forall_2 Q C_\Delta$.

Conversely, if $K \in \forall_2 Q C_\Delta$, then since $\forall_2 Q \subset Q_\omega$, $K \in Q_\omega C_\Delta$, so K is closed under ultraproducts and images of onto Q-relations, and $M^t \sim K$ closed under ultralimits. We leave for the reader (Problem 2.5.3) the verification that K is closed under unions of ascending chains.

(b) and (c) are special cases of (a).

Problems

‡2.5.1 (a) Prove Lemma 2.5.2.
(b) Derive Corollary 2.5.8 directly from Theorem 2.5.5.

‡2.5.2 (a) Show by induction (as in Section 1.2) that for $F \in QF^t$, $\mathfrak{A}$, $\mathfrak{C} \in M^t$, $\mathfrak{C} \subset \mathfrak{A}$, $a \in C^\omega$ we have $\mathfrak{C} \models F[a]$ iff $\mathfrak{A} \models F[a]$.
(b) Let $Q \subset QF$, $\{R_\gamma \mid t(\gamma) = 0\} \subset \mathscr{D}\varphi$, $\{S_\gamma \mid t(\gamma) = 0\} \subset \mathscr{R}\varphi$. Then $\varphi \colon \mathfrak{A} \; Q \; \mathfrak{B}$ iff $\varphi \colon \mathfrak{A} \mid \mathscr{D}\varphi \; Q \; \mathfrak{B} \mid \mathscr{R}\varphi$.

(c) Let $Q \subset QF^t$ be closed under the substitution of constants for variables. Then $\varphi\colon \mathfrak{A}\ Q\ \mathfrak{B}$ iff $\varphi'\colon \mathfrak{A}\ Q\ \mathfrak{B}$, φ' as in Problem 2.4.6 (b). (Note: This is connected to 2.4.12 (c).)

(d) If $\varphi\colon \mathfrak{A}\ Q\ \mathfrak{B}$ is a total Q-relation, Q as in (c), show that for some $\mathfrak{C} \subset \mathfrak{B}$ there is a total, onto Q-relation $\psi \subset \varphi$ with $\psi\colon \mathfrak{A}\ Q\ \mathfrak{C}$. If $\varphi\colon \mathfrak{A}\ Q\ \mathfrak{B}$ is an onto Q-relation show that for some $\mathfrak{C} \subset \mathfrak{A}$ there is a total onto Q-relation $\psi\colon \mathfrak{C}\ Q\ \mathfrak{B}$ such that $\varphi \subset \psi$.

(e) Use (d) to derive Corollary 2.5.9 (b)–(e) and fill the gap in 2.5.10.

‡2.5.3 Let $F \in \forall_2$, $\mathfrak{A}_1 \subset \mathfrak{A}_2 \subset \ldots$, $a \in A_1^{\omega}$, $\mathfrak{A} = \bigcup_{n<\omega} \mathfrak{A}_n$. If for every n, $\mathfrak{A}_n \models F[a]$, then show that $\mathfrak{A} \models F[a]$.

‡2.5.4 (a) Show that Δ may be removed from each of the parts of Corollary 2.5.7 if the condition "$M^t \sim K$ is closed under ultraproducts" is added. (For example: $K \in \forall QC$ iff K, $M^t \sim K$ are closed under ultraproducts and K closed under the images of onto partial Q-relations.)

(b) Prove the characterization of EC classes following Corollary 2.5.8.

(c) Formulate and prove Δ-less facts corresponding to those shown in Corollaries 2.5.9 and 2.5.10.

2.5.5 Facts established in this section show that the concept of Q-relation is often useful, but it is often useless as well. Show, for example, that if $Q \subset \Sigma^t$ then $\mathfrak{A}\ Q\ \mathfrak{B}$ iff $\varphi\colon \mathfrak{A}\ Q\ \mathfrak{B}$ for every $\varphi \subset A \times B$.

2.5.6 Use and extend the result of Problem 2.4.4 to derive characterizations of $\exists_n Q$ and $\forall_n Q$ classes, for Q as in Corollary 2.5.10 (a).

2.5.7 Show that if K is closed under substructures, direct products, and homomorphic images, then $K \in EC_\Delta$, and further that $K = M(S)$ for some $S \subset \forall_1$.

Give an example of $K = M(S)$, $S \subset \forall_1$, with K not closed under direct products and homomorphic images.

‡2.5.8 We say that K is elementarily closed and write $K \in ECL$ iff when $\mathfrak{A} \in K$ and $\mathfrak{A} \equiv \mathfrak{B}$ then $\mathfrak{B} \in K$.

(a) Show that if $K \in EC_\Delta$ then $K \in ECL$.

(b) Show that $K \in ECL$ iff K and $M^t \sim K$ are both closed under

(i) isomorphic images;

(ii) ultralimits.

2.5.9 Let $c(t) \leq \omega$ and assume the continuum hypothesis. Show that in this situation the word "ultralimits" may be replaced by "ultrapowers" (and eliminated completely for classes already closed under ultraproducts) in the statements of 2.5.7 (c), 2.5.8 (and statements following it), 2.5.9 (a) and 2.5.10 (a) through (c).

‡2.5.10 Use Lemma 2.5.4 and Theorems 2.3.2 and 2.4.1 to show that if $K \subset M^t$ and $T(K) \subset T(\mathfrak{B})$ then for some set $\mathbf{I}$, ultrafilter D on $\mathbf{I}$, and $\{\mathfrak{A}_{\mathbf{i}} \mid \mathbf{i} \in \mathbf{I}\} \subset K$, $\mathfrak{B} <' \prod_{\mathbf{I}} \mathfrak{A}_{\mathbf{i}}/D$.

2.5.11 Let $t' \subset t$, $t'(\delta) \neq 0$ for $\delta \in \mathscr{D}t'$.

$$N^{t,t'} = \{\mathfrak{A} \in M^t \mid \text{if } \delta \in \mathscr{D}t' \text{ then } \mathfrak{A} \models (\forall v_1)\cdots(\forall v_{t(\delta)-1})(\exists v_0)$$
$$(\forall v_{t(\delta)})(P(v_1, \ldots, v_{t(\delta)}) <\!-\!> v_{t(\delta)} = v_0)\}.$$

In other words, $N^{t,t'}$ is the class of structures of type t such that if $\delta \in \mathscr{D}t'$ then R_δ is a $t(\delta)$-1-ary operation.

Let $CS^{t,t'} = \{(\exists v_{t(\delta)})P_\delta(v_1, \ldots, v_{t(\delta)}) \mid \delta \in \mathscr{D}t'\} \cup QF^t$. A t'-closed substructure of $\mathfrak{A} \in M^t$ is a $\mathfrak{B} \subset \mathfrak{A}$ such that $\mathfrak{A}CS^{t,t'}\mathfrak{B}$.

(a) $\mathfrak{B} \in M^t$ is a t'-closed substructure of $\mathfrak{A} \in N^{t,t'}$ iff $\mathfrak{B} \subset \mathfrak{A}$ and $\mathfrak{B} \in N^{t,t'}$.

(b) $K \subset M^t$ is closed under ultraproducts, isomorphic images and t'-closed substructures iff K is an $\forall CSC_\Delta$-class.

(c) $K \subset M^t$ is closed under ultraproducts, homomorphic images, and t'-closed substructures iff K is an $(\forall CS) \cap (\forall POS_0)C_\Delta$-class.

(d) Translate these results into the language L'^t (with $J = \mathscr{D}t'$ here) discussed at the end of Section 1.2 to check that $K \subset N^{t,t'}$ is closed under ultraproducts, isomorphic images, and substructures (in $N^{t,t'}$) iff K is a $\forall QF_\Delta^{t,t'}$-class ($QF^{t,t'}$ the quantifier-free formulas in L'^t), closed under ultraproducts, homomorphic images, and substructures (in $N^{t,t'}$) iff it is a $\forall POS_{0\Delta}^{t,t'}$-class ($POS_0^{t,t'}$ the positive formulas in L'^t). You must make up reasonable definitions of quantifier-free and positive formulas in this new situation.

2.6 Limit Ultraproducts

Shortly after Kochen's ultralimit construction (discussed in Sections 2.4 and 2.5), the construction to be defined below under the name "limit ultrapower" was introduced by Keisler [1], and somewhat later, see [2], he discovered a construction equivalent to our "limit ultraproduct" construction. Reasons for these names will become apparent, although they are not in our definition. Our results, unless otherwise noted, are similar to some in Keisler [1] and [2].

Definition 2.6.1. Let $\{\mathfrak{A}_\mathbf{i} \mid \mathbf{i} \in \mathbf{I}\} \subset M^t$. $\prod_\mathbf{I} \mathfrak{A}_\mathbf{i}/D \mid G$ is a limit reduced product if:

(i) D is a filter on $\mathbf{I}$, G a filter on $\mathbf{I} \times \mathbf{I}$;

(ii) $eq(\mathfrak{A}_\mathbf{I}) \in G$, where $eq(\mathfrak{A}_\mathbf{I}) = \{\langle \mathbf{i}, \mathbf{j}\rangle \mid \mathfrak{A}_\mathbf{i} = \mathfrak{A}_\mathbf{j}\}$;

(iii) $\prod_\mathbf{I} \mathfrak{A}_\mathbf{i}/D \mid G = (\prod_\mathbf{I} \mathfrak{A}_\mathbf{i}/D) \mid (\prod_\mathbf{I} A_\mathbf{i}/D \mid G)$, where

$$\prod_\mathbf{I} A_\mathbf{i}/D \mid G = \left\{f/D \mid f \in \prod_\mathbf{I} A_\mathbf{i} \text{ and } eq(f) \in G\right\},$$

and

$$eq(f) = \{\langle \mathbf{i}, \mathbf{j}\rangle \mid f(\mathbf{i}) = f(\mathbf{j})\} \qquad \text{for } f \in \prod_\mathbf{I} A_\mathbf{i}$$

(this part of the definition is justified in Problem 6.1(b)).

If $\{\mathfrak{A}_\mathbf{i} \mid \mathbf{i} \in \mathbf{I}\} \subset K$, then a limit reduced product $\prod_\mathbf{I} \mathfrak{A}_\mathbf{i}/D \mid G$ is called a limit reduced product of elements of K, and if D is an ultrafilter, "ultraproduct" is substituted everywhere for "reduced product" above.

An important special case of the above occurs when $eq(\mathfrak{A}_\mathbf{I}) = \mathbf{I} \times \mathbf{I}$. Every filter G on $\mathbf{I} \times \mathbf{I}$ has the property $\mathbf{I} \times \mathbf{I} \in G$, thus we may write for any such filter

$$\prod_\mathbf{I} \mathfrak{A}_\mathbf{i}/D \mid G = \mathfrak{A}^\mathbf{I}/D \mid G,$$

where $\mathfrak{A}$ is the common value of the $\mathfrak{A}_\mathbf{i}$, and call the result a limit reduced (or ultra-) power of $\mathfrak{A}$.

$\prod_\mathbf{I} A_\mathbf{i}/D \mid G$ may be considered the set of equivalence classes (mod D) of functions that are "almost everywhere constant" with respect to G. If $G = \{\mathbf{I} \times \mathbf{I}\}$,

$$a/D \in A^\mathbf{I}/D \mid G \quad \text{iff for some} \quad f \in a/D, \quad eq(f) = \mathbf{I} \times \mathbf{I},$$

i.e., iff a/D contains a constant f. Thus $j_\mathfrak{A}$ (of Corollary 2.1.19) has the property

$$j_\mathfrak{A}\colon \mathfrak{A} \cong \mathfrak{A}^\mathbf{I}/D \mid \{\mathbf{I} \times \mathbf{I}\}.$$

This particular limit reduced power is called trivial for obvious reasons (we consider a related situation for limit reduced products in Problem 2.6.7).

If G, H are filters on $\mathbf{I} \times \mathbf{I}$ such that $eq(\mathfrak{A}_\mathbf{I}) \in G \subset H$, then let

$$f/D \in \prod_\mathbf{I} A_\mathbf{i}/D \mid G.$$

Thus for some $f' \in f/D$, $eq(f') \in G$, thus

$$eq(f') \in H, \qquad \text{so} \quad f/D = f'/D \in \prod_\mathbf{I} A_\mathbf{i}/D \mid H.$$

Thus

$$\prod_\mathbf{I} \mathfrak{A}_\mathbf{i}/D \mid G \subset \prod_\mathbf{I} \mathfrak{A}_\mathbf{i}/D \mid H.$$

In addition, it is possible to find a filter H on $\mathbf{I} \times \mathbf{I}$ such that

$$\prod_\mathbf{I} \mathfrak{A}_\mathbf{i}/D \mid H = \prod_\mathbf{I} \mathfrak{A}_\mathbf{i}/D,$$

for in general, if $\underline{=} \subset eq(\mathfrak{A}_\mathbf{I})$ is an equivalence relation on $\mathbf{I}$, let

$$G_{\underline{=}} = \{a \subset \mathbf{I} \times \mathbf{I} \mid \underline{=} \subset a\}.$$

Then $G_{\underline{=}}$ is clearly a filter on $\mathbf{I} \times \mathbf{I}$ and $eq(\mathfrak{A}_\mathbf{I}) \in G_{\underline{=}}$. If we now set $H = G_=$, then $eq(f) \in H$ for every $f \in \prod_\mathbf{I} A_\mathbf{i}$, so

$$\prod_\mathbf{I} \mathfrak{A}_\mathbf{i}/D \mid H = \prod_\mathbf{I} \mathfrak{A}_\mathbf{i}/D.$$

This discussion shows that for any filter G on $\mathbf{I} \times \mathbf{I}$ and filter D on $\mathbf{I}$ such that $eq(\mathfrak{A}_\mathbf{I}) \in G$,

$$\prod_\mathbf{I} \mathfrak{A}_\mathbf{i}/D \mid G_{eq(\mathfrak{A}_\mathbf{I})} \subset \prod_\mathbf{I} \mathfrak{A}_\mathbf{i}/D \mid G \subset \prod_\mathbf{I} \mathfrak{A}_\mathbf{i}/D \mid G_= = \prod_\mathbf{I} \mathfrak{A}_\mathbf{i}/D.$$

If $t' \subset t$, then

$$\left(\prod_\mathbf{I} \mathfrak{A}_\mathbf{i}/D \mid G\right)/t' = \prod_\mathbf{I} (\mathfrak{A}_\mathbf{i}/t')/D \mid G.$$

In Theorem 2.6.2 and Corollaries 2.6.3 and 2.6.4 we consider only the case in which D is an ultrafilter. The following generalizes Los' theorem:

THEOREM 2.6.2. Let $\prod_\mathbf{I} \mathfrak{A}_\mathbf{i}/D \mid G$ be a limit ultraproduct.

$$f \in \{g \in \prod_\mathbf{I} A_\mathbf{i} \mid eq(g) \in G\}^\omega \qquad \left(= \left(\prod_\mathbf{I} A_\mathbf{i} \mid G\right)^\omega\right).$$

For any $F \in L^t$,

$$\prod_\mathbf{I} \mathfrak{A}_\mathbf{i}/D \mid G \models F[f/D] \qquad \text{iff} \quad \{\mathbf{i} \mid \mathfrak{A}_\mathbf{i} \models F[f(\mathbf{i})]\} \in D.$$

Thus

$$\prod_\mathbf{I} \mathfrak{A}_\mathbf{i}/D \mid G \equiv \prod_\mathbf{I} \mathfrak{A}_\mathbf{i}/D.$$

Proof: The proof is identical to that of Theorem 2.1.13, except for the case $F = (\exists v_j)H$. In this case we have

$$\prod_\mathbf{I} \mathfrak{A}_\mathbf{i}/D \mid G \models F[f/D]$$

$$\text{iff for some} \quad g \in \prod_\mathbf{I} A_\mathbf{i} \mid G, \qquad \prod_\mathbf{I} \mathfrak{A}_\mathbf{i}/D \mid G \models H[f/D(j \mid g/D)]$$

$$\text{iff for some} \quad g \in \prod_\mathbf{I} \mathfrak{A}_\mathbf{i} \mid G, \qquad \{\mathbf{i} \mid \mathfrak{A}_\mathbf{i} \models H[f(j \mid g)(\mathbf{i})]\} \in D.$$

This clearly implies that $\{\mathbf{i} \mid \mathfrak{A}_\mathbf{i} \models F[f(\mathbf{i})]\} \in D$. However, conversely, if

$$\{\mathbf{i} \mid \mathfrak{A}_\mathbf{i} \models F[f(\mathbf{i})]\} \in D,$$

let $FV(F) = \{v_{j_1}, \ldots, v_{j_m}\}$. By our definition of f,

$$eq(f_{j_1}), \ldots, eq(f_{j_m}) \in G,$$

thus so is

$$\underline{=} = eq(\mathfrak{A}_\mathbf{I}) \cap eq(f_{j_1}) \cap \cdots \cap eq(f_{j_m})$$

$[eq(\mathfrak{A}_\mathbf{I})$ is needed if $m = 0]$. By the axiom of choice we can find $g' : \mathbf{I}/\underline{=} \to \bigcup_{\mathbf{i} \in \mathbf{I}} A_\mathbf{i}$ such that

$$\text{if} \quad \mathfrak{A}_\mathbf{k} \models F[f(\mathbf{k})] \qquad \text{then} \quad \mathfrak{A}_\mathbf{k} \models H[f(\mathbf{k})(j \mid g'(\mathbf{k}_{\underline{=}}))]$$

(where $\mathbf{k}_{\equiv}$ denotes the equivalence class of $\mathbf{k}$ with respect to $\equiv$) and in any case

$$g'(\mathbf{k}_{\equiv}) \in A_{\mathbf{k}}.$$

If g is defined by $g(\mathbf{k}) = g'(\mathbf{k}_{\equiv})$, then $\equiv \subset eq(g)$ and

$$\{\mathbf{i} \mid \mathfrak{A}_{\mathbf{i}} \models H[f(\mathbf{i})(j \mid g(\mathbf{i}))]\} = \{\mathbf{i} \mid \mathfrak{A}_{\mathbf{i}} \models F[f(\mathbf{i})]\} \in D,$$

and since $\equiv \in G$, $g \in \prod_{\mathbf{I}} A_{\mathbf{i}} \mid G$, so by induction

$$\prod_{\mathbf{I}} \mathfrak{A}_{\mathbf{i}}/D \mid G \models H[f(j \mid g)/D], \qquad \text{thus} \quad \prod_{\mathbf{I}} \mathfrak{A}_{\mathbf{i}}/D \mid G \models F[f/D].$$

COROLLARY 2.6.3. If $eq(\mathfrak{A}_{\mathbf{I}}) \in G \subset H$ then

$$\prod_{\mathbf{I}} \mathfrak{A}_{\mathbf{i}}/D \mid G < \prod_{\mathbf{I}} \mathfrak{A}_{\mathbf{i}}/D \mid H.$$

Proof: By Theorem 2.6.2 for $f/D \in (\prod_{\mathbf{I}} A_{\mathbf{i}}/D \mid G)^{\omega}$,

$$\prod_{\mathbf{I}} \mathfrak{A}_{\mathbf{i}}/D \mid G \models F[f/D] \qquad \text{iff} \quad \{\mathbf{i} \mid \mathfrak{A}_{\mathbf{i}} \models F[f(\mathbf{i})]\} \in D$$

iff

$$\prod_{\mathbf{I}} \mathfrak{A}_{\mathbf{i}}/D \mid H \models F[f/D].$$

COROLLARY 2.6.4. $j_{\mathfrak{A}}: \mathfrak{A} \ll' \mathfrak{A}^{\mathbf{I}}/D \mid G$.

Proof: Let $\mathfrak{B}/t = \mathfrak{A}$. Then

$$j_{\mathfrak{A}} = j_{\mathfrak{B}}: \mathfrak{B} \cong \mathfrak{B}^{\mathbf{I}}/D \mid \{\mathbf{I} \times \mathbf{I}\} < \mathfrak{B}^{\mathbf{I}}/D \mid G,$$

and

$$(\mathfrak{B}^{\mathbf{I}}/D \mid G)/t = \mathfrak{A}^{\mathbf{I}}/D \mid G.$$

We now proceed to show the converse, namely, if $\mathfrak{A} \ll' \mathfrak{B}$ then for some $\mathbf{I}$, D, G, $\mathfrak{B} \cong \mathfrak{A}^{\mathbf{I}}/D \mid G$. First we need:

LEMMA 2.6.5. Let $B \subset \prod_{\mathbf{I}} A_{\mathbf{i}}/D$. Then $B = \prod_{\mathbf{I}} A_{\mathbf{i}}/D \mid G$ for some filter G on $\mathbf{I} \times \mathbf{I}$ with $eq(\mathfrak{A}_{\mathbf{I}}) \in G$ iff for every $n < \omega$,

$$f_1/D, \ldots, f_n/D \in B \qquad \text{and} \qquad g/D \in \prod_{\mathbf{I}} A_{\mathbf{i}}/D,$$

$$\text{if} \quad eq(f_1) \cap \cdots \cap eq(f_n) \cap eq(\mathfrak{A}_{\mathbf{I}}) \subset eq(g),$$

$$\text{then} \quad g/D \in B.$$

Proof: If

$$B = \prod_{\mathbf{I}} A_{\mathbf{i}}/D \mid G \qquad \text{as above,}$$

$$f_1/D, \ldots, f_n/D \in B,$$

and

$$eq(f_1) \cap \cdots \cap eq(f_n) \cap eq(\mathfrak{A}_{\mathbf{I}}) \subset eq(g) \qquad \left(g/D \in \prod_{\mathbf{I}} A_{\mathbf{i}}/D\right),$$

then for some $f_1' \in f_1/D, \ldots, f_n' \in f_n/D$,

$$eq(f_1'), \ldots, eq(f_n') \in G.$$

Then there is a $g' \in g/D$ such that

$$eq(\mathfrak{A}_{\mathbf{I}}) \cap \cdots \cap eq(f_n') \subset eq(g')$$

(a proof we leave for the reader in Problem 2.6.2). But then

$$g/D = g'/D \in \prod_{\mathbf{I}} \mathfrak{A}_{\mathbf{i}}/D \mid G.$$

Conversely, let

$$G = \{a \subset \mathbf{I} \times \mathbf{I} \mid \text{for some } n < \omega,\ f_1, \ldots, f_n \in \textstyle\prod_{\mathbf{I}} A_{\mathbf{i}},\ f_1/D, \ldots, f_n/D \in B \text{ and } eq(\mathfrak{A}_{\mathbf{I}}) \cap \cdots \cap eq(f_n) \subset a\}.$$

Since $= \subset eq(f)$ for every $f \in \prod_{\mathbf{I}} A_{\mathbf{i}}$, G is a filter on $\mathbf{I} \times \mathbf{I}$; clearly

$$eq(\mathfrak{A}_{\mathbf{I}}) \in G.$$

If $f/D \in B$ then $eq(f) \in G$, so

$$f/D \in \prod_{\mathbf{I}} A_{\mathbf{i}}/D \mid G, \qquad \text{thus} \quad B \subset \prod_{\mathbf{I}} A_{\mathbf{i}}/D \mid G.$$

But if $g/D \in \prod_{\mathbf{I}} A_{\mathbf{i}}/D \mid G$, then for some $g' \in g/D$, $eq(g') \in G$, so

$$eq(\mathfrak{A}_{\mathbf{I}}) \cap \cdots \cap eq(f_n) \subset eq(g') \qquad \text{for some} \quad f_1/D, \ldots, f_n/D \in B,$$

so by hypothesis,

$$g/D \in B, \qquad \text{thus} \quad \prod_{\mathbf{I}} A_{\mathbf{i}}/D \mid G = B.$$

Since in the above proof (and in Problem 2.6.2) we at no point use the fact that D is an ultrafilter, our result holds for arbitrary limit reduced products.

THEOREM 2.6.6. $\mathfrak{A} \ll' \mathfrak{B}$ iff for some set $\mathbf{I}$, ultrafilter D on $\mathbf{I}$ and filter G on $\mathbf{I} \times \mathbf{I}$, $\mathfrak{B} \cong \mathfrak{A}^{\mathbf{I}}/D \mid G$.

Proof: One way has already been shown. Thus assume that $\mathfrak{A} \ll' \mathfrak{B}$. Then

$$\mathfrak{A}' <' \mathfrak{B}' \qquad \text{for some} \quad \mathfrak{A}', \mathfrak{B}'$$

such that

$$\mathfrak{A}'/t = \mathfrak{A}, \qquad \mathfrak{B}'/t = \mathfrak{B},$$

and $\mathfrak{A}'$ has on it all possible relations on A. By Lemma 2.4.2,

$$\mathfrak{B}' \cong \mathfrak{C} \qquad \text{for some} \quad \mathfrak{C} < \mathfrak{A}'^{\mathbf{I}}/D.$$

We would like to find a filter G on $\mathbf{I} \times \mathbf{I}$ such that $A^{\mathbf{I}}/D \mid G = C$. It will suffice by Lemma 2.6.5 to show that for each $f_1/D, \ldots, f_m/D \in C$, $g \in A^{\mathbf{I}}$,

$$\text{if} \quad eq(f_1) \cap \cdots \cap eq(f_m) \cap \mathbf{I} \times \mathbf{I} \subset eq(g), \qquad \text{then} \quad g/D \in C.$$

For such $f_1, \ldots, f_m, g$, let

$$k = \{\langle f_1(\mathbf{i}), \ldots, f_m(\mathbf{i}), g(\mathbf{i})\rangle \mid \mathbf{i} \in \mathbf{I}\}.$$

$$\mathfrak{A}' \models (\forall v_1) \cdots (\forall v_{m+2})(P_k(v_1, \ldots, v_{m+1}) \wedge P_k(v_1, \ldots, v_m, v_{m+2}) \\ \rightarrow v_{m+1} = v_{m+2})$$

(where P_k corresponds to k) thus so do $\mathfrak{A}'^{\mathbf{I}}/D$, $\mathfrak{C}$. Now let k' on $\mathfrak{C}$, k'' on $\mathfrak{A}^{\mathbf{I}}/D$, correspond to k. Since

$$\{\mathbf{i} \mid \langle f_1(\mathbf{i}), \ldots, f_m(\mathbf{i}), g(\mathbf{i})\rangle \in k\} = \mathbf{I} \in D,$$

$$\langle f_1/D, \ldots, f_m/D, g/D\rangle \in k'',$$

thus

$$\mathfrak{A}'^{\mathbf{I}}/D \models (\exists v_0)P_k(v_1, \ldots, v_m, v_0)[f_1/D, \ldots, f_m/D],$$

and since

$$\mathfrak{C} < \mathfrak{A}'^{\mathbf{I}}/D \qquad \text{and} \qquad f_1/D, \ldots, f_m/D \in C,$$

so does $\mathfrak{C}$. Thus let $\langle f_1/D, \ldots, f_m/D, x\rangle \in k'$. Then

$$\langle f_1/D, \ldots, f_m/D, x\rangle, \qquad \langle f_1/D, \ldots, f_m/D, g/D\rangle \in k'',$$

so $x = g/D$. Thus

$$\langle f_1/D, \ldots, f_m/D, g/D\rangle \in k' \subset C^{m+1},$$

so $g/D \in C$.

COROLLARY 2.6.7. φ: $\mathfrak{A} \ll' \mathfrak{B}$ iff there is a limit ultrapower $\mathfrak{A}^{\mathbf{I}}/D \mid G$ and an isomorphism ψ: $\mathfrak{B} \cong \mathfrak{A}^{\mathbf{I}}/D \mid G$ such that $j_{\mathfrak{A}} = \psi \circ \varphi$.

The proof is assigned as a problem.

COROLLARY 2.6.8. (a) If $\mathfrak{A}_\omega$ is an ultralimit of $\mathfrak{A}$, then $\mathfrak{A}_\omega$ is a limit ultrapower of $\mathfrak{A}$. (This justifies Keisler's use of the term "strong limit ultrapower" for ultralimit.)

(b) $\mathfrak{A} \equiv \mathfrak{B}$ iff for some $\mathbf{I}$, D, G, $\mathbf{J}$, E, H,

$$\mathfrak{A}^{\mathbf{I}}/D \mid G \cong \mathfrak{B}^{\mathbf{J}}/E \mid H.$$

Proof: (a) follows from the fact that $\mathfrak{A} \ll' \mathfrak{A}_\omega$ and from Theorem 2.6.6, while (b) follows from (a) and the fact that $\mathfrak{A} \equiv \mathfrak{B}$ iff $\mathfrak{A}$, $\mathfrak{B}$ have isomorphic ultralimits.

COROLLARY 2.6.9. (a) $K \in EC_\Delta$ iff K is closed under isomorphisms and limit ultraproducts and $M^t \sim K$ closed under limit ultrapowers.

(b) $K \in EC$ iff K, $M^t \sim K$ are both closed under isomorphisms and limit ultraproducts.

Naturally, corresponding changes may be made in other facts shown in Sections 2.4 and 2.5. At this point we alter Keisler's approach slightly. Keisler did not derive Theorem 2.6.12 in his papers, although he hinted at the result and did some related work. In what follows for the sake of convenience, if $\underline{=}' \subset \underline{=}$, $\underline{=}$, $\underline{=}'$ equivalence relations on $\mathbf{I}$, we identify $(\mathbf{I}/\underline{=}')/\underline{=}$ with $\mathbf{I}/\underline{=}$.

DEFINITION 2.6.10. Let $\{\mathfrak{A}_{\mathbf{i}} \mid \mathbf{i} \in \mathbf{I}\}$, $\mathbf{I}$, D, G, be as in Definition 2.6.1, $\underline{=}$ an equivalence relation on $\mathbf{I}$. For $\mathbf{i} \in \mathbf{I}$,

$$\mathbf{i}_{\underline{=}} = \{\mathbf{j} \mid \mathbf{j} \underline{=} \mathbf{i}\}, \qquad \mathbf{I}_{\underline{=}} = \mathbf{I}/\underline{=}, \qquad \text{and} \qquad D_{\underline{=}} = \{X \subset \mathbf{I}_{\underline{=}} \mid \bigcup X \in D\}.$$

If $\underline{=} \subset eq(\mathfrak{A}_{\mathbf{I}})$, $\underline{=} \in G$, define

$$\mathfrak{A}_{\mathbf{i}_{\underline{=}}} = \mathfrak{A}_{\mathbf{i}},$$

$$j^{\underline{=}}\colon \prod_{\mathbf{I}} \mathfrak{A}_{\mathbf{i}_{\underline{=}}}/D_{\underline{=}} \to \prod_{\mathbf{I}} \mathfrak{A}_{\mathbf{i}}/D \mid G \qquad \text{by} \quad j^{\underline{=}}(f/D_{\underline{=}}) = \hat{f}/D,$$

where for $\mathbf{i} \in \mathbf{I}$, $\hat{f}(\mathbf{i}) = f(\mathbf{i}_{\underline{=}})$. $j^{\underline{=}}$ is called the natural injection of

$$\prod_{\mathbf{I}_{\underline{=}}} \mathfrak{A}_{\mathbf{i}_{\underline{=}}}/D_{\underline{=}} \qquad \text{into} \qquad \prod_{\mathbf{I}} \mathfrak{A}_{\mathbf{i}}/D \mid G.$$

Our assertion that

$$j^{\underline{=}}\colon \prod_{\mathbf{I}_{\underline{=}}} \mathfrak{A}_{\mathbf{i}_{\underline{=}}}/D_{\underline{=}} \to \prod_{\mathbf{I}} \mathfrak{A}_{\mathbf{i}}/D \mid G$$

holds because

$$\text{if} \quad f\colon \mathbf{I}_{\underline{=}} \to \bigcup_{\mathbf{I}_{\underline{=}}} A_{\mathbf{i}_{\underline{=}}} \qquad \text{with} \quad f(\mathbf{i}_{\underline{=}}) \in A_{\mathbf{i}_{\underline{=}}}$$

$$\text{then} \quad \hat{f}\colon \mathbf{I} \to \bigcup_{\mathbf{I}} A_{\mathbf{i}} \qquad \text{with} \quad \hat{f}(\mathbf{i}) \in A_{\mathbf{i}}$$

and $\underline{=} \subset eq(f)$, since if $\mathbf{i} \underline{=} \mathbf{j}$ then

$$\hat{f}(\mathbf{i}) = f(\mathbf{i}_{\underline{=}}) = f(\mathbf{j}_{\underline{=}}) = \hat{f}(\mathbf{j}).$$

Also, for $f, g \in \prod_{\mathbf{I}_=} \mathfrak{A}_{\mathbf{i}_=}$,

$$\{\mathbf{i}_= \mid f(\mathbf{i}_=) = g(\mathbf{i}_=)\} \in D_=$$

iff

$$\{\mathbf{i} \mid \hat{f}(\mathbf{i}) = \hat{g}(\mathbf{i})\} = \bigcup \{\mathbf{i}_= \mid f(\mathbf{i}_=) = g(\mathbf{i}_=)\} \in D.$$

Thus f/D is well-defined; our definition of $D_=$ assures us that $j^=$ is an injection. This new definition of natural injection extends the one in 2.1.19, for $j_{\mathfrak{A}}\colon \mathfrak{A} \to \mathfrak{A}^{\mathbf{I}}/D$ is essentially

$$j^{\mathbf{I}\times\mathbf{I}}\colon \mathfrak{A}^{\mathbf{I}\mathbf{I}\times\mathbf{I}}/D_{\mathbf{I}\times\mathbf{I}} \to \mathfrak{A}^{\mathbf{I}}/D = \mathfrak{A}^{\mathbf{I}}/D \mid G_=.$$

Finally, we leave the verification that $D_=$ is in fact a filter (an ultrafilter if D is) to the reader.

Definition 2.6.11. A directed system of reduced (ultra-) products of $\{\mathfrak{A}_{\mathbf{i}} \mid \mathbf{i} \in \mathbf{I}\}$ and their natural injections is a directed set $\langle X, \leq\rangle$ together with a collection $\{\langle \mathbf{I}_x, D_x\rangle \mid x \in X\}$ of (ultra-) filter pairs, a set

$$\{\mathfrak{A}_{\mathbf{i}_x} \mid \mathbf{i}_x \in \mathbf{I}_x\}$$

for each $x \in X$, and a set of equivalence relations

$$\{\equiv_{yx} \mid x \leq y,\ x, y \in X\}$$

such that

(i) if $x \in X$, then $\{\mathfrak{A}_{\mathbf{i}_x} \mid \mathbf{i}_x \in \mathbf{I}_x\} = \{\mathfrak{A}_{\mathbf{i}} \mid \mathbf{i} \in \mathbf{I}\}$;
(ii) $\mathscr{D}_{\equiv yx} = \mathbf{I}_y$, $\mathbf{I}_{y\equiv yx} = \mathbf{I}_x$, $\equiv_{xx} = =$, $D_{y\equiv yx} = D_x$;
(iii) if $\mathbf{i}_y \in \mathbf{I}_y$, then $\mathfrak{A}_{\mathbf{i}_y} = \mathfrak{A}_{\mathbf{i}_{y\equiv yx}}$;
(iv) if $x \leq y \leq z$, then $\mathbf{i}_{z\equiv zx} = (\mathbf{i}_{z\equiv zy})_{\equiv yx}$.

The natural injections (indeed the reduced products) are not mentioned explicitly in the above definition, but clearly we have in mind $\prod_{\mathbf{I}_x} \mathfrak{A}_{\mathbf{i}_x}/D_x$, and for $x \leq y$,

$$j^{\equiv yx}\colon \prod_{\mathbf{I}_x} \mathfrak{A}_{\mathbf{i}_x}/D_x \to \prod_{\mathbf{I}_y} \mathfrak{A}_{\mathbf{i}_y}/D_y.$$

The conditions of our definition make

$$\mathscr{A} = \left\{\prod_{\mathbf{I}_x} \mathfrak{A}_{\mathbf{i}_x}/D_x \mid x \in X\right\} \cup \{j^{\equiv yx} \mid x \leq y,\ x, y \in X\}$$

a directed system, for $j^{\equiv xx}$ is always the identity map on $\prod_{\mathbf{I}_x} \mathfrak{A}_{\mathbf{i}_x}/D_x$, we have already verified

$$j^{\equiv yx}\colon \prod_{\mathbf{I}_x} \mathfrak{A}_{\mathbf{i}_x}/D_x \to \prod_{\mathbf{I}_y} \mathfrak{A}_{\mathbf{i}_y}/D_y$$

for $x \leq y$, and if $x \leq y \leq z$, then

$$j^{\equiv zx}(f/D_x) = h/D_z \qquad \text{for } f \in \prod_{\mathbf{I}_x} A_{\mathbf{i}_x},$$

where $f(\mathbf{i}_{z\equiv_{zx}}) = h(\mathbf{i}_z)$. However,

$$j^{\equiv_{zy}} \circ j^{\equiv_{yx}}(f/D_x) = j^{\equiv_{zy}}(g/D_y),$$

where $f(\mathbf{i}_{y\equiv_{yx}}) = g(\mathbf{i}_y)$, and $j^{\equiv_{zy}}(g/D_y) = h/D_z$ for

$$h(\mathbf{i}_z) = f(\mathbf{i}_{z\equiv_{zx}}) = f((\mathbf{i}_{z\equiv_{zy}})_{\equiv_{xy}}) = g(\mathbf{i}_{z\equiv_{zy}}).$$

The object limit (direct limit) of a system $\mathscr{A}$ obtained in this manner is called an object (direct) limit of a directed system of ultraproducts and their natural maps.

Theorem 2.6.12. If $\mathfrak{B}$ is isomorphic to a limit reduced product of $\{\mathfrak{A}_\mathbf{i} \mid \mathbf{i} \in \mathbf{I}\}$, then $\mathfrak{B}$ is an object limit of a directed system of reduced products of $\{\mathfrak{A}_\mathbf{i} \mid \mathbf{i} \in \mathbf{I}\}$ and their natural injections.

Proof: Let

$$X = \{\equiv \in G \mid \equiv \text{ is an equivalence relation on } \mathbf{I} \text{ and } \equiv \subset eq(\mathfrak{A}_\mathbf{I})\},$$

$\leq \; = \; \supset$. Then, since each $x \in X$ is an equivalence relation $\subset eq(\mathfrak{A}_\mathbf{I})$, $\langle \mathbf{I}_x, D_x \rangle$ are defined, as well as $\mathbf{i}_x$, $\mathfrak{A}_{\mathbf{i}_x}$ for $\mathbf{i} \in \mathbf{I}$ (thus $\mathbf{i}_x \in \mathbf{I}_x$). If $x \leq y$, $x, y \in X$, then $y \subset x \subset eq(\mathfrak{A}_\mathbf{I})$, so we may set

$$\equiv_{yx} = \{\langle \mathbf{i}_y, \mathbf{j}_y \rangle \mid \langle \mathbf{i}, \mathbf{j} \rangle \in x\}.$$

Verification of (i) through (iv) of Definition 2.6.11 are left to the reader. Thus we need only check that $\prod_\mathbf{I} \mathfrak{A}_\mathbf{i}/D \mid G$ is an object limit of the system $\mathscr{A}$ we obtain in the manner described in the discussion following Definition 2.6.11. In fact, we show that

$$\left\{\prod_\mathbf{I} \mathfrak{A}_\mathbf{i}/D \mid G\right\} \cup \left\{j^x : \prod_{\mathbf{I}_x} \mathfrak{A}_{\mathbf{i}_x}/D_x \to \prod_\mathbf{I} \mathfrak{A}_\mathbf{i}/D \mid G\right\}$$

is a direct limit for $\mathscr{A}$. The same proof that showed that $j^{\equiv_{zy}} \circ j^{\equiv_{yx}} = j^{\equiv_{zx}}$ now shows that $j^y \circ j^{\equiv_{yx}} = j^x$ for $x \leq y$, so it only remains to check that

$$\bigcup_{x \in X} j^x \left[\prod_{\mathbf{I}_x} A_{\mathbf{i}_x}/D_x\right] = \prod_\mathbf{I} A_\mathbf{i}/D \mid G \text{ (see Problem 2.4.5).}$$

However, if $f/D \in \prod_\mathbf{I} A_\mathbf{i}/D \mid G$, then for some $g \in \prod_\mathbf{I} A_\mathbf{i}$,

$$g \in f/D \qquad \text{and} \qquad eq(g) \in G.$$

Let $x = eq(\mathfrak{A}_\mathbf{I}) \cap eq(g)$, clearly $x \in X$. We may define $g' : \mathbf{I}_x \to \bigcup_\mathbf{I} A_\mathbf{i}$ by $g'(\mathbf{i}_x) = g(\mathbf{i})$, for

$$\text{if} \quad \langle \mathbf{i}, \mathbf{j} \rangle \in x \qquad \text{then} \quad g(\mathbf{i}) = g(\mathbf{j}),$$

so g' is well-defined. Thus

$$f/D = g/D = j^x(g'/D_x) \in j^x \left[\prod_{\mathbf{I}_x} A_{\mathbf{i}_x}/D_x\right].$$

COROLLARY 2.6.13. The following are equivalent:

(i) $\mathfrak{A} \ll' \mathfrak{B}$.
(ii) $\mathfrak{B}$ is isomorphic to a limit ultrapower of $\mathfrak{A}$.
(iii) $\mathfrak{B}$ is an object limit of a directed system of ultrapowers of $\mathfrak{A}$ and their natural injections.

Proof: (i) –> (ii) by Theorem 2.6.6 and (ii) –> (iii) by Theorem 2.6.12. For (iii) –> (i), note that such an object limit is the reduct of the union of a system directed by $<$ in the type having a predicate for each possible relation on A (see, for example, the proof of Theorem 2.1.18(c)), and any such union has the property that $\mathfrak{A}' <' \mathfrak{B}'$ (where $\mathfrak{B}'$ is our union, $\mathfrak{A}'$ a structure with appropriate reduct $\mathfrak{A}$ and each possible relation on A), thus $\mathfrak{A} \ll' \mathfrak{B}$.

Note that for some theorems on limit ultrapowers we have not stated corresponding facts on limit ultraproducts. The statement of a theorem closing this gap is below (Theorem 2.6.15), but we postpone the proof and leave it for the reader in Problem 2.6.13.

DEFINITION 2.6.14. Let $K \subset M^t$, $\mathfrak{B} \in M^t$. $K \ll' \mathfrak{B}$ iff whenever $t \subset t'$ and $K = K'/t = \{\mathfrak{A}/t \mid \mathfrak{A} \in K'\}$, $K' \subset M^{t'}$, then for some $\mathfrak{B}' \in M^{t'}$, $T(K') \subset T(\mathfrak{B}')$ and $\mathfrak{B}'/t = \mathfrak{B}$.

THEOREM 2.6.15. The following are equivalent:

(i) $K \ll' \mathfrak{B}$.
(ii) $\mathfrak{B}$ is isomorphic to a limit ultraproduct of elements of K.
(iii) $\mathfrak{B}$ is an object limit of a directed system of ultraproducts of elements of K and their natural injections.

Problems

‡2.6.1 (a) Give an example of a filter $G \subset \mathscr{P}\mathbf{I} \times \mathbf{I}$ such that $\{\mathbf{I} \times \mathbf{I}) \neq G$ but

$$\mathfrak{A}^{\mathbf{I}}/D \mid \{\mathbf{I} \times \mathbf{I}\} = \mathfrak{A}^{\mathbf{I}}/D \mid G.$$

Also give an example of a filter H such that

$$\mathfrak{A}^{\mathbf{I}}/D \mid H = \mathfrak{A}^{\mathbf{I}}/D, \qquad \text{but} \qquad H \neq G_{=}.$$

(b) Show that $X = \prod_{\mathrm{I}} A_{\mathrm{i}}/D \mid G$ contains all distinguished elements of $\prod_{\mathrm{I}} \mathfrak{A}_{\mathrm{i}}/D$ to justify the definition $\prod_{\mathrm{I}} \mathfrak{A}_{\mathrm{i}}/D \mid G = (\prod_{\mathrm{I}} \mathfrak{A}_{\mathrm{i}}/D) \mid X$ used in (iii).
(c) Prove Corollaries 6.7 and 6.9.

‡2.6.2 (a) Let

$$f_1/D, \ldots, f_n/D \in \prod_{\mathbf{I}} A_{\mathbf{i}}/D \mid G,$$

$$eq(\mathfrak{A}_{\mathbf{I}}) \cap eq(f_1) \cap \cdots \cap eq(f_n) \subset eq(g),$$

$$g \in \prod_{\mathbf{I}} A_{\mathbf{i}}.$$

Show that for some $e \in G$, $d \in D$, e is an equivalence relation and $e \cap d \times d \subset eq(g)$.

(b) Let $h: d \to \cup_{\mathbf{i} \in d} A_{\mathbf{i}}$ be such that $h(\mathbf{i}) \in A_{\mathbf{i}}$, and let $e \cap \mathscr{D}h \times \mathscr{D}h \subset eq(h)$. Show that h can be extended to a function $g' \in \prod_{\mathbf{I}} A_{\mathbf{i}}$ such that $e \subset eq(g')$. (HINT: By Zorn's lemma find a maximal h^* such that $h \subset h^*$ and $e \cap \mathscr{D}h^* \times \mathscr{D}h^* \subset eq(h^*)$. Then show that $\mathscr{D}h^* = \mathbf{I}$.)

(c) Use (a) and (b) to show that if

$$f_1/D, \ldots, f_n/D \in \prod_{\mathbf{I}} A_{\mathbf{i}}/D \mid G$$

and

$$eq(\mathfrak{A}_{\mathbf{I}}) \cap eq(f_1) \cap \cdots \cap eq(f_n) \subset eq(g),$$

then

$$g/D \in \prod_{\mathbf{I}} A_{\mathbf{i}}/D \mid G.$$

DEFINITION 2.6.16. Let X be a set of structures of type t. X is complete iff $X \neq \phi$, and for every integer $n \geq 1$, every $f \in \prod_{\mathfrak{A} \in X} \mathscr{P}(A^n)$ and every $f \in \prod_{\mathfrak{A} \in X} A$, there is a $\gamma \in \Gamma$ such that for each $\mathfrak{A} \in X$, $f(\mathfrak{A}) = R_\gamma^{\mathfrak{A}}$. $\mathfrak{A}$ is a complete structure iff $\{\mathfrak{A}\}$ is a complete set of structures. (The definition of a complete set of structures, which is after Keisler, is based on Rabin's earlier definition of a complete structure.)

Intuitively, for every possible collection of relations, we can find a γ giving us that particular set. A single structure is complete iff it already has on it every possible relation. Note that a structure $\mathfrak{A}$ of infinite cardinality has

$$c(A) + c(\mathscr{P}A) + c(\mathscr{P}(A \times A)) + c(\mathscr{P}(A^3)) + \cdots = 2^{c(A)}$$

possible relations on it.

2.6.3 (a) Show that every structure is the reduct of a complete structure.

(b) If X is a set of structures of type t, prove that X is the set of t-reducts of a complete set of structures X'. If $X' \subset M^{t'}$, what is $c(t')$?

2.6.4 (a) Let $\mathfrak{A}$ be a complete structure. Show that $\mathfrak{A} \equiv \mathfrak{B}$ iff $\mathfrak{A} \ll' \mathfrak{B}$.

(b) If $\mathfrak{A}_{\mathbf{i}} \mid \mathbf{i} \in \mathbf{I}\}$ is a complete set of structures, then for each $\mathbf{i}, \mathbf{j} \in \mathbf{I}$, if $\mathfrak{A}_{\mathbf{i}} \equiv \mathfrak{A}_{\mathbf{j}}$, $\mathfrak{A}_{\mathbf{i}} \cong \mathfrak{A}_{\mathbf{j}}$. How does this make itself compatible with Löwenheim-Skolem?

2.6.5 (a) If $\mathfrak{A} \equiv \mathfrak{B}$, show that there is a $\mathfrak{C}$ such that

$$\mathfrak{A} \ll' \mathfrak{C}, \qquad \mathfrak{B} \ll' \mathfrak{C}, \qquad \text{and} \qquad c(\mathfrak{C}) \leq 2^{c(\mathfrak{A})} + 2^{c(\mathfrak{B})}.$$

(HINT: Use Definition 2.6.16, Problem 2.6.3.)

(b) If $\mathfrak{A} \equiv \mathfrak{B}$, show that there are isomorphic limit ultrapowers of $\mathfrak{A}$ and $\mathfrak{B}$ of cardinality at most $2^{c(\mathfrak{A})} + 2^{c(\mathfrak{B})}$.

2.6.6 (a) Show that $K \in EC_\Delta$ iff K is closed under limit ultraproducts and isomorphic images, and $M^t \sim K$ closed under ultralimits (strong limit ultrapowers).

(b) Let $K \in EC_\Delta$, $L = \{\mathfrak{B} \mid \text{for some } \mathfrak{A} \in K, \mathfrak{B} \subset \mathfrak{A}\}$. Show that $L \in \forall C_\Delta$.

2.6.7 If $\equiv$ is an equivalence relation on $\mathbf{I}$ such that if $\mathbf{i} \equiv \mathbf{j}$ then $\mathfrak{A}_\mathbf{i} = \mathfrak{A}_\mathbf{j}$, show that

$$\prod_{\mathbf{I}} \mathfrak{A}_\mathbf{i}/D \mid G_{\equiv} \cong \prod_{\mathbf{I}_{\equiv}} \mathfrak{A}_{\mathbf{i}_{\equiv}}/D_{\equiv}.$$

(Note that this generalizes the "triviality" comments following Definition 2.6.1.)

2.6.8 Let t be countable. Show that for some $\mathfrak{A}, \mathfrak{B} \in M^t$, $\mathfrak{A} <' \mathfrak{B}$ but not $\mathfrak{A} \ll' \mathfrak{B}$. Is this true for general t?

2.6.9 Let $\mathfrak{m}$ be an infinite cardinal, $c(\mathfrak{m}^\omega) = \mathfrak{m}$. Show that if $c(\mathfrak{A}) = \mathfrak{m}$, there is a $\mathfrak{B}$ such that $c(\mathfrak{B}) = \mathfrak{m}$ and $\mathfrak{A} < \mathfrak{B}$ ($\mathfrak{A} \neq \mathfrak{B}$). (Some of the above result and that in 2.6.8 was shown in Rabin [2].)

2.6.10 Keisler originally defined limit ultraproducts as follows: Let $\mathbf{I}$, $\mathbf{J}$ be sets and define

$$\prod_{\mathbf{I}\times\mathbf{J}} A_\mathbf{i}/D = \prod_{\mathbf{I}\times\mathbf{J}} A_{\langle \mathbf{i},\mathbf{j}\rangle}/D$$

for D a filter on $\mathbf{I} \times \mathbf{J}$, where $A_{\langle \mathbf{i},\mathbf{j}\rangle} = A_\mathbf{i}$, and we are given $\{A_\mathbf{i} \mid \mathbf{i} \in \mathbf{I}\}$. $\prod_{\mathbf{I}\times\mathbf{J}} \mathfrak{A}_\mathbf{i}/D$ is defined similarly. For $f \in \prod_{\mathbf{I}\times\mathbf{J}} A_\mathbf{i}$, set

$$el(f) = \{\langle \mathbf{i}, \mathbf{j}, \mathbf{j}'\rangle \mid f(\langle \mathbf{i}, \mathbf{j}\rangle) = f(\langle \mathbf{i}, \mathbf{j}'\rangle)\}.$$

If D is a filter on $\mathbf{I} \times \mathbf{J}$, G a filter on $\mathbf{I} \times \mathbf{J} \times \mathbf{J}$ then

$$\prod_{\mathbf{I}\times\mathbf{J}} A_\mathbf{i}/D \mid G = \{f/D \in \prod_{\mathbf{I}\times\mathbf{J}} A_\mathbf{i}/D \mid el(f) \in G\},$$

$$\prod_{\mathbf{I}\times\mathbf{J}} \mathfrak{A}_\mathbf{i}/D \mid G = (\prod_{\mathbf{I}\times\mathbf{J}} \mathfrak{A}_\mathbf{i}/D) \mid (\prod_{\mathbf{I}\times\mathbf{J}} A_\mathbf{i}/D \mid G).$$

The result is called a limit reduced product and a limit ultraproduct if D is an ultrafilter.

(a) Show each of Keisler's limit reduced products to be one of ours.

(b) Show each of ours to be isomorphic to one of his. (HINT: Let $\mathbf{I}' = \mathbf{I}_{eq(\mathfrak{A}_\mathbf{I})}$ and show that there is a $\mathbf{J}$ and an equivalence relation $\equiv$ on $\mathbf{I}' \times \mathbf{J}$ such that $\mathbf{I} = (\mathbf{I}' \times \mathbf{J})_{\equiv}$ and an ultrafilter D' on $\mathbf{I}' \times \mathbf{J}$ such that $D'_{\equiv} = D$. Now find an appropriate G'.)

We now ask whether the limit ultrapower construction actually gives more structures than the ultralimit construction. This and similar questions are answered in an example from Keisler [1], which we study in Problems 2.6.11 and 2.6.12. We shall use the following notations throughout: Let $\mathfrak{A} \in M^t$. Then

$K_0(\mathfrak{A}) = \{\mathfrak{B} \mid \mathfrak{B} \cong \mathfrak{A}\}$.
$K_1(\mathfrak{A}) = \{\mathfrak{B} \mid \text{for some ultrafilter pair, } \langle \mathbf{I}, D\rangle, \mathfrak{B} \cong \mathfrak{A}^\mathbf{I}/D\}$.
$K_2(\mathfrak{A}) = \{\mathfrak{B} \mid \text{for some ultralimit } \mathfrak{A}_\omega \text{ of } \mathfrak{A}, \mathfrak{B} \cong \mathfrak{A}_\omega\}$.
$K_3(\mathfrak{A}) = \{\mathfrak{B} \mid \mathfrak{A} \ll' \mathfrak{B}\}$.
$K_4(\mathfrak{A}) = \{\mathfrak{B} \mid \mathfrak{A} <' \mathfrak{B}\}$.

Clearly, for every $\mathfrak{A}$,

$$K_0(\mathfrak{A}) \subset K_1(\mathfrak{A}) \subset K_2(\mathfrak{A}) \subset K_3(\mathfrak{A}) \subset K_4(\mathfrak{A});$$

and Keisler provides us with a single $\mathfrak{A}$ for which all the inclusions just mentioned are proper. For the problems to follow, let $\mathfrak{A} = \langle \mathbb{Q}, < \rangle$.

2.6.11 (a) ($K_0(\mathfrak{A}) \neq K_1(\mathfrak{A})$) Show that for no nontrivial ultrapower do we have $\mathfrak{A} \cong \mathfrak{A}^{\mathbf{I}}/D$ (i.e., if $j_{\mathfrak{A}}[A] \neq A^{\mathbf{I}}/D$, $\mathfrak{A} \not\cong \mathfrak{A}^{\mathbf{I}}/D$).

(b) ($K_1(\mathfrak{A}) \neq K_2(\mathfrak{A})$) Let $\mathfrak{A}_0 = \mathfrak{A}$, and assume that we have $\mathfrak{A}_n$. Then we can find an ultrafilter pair such that $j_{\mathfrak{A}_n}(\mathfrak{A}_n)$ is bounded in $\mathfrak{A}_n^{\mathbf{I}}/D$. Then set

$$\langle \mathbf{I}, D\rangle = \langle \mathbf{I}_{n+1}, D_{n+1}\rangle, \ \mathfrak{A}_{n+1} = \mathfrak{A}_n^{\mathbf{I}}/D.$$

Check that the ultralimit of this sequence has a countable cofinal set, and that we can actually find these ultrafilter pairs. Now show that no nontrivial ultrapower of $\mathfrak{A}$ has a countable cofinal set, and thus that $\mathfrak{A}_\omega \notin K_1(\mathfrak{A})$.

(c) ($K_3(\mathfrak{A}) \neq K_4(\mathfrak{A})$) Let $\mathfrak{B} = \langle \mathbb{R} \sim \{0\}, < \rangle$. Show that $\mathfrak{A} <' \mathfrak{B}$, and that while there are relations $+, \cdot, 0, 1$ that when added to $\mathfrak{A}$ give us an ordered field, there are no such for $\mathfrak{B}$.

The most difficult fact to prove, $K_2(\mathfrak{A}) \neq K_3(\mathfrak{A})$, is shown in the following problem.

2.6.12 Now we assume the continuum hypothesis, $2^\omega = \omega^+$. Thus there is a complete structure $\mathfrak{A}'$ with ω^+ relations and $\mathfrak{A}$ as a $\langle 2\rangle$-reduct.

(a) Show that there is a sequence $\mathfrak{A}'_0 = \mathfrak{A}', \mathfrak{A}'_1, \mathfrak{A}'_2, \ldots$ such that for every $n < \omega$, A'_n has an upper bound b_n in the $\langle 2\rangle$-reduct of $\mathfrak{A}'_{n+1}$, and $c(\mathfrak{A}'_n) = \omega^+$, and $\mathfrak{A}'_n < \mathfrak{A}'_{n+1}$. Now let $\mathfrak{B}' = \bigcup_{n<\omega} \mathfrak{A}'_n$, $\mathfrak{B}$ be the $\langle 2\rangle$-reduct of $\mathfrak{B}'$. Show that

$$\mathfrak{A} \ll \mathfrak{B}, \qquad cf(\mathfrak{B}) = \omega, \qquad \text{and} \qquad c(\mathfrak{B}) = \omega^+.$$

(b) Assume now that $\mathfrak{B} \cong \mathfrak{C} = \bigcup_{n<\omega} \mathfrak{C}_n$, where for each n,

$$\mathfrak{C}_{n+1} \cong \mathfrak{C}_n^{\mathbf{I}_{n+1}}/D_{n+1}, \qquad \mathfrak{C}_0 = \mathfrak{A}.$$

Show that for some p, $c(\mathfrak{C}_p) = \omega^+$.

Show that for every $m \geq p$, $\mathfrak{C}_p$ is unbounded in $\mathfrak{C}_m$. Then show that $\mathfrak{C}_p$ is unbounded in $\mathfrak{C}$, thus $cf(\mathfrak{C}) \neq \omega$, a contradiction. Thus $\mathfrak{C} \notin K_2(\mathfrak{A})$. (HINT: The result of Problem 2.2.6 is useful for showing $\mathfrak{C}_p$ unbounded in $\mathfrak{C}_m$.)

‡2.6.13 We prove Theorem 2.6.15.

(a) If $K \ll' \mathfrak{B}$ show $\mathfrak{B} \cong \prod_{\mathbf{I}} \mathfrak{A}_{\mathbf{i}}/D \mid G$ for some $\{\mathfrak{A}_{\mathbf{i}} \mid \mathbf{i} \in \mathbf{I}\} \subset K$, ultrafilter D on $\mathbf{I}$ and filter G on $\mathbf{I} \times \mathbf{I}$ such that $eq(\mathfrak{A}_{\mathbf{I}}) \in G$. (This is (i) –> (ii) of Theorem 2.6.15. For its proof use Problem 2.5.10.) (ii) –> (iii) of Theorem 2.6.15 results from Theorem 2.6.12.

(b) Show that if $\underline{=} \subset eq(\mathfrak{A}_{\mathbf{I}})$ then $j^{=}: \prod_{\mathbf{I}_{=}} \mathfrak{A}_{\mathbf{i}_{=}}/D_{=} <' \prod_{\mathbf{I}} \mathfrak{A}_{\mathbf{i}}/D$, and if in addition, $\{\mathfrak{A}_{\mathbf{i}} \mid \mathbf{i} \in \mathbf{I}\} \subset K$ then $K \ll' \prod_{\mathbf{I}} \mathfrak{A}_{\mathbf{i}}/D$. Use these facts to show that if $\mathfrak{B}$ is the object limit of a directed system of ultraproducts of elements of K and their natural injections, then $K \ll' \mathfrak{B}$.

2.7 Saturated Models

In Sections 2.4 and 2.6 we have obtained results on generalizations of the ultraproduct and ultrapower constructions. Here we consider special cases of the generalized constructions.

Let $\mathfrak{A}$ be a structure, Δ any set, $a \in A^{\Delta}$. Then

$$(\mathfrak{A}, a) = \langle A, R_{\gamma}, a_{\delta}\rangle_{\gamma \in \Gamma, \delta \in \Delta}.$$

DEFINITION 2.7.1. Let $\mathfrak{m}$ be a cardinal, $\mathfrak{A} \in M^t$. Then $\mathfrak{A}$ is $\mathfrak{m}$-saturated iff whenever $c(\Delta) < \mathfrak{m}$ and $a \in A^{\Delta}$, $(\mathfrak{A}, a)$ has the finite satisfaction property.

By Theorem 2.3.10, if D is countably incomplete then $\mathfrak{A} = \prod_{\mathbf{I}} \mathfrak{A}_{\mathbf{i}}/D$ is ω^+-saturated, for if $a/D \in A^{\omega}$ then $(\mathfrak{A}, a/D) = \prod_{\mathbf{I}} (\mathfrak{A}_{\mathbf{i}}, a(\mathbf{i}))/D$ has the finite satisfaction property. The proofs of 2.7.2 and 2.7.3 are left for the reader.

LEMMA 2.7.2. The following are equivalent for infinite $\mathfrak{m}$.

(a) $\mathfrak{A}$ is $\mathfrak{m}$-saturated.

(b) For every Δ with $c(\Delta) < \mathfrak{m}$, $a \in A^{\Delta}$, $(\mathfrak{A}, a)$ is $\mathfrak{m}$-saturated.

(c) For every Δ with $c(\Delta) < \mathfrak{m}$, $a \in A^{\Delta}$, $(\mathfrak{A}, a)$ is 1-saturated.

LEMMA 2.7.3. (a) $\mathfrak{A}$ is $\mathfrak{m}$-saturated iff $\mathfrak{A}$ is $\mathfrak{n}$-saturated for every $\mathfrak{n} \leq \mathfrak{m}$.

(b) If $\mathfrak{m}$ is a limit cardinal, then $\mathfrak{A}$ is $\mathfrak{m}$-saturated iff $\mathfrak{A}$ is $\mathfrak{n}$-saturated for every $\mathfrak{n} < \mathfrak{m}$.

(c) $\mathfrak{A}$ is $\mathfrak{m}^+$-saturated iff for every Δ such that $c(\Delta) = \mathfrak{m}$ and every $a \in A^{\Delta}$, $(\mathfrak{A}, a)$ is 1-saturated, i.e., has the finite satisfaction property.

LEMMA 2.7.4. Let $c(t) + \omega \leq \mathfrak{m}$, $\mathscr{A} = \{\mathfrak{A}_{\alpha} \mid \alpha \in \mathfrak{m}^+\}$ be such that for every $\alpha, \beta \in \mathfrak{m}^+$, if $\alpha < \beta$ then $\mathfrak{A}_{\alpha} < \mathfrak{A}_{\beta}$, and such that for some $\gamma \in \mathfrak{m}^+$, if $\alpha \geq \gamma$ then $\mathfrak{A}_{\alpha+1}$ always has the finite satisfaction property for A_{α}. Then $\mathfrak{A} = \bigcup \mathscr{A}$ has the finite satisfaction property.

Proof: Let $S \subset V_0^t$, and suppose that for every $S' \in \mathscr{P}^{\omega}(S)$ we have an $a_{S'} \in A$ such that $\mathfrak{A} \models F[a_{S'}]$ for every $F \in S'$. For each S', let $a_{S'} \in A_{\alpha_{S'}}$, as we may by Theorem 1.7.6, since $\mathfrak{A}_{\alpha} < \mathfrak{A}$ for $\alpha < \mathfrak{m}^+$ (by Theorem 1.7.8 on ascending unions of $<$-chains).

However, $c(S) \leq \mathfrak{m}$ and $c(\mathscr{P}^{\omega}(S)) \leq c(S) + \omega \leq \mathfrak{m}$. Let

$$\alpha = \bigcup_{S' \in \mathscr{P}^{\omega}(S)} \alpha_{S'}.$$

$$c(\alpha) \leq \sum_{S' \in \mathscr{P}^{\omega}(S)} c(\alpha_{S'}) \leq \sum_{S' \in \mathscr{P}^{\omega}(S)} \mathfrak{m} \leq \mathfrak{m} \cdot \mathfrak{m} = \mathfrak{m} < \mathfrak{m}^+.$$

Thus $\alpha \in \mathfrak{m}^+$ and $\alpha_{S'} \leq \alpha$ for each S'. Therefore $a_{S'} \in A_\alpha$ for each S' so $a_{S'} \in A_\beta$, where $\beta = \max\{\alpha, \gamma\}$. Thus for some $y \in A_{\beta+1}$,

$$\mathfrak{A}_{\beta+1} \models F[y] \qquad \text{for every} \quad F \in S;$$

thus since $\mathfrak{A}_{\beta+1} < \mathfrak{A}$,

$$\mathfrak{A} \models F[y] \qquad \text{for each} \quad F \in S.$$

COROLLARY 2.7.5. (a) Assume that in the above each $\mathfrak{A}_\alpha$ is $\mathfrak{m}^+$-saturated. Then so is $\bigcup \mathscr{A}$.

(b) Assume that each $\mathfrak{A}_\alpha$ is $c(\alpha)^+$-saturated. Then $\bigcup \mathscr{A}$ is $\mathfrak{m}^+$-saturated.

The above is assigned as Problem 2.7.2. Note that in the proof of Corollary 2.7.5 we make strong use of the fact that $\mathfrak{m}^+$ is our index set. In fact, counterexamples exist for other index sets.

PROPOSITION 2.7.6. If $\mathfrak{A}$ is infinite and $\mathfrak{m}$-saturated, then $c(\mathfrak{A}) \geq \mathfrak{m}$.

Proof: If $c(\mathfrak{A}) = \mathfrak{n} < \mathfrak{m}$, let $a\colon \mathfrak{n} \to A$ be onto, and let

$$S = \{v_0 \neq c_{a_q} \mid q < \mathfrak{n}\} \subset V_0^{t\oplus\mathfrak{n}}.$$

Since $\mathfrak{A}$ is infinite, any finite subset of S can be satisfied in $(\mathfrak{A}, a)$, but by our construction of a, S cannot be satisfied.

COROLLARY 2.7.7. $\mathfrak{A}$ is finite iff $\mathfrak{A}$ is $\mathfrak{m}$-saturated for every $\mathfrak{m}$.

Proof: If $\mathfrak{A}$ is finite, let $a \in A^{\mathfrak{m}}$ for any $\mathfrak{m}$, $A = \{b_1, \ldots, b_n\}$, $S \subset V_0^{t\oplus\mathfrak{m}}$. If S is not satisfiable in $(\mathfrak{A}, a)$, then we can find $F_1, \ldots, F_n \in S$ such that

$$(\mathfrak{A}, a) \models \neg F_1[b_1], \ldots, (\mathfrak{A}, a) \models \neg F_n[b_n].$$

Thus $S' = \{F_1, \ldots, F_n\}$ is a finite subset of S not satisfiable in $(\mathfrak{A}, a)$.

The converse also holds, since otherwise, by Proposition 2.7.7, $c(\mathfrak{A}) \geq \mathfrak{m}$ for every cardinal $\mathfrak{m}$.

Example: $\langle \mathbb{Q}, < \rangle$ is ω-saturated, for let $a_1, \ldots, a_n \in \mathbb{Q}$, $S \subset V_0^{t\oplus n}$, and assume that for every finite subset $S' \subset S$, we have a $b_{S'} \in \mathbb{Q}$ such that for every $F \in S'$,

$$\langle \mathbb{Q}, <, a_1, \ldots, a_n \rangle \models F[b_{S'}].$$

By Löwenheim-Skolem and compactness, we can find a countable model $\langle B, <', b_1, \ldots, b_n \rangle$ and a $c \in B$ such that for every $F \in S$,

$$\langle B, <', b_1, \ldots, b_n \rangle \models F[c], \qquad b_{j_1} <' \cdots <' b_{j_n}$$

iff

$$a_{j_1} < \cdots < a_{j_n},$$

and $\langle B, <' \rangle$ is a dense totally ordered set with no first or last element. There is an isomorphism

$$\varphi: \langle B, <', b_1, \ldots, b_n \rangle \to \langle \mathbb{Q}, <, a_1, \ldots, a_n \rangle,$$

thus

$$\langle \mathbb{Q}, <, a_1, \ldots, a_n \rangle \models F[\varphi(c)] \qquad \text{for every} \quad F \in S.$$

Other examples will be presented in the problems of this and the next section.

LEMMA 2.7.8. Suppose $c(t) \leq \mathfrak{A}$ and $\omega \leq c(\mathfrak{A}) \leq 2^{\alpha}$. Then there is a $\mathfrak{B}$ such that $\mathfrak{A} < \mathfrak{B}$ and for every $a: \alpha \to A$, $(\mathfrak{B}, a)$ has the finite satisfaction property for A. Also, $c(\mathfrak{B}) = 2^{\alpha}$.

Proof: Let D be a regular ultrafilter on α, $\mathfrak{B}^* = \mathfrak{A}^{\alpha}/D$, $\mathfrak{A}^* = \mathfrak{B}^* \mid j_{\mathfrak{A}}[A]$. Then

$$\mathfrak{A}^* < \mathfrak{B}^*, \qquad c(\mathfrak{B}^*) = c(\mathfrak{A})^{\alpha} = 2^{\alpha},$$

$$c(t \oplus \alpha) = c(t) + \alpha = \alpha,$$

so by Theorem 2.3.8, $(\mathfrak{A}, a)^{\alpha}/D$ has the finite satisfaction property for $j_{\mathfrak{A}}[A]$. But

$$(\mathfrak{A}, a)^{\alpha}/D = (\mathfrak{A}^{\alpha}/D, j_{\mathfrak{A}}(a)) = (\mathfrak{B}^*, j_{\mathfrak{A}}(a)).$$

We can now take $\mathfrak{B} \cong \mathfrak{B}^*$, with $\mathfrak{A} < \mathfrak{B}$, and we are through.

THEOREM 2.7.9. Let $c(t) \leq \alpha$, $\omega \leq c(A) \leq 2^{\alpha}$. Then there is a $\mathfrak{B}$ such that $c(\mathfrak{B}) = 2^{\alpha}$, $\mathfrak{A} < \mathfrak{B}$, and $\mathfrak{B}$ is α^+-saturated.

Proof: We construct a sequence of models $\mathfrak{A}_{\eta}$, $\eta \leq \alpha^+$ as follows:

$$\mathfrak{A} = \mathfrak{A}_0, \qquad \mathfrak{A}_{\eta} < \mathfrak{A}_{\eta+1}, \qquad c(\mathfrak{A}_{\eta+1}) = 2^{\alpha}$$

and for every $a \in A_{\eta}^{\alpha}$, $(\mathfrak{A}_{\eta+1}, a)$ has the finite satisfaction property for A_{η}. For limit $\eta \leq \alpha^+$,

$$\mathfrak{A}_{\eta} = \bigcup_{\beta<\eta} \mathfrak{A}_{\beta}.$$

We can form the above by Lemma 2.7.8. Now let $\mathfrak{B} = \mathfrak{A}_{\alpha^+}$. The fact that $\mathfrak{B}$ is α^+-saturated is shown by applying Lemma 2.7.4 to the language $L^{t\oplus\alpha}$ for any map $a \in B^{\alpha}$. Finally, it is clear that the cardinality

$$c(\mathfrak{B}) \leq \sum_{\eta<\alpha} c(\mathfrak{A}_{\eta}) \leq \alpha^+ \cdot 2^{\alpha} = 2^{\alpha}.$$

Problems

‡2.7.1 (a) Prove Lemma 2.7.2.
(b) Prove Lemma 2.7.3.
(c) Prove Corollary 2.7.5.

2.7.2 (a) Give an example of an ascending chain of $\mathfrak{m}$-saturated structures whose union is not $\mathfrak{m}$-saturated.
(b) Give an example of an $\mathfrak{m}$-saturated $\mathfrak{A}$ and an $\mathfrak{B}$ with $\mathfrak{A} < \mathfrak{B}$, and $\mathfrak{B}$ not ω-saturated.

2.7.3 A filter D on $\mathbf{I}$ is called $\mathfrak{a}$-good iff for every $\beta < \mathfrak{a}$ and every $G: \mathscr{P}_\omega(\rho) \to D$, such that for every pair $S_1, S_2 \in \mathscr{P}_\omega(\beta)$ with $S_1 \subset S_2$, we have $G(S_1) \subset G(S_2)$, there is an $H: \mathscr{P}_\omega(\beta) \to D$ such that
(i) for $S' \in \mathscr{P}_\omega(\beta)$, $H(S') \subset G(S')$;
(ii) for $S', S'' \in \mathscr{P}_\omega(\beta)$, $H(S' \cap S'') = H(S') \cap H(S'')$.
By Lemma 2.3.9, every countably incomplete ultrafilter is ω^+-good.
Show that if D is an $\mathfrak{a}$-good ultrafilter on $\mathbf{I}$, which is not countably complete, if

$$c(t) < \mathfrak{a} \qquad \text{and} \qquad \{\mathfrak{A}_\mathbf{i} \mid \mathbf{i} \in \mathbf{I}\} \subset M^t,$$

then $\prod_\mathbf{I} \mathfrak{A}_\mathbf{i}/D$ is $\mathfrak{a}$-saturated.
Keisler has studied these ultrafilters and ultraproducts in his [5] and [6].

2.7.4 Show that any uncountable algebraically closed field $\mathfrak{A}$ is $c(\mathfrak{A})$-saturated.

2.8 Special Models

DEFINITION 2.8.1. $\mathfrak{A} \in M^t$ is special iff $\mathfrak{A} = \bigcup \{\mathfrak{A}_\mathfrak{b} \mid \mathfrak{b}$ a cardinal, $\mathfrak{b} < c(\mathfrak{A})\}$ for some set of structures indexed by the set of cardinals smaller than $c(\mathfrak{A})$, such that for $\mathfrak{b} < c(\mathfrak{A})$, $\mathfrak{A}_\mathfrak{b}$ is $\mathfrak{b}^+$-saturated, and for

$$\mathfrak{b} < \mathfrak{c} < c(\mathfrak{A}), \qquad \mathfrak{A}_\mathfrak{b} < \mathfrak{A}_\mathfrak{c}.$$

The set $\{\mathfrak{A}_\mathfrak{b} \mid \mathfrak{b} < c(\mathfrak{A})\}$ is called a specializing chain for $\mathfrak{A}$.

COROLLARY 2.8.2. If $c(\mathfrak{A}) = \mathfrak{a}$ and $\mathfrak{A}$ is $\mathfrak{a}$-saturated, then $\mathfrak{A}$ is special.

Proof: Let each $\mathfrak{A}_\mathfrak{b}$ be $\mathfrak{A}$.

COROLLARY 2.8.3. Every finite structure is special.

THEOREM 2.8.4. If $c(\mathfrak{A}) = \mathfrak{a}^+$, then $\mathfrak{A}$ is special iff $\mathfrak{A}$ is $\mathfrak{a}^+$-saturated.

Proof: Half has already been shown. If $\mathfrak{A}$ is special, consider $\mathfrak{A}_\mathfrak{a} < \mathfrak{A}$, $\mathfrak{A}_\mathfrak{a}$ $\mathfrak{a}^+$-saturated. However, since $\mathfrak{a}$ is the last cardinal less than $\mathfrak{a}^+$, $\mathfrak{A}_\mathfrak{a} = \mathfrak{A}$.

Now let $\mathfrak{a}^* = \sum_{\mathfrak{b}<\mathfrak{a}} 2^{\mathfrak{b}}$. Recall that in the introduction we defined for each cardinal $\mathfrak{m}$ a cardinal $\mathfrak{p}$ such that $\mathfrak{m} \leq cf(\mathfrak{p})$ and $\mathfrak{p} = \mathfrak{p}^*$.

THEOREM 2.8.5. Let $\mathfrak{a} = \mathfrak{a}^*$, $c(t) < \mathfrak{a}$, $\omega \leq c(\mathfrak{A}) < \mathfrak{a}$. Then there is a special $\mathfrak{B}$ such that $c(\mathfrak{B}) = \mathfrak{a}$ and $\mathfrak{A} < \mathfrak{B}$.

Proof: If $\mathfrak{a} = \mathfrak{b}^+$, then $\mathfrak{a} = 2^{\mathfrak{b}}$. By Theorem 2.7.9, there is a $\mathfrak{b}^+$-saturated $\mathfrak{B}$ with $\mathfrak{A} < \mathfrak{B}$ and $c(\mathfrak{B}) = 2^{\mathfrak{b}} = \mathfrak{b}^+$. But by Theorem 2.8.4, $\mathfrak{B}$ is special.

If $\mathfrak{a}$ is a limit cardinal, then for $\mathfrak{b} < \mathfrak{a}$,

$$\mathfrak{b}^+ < \mathfrak{a}, \qquad 2^{\mathfrak{b}} \leq \mathfrak{a}.$$

Let $c(t) \cup c(A) = \mathfrak{c}$, $\mathfrak{b} < \mathfrak{a}$. We construct $\mathfrak{A}_{\mathfrak{b}}$ by (cardinal) induction as follows: If $\mathfrak{b} \leq \mathfrak{c}$, $\mathfrak{A}_{\mathfrak{b}} = \mathfrak{A}_{\mathfrak{c}}$, a $\mathfrak{c}^+$-saturated elementary extension of $\mathfrak{A}$ of cardinality $2^{\mathfrak{c}}$. For each successor cardinal $\mathfrak{b}^+$, $\mathfrak{A}_{\mathfrak{b}^+}$ is a $\mathfrak{b}^{++}$-saturated elementary extension of $\mathfrak{A}_{\mathfrak{b}}$, which has cardinality $2^{\mathfrak{b}^+}$. For limit cardinals $\mathfrak{d}$, $\mathfrak{A}_{\mathfrak{d}} = \bigcup_{\mathfrak{b}<\mathfrak{d}} \mathfrak{A}_{\mathfrak{b}}$. Now let $\mathfrak{B} = \bigcup_{\mathfrak{b}<\mathfrak{a}} \mathfrak{A}_{\mathfrak{b}}$, then if $\mathfrak{b} < \mathfrak{a}$, $c(B) \geq c(A_{\mathfrak{b}}) \geq \mathfrak{b}$, but

$$c(B) \leq \sum_{\mathfrak{b}<\mathfrak{a}} c(A_{\mathfrak{b}}) \leq \mathfrak{a} \cdot \mathfrak{a} = \mathfrak{a},$$

so $c(B) = \mathfrak{a}$, and the $\mathfrak{A}_{\mathfrak{b}^+}$ form a specializing chain.

COROLLARY 2.8.6. Every consistent theory has special models.

COROLLARY 2.8.7. Let $\omega + c(t) < \mathfrak{m} = \mathfrak{m}^*$. If all special models of T in cardinality $\mathfrak{m}$ are isomorphic and T has no finite models then T is complete.

Proof: Let $\mathfrak{A}, \mathfrak{B} \in M(T)$, and find $\mathfrak{C} \equiv \mathfrak{A}$, $\mathfrak{D} \equiv \mathfrak{B}$ with $c(\mathfrak{C}) = c(\mathfrak{D}) = \omega + c(t)$. Thus by Theorem 2.8.5, $\mathfrak{C}, \mathfrak{D}$ can be extended to special models $\mathfrak{E}, \mathfrak{F} \in M(T)$ with $c(\mathfrak{E}) = c(\mathfrak{F}) = \mathfrak{m}$, $\mathfrak{C} < \mathfrak{E}$, $\mathfrak{D} < \mathfrak{F}$. But $\mathfrak{E} \cong \mathfrak{F}$, so

$$\mathfrak{A} \equiv \mathfrak{C} \equiv \mathfrak{E} \equiv \mathfrak{F} \equiv \mathfrak{D} \equiv \mathfrak{B}.$$

Beginning now, and until otherwise indicated, we assume Q to be well-closed.

THEOREM 2.8.8. (a) If $\mathfrak{A} \; \exists Q \; \mathfrak{B}$, $x_r \in A$, $\mathfrak{B}$ $\mathfrak{m}$-saturated, $\mathfrak{m} \geq 1$, then for some $y_r \in B$,

$$(\mathfrak{A}, x_r) \; \exists Sb^V_{\{c_r\}} \, Q \; (\mathfrak{B}, y_r).$$

(b) Let $\mathfrak{B}$ be $\mathfrak{m}$-saturated, $\varphi\colon \mathfrak{A} \; \exists Q \; \mathfrak{B}$, $c(\varphi) < \mathfrak{m}$, $z \in A$. Then for some $y \in B$, $\varphi \cup \{\langle z, y\rangle\}\colon \mathfrak{A} \; \exists Q \; \mathfrak{B}$.

Proof: (a) Let $S = \{F \in V_0^t \cap \exists Q \mid \mathfrak{A} \models F[x_r]\}$. If

$$S' = \{G_1, \ldots, G_m\} \subset S,$$

then $G_1 \wedge \cdots \wedge G_m \in S$ so

$$\mathfrak{A} \models (\exists v_0)(G_1 \wedge \cdots \wedge G_m) \in \exists Q, \qquad \text{thus} \qquad \mathfrak{B} \models (\exists v_0)(G_1 \wedge \cdots \wedge G_m),$$

so for some $y_{S'} \in B$,

$$\mathfrak{B} \models G_1 \wedge \cdots \wedge G_m[y_{S'}],$$

i.e., if $S' \subset S$ is finite there is a $y_{S'} \in B$ such that for every $G \in S'$, $\mathfrak{B} \models G[y_{S'}]$, so S is finitely satisfiable in $\mathfrak{B}$. Since $\mathfrak{B}$ is $\mathfrak{m}$-saturated, $\mathfrak{m} \geq 1$, we can find $y_r \in B$ such that for every $G \in S$, $\mathfrak{B} \models G[y_r]$. But by Theorem 1.2.15, this is equivalent to the statement that for every $G \in S$, $(\mathfrak{A}, x_r) \models Sb_{c_r}^{v_0} G$ implies $(\mathfrak{B}, y_r) \models Sb_{c_r}^{v_0} G$, i.e.,

$$(\mathfrak{A}, x_r)\ Sb_{\{c_r\}}^V \exists Q\ (\mathfrak{B}, y_r).$$

(b) By Corollary 2.4.12(c), $\varphi\colon \mathfrak{A}\ \exists Q\ \mathfrak{B}$ iff

$$(\mathfrak{A}, a_\alpha)_{\alpha < c(\varphi)}\ Sb_C^V \exists Q\ (\mathfrak{B}, b_\alpha)_{\alpha < c(\varphi)},$$

where

$$\varphi = \{\langle a_\alpha, b_\alpha \rangle \mid \alpha < c(\varphi)\}, \qquad C = \{c_\alpha \mid \alpha < c(\varphi)\}.$$

But since $Sb_C^V \exists Q = \exists Sb_C^V Q$ we have

$$(\mathfrak{A}, a_\alpha)_{\alpha < c(\varphi)}\ \exists Sb_C^V Q\ (\mathfrak{B}, b_\alpha)_{\alpha < c(\varphi)}.$$

Let $z = a_{c(\varphi)}$. Since $\mathfrak{B}$ is $\mathfrak{m}$-saturated, $c(\varphi) < \mathfrak{m}$, we can find $y = b_{c(\varphi)} \in B$ such that

$$\begin{aligned}(\mathfrak{A}, a_\alpha)_{\alpha \leq c(\varphi)} &= ((\mathfrak{A}, a_\alpha)_{\alpha < c(\varphi)}, a_{c(\varphi)}) Sb_{\{c_{c(\varphi)}\}}^V\ \exists Sb_C^V Q\ ((\mathfrak{B}, b_\alpha)_{\alpha < c(\varphi)}, b_{c(\varphi)}) \\ &= (\mathfrak{B}, b_\alpha)_{\alpha \leq c(\varphi)},\end{aligned}$$

so

$$(\mathfrak{A}, a_\alpha)_{\alpha \leq c(\varphi)}\ Sb_{C'}^V \exists Q\ (\mathfrak{B}, b_\alpha)_{\alpha \leq c(\varphi)}$$

with

$$C' = C \cup \{c_{c(\varphi)}\},$$

and a second application of Lemma 2.4.12(c) assures us that

$$\varphi \cup \{\langle a_{c(\varphi)}, b_{c(\varphi)} \rangle\}$$

is an $\exists Q$-relation.

Before proceeding, the reader should review or recall the discussion of cofinality in the introduction.

THEOREM 2.8.9. (a) Let $\varphi: \mathfrak{A} \exists Q \mathfrak{B}$, $\mathfrak{B}$ be $c(\varphi)^{+} + c(\mathfrak{A})$-saturated. Then for some total Q-relation ψ, $\varphi \subset \psi: \mathfrak{A}\ Q\ \mathfrak{B}$.

(b) Let $\mathfrak{A}$, $\mathfrak{B}$ be special, $\varphi: \mathfrak{A}\ Q_{\omega}\ \mathfrak{B}$, and

(i) $\mathfrak{A}$, $\mathfrak{B}$ finite; or

(ii) one of $\mathfrak{A}$, $\mathfrak{B}$ finite, $c(\varphi) < \mathfrak{t}$, $\mathfrak{t}$ the cofinality of the other, $c(t) <$ the cardinality of the other; or

(iii) $c(\mathfrak{A}) = c(\mathfrak{B}) \geq \omega$, $c(\varphi) < cf(c(\mathfrak{B}))$, $c(t) < c(\mathfrak{B})$.

Then for some onto total Q-relation ψ, $\varphi \subset \psi: \mathfrak{A}\ Q\ \mathfrak{B}$.

Proof: (a) Let

$$\varphi = \{\langle a_{\alpha}, b_{\alpha}\rangle \mid \alpha < c(\varphi)\},$$

$$A \sim \mathscr{D}\varphi = \{a_{\alpha} \mid c(\varphi) \leq \alpha < c(\varphi) + c(A \sim \mathscr{D}\varphi) \text{ (ordinal sum)}\}.$$

We define an ascending collection

$$\{\varphi_{\beta} \mid \beta \leq c(A \sim \mathscr{D}\varphi)\}$$

such that for each such β,

$$\varphi_{\beta}: \mathfrak{A} \exists Q \mathfrak{B} \qquad \text{and} \qquad c(\varphi_{\beta}) \leq c(c(\varphi) + \beta),$$

as follows: Let $\varphi_0 = \varphi$, if we have φ_{β} for $\beta < c(A \sim \mathscr{D}\varphi)$, note that $c(\beta) < c(\mathfrak{A})$, so

$$c(\varphi_{\beta}) < c(\varphi)^{+} + c(\mathfrak{A}).$$

Thus by Theorem 2.8.8.(b) we have a $y = b_{c(\varphi)+\beta} \in B$ such that

$$\varphi_{\beta+1} = \varphi_{\beta} \cup \{\langle a_{c(\varphi)+\beta}, b_{c(\varphi)+\beta}\rangle\}: \mathfrak{A} \exists Q \mathfrak{B}.$$

If β is a limit ordinal,

$$\beta \leq c(A \sim \mathscr{D}\varphi), \qquad \varphi_{\beta} = \bigcup_{\gamma<\beta} \varphi_{\gamma},$$

and $\varphi_{\beta}: \mathfrak{A} \exists Q \mathfrak{B}$ as an ascending union of $\exists Q$-relations (see Problem 2.4.5(b)).

Finally, note that by our construction, for $\beta \leq c(A \sim \mathscr{D}\varphi)$,

$$\mathscr{D}\varphi_{\beta} = \{a_{\alpha} \mid \alpha < c(\varphi) + \beta\},$$

thus $\varphi_{c(A\sim\mathscr{D}\varphi)}$ is our relation.

(b) Once again let

$$\varphi = \{\langle a_{\alpha}, b_{\alpha}\rangle \mid \alpha < c(\varphi)\},$$

and set

$$\mathfrak{k} = c(A \cup B \cup \omega), \qquad a_{\alpha} \in A_{\mathfrak{c}_{\alpha}}, \qquad b_{\alpha} \in B_{\mathfrak{c}_{\alpha}},$$

where

$$\{\mathfrak{A}_{\mathfrak{b}} \mid \mathfrak{b} < \mathfrak{k}\}, \qquad \{\mathfrak{B}_{\mathfrak{c}} \mid \mathfrak{c} < \mathfrak{k}\}$$

are specializing chains for $\mathfrak{A}$, $\mathfrak{B}$ respectively if $\mathfrak{A}$, $\mathfrak{B}$ are infinite, otherwise if $\mathfrak{A}$ is finite, $\mathfrak{A}_{\mathfrak{b}} = \mathfrak{A}$ for each $\mathfrak{b} < \mathfrak{k}$, and $\mathfrak{B}$ is treated similarly. Let

$$\mathfrak{d} = \bigcup_{\alpha < c(\varphi)} (\mathfrak{b}_\alpha \cup \mathfrak{c}_\alpha \cup c(\varphi)) < \mathfrak{k}.$$

Thus in any of the cases (i) through (iii) for each $\alpha < c(\varphi)$,

$$a_\alpha \in A_{\mathfrak{d}} \qquad \text{and} \qquad b_\alpha \in B_{\mathfrak{d}}.$$

We now show that a, b can be extended to $d\colon \mathfrak{k} \to A$, $e\colon \mathfrak{k} \to B$, both onto, such that for $\mathfrak{d} \leq \mathfrak{l} < \mathfrak{k}$,

$$\mathscr{R}(d \mid \mathfrak{l}^+) \subset A_{\mathfrak{l}} \qquad \text{and} \qquad \mathscr{R}(e \mid \mathfrak{l}^+) \subset B_{\mathfrak{l}}.$$

Let $c\colon \mathfrak{k} \to A$ be onto and such that $c \mid c(\varphi) = a$ (such a c exists because $c(\varphi) < \mathfrak{k}$, thus

$$c(A) \leq \mathfrak{k} = c(\mathfrak{k} \sim c(\varphi)),$$

so let $c = a \cup c'$, where $c'\colon (\mathfrak{k} \sim c(\varphi)) \to A$ onto). Define an ascending chain of maps

$$\{d^\mu \mid c(\varphi) \leq \mu \leq \mathfrak{k}\}$$

such that

$$\mathscr{D}d^\mu = \mu \qquad \text{and} \qquad A_{c(\mu+\mathfrak{d})} \cap \mathscr{R}(c \mid \mu) \subset \mathscr{R}d^\mu \subset A_{c(\mu+\mathfrak{d})}$$

as follows:

$$d^{c(\varphi)} = a,$$

$$\text{for} \quad c(\varphi) \leq \mu < \mathfrak{k}, \quad d^{\mu+1} = d^\mu \cup \{\langle \mu, c_\pi \rangle\},$$

π least such that

$$c_\pi \in A_{c(\mu+\mathfrak{d})} \sim \mathscr{R}d^\mu \qquad \text{if} \quad A_{c(\mu+\mathfrak{d})} \sim \mathscr{R}d^\mu \neq \phi,$$

arbitrary otherwise; if $\omega \leq c(A)$, then

$$c(\mathscr{R}d^\mu) \leq c(d^\mu) \leq c(\mu) < c(\mu + \mathfrak{d})^+,$$

and $\mathfrak{A}_{c(\mu+\mathfrak{d})}$ is $c(\mu + \mathfrak{d})^+$-saturated so

$$c(\mu + \mathfrak{d})^+ \leq c(A_{c(\mu+\mathfrak{d})}),$$

so

$$A_{c(\mu+\mathfrak{d})} \sim \mathscr{R}d^\mu \neq \phi.$$

For limit ordinals λ with $c(\varphi) < \lambda \leq \mathfrak{k}$,

$$d^\lambda = \bigcup_{c(\varphi) \leq \mu < \lambda} d^\mu;$$

finally set $d = d^{\mathfrak{k}}$. We leave the reader to check by transfinite induction the conditions on the d^λ.

$$\mathscr{D}d = \bigcup_{c(\varphi) \leq \lambda < \mathfrak{k}} \mathscr{D}d^\lambda = \bigcup_{c(\varphi) \leq \lambda < \mathfrak{k}} \lambda = \mathfrak{k}, \qquad \text{and} \qquad a \subset d.$$

Also

$$\mathscr{R}d = \bigcup_{c(\varphi) \leq \lambda < \mathfrak{k}} \mathscr{R}d^{\lambda},$$

and if $\mu < \mathfrak{k}$, we can find $\lambda' < \mathfrak{k}$ such that $c_\mu \in A_{c(\lambda' + \mathfrak{d})}$, and if $\lambda = \max\{\mu + 1, \lambda'\} < \mathfrak{k}$,

$$c_\mu \in A_{c(\lambda + \mathfrak{d})} \cap \mathscr{R}(c \mid \lambda) \subset \mathscr{R}d^{\lambda} \subset \mathscr{R}d.$$

This shows d to be our map; e is produced similarly.

We next produce an ascending chain

$$\{\varphi_{\mathfrak{n}} \mid c(\varphi \cup t \cup \omega) \leq \mathfrak{n} \leq \mathfrak{k}, \qquad \mathfrak{n} \text{ a cardinal}\}$$

of Q_ω-relations, $\varphi_{\mathfrak{n}}\colon \mathfrak{A}\ Q_\omega\ \mathfrak{B}$ such that for each such $\mathfrak{n}$,

$$\varphi_{\mathfrak{n}} \subset \mathscr{R}(d \mid \mathfrak{n}) \times \mathscr{R}(e \mid \mathfrak{n}),$$

and if $c(t \cup \varphi \cup \omega) < \mathfrak{n}$, then

$$\mathscr{D}\varphi_{\mathfrak{n}} = \mathscr{R}(d \mid \mathfrak{n}) \qquad \text{and} \qquad \mathscr{R}\varphi_{\mathfrak{n}} = \mathscr{R}(e \mid \mathfrak{n}).$$

Let $\varphi_{c(t \cup \varphi \cup \omega)} = \varphi$; if we have

$$\varphi_{\mathfrak{n}}, \qquad c(t \cup \varphi \cup \omega) \leq \mathfrak{n} < \mathfrak{k},$$

$\varphi_{\mathfrak{n}^+}$ is defined as follows:

$$\mathscr{R}\varphi_{\mathfrak{n}} \subset \mathscr{R}(e \mid \mathfrak{n}) \subset \mathfrak{B}_{c(\mathfrak{d} + \mathfrak{n})} \qquad \text{and} \qquad c(\varphi_{\mathfrak{n}}) \leq \mathfrak{n},$$

so by (a) of this theorem and Problem 2.8.12, we have

$$\psi'\colon \mathfrak{A}'\ Q_\omega\ \mathfrak{B}_{c(\mathfrak{d} + \mathfrak{n})},$$

where $\mathscr{D}\psi' = A'$, $\mathfrak{A}'$ is such that

$$\mathscr{R}(d \mid \mathfrak{n}^+) \subset \mathfrak{A}' < \mathfrak{A},$$

and if $\omega \leq c(\mathfrak{A})$, $c(\mathfrak{A}') = \mathfrak{n}^+$ (such an $\mathfrak{A}'$ exists by Theorem 1.7.7). Thus

$$\psi = \psi' \cap \mathscr{R}(d \mid \mathfrak{n}^+) \times \mathscr{R}(e \mid \mathfrak{n}^+)\colon \mathfrak{A}'\ Q_\omega\ \mathfrak{B}_{c(\mathfrak{d} + \mathfrak{n})}$$

(see Corollary 2.4.12(d)) so

$$\mathscr{R}\psi^{-1} \subset \mathfrak{A}_{c(\mathfrak{d} + \mathfrak{n})}, \qquad c(\psi^{-1}) \leq \mathfrak{n}^+,$$

thus we may once again use part (a) of this theorem, this time to obtain

$$\varphi'^{-1}_{\mathfrak{n}^+}\colon \mathfrak{B}'\ \bar{Q}_\omega\ \mathfrak{A}_{c(\mathfrak{d} + \mathfrak{n})},$$

so

$$\varphi_{\mathfrak{n}^+} = \varphi'_{\mathfrak{n}^+} \cap \mathscr{R}(d \mid \mathfrak{n}^+) \times \mathscr{R}(e \mid \mathfrak{n}^+)$$

satisfies our conditions, as the reader can easily check; it is also simple to check that for limit cardinals,

$$\varphi_{\mathfrak{n}} = \bigcup_{c(t \cup \varphi \cup \omega) \leq \mathfrak{n}' < \mathfrak{n}} \varphi_{\mathfrak{n}'}$$

satisfies our conditions. However, these conditions imply that

$$\varphi_{\mathfrak{k}}\colon \mathfrak{A}\ Q\ \mathfrak{B} \qquad \text{with domain} \quad \mathscr{D}\varphi_{\mathfrak{k}} = \mathscr{R}(d \mid \mathfrak{k}) = A, \quad \mathscr{R}\varphi_{\mathfrak{k}} = B.$$

COROLLARY 2.8.10. (a) A theory T with no finite models is complete iff for some cardinal $\mathfrak{m}$,

$$c(t \cup \omega) < \mathfrak{m} = \mathfrak{m}^*$$

and all special models of T of cardinality $\mathfrak{m}$ are isomorphic.

(b) If $c(\mathfrak{A}) \leq c(\mathfrak{B})$, $\mathfrak{A} \equiv \mathfrak{B}$, and $\mathfrak{B}$ is special then $\mathfrak{A} <' \mathfrak{B}$.

Proof: Half the above was Corollary 2.8.7. The other half is due to the fact that if T is complete with infinite models it has a special model of cardinality $\mathfrak{m}$ for some $\mathfrak{m} = \mathfrak{m}^* > \omega + c(t)$, and by Theorem 2.8.9 any two such are isomorphic.

The proof of (b) is left for the reader.

Many other corollaries, corresponding in some way to 2.4.14, etc. can be found to Theorem 2.8.9. For example: If $\mathfrak{A}$ and $\mathfrak{B}$ are special, $\mathfrak{A}\ POS\ \mathfrak{B}$, and either $c(\mathfrak{A}) = c(\mathfrak{B})$ or $\mathfrak{B}$ is finite, then there is a homomorphism $\varphi\colon \mathfrak{A} \to \mathfrak{B}$ that is onto. These corollaries give rise to preservation theorems such as those in Section 2.5, again for example: $K \in POSC_\Delta$ iff K is closed under ultraproducts and homomorphic images, and K, $M^t \sim K$ both closed under ultralimits. By Theorem 2.5.5, to prove this we must simply demonstrate that if $\mathfrak{A} \in K$, $\mathfrak{A}\ POS\ \mathfrak{B}$, then $\mathfrak{B} \in K$. But by the closure of K, $M^t \sim K$ under ultralimits, we can show K (thus $M^t \sim K$) $\in ECL$ (see Problem 2.5.8); thus there are

$$\mathfrak{C} \in K, \qquad \mathfrak{D} \in M^t \sim K \qquad (\text{if} \quad \mathfrak{B} \in M^t \sim K),$$

both special and such that

$$\mathfrak{A} \equiv \mathfrak{C}, \qquad \mathfrak{B} \equiv \mathfrak{D}, \qquad \text{thus} \qquad \mathfrak{C}\ POS\ \mathfrak{D}.$$

We can also require, if $\mathfrak{A}$, $\mathfrak{B}$ are both infinite, that $c(\mathfrak{C}) = c(\mathfrak{D})$, otherwise they are finite or $\mathfrak{D}$ is finite. Thus there is an onto homomorphism $\varphi\colon \mathfrak{C} \to \mathfrak{D}$, so $\mathfrak{D} \in K$, a contradiction.

DEFINITION 2.8.11. Let $\mathfrak{A} \in M^t$. $\mathfrak{A}$ is $\mathfrak{l}$-homogeneous iff for every isomorphism $\varphi\colon \mathfrak{C} \cong \mathfrak{D}$, for

$$\mathfrak{C}, \mathfrak{D} < \mathfrak{A}, \qquad c(\mathfrak{C}) = c(\mathfrak{D}) < \mathfrak{l},$$

there is an automorphism ψ of $\mathfrak{A}$ such that $\varphi \subset \psi$. $\mathfrak{A}$ is $\mathfrak{l}$-universal iff for every $\mathfrak{B} \in M(T(\mathfrak{A}))$ with $c(\mathfrak{B}) < \mathfrak{l}$, we can find an imbedding $\psi\colon \mathfrak{B} <' \mathfrak{A}$.

$\mathfrak{A}$ is homogeneous-universal iff $\mathfrak{A}$ is $c(\mathfrak{A})$-homogeneous and $c(\mathfrak{A})^+$-universal.

Corollary 2.8.10(b) showed us that a special model $\mathfrak{A}$ is always $c(\mathfrak{A})^+$-universal. However:

COROLLARY 2.8.12. If $\mathfrak{A}$ is special and $c(t) + \omega < c(\mathfrak{A})$, then $\mathfrak{A}$ is $cf(c(\mathfrak{A}))$-homogeneous.

Proof: Let $\mathfrak{C}, \mathfrak{D} < \mathfrak{A}$, $c(\mathfrak{C}) < cf(c(\mathfrak{A}))$, $\varphi: \mathfrak{C} \cong \mathfrak{D}$. Thus

$$c(\varphi) = c(\mathfrak{C}) < cf(c(\mathfrak{A})), \qquad \varphi: \mathfrak{C} \cong \mathfrak{D},$$

and

$$\varphi: \mathfrak{C}\ L^t\ \mathfrak{D}.$$

Since $\mathfrak{C} < \mathfrak{A}$, $\mathfrak{D} < \mathfrak{A}$, $\varphi: \mathfrak{A}\ L^t\ \mathfrak{A}$; and by Theorem 2.8.9, there is therefore an onto, total L^t-relation $\psi \supset \varphi$ such that $\psi: \mathfrak{A}\ L^t\ \mathfrak{A}$; but then $\psi: \mathfrak{A} \cong \mathfrak{A}$.

Thus special models are indeed special. Any two of the same cardinality and with the same theories must be isomorphic; any structure with the same theory as that of our special structure can be imbedded elementarily in it, provided only that its cardinality enables us to do this; and many isomorphisms between elementary substructures of it can be extended to an automorphism of it. Other uses of the concept will be discussed.

It should be mentioned that our concepts of universality, homogeneity, and speciality differ from those discussed in one of the best-known papers on the subject by Morley and Vaught. These authors discuss structures that contain all models of a given theory up to their cardinalities, and for which automorphisms can be found extending isomorphisms between arbitrary submodels of prescribed cardinalities, rather than only elementary submodels. To some extent, it could be said that we are discussing their work for complete theories.

Special models have many nontrivial automorphisms, a fact we now show. For the remainder of this section, if S is an infinite set, $1 \leq n \in \omega$, then

$$S^{[n]} = \mathscr{P}^n(S) \sim \mathscr{P}^{n-1}(S),$$

and is thus the collection of subsets of S with exactly n elements.

LEMMA 2.8.13 (Ramsey's Theorem). Let S be an infinite set, m, n positive integers, $S^{[n]} \subset C_1 \cup \cdots \cup C_m$. Then for some infinite $S_0 \subset S$, $r \leq m$, $S_0^{[n]} \subset C_r$.

Proof: We proceed by induction on n; the case $n = 1$ is trivial since once $S^{[1]}$ is infinite, one of the C_r must be infinite, and for that r,

$$\{x \mid \{x\} \in C_r\} = S_0$$

works.

Now assume our result for $n - 1$. We select by induction on p for each $p \in \omega$, $x_1, \ldots, x_p \in S$, $S_p \subset \cdots \subset S_1 \subset S$, $r_1, \ldots, r_p \in \{1, \ldots, m\}$ such that for $j = 1, \ldots, p$, $x_j \in S_{j-1} \sim S_j$ and if $a \in S_j^{[n-1]}$ then $\{x_j\} \cup a \in C_{r_j}$ (here we allow $p = 0$). If we have $x_1, \ldots, x_p$, $S_1, \ldots, S_p$, $r_1, \ldots, r_p$, let $x_{p+1} \in S_p$ be arbitrary and note that

$$(S_p \sim \{x_{p+1}\})^{[n-1]} \subset D_1 \cup \cdots \cup D_m,$$

where for $1 \leq r \leq m$,

$$D_r = \{a \in S_p^{[n-1]} \mid \{x_{p+1}\} \cup a \in C_r\}.$$

Thus for some r_{p+1} and infinite $S_{p+1} \subset S_p$, $S_{p+1}^{[n-1]} \subset D_{r_{p+1}}$ (note that this requires $x_{p+1} \notin S_{p+1}$). Clearly $x_1, \ldots, x_{p+1}$, $S_1, \ldots, S_{p+1}$, $r_1, \ldots, r_{p+1}$ satisfy our inductive hypotheses. Let $X = \{x_1, x_2, \ldots\}$, and for $r = 1, \ldots, m$, $X_r = \{x_p \in X \mid r_p = r\}$. $X = X_1 \cup \cdots \cup X_m$, so one of the X_r, say X_s, is infinite. If $a \in X_s^{[n]}$ let $a = \{x_{j_1}, \ldots, x_{j_n}\}$, $j_1 < \cdots < j_n$; then $x_{j_2}, \ldots, x_{j_n} \in S_{j_1}^{[n-1]}$, thus $a = \{x_{j_1}\} \cup b$, $b \in S_{j_1}^{[n-1]}$, so $a \in C_s$. Thus $X_s^{[n]} \subset C_s$, so $S_0 = X_s$ is our infinite subset.

We now recall a situation that occurred several times in Section 1.6. If $\mathfrak{G}$ is an algebraically closed field, let $\mathfrak{G}$ be the algebraic closure of $\mathfrak{F}(S)$, $\mathfrak{F}$ the prime field in the characteristic of $\mathfrak{G}$, S a transcendence base for $\mathfrak{F}(S)$. If $\varphi \subset S \times S$ is a one-one mapping then φ can be extended to an automorphism of $\mathfrak{G}$.

If $\mathfrak{M}$ is a torsion-free divisible Abelian group, let S be a basis for $\mathfrak{M}$ considered as a vector space over $\mathbb{Q}$. Again if $\varphi \subset S \times S$ is a one-one map then φ can be extended to an automorphism.

If A is a set with no relations (other than equality), $S \subset A$, $\varphi \subset S \times S$ a one-one map, then φ can be extended to an automorphism.

Clearly if the above situation holds for $\mathfrak{A}$, S, and F is a formula of the appropriate language, $\varphi \subset S \times S$ a one-one map, $\langle a, b\rangle \in \varphi^{(FV(F))}$, then $\mathfrak{A} \models F[a]$ iff $\mathfrak{A} \models F[b]$.

One might thus say that if $S \subset A$, $\mathfrak{A} \in M^t$, then S is a set of indiscernables in $\mathfrak{A}$ iff for each one-one map $\varphi \subset S \times S$, $\varphi\colon \mathfrak{A}\ L^t\ \mathfrak{A}$. A reasonable question then is how generally such sets of indiscernables exist. They do not always exist (other than trivially), for if $\langle A, <\rangle$ is totally ordered then no set $S \subset A$ of indiscernables can have more than one element, for in $s_1 < s_2$, $s_1, s_2 \in S$, then

$$\mathfrak{A} \models (v_0 < v_1)[s_1, s_2] \qquad \text{and} \qquad \mathfrak{A} \not\models (v_0 < v_1)[s_2, s_1].$$

Surprisingly this epitomizes the essential obstacle. Thus:

DEFINITION 2.8.14. Let $\mathfrak{A} \in M^t$, $I \subset A$, $\langle I, <\rangle$ totally ordered, $Q \subset L^t$. Then $\langle I, <\rangle$ is a set of Q-order-indiscernables in $\mathfrak{A}$ iff for each order-preserving map $\varphi \subset I \times I$ (i.e., each $\varphi: \langle I, <\rangle L^{\langle 2\rangle}(0)\langle I, <\rangle$), $\varphi: \mathfrak{A}\, Q\, \mathfrak{A}$. (Note that for such φ, φ^{-1} is also order-preserving so $\varphi^{-1}: \mathfrak{A}\, Q\, \mathfrak{A}$, thus $\varphi: \mathfrak{A}(Q \cup \bar{Q})\mathfrak{A}$). A set of L^t-order-indiscernables is called a set of order-indiscernables.

PROPOSITION 2.8.15. Let $Q \subset L^t$ be finite, $\mathfrak{A} \in M^t$ infinite. Then there is an infinite set of Q-order-indiscernables $\langle I, <\rangle$ in $\mathfrak{A}$.

Proof: Let $<'$ totally order A, let $Q = \{F_1, \ldots, F_m\}$, and let

$$FV(F_1) \cup \cdots \cup FV(F_m) \subset \{v_0, \ldots, v_{n-1}\}.$$

For the sake of convenience if $A_0 \in A^{[n]}$ let $A_0 = \{a_0, \ldots, a_{n-1}\}$ with $a_0 < \cdots < a_{n-1}$, $\langle A_0\rangle - \langle a_0, \ldots, a_{n-1}\rangle$; recall that if $\kappa \in n^n$, $a \in A^n$, then $a \circ \kappa = \langle a_{\kappa(0)}, \ldots, a_{\kappa(n-1)}\rangle$. Let $n^n = \{\kappa_1, \ldots, \kappa_{n^n}\}$ and consider the $n^n m$ questions:

$$\mathfrak{A} \models F_1[\langle A_0\rangle \circ \kappa_1]?, \ldots, \mathfrak{A} \models F_m[\langle A_0\rangle \circ \kappa_{n^n}]?$$

There are $p = 2^{n^n m}$ possible sets of answers, $P_1(A_0), \ldots, P_p(A_0)$, thus if $C_k = \{A_0 \in A^{[n]} \mid P_k(A_0)\}$ for $1 \leq k \leq p$,

$$A^{[n]} = C_1 \cup \cdots \cup C_p.$$

Thus by Ramsey's Theorem we may choose $r \in \{1, \ldots, p\}$ and an infinite $I \subset A$ such that $I^{[n]} \subset C_r$. Let $< \, = \, <' \restriction I$; we show that $\langle I, <\rangle$ is a set of Q-order-indiscernables in $\mathfrak{A}$.

Let $F \in Q$, $\varphi \subset I \times I$ be an order-preserving map,

$$\langle a, b\rangle \in \varphi^{(\{v_0,\ldots,v_{n-1}\})}.$$

Then there are unique $A_0, B_0 \in A^{[n]}$, $\kappa, \eta \in n^n$ such that $a = \langle A_0\rangle \circ \kappa$, $b = \langle B_0\rangle \circ \eta$. Since

$$\langle\langle A_0\rangle \circ \kappa, \langle B_0\rangle \circ \eta\rangle \in \varphi^{(\{v_0,\ldots,v_{n-1}\})}, \qquad \langle B_0\rangle \circ \eta = \varphi \circ \langle A_0\rangle \circ \kappa,$$

so $\eta = \langle B_0\rangle^{-1} \circ \varphi \circ \langle A_0\rangle \circ \kappa = \kappa$. Thus $\mathfrak{A} \models F[a]$ iff $\mathfrak{A} \models F[\langle A_0\rangle \circ \kappa]$ iff $\mathfrak{A} \models F[\langle B_0\rangle \circ \eta]$ (since $A_0, B_0 \in C_r$) iff $\mathfrak{A} \models F[b]$.

THEOREM 2.8.16 (Ehrenfeucht–Mostowski). Let $\langle I, <\rangle$ be totally ordered, $\mathfrak{A} \in M^t$ be infinite. Then for some $\mathfrak{B} \in M^t$, $\mathfrak{A} \equiv \mathfrak{B}$, $\langle I, <\rangle$ is a set of order-indiscernables in $\mathfrak{B}$, and

$$c(\mathfrak{B}) \leq \max\{c(t), \omega, c(I)\}.$$

Proof: $\langle I, <\rangle$ is a set of order-indiscernables in $\mathfrak{B} \equiv \mathfrak{A}$ iff

$$(\mathfrak{B}, i)_{i \in I} \models T(\mathfrak{A})$$
$$\cup \{Sb_{\varphi \circ \kappa}F \leftrightarrow Sb_{\kappa}F \mid \kappa \in I^{FV(F)}, \varphi \subset I \times I \text{ order-preserving}\}.$$

This set of axioms is consistent by compactness (applied to Proposition 2.8.15), and by Löwenheim-Skolem (Theorem 1.4.1) we may choose

$$c(\mathfrak{B}) \leq c(L^{t \oplus I}) = \max\{c(t), \omega, c(I)\}.$$

THEOREM 2.8.17. Let $\mathfrak{A} \in M^t$ be special, $\max\{c(t), \omega\} < c(\mathfrak{A})$, $\langle I, <\rangle$ be totally ordered, $c(I) \leq c(\mathfrak{A})$. Then for some $I' \subset A$, $<' \subset I' \times I'$, $\langle I, <\rangle \cong \langle I', <'\rangle$, and if $\varphi \subset I' \times I'$ is an order-preserving map, $c(\varphi) < cf(c(\mathfrak{A}))$ then for some automorphism $\psi: \mathfrak{A} \cong \mathfrak{A}$, $\varphi \subset \psi$.

Proof: Let $\langle I, <\rangle$ be a set of order-indiscernables in $\mathfrak{B}$, $c(\mathfrak{B}) \leq \max\{c(t), \omega, c(I)\} = c(I)$ (of course, but irrelevantly $c(I) = c(\mathfrak{B})$). Then $\rho: \mathfrak{B} <' \mathfrak{A}$ for some ρ so let

$$I' = \rho[I], \qquad <' = \{\langle \rho(x), \rho(y)\rangle \mid \langle x, y\rangle \in <\}.$$

Clearly $\rho \mid I: \langle I, <\rangle \cong \langle I', <'\rangle$; we show $\langle I', <'\rangle$ to be a set of order-indiscernables in $\mathfrak{A}$.

If $F \in L^t$, $\langle a, b\rangle \in \varphi^{(FV(F))}$, $\varphi \subset I \times I$ an order-preserving map, then let $\langle x, a\rangle \in \varphi^{(FV(F))}$, $\langle y, b\rangle \in \varphi^{(FV(F))}$ (possible since a_n, $b_n \in I'$ for $v_n \in FV(F)$). Thus

$$y = \rho^{-1} \circ b = \rho^{-1} \circ \varphi \circ a = \rho^{-1} \circ \varphi \circ \rho \circ x,$$

and since ρ, φ are order-preserving, so is $\rho^{-1} \circ \varphi \circ \rho$. Thus $\mathfrak{A} \models F[a]$ iff $\mathfrak{B} \models F[x]$ iff $\mathfrak{B} \models F[y]$ iff $\mathfrak{A} \models F[b]$.

The above shows that if $\varphi \subset I' \times I'$ is an order-preserving map then $\varphi: \mathfrak{A}\ L^t\ \mathfrak{A}$. If in addition $c(\varphi) < cf(c(\mathfrak{A}))$, Theorem 2.8.9(b)(iii) assures us that for some total, onto $\psi: \mathfrak{A}\ L^t\ \mathfrak{A}$, $\varphi \subset \psi$, i.e., $\varphi \subset \psi: \mathfrak{A} \cong \mathfrak{A}$.

COROLLARY 2.8.18. If T has infinite models then T has a model with a nontrivial automorphism.

Problems

2.8.1 (a) Show that $\langle \mathbb{R}, <\rangle$ is not special.

(b) Find two countable subsets $C, D \subset \mathbb{Q}$ such that $\langle C, < \mid C\rangle \cong \langle D, < \mid D\rangle$, but such that no isomorphism between them can be extended to an automorphism of $\langle \mathbb{Q}, <\rangle$.

2.8.2 (a) If $\mathfrak{l} > c(t \cup \omega)$ and $\mathfrak{A}$ is $\mathfrak{l}$-homogeneous and $\mathfrak{l}$-universal, show that $\mathfrak{A}$ is $\mathfrak{l}^+$-universal. (HINT: If $c(\mathfrak{B}) = \mathfrak{l}$ then $\mathfrak{B} = \bigcup_{\tau<\mathfrak{l}} \mathfrak{B}_\tau$, a union of an ascending $<$-chain, with $c(\mathfrak{B}_\tau) < \mathfrak{l}$ for each τ.)

(b) If $c(\mathfrak{A}) > c(t \cup \omega)$, show that $\mathfrak{A}$ cannot be more than $c(\mathfrak{A})^+$-universal and if $\mathfrak{A}$ is $c(t \cup \omega)^+$-universal prove that $\mathfrak{A}$ cannot be more than $c(\mathfrak{A})$-homogeneous.

(c) Find a structure $\mathfrak{A}$ that is more than $c(\mathfrak{A})$-homogeneous and more than $c(\mathfrak{A})^+$-universal.

2.8.3 One of the first and one of the most famous generalizations of Cantor's argument was given by Hausdorff [1] in 1914. He defined a totally ordered set $\langle A, < \rangle$ to be an $\eta_\mathfrak{a}$-set iff for every $X, Y \subset A$ such that for every $x \in X, y \in Y, x < y$ and $c(X), c(Y) < \mathfrak{a}$, there could be found a $z \in A$ such that for every $x \in X, y \in Y, x < z < y$.

(a) Show that an infinite $\mathfrak{A} = \langle A, < \rangle$ is an $\eta_\mathfrak{a}$-set iff $\mathfrak{A}$ is $\mathfrak{a}$-saturated.

(b) Show that an $\eta_\mathfrak{a}$-set of cardinality $\mathfrak{a}$ is special.

2.8.4 (a) Let $\mathfrak{A}$ be $\mathfrak{l}$-homogeneous and $\mathfrak{l}$-universal. Show that if $c(t) < \mathfrak{l}$ then $\mathfrak{A}$ is $\mathfrak{l}$-saturated.

(b) If $c(t_\mathfrak{A}) < c(\mathfrak{A}) = cf(c(\mathfrak{A}))$, then prove the following equivalent:

(i) $\mathfrak{A}$ is homogeneous-universal.

(ii) $\mathfrak{A}$ is $c(\mathfrak{A})$-saturated.

(iii) $\mathfrak{A}$ is special.

2.8.5 (a) Show that $\langle \mathbb{C}, +, \cdot, 0, 1 \rangle$ is special.

(b) Show that any uncountable divisible torsion-free group is special.

(c) Let V be a vector space over a field $\mathfrak{F}$ such that $c(V) > c(\mathfrak{F})$. Show that V is special.

2.8.6 Let $\mathfrak{A}$ be $\mathfrak{l}$-saturated, and let $c(t_\mathfrak{A}) < \mathfrak{l}, \omega \leq \mathfrak{l}, S \subset L^{t \oplus \tau}, \tau < \mathfrak{l}$. If for every finite subset $S' \subset S$ we can find an $a_{S'} \in A^\omega$ such that for every $F \in S'$, $\mathfrak{A} \models F[a_{S'}]$, show that we can find an $a \in A^\omega$ such that for every $F \in S$, $\mathfrak{A} \models F[a]$.

Now improve the result of Problem 1.6.6 as follows: Let $f_1, f_2, \ldots$ be a sequence of polynomials with $f_n \in \mathbb{C}[X_1, \ldots, X_{j_n}]$. If for every m, $\{f_1, \ldots, f_m\}$ has a common root in $\mathbb{C}$, then $\{f_1, f_2, \ldots\}$ has a common root in $\mathbb{C}$. Does this also hold for uncountable algebraically closed fields of other characteristics?

Keisler [5] has shown that if

$$2^\mathfrak{a} = \mathfrak{a}^+, \qquad S \subset \mathscr{P}\mathfrak{a}, \qquad c(S) \leq \mathfrak{a},$$

and for

$$a, b \in S, \qquad a \cap b \in S, \qquad \text{and} \qquad c(a) = \mathfrak{a},$$

then there is an $\mathfrak{a}^+$-good ultrafilter D on $\mathfrak{a}$ such that $S \subset D$ (see Problem 2.7.3). Assume this result and that of Problem 2.7.3 in Problem 2.8.7.

2.8.7 (a) If

$$\omega \leq c(\mathfrak{A}), \qquad c(\mathfrak{B}) \leq 2^\mathfrak{a}, \qquad c(t) \leq \mathfrak{a},$$

$$\mathfrak{A}, \mathfrak{B} \in M^t, \qquad \mathfrak{a}^+ = 2^\mathfrak{a}$$

and D is an $\mathfrak{a}^+$-good ultrafilter on $\mathfrak{a}$, then

$$\mathfrak{A}^{\mathfrak{a}}/D \cong \mathfrak{B}^{\mathfrak{a}}/D \quad \text{iff} \quad \mathfrak{A} \equiv \mathfrak{B}.$$

(b) If we assume the generalized continuum hypothesis [or the weaker hypothesis (*) that for all $\mathfrak{m}$ there is an $\mathfrak{a}$ with $\mathfrak{m} \leq \mathfrak{a}$ such that $\mathfrak{a}^+ = 2^{\mathfrak{a}}$], then $\mathfrak{A} \equiv \mathfrak{B}$, iff for some ultrafilter pair $\langle \mathbf{I}, D\rangle$, $\mathfrak{A}^{\mathbf{I}}/D \cong \mathfrak{B}^{\mathbf{I}}/D$.

(c) If we assume the generalized continuum hypothesis [or (*)], then $K \in EC_\Delta$ iff K is closed under isomorphic images and ultraproducts and $M^t \sim K$ is closed under ultrapowers.

2.8.8 (a) If $\mathfrak{A}$ is special and $t \subset t_{\mathfrak{A}}$, then $\mathfrak{A}/t$ is special.

(b) If $\mathfrak{m} = \mathfrak{m}^* = c(\mathfrak{A})$, $c(t) + \omega < \mathfrak{m}$, $\mathfrak{A}$ is special, $t \subset t'$ and $c(t') < \mathfrak{m}$, prove that there is a special $\mathfrak{B}$ such that $\mathfrak{B}/t \cong \mathfrak{A}$, $\mathfrak{B}$ of type t'.

(c) Morley and Vaught define $\mathfrak{A}$ to be relation-universal iff for every t such that $t_{\mathfrak{A}} \subset t$, $c(t) + \omega < c(\mathfrak{A})$ and every $\mathfrak{B} \in M^t$ such that $\mathfrak{B}/t_{\mathfrak{A}} \equiv \mathfrak{A}$, there is a $\mathfrak{C} \equiv \mathfrak{B}$ such that $\mathfrak{C}/t_{\mathfrak{A}} = \mathfrak{A}$. Show that every special $\mathfrak{A}$ such that $c(\mathfrak{A}) = c(\mathfrak{A})^*$ is relation-universal.

‡2.8.9 Let $\mathfrak{A}, \mathfrak{B} \in M^t$, $\mathfrak{B} \subset \mathfrak{A}$. Then $\mathfrak{B} < \mathfrak{A}$ iff for every $\mathfrak{C} \in M^t$, $\varphi \subset C \times B$, $Q \subset L^t$,

$$\varphi\colon \mathfrak{C}\ Q\ \mathfrak{B} \quad \text{iff} \quad \varphi\colon \mathfrak{C}\ Q\ \mathfrak{A}$$

2.8.10 We can establish the fact that special models have many automorphisms (though not as many as shown in Theorem 2.8.18) much more simply.

By counting $\{T((\mathfrak{A}, a)) \mid a \in A\}$ show that if $c(t) + \omega < c(\mathfrak{A})$ and $\mathfrak{A}$ is special, then $\mathfrak{A}$ has at least $c(\mathfrak{A})$ distinct automorphisms.

3

Relationships with Logic

3.1 Proofs

To this point, our consideration of formal logic has been largely submerged. There is, however, one question we should not ignore. Consider the relation $S \models F$, with $S \subset \Sigma^t$, $F \in L^t$. At the moment, the best way we know to check whether the relation holds or not is to look through the models of S of cardinality $\leq c(S) + \omega$ and see whether or not each one of them satisfies F at every possible point. The relation, however, is one between sets in Σ^t and elements of L^t, and it might well be asked whether there is a method of verifying the relation considering only sets and elements of L^t. The well-known answer to this question is Yes, and the method is that of formal proof. Throughout this chapter we study this method and show that it does indeed solve the above problem.

The following is motivated by Theorem 1.2.15 and Problem 1.2.13 of Chapter 1.

Definition 3.1.1. Let $F \in L^t$, $v_j \in V$. F admits $x \in K_t$ for v_j iff either $v_j \notin FV(F)$ or $x \notin BV(F)$.

Definition 3.1.2. Let $S \subset \Sigma^t$. Then $T(S)$ is the smallest subset T' of L^t such that $S \subset T'$ and for every $P, Q, R \in L^t$, $v_j \in V$, $x \in K_t$,

(a1) $P \rightarrow (Q \rightarrow P) \in T'$;
(a2) $[R \rightarrow (P \rightarrow Q)] \rightarrow [(R \rightarrow P) \rightarrow (R \rightarrow Q)] \in T'$;
(a3) $(\neg Q \rightarrow \neg P) \rightarrow (P \rightarrow Q) \in T'$;

(a4) $(\forall v_j)(P \to Q) \to (P \to (\forall v_j)Q) \in T'$ if $v_j \notin FV(P)$;
(a5) $(\forall v_j)P \to Sb_x^{v_j}P \in T'$ if P admits x for v_j or $x = v_j$;
(a6) if P_i is any of the predicates of our language or $=$, and

$$x_1, \ldots, x_{t(i)}, \qquad y_1, \ldots, y_{t(i)} \in K_t$$

then

$$(x_1 = y_1) \to ((x_2 = y_2) \to ((x_3 = y_3) \to \cdots \to ((x_{t(i)} = y_{t(i)}) \to (P_i(x_1, \ldots, x_{t(i)}) \to P_i(y_1, \ldots, y_{t(i)}))))\cdots) \in T';$$

(a7) $x = x \in T'$;

and

(r1) if $P, P \to Q \in T'$, then $Q \in T'$;
(r2) if $P \in T'$, $v_k \in V$, then $(\forall v_k)P \in T'$.

Here (a1) to (a5) are referred to as the logical axioms, although each is an axiom schema since it gives a different axiom for each choice of P (and if they appear Q, R, v_j, and x). (a6) and (a7) are referred to as the axioms of equality. (r1) and (r2) are called the rules of inference, and (r1) is called modus ponens, (r2), generalization. (The restrictions in (a4) and (a5) are discussed in Problem 3.1.8.)

Here we have written all our axioms and rules in terms of $\forall$, $\to$, $\neg$, and we define $\exists$, $\vee$, $\wedge$ all in terms of these, rather than reversing the procedure for some of them as we did in Chapter 1.

DEFINITION 3.1.3. If $F \in T(S)$, we say that S syntactically implies F, and we write $S \vdash F$. $\vdash F$ will stand for $\phi \vdash F$.

PROPOSITION 3.1.4. (a) $T(S) = \bigcup_{n<\omega} T_n(S)$, where

$$T_0(S) = S \cup \{F \mid F \text{ is of one of the forms (a1), \ldots, (a7)}\},$$

and

$$T_{n+1}(S) = T_n(S) \cup \{Q \mid P, P \to Q \in T_n(S)\} \cup \{(\forall v_k)P \mid v_k \in V, P \in T_n(S)\}.$$

(b) If $S' \subset S$, then $T(S') \subset T(S)$.
(c) $T(S) = \bigcup \{T(S_0) \mid S_0 \subset S, S_0 \text{ finite}\}$.

Proof: (a) Set $T = \bigcup_{n<\omega} T_n(S)$. Then $S \subset T$, T contains all the logical axioms, and T is closed under (r1) and (r2), so by definition $T(S) \subset T$.

However, if $T \neq T(S)$, then for some least n,

$$T_n(S) \not\subset T(S).$$

Obviously $n > 0$, and just as clearly if $n > k$, then $n > k + 1$.

(b) $T(S)$ contains S', the logical axioms, and is closed under the rules of inference, so by definition

$$T(S') \subset T(S).$$

(c) By (b), $T^* \subset T(S)$, where

$$T^* = \bigcup \{T(S') \mid S' \text{ finite}, S' \subset S\}.$$

But if $F \in T(S)$, then $F \in T_n(S)$ for some n. We now show by induction that $T_n(S) \subset T^*$ for each n. This is clear for $n = 0$; if we assume it for $n = k$ and

$$F \in T_{k+1}(S) \sim T_k(S),$$

then

$$F = Q, \qquad \text{with} \quad P, P \to Q \in T_k(S),$$

or

$$F = (\forall v_j)P \qquad \text{with} \quad P \in T_k(S).$$

In the first case, $P, P \to Q \in T^*$, so let

$$P \in T(S'), \qquad P \to Q \in T(S''),$$

with S' and S'' finite subsets of S. Then

$$P, P \to Q \in T(S' \cup S''),$$

thus so is Q. Therefore $Q \in T^*$. The other case is similar. Thus

$$T_{k+1}(S) \subset T^*, \qquad \text{so} \qquad T(S) \subset T^*.$$

Lemma 3.1.5. For every $P \in L^t$, $\vdash (P \to P)$.

Proof:

$$[P \to ((P \to P) \to P)] \to [(P \to (P \to P)) \to (P \to P)]$$

is of the form (a2) and thus in $T_0(\phi)$;

$$P \to ((P \to P) \to P)$$

is of the form (a1), thus also in $T_0(\phi)$. By (r1),

$$(P \to (P \to P)) \to (P \to P) \in T_1(\phi).$$

But

$$P \to (P \to P) \in T_0(\phi),$$

thus a second use of (r1) puts

$$P \to P \in T_2(\phi), \qquad \text{so} \qquad \vdash (P \to P).$$

THEOREM 3.1.6 (Deduction Theorem). Let $S \subset \Sigma^t$, $F \in \Sigma^t$. Then for $G \in L^t$,

$$S \vdash (F \to G) \quad \text{iff} \quad S \cup \{F\} \vdash G.$$

Proof: If $S \vdash (F \to G)$, then $S \cup \{F\} \vdash F, (F \to G)$, thus by (r1),

$$S \cup \{F\} \vdash G.$$

Conversely, let

$$G \in T_0(S \cup \{F\}) = T_0(S) \cup \{F\}.$$

If $G \in T_0(S)$, then since $G \to (F \to G) \in T_0(S)$,

$$F \to G \in T_1(S), \qquad \text{so} \qquad S \vdash F \to G.$$

If $G = F$, then

$$F \to G = F \to F \in T_2(\phi) \subset T_2(S), \qquad \text{so} \qquad S \vdash F \to G.$$

Assume now that our converse holds for each $G \in T_n(S \cup \{F\})$ and we have $H \in T_{n+1}(S \cup \{F\})$. If we have $G, G \to H \in T_n(S \cup \{F\})$ for some $G \in L^t$, then $F \to G, F \to (G \to H) \in T_m(S)$ for some m by our induction hypothesis. By (a2),

$$[F \to (G \to H)] \to [(F \to G) \to (F \to H)] \in T_m(S),$$

so by (r1),

$$(F \to G) \to (F \to H) \in T_{m+1}(S),$$

thus

$$F \to H \in T_{m+2}(S), \qquad \text{so} \qquad S \vdash F \to H.$$

If $H = (\forall v_k)G$, $G \in T_n(S)$, then again by induction,

$$F \to G \in T_m(S) \qquad \text{for some } m.$$

By (r2),

$$(\forall v_k)(F \to G) \in T_{m+1}(S),$$

and since $FV(F) = \phi$,

$$(\forall v_k)(F \to G) \to (F \to (\forall v_k)G)$$

is an occurrence of (a4). Now by modus ponens,

$$F \to (\forall v_k)G \in T_{n+2}(S), \qquad \text{so} \qquad S \vdash F \to H,$$

completing the induction.

It is somewhat irregular to have a "deduction theorem" with no definition of deduction. We fill this gap.

DEFINITION 3.1.7. A sequence $F_1, \ldots, F_n$ is a deduction of F from S, where $S \subset \Sigma^t$, $F \in L^t$, iff $F_1, \ldots, F_n \in L^t$, $F = F_n$, and for each $m \leq n$, one of the following holds: $F_m \in S$, F_m is a logical axiom or an axiom of equality,

$$F_r = (F_k \rightarrow F_m) \qquad \text{for some } r, k < m,$$

or

$$F_m = (\forall v_j)F_k \qquad \text{for some } v_j \in V, \qquad k < m.$$

$F_1, \ldots, F_n$ is a (formal) proof of F iff $F_1, \ldots, F_n$ is a deduction of F from ϕ.

COROLLARY 3.1.8. $S \vdash F$ iff there is a deduction of F from S.

The proof is assigned as a problem.

Obviously none of our proofs to this point have been formal proofs, however, the deletion of all but the formulas of the proof of Lemma 3.1.5 leaves the following formal proof of $P \rightarrow P$:

$$[P \rightarrow ((P \rightarrow P) \rightarrow P)] \rightarrow [(P \rightarrow (P \rightarrow P)) \rightarrow (P \rightarrow P)]$$
$$P \rightarrow ((P \rightarrow P) \rightarrow P)$$
$$(P \rightarrow (P \rightarrow P)) \rightarrow (P \rightarrow P)$$
$$P \rightarrow (P \rightarrow P)$$
$$P \rightarrow P.$$

In the future, few of our proofs will be formal.

While our interest is in the existence of formal proofs or deductions, by Corollary 3.1.8 it will do to look at the relation $\vdash$ to discover whether they exist.

DEFINITION 3.1.9. S is syntactically consistent iff $T(S) \neq L^t$, syntactically inconsistent otherwise.

LEMMA 3.1.10. (a) $\vdash (\neg F) \rightarrow (F \rightarrow G)$.
(b) $\vdash (\neg(F \rightarrow F)) \rightarrow G$
where $F \in \Sigma^t$, $G \in L^t$.

Proof: For (a), we show that $\{\neg F\} \vdash F \rightarrow G$ and use the deduction theorem. The following is a deduction of $F \rightarrow G$ from $\{\neg F\}$:

$$\neg F$$
$$\neg F \rightarrow (\neg G \rightarrow \neg F)$$
$$\neg G \rightarrow \neg F$$
$$(\neg G \rightarrow \neg F) \rightarrow (F \rightarrow G)$$
$$F \rightarrow G.$$

For (b) it will again do to show $\{\neg(F \rightarrow F)\} \vdash G$. However, by (a),

$$\vdash (\neg(F \rightarrow F)) \rightarrow [(F \rightarrow F) \rightarrow G].$$

Thus by (r1),

$$\{\neg(F \rightarrow F)\} \vdash (F \rightarrow F) \rightarrow G,$$

and by 3.1.4(b) and 3.1.5,

$$\{\neg(F \rightarrow F)\} \vdash F \rightarrow F,$$

so a second use of modus ponens yields

$$\{\neg(F \rightarrow F)\} \vdash G.$$

PROPOSITION 3.1.11. (a) If $S' \subset S$ and S is syntactically consistent, then so is S'.

(b) S is syntactically inconsistent iff for some $F \in \Sigma^t$,

$$S \vdash \neg(F \rightarrow F)$$

(iff for every $F \in L^t$, $S \vdash \neg(F \rightarrow F)$).

(c) S is syntactically consistent iff every finite subset of S is syntactically consistent.

Proof: (a) is immediate from Proposition 3.1.4(b).

(b) If S is syntactically inconsistent, then clearly for every $F \in L^t$,

$$S \vdash \neg(F \rightarrow F),$$

so for some $F \in \Sigma^t$,

$$S \vdash \neg(F \rightarrow F).$$

Conversely, if $F \in \Sigma^t$ and $S \vdash \neg(F \rightarrow F)$, then by Lemma 3.1.10(b) and modus ponens,

$$S \vdash G \qquad \text{for every} \quad G \in L^t.$$

(c) Clearly if S is syntactically consistent, then S_0 is syntactically consistent for every finite $S_0 \subset S$. Conversely, let S_0 be consistent for every finite $S_0 \subset S$, $F \in \Sigma^t$. Then for no finite $S_0 \subset S$ do we have

$$S_0 \vdash \neg(F \rightarrow F),$$

so by Proposition 3.1.4(c),

$$S \nvdash \neg(F \rightarrow F),$$

so S is syntactically consistent.

COROLLARY 3.1.12. The following are equivalent for $F \in \Sigma^t$:

(i) $S \vdash F$.
(ii) $S \cup \{\neg F\}$ is syntactically inconsistent.

Proof: If $S \vdash F$, then $F \in T(S)$, thus

$$F, \neg F \in T(S \cup \{\neg F\}).$$

By Lemma 3.1.10(a),

$$\neg F \to (F \to G) \in T(S \cup \{\neg F\}).$$

Two applications of modus ponens give us

$$G \in T(S \cup \{\neg F\}),$$

but here $G \in L^t$ was arbitrary.

Conversely, let $S \cup \{\neg F\}$ be syntactically inconsistent. Thus

$$S \cup \{\neg F\} \vdash \neg(F \to F),$$

so

$$S \vdash \neg F \to \neg(F \to F).$$

But

$$[\neg F \to \neg(F \to F)] \to [(F \to F) \to F]$$

is of the form (a3), so by modus ponens,

$$S \vdash (F \to F) \to F,$$

and a second application of it yields $S \vdash F$.

Problems

‡3.1.1 Prove Corollary 3.1.8.

3.1.2 The notion of $T(S)$ can be defined for arbitrary $S \subset L^t$ using Definition 3.1.2. Furthermore, with the exception of the deduction theorem, almost every Theorem, Lemma, and so on, of this section holds for arbitrary $F \in L^t$, $S \subset L^t$. The deduction theorem must be changed to read:

Let $S \subset L^t$, $F, G \in L^t$. Then if $S \cup \{F\} \vdash G$, and generalization is never used on any

$$H \in T(S \cup \{F\}) \sim T(S)$$

for a variable v_k free in F, then $S \vdash F \to G$. (The converse, that if $S \vdash F \to G$ then $S \cup \{F\} \vdash G$, needs no change.)

Verify all the above assertions and give a counterexample to the statement: If $S \subset L^t$, $F, G \in L^t$ and $S \cup \{F\} \vdash G$, then $S \vdash F \to G$.

3.1.3 Supply formal proofs:

(a) $F \to \neg\neg F$.
(b) $\neg\neg F \to F$.

(c) $\{P \to Q, Q \to R\} \vdash P \to R$.
(d) $P \to (Q \to P \wedge Q)$.
(e) $A \to A \vee B$.

3.1.4 Show:
(a) $\{F_1, \ldots, F_n\} \vdash F_1 \wedge \cdots \wedge F_n$.
(b) $(\forall v_1)(\forall v_2)(v_1 = v_2 \to v_2 = v_1)$.
(c) $(\forall v_1)(\forall v_2)(\forall v_3)((v_1 = v_2 \wedge v_2 = v_3) \to v_1 = v_3)$.
(d) $S \vdash F \to G$ if $S \vdash G$ or $S \vdash \neg F$.

3.1.5 (a) Let $F \in L^t$, $FV(F) \cap BV(F) = \phi$, $v_k \notin V(F)$. Show that $F = Sb^{v_k}_{v_j} Sb^{v_j}_{v_k} F$ and that $\vdash (\forall v_j)F \to (\forall v_k) Sb^{v_j}_{v_k} F$, $\vdash (\forall v_k) Sb^{v_j}_{v_k} F \to (\forall v_j)F$.
(b) Let $F \in L^t$. Show that for some $F' \in L^t$, $\vdash F \to F'$, $\vdash F' \to F$, and $FV(F') \cap BV(F') = \phi$. (Hint: use an induction based on $\neg$, $\to$, and $\forall$, the connectives and quantifiers used in Definition 3.1.2.)
(c) Let $F, F' \in L^t$, $\vdash F \to F'$. Then for each constant c,

$$\vdash Sb^{v_j}_c F \to Sb^{v_j}_c F'.$$

3.1.6 Show that the following rules and axioms provide an alternative to (a1), ..., (a7), (r1), (r2).
(a′1) $\neg P \vee P \in T'$.
(a′2) $Sb^{v_k}_x F \to (\exists v_k)F \in T'$ if F admits x for v_j.
(a′3) $x = x \in T'$.
(a′4) $(\forall v_1) \cdots (\forall v_{2t(i)})(v_1 = v_{t(i)+1} \wedge \cdots \wedge v_{t(i)} = v_{2t(i)}$
$\to [P_i(v_1, \ldots, v_{t(i)}) \to P_i(v_{t(i)+1}, \ldots, v_{2t(i)})]) \in T'$
for P_i any predicate or $=$.
(r′1) If $A \in T'$, then $A \vee B \in T'$.
(r′2) If $A \vee A \in T'$, then $A \in T'$.
(r′3) If $A \vee (B \vee C) \in T'$, then $(A \vee B) \vee C \in T'$.
(r′4) If $A \vee B$, $(\neg A) \vee C \in T'$, then $B \vee C \in T'$.
(r′5) If v_k is not free in B and $A \to B \in T'$, then $((\exists v_k)A) \to B \in T'$.

3.1.7 Give a collection of axioms and rules formulated without use of $\forall$, $\wedge$, $\to$ that may be used in place of (a1), ..., (r2).

3.1.8 Check that the following are not always true and thus would be counterexamples to (a4) and (a5) respectively if the restrictions on these axioms were removed.
(a) $(\forall v_1)(v_1 \neq v_2 \to v_1 \neq v_2) \to (v_1 \neq v_2 \to (\forall v_1)(v_1 \neq v_2))$.
(b) $(\forall v_1)(\exists v_2)(v_1 \neq v_2) \to (\exists v_2)(v_2 \neq v_2)$.

3.2 The Completeness Theorems

THEOREM 3.2.1. If $S \vdash F$, then $S \models F$ (for $S \subset \Sigma^t$, $F \in L^t$).

Proof: Let $\mathfrak{A} \in M(S)$, and consider $T(\mathfrak{A})$. If $P, Q \in L^t$, $a \in A^\omega$, then

$$\mathscr{V}^{\mathfrak{A}}(P \to (Q \to P), a) = 0$$

iff

$$\mathscr{V}^{\mathfrak{A}}(P, a) = 1 \quad \text{and} \quad \mathscr{V}^{\mathfrak{A}}(Q \to P, a) = 0.$$

However,

$$\mathscr{V}^{\mathfrak{A}}(Q \to P, a) = 0 \quad \text{iff} \quad \mathscr{V}^{\mathfrak{A}}(Q, a) = 1 \quad \text{and} \quad \mathscr{V}^{\mathfrak{A}}(P, a) = 0,$$

contradicting our remark above. Thus

$$\mathscr{V}^{\mathfrak{A}}(P \to (Q \to P), a) = 1,$$

and since this holds for any $\mathfrak{A} \in M(S)$, $a \in A^{\omega}$, we have

$$S \models P \to (Q \to P).$$

Our other logical axioms and axioms of equality are shown similarly, so S together with all the logical axioms is contained in the set $\{F \mid S \models F\}$. If

$$F, F \to G \in \{F \mid S \models F\},$$

then we must have

$$\mathfrak{A} \models F[a], \qquad \mathfrak{A} \models (F \to G)[a]$$

for every appropriate $\mathfrak{A}$, a, thus $\mathfrak{A} \models G[a]$ for every appropriate $\mathfrak{A}$, a, so $S \models G$. Finally, if for every $\mathfrak{A} \in M(S)$, $a \in A^{\omega}$ we have $\mathfrak{A} \models P[a]$, then for every $\mathfrak{A} \in M(S)$, $a \in A^{\omega}$

$$\mathfrak{A} \models (\forall v_k)P[a] \qquad \text{for} \quad v_k \in V.$$

Thus $\{F \mid S \models F\}$ is also closed under the rules of inference, so

$$T(S) \subset \{F \in L^t \mid S \models F\}.$$

Are these sets of formulas equal (i.e., are $T(S)$, $\{F \in L^t \mid S \models F\}$ equal)?

THEOREM 3.2.2 (The Gödel-Henkin Completeness Theorem). For $S \subset \Sigma^t$, $F \in L^t$, $S \models F$ iff $S \vdash F$.

In other words, our collection of axioms and rules is sufficient to prove every true formula, so we need no more of them—our collection is "complete." This completeness theorem, then, has little to do with the complete theories or model-complete theories mentioned in Chapter 1 or the complete sets of structures mentioned in Chapter 2, indeed little to do with most of the legion of concepts called "complete" in mathematics.

The Gödel completeness theorem below deals with finite types only, since each $F \in L^t$ for some finite t. Henkin, as well as Robinson and Malcev were responsible for bringing under consideration languages with arbitrarily large types and this lends significance to the Gödel-Henkin formulation despite its formal equivalence to the Gödel completeness theorem in our system.

Theorem 3.2.3 (Gödel Completeness Theorem). If $\models F$, then $\vdash F$.

Proposition 3.2.4. The Gödel completeness theorem implies the Gödel-Henkin completeness theorem.

Proof: Let $S \models F$. By compactness, see Problem 1.5.13, Chapter 1, $\{F_1, \ldots, F_n\} \models F$ for some $F_1, \ldots, F_n \in S$,

$$\text{thus} \quad \models F_1 \wedge \cdots \wedge F_n \to F, \qquad \text{so} \quad \vdash F_1 \wedge \cdots \wedge F_n \to F, \text{ and}$$

$$\text{so} \quad \{F_1, \ldots, F_n\} \vdash F, \qquad \text{so} \quad S \vdash F.$$

Thus

$$\{F \mid S \models F\} \subset T(S),$$

and by Theorem 3.2.1 we are through.

Definition 3.2.5. A syntactical theory is a set $T \subset L^t$ such that for some $S \subset \Sigma^t$, $T = T(S)$.

A syntactical theory is complete iff for every $F \in \Sigma^t$, either $F \in T$ or $\neg F \in T$, but not both. A set $S \subset \Sigma^t$ is syntactically complete iff $T(S)$ is a complete syntactical theory.

A syntactical theory is closed iff $T \subset L^t$ is such that for some i, $t(i) = 0$ and for every $F \in \Sigma^t$ of the form $F = (\forall v_j)P$, $F \in T$ iff $Sb^{v_j}_{c_i}P \in T$ for every i such that $t(i) = 0$.

Lemma 3.2.6. If $S \subset \Sigma^t$ is syntactically consistent, then $S \subset T$ for some complete syntactical theory $T \subset L^t$.

Proof: Zorn's lemma, applied to Proposition 3.1.11(b).

Lemma 3.2.7. Throughout this lemma,

$$i \notin \mathcal{D}t, \qquad t' = t \cup \{\langle i, 0\rangle\}, \qquad S \subset \Sigma^t.$$

(a) If $F \in T'(S) = \{F \in L^{t'} \mid S \vdash F\}$, then for all but a finite number of j,

$$Sb^{c_i}_{v_j}F \in T(S) = \{F \in L^t \mid S \vdash F\}.$$

(b) If $S \subset \Sigma^t$ is syntactically consistent, then S is syntactically consistent in $\Sigma^{t \oplus \omega}$ ($t \oplus X$ is the disjoint union of t and $\{\langle n, 0\rangle \mid n \in X\}$).

(c) Let $S \subset \Sigma^t$, and define $S' \subset \Sigma^{t'}$ by $S' = S \cup \{Sb^{v_j}_{c_i}F \to (\forall v_j)F\}$ for some $F \in L^t$ such that $v_j \in FV(F)$. If S is syntactically consistent in L^t, then S' is syntactically consistent in $L^{t'}$. In fact $T(S) = T(S') \cap L^t$.

Proof: (a) If $F \in T'(S)$ then for some n, $F \in T'_n(S)$. We show by induction on n that for all but a finite number of j,

$$Sb^{ci}_{vj}F \in T'(S).$$

We leave it for the reader to check all axioms of the form (a1), . . . , (a7). For $F \in S$, $Sb^{ci}_{vj}F = F$. Thus if $n = 0$, we are through.

Assume (a) for $n = k$ and let

$$F \in T'_{k+1}(S) \sim T'_k(S).$$

Then we have for some $G \in T'_k(S)$,

$$G \mathrel{-\!>} F \in T'_k(S) \qquad \text{or} \qquad F = (\forall v_m)G.$$

In either case, for all but a finite number of $j \neq m$,

$$Sb^{ci}_{vj}G,\ Sb^{ci}_{vj}(G \mathrel{-\!>} F) \in T(S),$$

and

$$Sb^{ci}_{vj}(G \mathrel{-\!>} F) = Sb^{ci}_{vj}G \mathrel{-\!>} Sb^{ci}_{vj}F,$$

so in either case

$$Sb^{ci}_{vj}F \in T(S).$$

(b) By (a), $T'(S) \cap L^t \subset T(S)$, for if $F \in T'(S) \cap L^t$, then for some $v_j \in V$,

$$F = Sb^{ci}_{vj}F \in T(S).$$

Thus if $T(S) \neq L^t$, then $T'(S) \neq L^{t'}$. Using this, we can show by induction that if

$$\omega \cap \mathscr{D}t = \phi, \qquad \text{and} \qquad T(S) \neq L^t, \qquad m \leq \omega,$$

then

$$T^m(S) \cap L^t \subset T(S), \qquad \text{where} \quad T^m(S) = \{F \in L^{t\oplus m} \mid S \vdash F\}.$$

If $\neg(F \mathrel{-\!>} F) \in T^\omega(S) \cap L^t$, then for an m,

$$\neg(F \mathrel{-\!>} F) \in T^m(S) \cap L^t$$

(Problem 3.2.1), which is impossible by the above if S is syntactically consistent.

(c) If S' is inconsistent, then by Corollary 3.1.12,

$$\neg(Sb^{vj}_{ci}F \mathrel{-\!>} (\forall v_j)F) \in T'(S)$$

and by Problem 3.1.5 we may assume

$$FV(F) \cap BV(F) = \phi.$$

Thus

$$Sb^{vj}_{ci}F \in T'(S), \qquad \text{and} \qquad \neg(\forall v_j)F \in T'(S)$$

(by Axiom (a1) and Lemma 3.1.10(a)). Now choose v_k such that

$$Sb^{ci}_{vk}Sb^{vj}_{ci}F \in T(S)$$

and such that $v_k \notin V(F)$, so

$$Sb^{v_k}_{v_j}G = F, \qquad \text{where} \quad G = Sb^{v_j}_{v_k}F = Sb^{c_i}_{v_k}Sb^{v_j}_{c_i}F,$$

a choice possible by (a) and Problem 3.1.5. However, since $G \in T(S)$,

$$(\forall v_k)G \in T(S), \qquad \text{thus} \qquad (\forall v_j)F \in T(S),$$

by Problem 3.1.5, contradicting

$$\neg(\forall v_j)F \in T'(S) \cap L^t \subset T(S).$$

PROPOSITION 3.2.8. If t is countable, $S \subset \Sigma^t$ syntactically consistent, then there is a complete closed syntactical theory $T \subset L^{t\oplus\omega}$ such that $S \subset T$.

Proof: Let $T_0 = T^{\omega}(S)$, consistent by Lemma 3.2.7(b). Now let $(\forall v_{j_1})Q_1$, $(\forall v_{j_2})Q_2, \ldots$ be all elements of $\Sigma^{t\oplus\omega}$, which are of the form $(\forall v_j)Q$, $Q \in L^{t\oplus\omega}$.

We define T_k by induction as follows:

$$T_{k+1} = T_k \cup \{Sb^{v_{j_k}}_{c_k} Q_k \text{ -> } (\forall v_{j_k})Q_k\}.$$

By induction using Lemma 3.2.7(c), we see that for each k, T_k is syntactically consistent. Thus $T^* = \bigcup_{k<\omega} T_k$ is syntactically consistent (in fact, each finite subset of T^* is contained in one of the T_k). Thus we can find a complete syntactical theory T with $T^* \subset T \subset L^{t\oplus\omega}$. We now show that T is closed. Suppose that

$$(\forall v_j)Q \in \Sigma^{t\oplus\omega} \qquad \text{and} \qquad Sb^{v_j}_{c_i}Q \in T \qquad \text{for every} \quad i$$

such that $t \oplus \omega(i) = 0$. For some n,

$$(\forall v_j)Q = (\forall v_{j_n})Q_n, \qquad \text{so} \qquad Sb^{v_{j_n}}_{c_n} Q_n \text{ -> } (\forall v_{j_n})Q_n \in T.$$

But since $Sb^{v_{j_n}}_{c_n} Q_n \in T$,

$$(\forall v_{j_n})Q_n \in T$$

by modus ponens. "Conversely" if $(\forall v_j)Q \in T$ then by (a5), $Sb^{v_j}_{c_i}Q \in T$ for each c_i.

The following includes the remainder of the work involved in the proof of the Gödel completeness theorem:

THEOREM 3.2.9. If t is countable, $T \subset L^t$ a complete, closed syntactical theory, then T has a countable model.

Proof: For $c_i \in C_t$, let

$$[c_i] = \{c_j \mid (c_i = c_j) \in T\},$$

and define $\mathfrak{A}$ as follows:

$$A = \{[c_i] \quad \mid t(i) = 0\} = \{a_1, \ldots, a_n, \ldots\}.$$

For $t(j) > 0$, set

$$R_j = \{\langle a_{r_1}, \ldots, a_{r_{t(j)}}\rangle \mid \text{for some } c_{s_1}, \ldots, c_{s_{t(j)}},$$

$$a_{r_1} = [c_{s_1}], \ldots, a_{r_{t(j)}} = [c_{s_{t(j)}}] \quad \text{and} \quad T \vdash P_j(c_{s_1}, \ldots, c_{s_{t(j)}})\}$$

$$\text{for} \quad t(j) = 0, \quad R_j = [c_j],$$

finally,

$$\mathfrak{A} = \langle A, R_j\rangle_{j \in \mathscr{D}t}.$$

We now show that for every $F \in \Sigma^t$, $F \in T$ iff $\mathfrak{A} \models F$. The induction we use is based on $\rightarrow$, $\neg$, $\forall$, rather than $\vee$, $\neg$, $\exists$.

First let $F = P_j(x_1, \ldots, x_{t(j)})$. Since $F \in \Sigma^t$,

$$x_1, \ldots, x_{t(j)} \in C_t,$$

so set

$$x_1 = c_{s_1}, \ldots, x_{t(j)} = c_{s_{t(j)}}.$$

If $T \vdash F$, then

$$\langle [c_{s_1}], \ldots, [c_{s_{t(j)}}]\rangle \in R_j.$$

Thus by definition of $\models$,

$$\mathfrak{A} \models P_j(c_{s_1}, \ldots, c_{s_{t(j)}}) = P_j(x_1, \ldots, x_{t(j)}).$$

The fact that if $\mathfrak{A} \models F$ then $T \vdash F$ holds here by definition, and the case where we have $x_1 = x_2$ is handled similarly.

Now let $F = G \rightarrow H$; by induction if $G \in T \cap \Sigma^t$, then $\mathfrak{A} \models G$, and the same holds for H. $\mathfrak{A} \models F$ iff $\mathfrak{A} \models H$ or $\mathfrak{A} \models \neg G$ iff $\mathfrak{A} \models H$ or $\mathfrak{A} \not\models G$ iff $T \vdash H$ or $T \nvdash G$ iff $T \vdash H$ or $T \vdash \neg G$ iff $T \vdash G \rightarrow H$ iff $T \vdash F$, where we have used the syntactical completeness of T here. A similar proof establishes our inductive step for $\neg$.

Now let $F = (\forall v_k)G$, $t(i) = 0$, and $\mathfrak{A} \models F$. Then

$$\mathfrak{A} \models (\forall v_k)G \rightarrow Sb^{v_k}_{ci}G, \qquad \text{thus} \qquad \mathfrak{A} \models Sb^{v_k}_{ci}G,$$

so by our induction hypothesis,

$$T \vdash Sb^{v_k}_{ci}G,\dagger$$

thus since c_i is arbitrary and T is closed,

$$T \vdash (\forall v_k)G.$$

† If we define L^t as in 1.2.1, but in terms of $\neg$, $\rightarrow$, $\forall$, it is clear that for $G \in L^t(n)$, $Sb^{v_n}_{c_i}G \in L^t(n)$.

Conversely, let $T \vdash F$. Then by (a5) and (r1) $T \vdash Sb^{v_k}_{c_i}G$ for every c_i. By induction, $\mathfrak{A} \models Sb^{v_k}_{c_i}G$ for every c_i, but by the construction of $\mathfrak{A}$, $\mathfrak{A} \models G[a]$ for every $a \in A$, so $\mathfrak{A} \models (\forall v_k)G$.

Proof of Theorem 3.2.3 (*Gödel Completeness*): Let $F \in \Sigma^t$ and assume not $\vdash F$. Then $\{\neg F\}$ is syntactically consistent, so we can find a complete closed syntactical theory T with $\{\neg F\} \subset T$, and a structure $\mathfrak{A}$ such that for every sentence $G \in T$, $\mathfrak{A} \models G$. Thus $\mathfrak{A} \models \neg F$, so not $\models F$. Conversely, by Theorem 3.2.1, if not $\models F$, then not $\vdash F$. Thus not $\vdash F$ iff not $\models F$, so $\vdash F$ iff $\models F$.

Problems

‡3.2.1 (a) Check the remaining axioms in the proofs of Theorem 3.2.1 and Lemma 3.2.7(a).

(b) Check the fact that $T^{\omega}(S) = \bigcup_{m<\omega} T^m(S)$, where these are as in the proof of Lemma 3.2.7 (b).

(c) Complete the proof of Lemma 3.2.6.

3.2.2 Show that the Gödel-Henkin completeness theorem implies the compactness theorem. (Before the discovery that ultraproducts could be applied to model theory, compactness was deduced from the Gödel-Henkin completeness theorem.)

3.2.3 Prove the Gödel-Henkin completeness theorem directly, without any application of compactness, thus completing a second proof of the compactness theorem, the only one known until the mid 1950s, thus the one used when most of the work in Chapter 1 was originally done.

4

An Application to Algebra

4.1 Valued Fields

We have seen in Chapters 1 and 2 that model theory and algebra often run parallel courses and can be applied to each other. Here we select a particular application and study it in some detail. We choose the solution by Ax and Kochen of a problem raised by E. Artin.

We select this example for various reasons. Artin's conjecture was a quarter of a century old and had received much attention prior to the solution. For their work Ax and Kochen shared the 1967 Cole Prize in Number Theory for the best contribution to that subject during the preceding five years.

The solution by Ax and Kochen—that Artin's conjecture was almost true—and the subsequent discovery of counterexamples to the full conjecture indicates a type of problem particularly amenable to model-theoretic solution.

In this section we set down preliminaries, mostly algebraic, to the work done by Ax and Kochen. A more recent alternate approach is found in P. J. Cohen.

DEFINITION 4.1.1. A valued field is an ordered triple $\langle \mathfrak{F}, \mathfrak{M}, v \rangle$, where $\mathfrak{F} = \langle F, +, \cdot, 0, 1 \rangle$ is a field, $\mathfrak{M} = \langle M, +, e, < \rangle$ an ordered Abelian group, and $v \colon F \sim \{0\} \to M$ is an *onto* map satisfying:

(va) if $a, b \in F \sim \{0\}$, $v(ab) = v(a) + v(b)$;

(vb) if $a, b, a + b \in F \sim \{0\}$, then $v(a + b) \leq \max\{v(a), v(b)\}$.

Note that v is therefore a homomorphism from $\langle F \sim \{0\}, \cdot, 1\rangle$ onto $\langle M, +, e\rangle$. Little confusion should arise from the fact that the group operation and additive field operation are both denoted by $+$.

COROLLARY 4.1.2. (a) Let $\mathfrak{F}$ be any field. Then $\langle \mathfrak{F}(X), \mathbb{Z}, v\rangle$ is a valued field where

$$\mathfrak{F}(X) = \{f/g \mid f, g \in \mathfrak{F}[X] \text{ and } g \neq 0\}$$

with the usual operations, and

$$v(f/g) = \deg(f) - \deg(g).$$

(b) Let p be a prime. If

$$a/b \in \mathbb{Q} \sim \{0\} \qquad (\mathbb{Q} \text{ the rationals}),$$

then $a/b = p^r(c/d)$ where p divides neither c nor d, c/d is in lowest terms and $r \in \mathbb{Z}$. This representation is unique.

If

$$v_p(a/b) = -r \qquad \text{for} \quad a/b \in \mathbb{Q} \sim \{0\},$$

then $\langle \mathbb{Q}, \mathbb{Z}, v_p\rangle$ is a valued field. v_p is called the p-adic valuation.

(c) Again let $\mathfrak{F}$ be any field and consider $\langle \mathfrak{F}(X), \mathbb{Z}, v_f\rangle$, where f is a polynomial irreducible in $\mathfrak{F}[X]$ and v_f is defined as follows: Let $g/h \in \mathfrak{F}(X)$. Let $g/h = f^r(g'/h')$ with $r \in \mathbb{Z}$, f dividing neither g' nor h', g'/h' in lowest terms (this exists and is unique), and set $v_f(g/h) = -r$.

Proof of the above is left for the reader (see Problem 4.1.1).

The concept of valued field can be axiomatized in a first-order language, in particular $L^{\langle 1,3,3,0,0,1,0,2,2\rangle}$. For many purposes it might be best to consider $\langle \mathfrak{F}, \mathfrak{M}, v\rangle$ an abbreviation for $\langle A, F, \cdot, +, 0, 1, M, e, <, v\rangle$, where A is the disjoint union of F and M and $+$ the disjoint union of the group operation and additive field operation. We leave details for the reader in Problem 4.1.2.

Throughout this chapter, unless otherwise noted, we allow $\mathfrak{F} = \{0\}$ to be a field. We also refer to subgroups of $\langle M, +, e\rangle$ as subgroups of $\mathfrak{M}$.

NOTATION. Let $\mathfrak{R}$ be a commutative ring, I an ideal of $\mathfrak{R}$. Then by $\mathfrak{R}/I$ we mean $\{a + I \mid a \in R\}$ together with the usual operations on it

$$((a + b) + I = (a + I) + (b + I), \qquad (a + I)(b + I) = ab + I).$$

The homomorphism $^{-}: R \to R/I$ defined by $\bar{a} = a + I$ is called the canonical homomorphism and can be "extended" to a map $R[X] \to (R/I)[X]$ by setting

$$\overline{a_0 + \cdots + a_n X^n} = \overline{a_0} + \cdots + \overline{a_n} X^n.$$

Clearly if $f \in R[X]$, $\bar{r}$ is a root of $\bar{f}$ iff $f(r) \in I$.

THEOREM 4.1.3. Let $\mathfrak{A} = \langle \mathfrak{F}, \mathfrak{M}, v \rangle$ be a valued field, $\mathfrak{N} = \mathfrak{M} \mid N$ a subgroup of $\mathfrak{M}$, and let

$$R_{\mathfrak{A},\mathfrak{N}} = \{a \in F \mid \text{for some } x \in \mathfrak{N},\ v(a) \leq x\} \cup \{0\} \quad (= R_{\mathfrak{F},\mathfrak{N}})$$

$$I_{\mathfrak{A},\mathfrak{N}} = \{a \in F \mid \text{for every } x \in \mathfrak{N},\ v(a) < x\} \cup \{0\} \quad (= I_{\mathfrak{F},\mathfrak{N}}).$$

Then

(a) $\mathfrak{R}_{\mathfrak{A},\mathfrak{N}} = \mathfrak{F} \mid R_{\mathfrak{A},\mathfrak{N}}$ is an integral domain whose field of quotients is $\mathfrak{F}$;
(b) $I_{\mathfrak{A},\mathfrak{N}}$ is a maximal ideal of $\mathfrak{R}_{\mathfrak{A},\mathfrak{N}}$.

Proof: (a) Any subring of a field must be an integral domain, so we need only check that for every $a, b \in R_{\mathfrak{A},\mathfrak{N}}$, ab, $a + b \in R_{\mathfrak{A},\mathfrak{N}}$, and that $-1 \in R_{\mathfrak{A},\mathfrak{N}}$. But

$$e = v(1) = v((-1)(-1)) = v(-1) + v(-1).$$

Since $\mathfrak{M}$ is ordered, $v(-1) = e$, so $-1 \in R_{\mathfrak{A},\mathfrak{N}}$. If $a, b \in R_{\mathfrak{A},\mathfrak{N}}$ let

$$v(a) \leq x, \qquad v(b) \leq y, \qquad x, y \in \mathfrak{N}.$$

Thus

$$v(ab) \leq x + y, \qquad v(a + b) \leq \max\{x, y\},$$

so ab, $a + b \in R_{\mathfrak{A},\mathfrak{N}}$.

Now let $a \in F$. Then if $a \notin R_{\mathfrak{A},\mathfrak{N}}$, $v(a) > e$. Thus

$$v(a^{-1}) = -v(a) < e$$

(for if $v(a) > e$, $-v(a) \geq e$, then

$$e = v(aa^{-1}) = v(a) + -v(a) > e).$$

Thus since $e \in \mathfrak{N}$, $a^{-1} \in R_{\mathfrak{A},\mathfrak{N}}$. Thus $a = 1/(a^{-1})$, an element of the field of quotients of $\mathfrak{R}_{\mathfrak{A},\mathfrak{N}}$.

(b) It is simple to show that $I_{\mathfrak{A},\mathfrak{N}}$ is closed under $+$. Now let $a \in I_{\mathfrak{A},\mathfrak{N}}$, $b \in R_{\mathfrak{A},\mathfrak{N}}$. If $v(ab) \geq x$ for some $x \in N$, let $v(a) = y$, $v(b) \leq z \in N$. Then $y + z \geq x$, so $y \geq x + -z \in N$, a contradiction to the fact that if $q \in N$ then $y < q$. $I_{\mathfrak{A},\mathfrak{N}}$ is maximal, for if $r \in R_{\mathfrak{A},\mathfrak{N}} \sim I_{\mathfrak{A},\mathfrak{N}}$, then for some $x \in \mathfrak{N}$, $v(r) \geq x$. Then

$$v(r^{-1}) \leq -x \in \mathfrak{N}, \qquad \text{so} \qquad r^{-1} \in R_{\mathfrak{A},\mathfrak{N}}.$$

Thus r is a unit in $R_{\mathfrak{A},\mathfrak{N}}$ and so cannot be in any proper ideal.

Lemma 4.1.4. Let $\mathfrak{H}$ be a subfield of $\mathfrak{R}_{\mathfrak{A},\mathfrak{N}}$, then $^{-} \mid \mathfrak{H}$ is an injection into $\mathfrak{R}_{\mathfrak{A},\mathfrak{N}}/I_{\mathfrak{A},\mathfrak{N}}$. It is an isomorphism iff for every $a \in R_{\mathfrak{A},\mathfrak{N}}$ there is a $b \in H$ such that $a - b \in I_{\mathfrak{A},\mathfrak{N}}$.

The proof is trivial. We are now interested in less trivial conditions under which this map is an isomorphism. Obviously we have no hope unless $\mathfrak{H}$ is a maximal subfield of $R_{\mathfrak{A},\mathfrak{N}}$ (for if $\mathfrak{H} \subset \mathfrak{K}$, $^{-}[H] \subset {}^{-}[K]$). Note that here and throughout this chapter, except when making comments in which the distinctions are essential, we adopt the algebraists convention of not distinguishing between a structure (such as $\mathfrak{H}$) and its universe (H).

Definition 4.1.5. Let $\mathfrak{F}$ be a subfield of the field $\mathfrak{G}$. Then $\mathfrak{F}$ is relatively algebraically closed in $\mathfrak{G}$ iff every polynomial $f \in \mathfrak{F}[X]$ with roots in G has all these roots in F. (Note that this holds iff every such polynomial has a root in F.)

An extension field $\mathfrak{G}$ of $\mathfrak{F}$ is called an algebraic extension of $\mathfrak{F}$ iff every element of G is a root of some polynomial in $\mathfrak{F}[X]$, and we note in passing that if $\mathfrak{F} \subset \mathfrak{H}$, $a \in H$ is the root of some polynomial over $\mathfrak{F}$ iff $\mathfrak{F}(a)$ is finite-dimensional as a vector space over $\mathfrak{F}$. This clearly implies that if $b \in \mathfrak{F}(a)$, a a root of some polynomial over $\mathfrak{F}$, then b is the root of some polynomial over $\mathfrak{F}$, so $\mathfrak{F}(a)$ is an algebraic extension of $\mathfrak{F}$.

Proposition 4.1.6. Let $\mathfrak{H}$ be a maximal subfield of $\mathfrak{R}_{\mathfrak{A},\mathfrak{N}}$. Then:

(a) $\mathfrak{H}$ is relatively algebraically closed in $\mathfrak{F}$;

(b) if $^{-}[\mathfrak{H}]$ is relatively algebraically closed in $\overline{\mathfrak{F}_{\mathfrak{N}}} = \mathfrak{R}_{\mathfrak{A},\mathfrak{N}}/I_{\mathfrak{A},\mathfrak{N}}$, and $H \neq \{0\}$, then $^{-} \mid \mathfrak{H}$ is an isomorphism.

Proof: (a) Let $f \in \mathfrak{H}[X]$ have a root $r \in F$, i.e., let

$$a_0 + \cdots + a_n r^n = 0 \qquad \text{where} \quad f = a_0 + \cdots + a_n X^n,$$

and assume that $a_0 \neq 0$ (what if $\mathfrak{H} = \{0\}$?). $r \notin I_{\mathfrak{A},\mathfrak{N}}$, for if $v(r) < x$ for every $x \in N$, then

$$\max\{v(a_1) + v(r), \ldots, v(a_n) + nv(r)\} < x$$

for every $x \in N$. Thus

$$v(a_0) > \max\{v(a_1) + v(r), \ldots, v(a_n) + nv(r)\},$$

and since $v(-a_0) = v(a_0)$,

$$-a_0 \neq a_1 r + \cdots + a_n r^n,$$

a contradiction.

It is also impossible that for every $x \in \mathfrak{N}$, $v(r) > x$, for if this were the case,

$$0 = (a_0 + \cdots + a_n r^n) = r^n(a_0(r^{-1})^n + \cdots + a_n),$$

so r^{-1} is a root of $a_0 X^n + \cdots + a_n$, $a_n \neq 0$, and $v(r^{-1}) < x$ for every $x \in \mathfrak{N}$. Thus if r is a root of some polynomial in $\mathfrak{H}[X]$, then $r \in R_{\mathfrak{A},\mathfrak{N}}$.

Now let $r \in F$ be a root of some $f \in \mathfrak{H}[X]$ and consider $\mathfrak{H}(r)$. Every element of $\mathfrak{H}(r)$ is a root of some polynomial over $\mathfrak{H}$, thus every element of $\mathfrak{H}(r)$ is contained in $R_{\mathfrak{A},\mathfrak{N}}$, thus

$$\mathfrak{H} \subset \mathfrak{H}(r) \subset R_{\mathfrak{A},\mathfrak{N}},$$

so by the maximality of $\mathfrak{H}$,

$$\mathfrak{H} = \mathfrak{H}(r), \qquad \text{so} \quad r \in H.$$

(b) If (by way of contradiction) $c \in \bar{\mathfrak{F}}_{\mathfrak{N}} \sim {}^{-}[\mathfrak{H}]$ then c is not the root of a polynomial over ${}^{-}[\mathfrak{H}]$ because of our assumption. Let $k \in R_{\mathfrak{A},\mathfrak{N}}$, $\bar{k} = c$. Then $k \notin H$; let $f \in \mathfrak{H}[X]$, $f \neq 0$. Then clearly if $f(k) \in I_{\mathfrak{A},\mathfrak{N}}$, $\bar{f}(c) = 0$, a contradiction.

Thus for every nonzero $f \in \mathfrak{H}[X]$, $f(k) \notin I_{\mathfrak{A},\mathfrak{N}}$, so $f(k)$ is a unit in $R_{\mathfrak{A},\mathfrak{N}}$. Thus

$$\{f(k)/g(k) \mid f, g \in \mathfrak{H}[X], g \neq 0\}$$

yields a proper extension of $\mathfrak{H}$, which is contained in $\mathfrak{R}_{\mathfrak{A},\mathfrak{N}}$, contradicting the maximality of $\mathfrak{H}$.

For the remainder of this chapter we shall use the following notations: $\bar{\mathfrak{F}} = \bar{\mathfrak{F}}_{\{e\}}$, $R_{\mathfrak{A}} = R_{\mathfrak{F}} = R_{\mathfrak{A},\{e\}}$, etc., and $\mathfrak{H}$ or $\mathfrak{H}_{\mathfrak{A}}$ will denote a maximal subfield of $\mathfrak{R}_{\mathfrak{A}}$. For any field $\mathfrak{F}$, $\tilde{\mathfrak{F}}$ will denote the algebraic closure of $\mathfrak{F}$.

We shall on occasion be using some fairly nonobvious facts from field theory and we suggest that the reader have available references in the subject, such as *Algebraic Extensions of Fields* by P. McCarthy.

In a valued field, $v(a + b) \leq \max\{v(a), v(b)\}$. If, however, $v(a) \neq v(b)$, then

$$v(a + b) = \max\{v(a), v(b)\},$$

for otherwise, $v(a), v(a + b) < v(b)$, so

$$v(-a), v(a + b) < v(b),$$

so

$$v(b) \leq \max\{v(a + b), v(-a)\} < v(b),$$

a contradiction.

Ax and Kochen make considerable use of the following well-known property studied by Hensel and called Hensel's lemma:

Let $f \in \mathfrak{R}_{\mathfrak{F}}[X]$, $\bar{f} = F \in \bar{\mathfrak{F}}[X]$. If $F = GH$ with $G, H \in \bar{\mathfrak{F}}[X]$ relatively prime (see Problem 4.1.12), then $f = gh$ for some $g, h \in \mathfrak{F}[X]$ such that $\deg(g) = \deg(G)$.

Not every valued field satisfies Hensel's lemma, but we shall be interested in those that do, and shall therefore study some of its consequences. The proof of the following theorem is rather difficult, but can be found in McCarthy (in a special case, but the generalization is clear).

THEOREM 4.1.7. $\langle \mathfrak{F}, \mathfrak{M}, v \rangle$ satisfies Hensel's lemma iff $\langle \mathfrak{F}, \mathfrak{M}, v \rangle$ has the uniqueness property, where:

DEFINITION 4.1.8. Let $\mathfrak{A} = \langle \mathfrak{F}, \mathfrak{M}, v \rangle$ be a valued field. Then $\mathfrak{A}$ is said to have the uniqueness property iff for every algebraic extension $\mathfrak{G}$ of $\mathfrak{F}$ there is an $\mathfrak{N}$, w such that $\mathfrak{B} = \langle \mathfrak{G}, \mathfrak{N}, w \rangle$ is a valued field and $\mathfrak{A} \subset \mathfrak{B}$, and further, this $\mathfrak{B}$ is unique up to isomorphism. (NOTE: By an isomorphism, we mean an isomorphism of the first-order structures associated with our valued fields; see Problem 4.1.2).

LEMMA 4.1.9. (a) Let $\mathfrak{F}$ be a field of characteristic 0, $\langle \mathfrak{F}, \mathfrak{M}, v \rangle$ satisfy Hensel's Lemma, $f \in R_{\mathfrak{F}}[X]$ be monic. If $r_1, \ldots, r_n$ are the roots of f (possibly in an extension field $\mathfrak{G}$ of $\mathfrak{F}$), and

$$v(f(a)) < \sum_{i \neq j} w(r_i - r_j) \qquad (= v(D(f)))$$

for some $a \in R_{\mathfrak{F}}$ (where w is given by 4.1.7 and 4.1.8), f has a root in $R_{\mathfrak{F}}$.

(b) Let $\mathfrak{F}$ be a field of characteristic 0, $\langle \mathfrak{F}, \mathfrak{M}, v \rangle$ satisfy Hensel's lemma, $\mathfrak{H}$ be a maximal subfield of $\mathfrak{R}_{\mathfrak{A}}$, and $f \in \mathfrak{H}[X]$. If for some $a \in R_{\mathfrak{A}}$, $v(f(a)) < e$, then f has a root in $R_{\mathfrak{A}}$.

(c) If $\langle \mathfrak{F}, \mathfrak{M}, v \rangle$ satisfies Hensel's lemma and $\mathfrak{F}$, $\bar{\mathfrak{F}}$ are both of characteristic 0, then $^{-} \mid \mathfrak{H}$ is an isomorphism.

Proof: (b) is a special case of (a), for if $\mathfrak{H}'$ is algebraic over $\mathfrak{H}$, part of the proof of 4.1.6(a) shows w to be trivial on $\mathfrak{H}'$, so

$$\sum_{i \neq j} w(r_i - r_j) = e.$$

For (a), note first that if $f(r) = 0$ then $w(r) \leq e$, since if $f = b_0 + \cdots + X^n$, $b_0 + \cdots + r^n = 0$, and $w(r) > e$, then

$$w(-r^n) = nw(r) > jw(r) \geq jw(r) + w(b_j) = w(b_j r^j) \qquad \text{for} \quad j < n,$$

so

$$-r^n \neq b_0 + \cdots + b_{n-1} r^{n-1},$$

a contradiction. Also, if r_i and r_j are roots,

$$w(r_i - r_j) \leq \max\{w(r_i), w(-r_j)\} \leq e.$$

There is a j such that if $k \neq j$,

$$w(a - r_j) < w(r_j - r_k),$$

since otherwise we have for $j = 1, \ldots, n$, $s(j)$ such that

$$w(a - r_j) \geq w(r_j - r_{s(j)}),$$

thus

$$v(f(a)) = v((a - r_1)\cdots(a - r_n)) \geq \sum_{j=1} w(r_j - r_{s(j)}) \geq \sum_{i \neq j} w(r_j - r_i),$$

a contradiction.

Assume now, by way of contradiction, that $\mathfrak{F} \neq \mathfrak{F}(r_j)$. By field theory there is an isomorphism $\varphi\colon \tilde{\mathfrak{F}} \to \tilde{\mathfrak{F}}$ such that the restriction of φ to $\mathfrak{F}$ is the identity map and $\varphi(r_j) = r_i$ for some $i \neq j$. Thus $\varphi(a - r_j) = a - r_i$, and so $w(a - r_j) = w(a - r_i)$, for otherwise $w'(b) = w(\varphi(b))$ would be a new valuation on $\tilde{\mathfrak{F}}$ and by Problem 4.1.6, no such w' exists. But

$$w(r_i - r_j) \leq \max\{w(a - r_i), w(a - r_j)\} \leq w(a - r_j),$$

a contradiction.

(c) Since $\mathfrak{F}$, $\overline{\mathfrak{F}}$ both have characteristic 0 they both have prime fields isomorphic to $\mathbb{Q}$. We first show $\mathbb{Q} \subset \mathfrak{R}_{\mathfrak{F}}$, thus assuring $H \neq \{0\}$. $v(1) = e$, and if $v(n) \leq e$, then

$$v(n + 1) \leq \max\{e, v(n)\} \leq e.$$

Also, $v(-n) = v(n) \leq e$, so in any valued field, $v(n) \leq e$ for every integer n. However, $v(n) = e$, for if $v(n) < e$, then $\bar{n} = 0$ in $\overline{\mathfrak{F}}$, contradicting the fact that $\overline{\mathfrak{F}}$ is of characteristic 0. If $a/b \in Q$, then

$$v(a/b) = v(a) - v(b) = e, \qquad \text{so} \qquad \mathbb{Q} \subset \mathfrak{R}_{\mathfrak{F}}.$$

We now show that $\overline{\mathfrak{H}}$ is algebraically closed in $\overline{\mathfrak{F}}$. Let r represent a root of $f \in \overline{\mathfrak{H}}[X]$, $r \in \bar{F} \sim \bar{H}$; and let $f = \bar{g}$, $r = \bar{s}$, $g \in \mathfrak{H}[X]$, $s \in \mathfrak{R}_{\mathfrak{F}}$. Thus $v(g(s)) < e$, so by (a), g has a root in $\mathfrak{F}$, and since $\mathfrak{H}$ is algebraically closed in $\mathfrak{F}$, this root is in $\mathfrak{H}$. Thus f has a root in $\overline{\mathfrak{H}}$, so $\overline{\mathfrak{H}}$ is algebracally closed in $\overline{\mathfrak{F}}$, and an application of Proposition 4.1.6 completes the proof.

From now on, we take notational advantage of the uniqueness of the extension of our valuation by calling it v rather than w. Recall now that a polynomial is called factorable iff it is the product of two polynomials of positive degree (otherwise it is irreducible).

PROPOSITION 4.1.10. (a) Let $\langle \mathfrak{F}, \mathfrak{M}, v\rangle$ satisfy Hensel's lemma, and let

$$f = a_0 + \cdots + a_nX^n \in \mathfrak{F}[X]$$

be such that for some integer r,

$$0 < r < n \qquad \text{and} \qquad v(a_r) > \max\{v(a_0), v(a_n)\}.$$

Then f is factorable.

(b) Let $\langle \mathfrak{F}, \mathfrak{M}, v\rangle$ satisfy Hensel's lemma and let $\text{char}(\mathfrak{F}) = \text{char}(\overline{\mathfrak{F}}) = 0$, $\overline{\mathfrak{F}}$ be algebraically closed, $\mathfrak{M}$ divisible. Then $\mathfrak{F}$ is algebraically closed.

Proof: (a) Let

$$v(a_s) = \max\{v(a_i) \mid 0 \leq i \leq n\},$$

$$f^* = (1/a_s)f = (a_0/a_s) + \cdots + (a_n/a_s)X^n \in \mathfrak{R}_{\mathfrak{F}}[X].$$

$\overline{f^*} = \overline{f^*}1$, where $\overline{f^*}, 1 \in \overline{\mathfrak{F}}[X]$ and are obviously relatively prime. Also since $v(a_0/a_s), v(a_n/a_s) < e$,

$$0 < \deg(\overline{f^*}) < \deg(f^*).$$

Thus f^* (and therefore f) is factorable by Hensel's lemma.

(b) We first note that it will suffice to show that every polynomial of degree > 1 is factorable, for once this is known, repeated factorization can be carried out until linear factors, thus roots, are found for each polynomial.

Familiar algebraic manipulations show that a polynomial $a_0 + \cdots + a_nX^n$ is factorable iff $a_0 + \cdots + a_n(X + b)^n$ is, where $b \in F$, also that it is factorable iff $a_0 + \cdots + a_n(bX)^n$ is, where $b \in F \sim \{0\}$. We also know that for each polynomial there is a $b \in F$ such that

$$a_0 + \cdots + a_n(X + b)^n = c_0 + \cdots + c_nX^n, \qquad \text{and} \qquad c_{n-1} = 0.$$

We now proceed to show that each polynomial of this last form is factorable.

Thus let $f \in \mathfrak{F}[X]$, $f = a_0 + \cdots + a_nX^n$, $a_{n-1} = 0$. First select $a \in F$ such that

$$nv(a) = v(a_0) - v(a_n)$$

(a selection possible by the divisibility of $\mathfrak{M}$) and consider

$$a_0 + \cdots + a_n(aX)^n = a_0 + \cdots + a_na^nX^n.$$

Since $\overline{\mathfrak{H}} = \overline{\mathfrak{F}}$, we can find $b_0, \ldots, b_n \in H$ (with $b_{n-1} = 0$) such that for $0 \leq j \leq n$,

$$\overline{b_j} = \overline{a_ja^j} \qquad (\text{thus } b_j - a_ja^j \in I_{\mathfrak{F}}).$$

Since $\mathfrak{H} \cong \overline{\mathfrak{F}}$, $\mathfrak{H}$ is algebraically closed, so $h = b_0 + \cdots + b_nX^n$ has a root $r \in H$, thus $h(r) = 0$, so

$$g(r) = g(r) - h(r) = (a_0 - b_0) + \cdots + (a_na^n - b_n)r^n,$$

and since $a_ja^j - b_j \in I_{\mathfrak{F}}$, $r^j \in R_{\mathfrak{F}}$,

$$g(r) \in I_{\mathfrak{F}}.$$

Now consider

$$c_0 + \cdots + c_nX^n = a_0 + \cdots + a_na^n(X - r)^n.$$

$c_0 = g(r) \in I_{\mathfrak{F}}$, and expanding the right side of our equation, we see that

$$v(c_{n-1}) = v(-n) + v(r) = e.$$

Choose d such that $nv(d) = v(c_0)$ and consider that

$$k = c_0 + \cdots + c_n(dX)^n.$$

Then $v(d) < e$ (since $nv(d) < e$) and

$$v(c_{n-1}d^{n-1}) = v(c_0) - v(d) > v(c_0),$$
$$v(c_{n+1}d^{n-1}) > v(c_n) + nv(d) = v(c_nd^n),$$

so by (a), k is factorable, and thus so is f. Thus each polynomial over $\mathfrak{F}$ is factorable.

We now consider a concept closely related to completeness (in the sense of topology, not of logic).

Definition 4.1.11. Let λ be a limit ordinal, $a: \lambda \to F$, $\langle \mathfrak{F}, \mathfrak{M}, v\rangle$ a valued field, $S \subset M$, a is S-Cauchy iff for every $s \in S$ there is a $\sigma < \lambda$ such that if $\sigma < \tau < \beta < \lambda$, then $v(a_\tau - a_\beta) < s$. Here and henceforth we use the convention that $v(x - y) < s$ really means $v(x - y) < s$ or $x = y$.

If $a: \lambda \to F$, $b \in F$ is an S-limit for a iff for every $s \in S$ there is a $\sigma < \lambda$ such that if $\sigma < \tau < \lambda$ then $v(a_\tau - b) < s$.

$\langle \mathfrak{F}, \mathfrak{M}, v\rangle$ is pseudocomplete iff for every $S \subset M$, every limit ordinal λ, every S-Cauchy λ-sequence has an S-limit. It is called $\leq \kappa$-pseudocomplete iff every S-Cauchy λ-sequence has an S-limit when $c(S) \leq \kappa$.

If a has an S-limit, then a is S-Cauchy, for if $s \in S$, choose σ such that if $\sigma < \tau < \lambda$, then $v(a_\tau - b) < s$. Then if $\sigma < \tau < \beta < \lambda$, we have

$$v(a_\tau - a_\beta) \leq \max\{v(a_\tau - b), v(a_\beta - b)\} < s.$$

It should be noted that S-limits are not necessarily unique. In fact, let

$$J_S = \{x \in F \mid \text{if } s \in S, \text{ then } v(x) < s\} \cup \{0\}.$$

Then:

COROLLARY 4.1.12. (a) J_S is a subgroup of $\langle F, +, 0\rangle$ and if for some $s \in S$, $s \leq e$, then J_S is an ideal in $\mathfrak{R}_{\mathfrak{F}}$.

(b) Let b be an S-limit of the λ-sequence a. Then c is an S-limit of a iff $b - c \in J_S$.

The proof is not difficult and is left for the reader. Thus S-limits are unique iff $J_S = \{0\}$, i.e., iff for every $x \in M$ and $s \in S$ can be found such that $s < x$.

Suppose that $\mathfrak{M} \subset \langle \mathbb{R}, +, 0, <\rangle$. We define

$$\varphi: \mathfrak{M} \to \langle \{x \in \mathbb{R} \mid x > 0\}, \cdot, 1, <\rangle$$

by $\varphi(x) = 2^x$. Note that φ is an injection, and for $b, c \in F$, define $d(b, c) = \varphi(v(b - c))$. It is simple to check that d is a metric and that if

$$\mathfrak{M} = \langle \mathbb{Z}, +, 0, <\rangle,$$

$\langle \mathfrak{F}, \mathfrak{M}, v\rangle$ is pseudocomplete iff $\langle F, d\rangle$ is a complete metric space (see Problem 4.1.8). Thus we call such an $\langle \mathfrak{F}, \mathfrak{M}, v\rangle$ complete iff it is pseudocomplete. No countable metric space with non-open points is complete (by the Baire category theorem), thus $\langle \mathbb{Q}, \mathbb{Z}, v_p\rangle$ is never complete, and neither is

$$\langle \mathfrak{F}(X), \mathbb{Z}, v_f\rangle \qquad \text{or} \qquad \langle \mathfrak{F}(X), \mathbb{Z}, v\rangle$$

for any countable $\mathfrak{F}$. However, these all have completions, and among their completions are valued fields with which we shall be concerned, namely $\langle \mathbb{Q}_p, \mathbb{Z}, v_p\rangle$ the p-adic numbers (the completion of $\langle \mathbb{Q}, \mathbb{Z}, v_p\rangle$) and $\langle \mathbb{Z}_p((X)), \mathbb{Z}, v_x\rangle$ (the completion of $\langle \mathbb{Z}_p(X), \mathbb{Z}, v_x\rangle$,† where $x = X$, $\mathbb{Z}_p = \mathbb{Z}/p\mathbb{Z}$). We shall study these more closely in the problems. We close this section with a connection between pseudocompleteness and Hensel's lemma.

† In general, we define $\langle \mathfrak{F}((X)), \mathbb{Z}, v_x\rangle$ to be the completion of $\langle \mathfrak{F}(X), \mathbb{Z}, v_x\rangle$. In Problem 4.1.5, it is shown that

$$\mathfrak{F}((X)) = \left\{\sum_n^\infty a_j X^j \mid n \in \mathbb{Z}, \text{each } a_j \in \mathfrak{F}\right\}$$

with addition defined coordinatewise, multiplication by

$$\left(\sum_n^\infty a_j X^j\right)\left(\sum_m^\infty b_j X^j\right) = \sum_{m+n}^\infty \left(\sum_{j+k=r} a_j b_k\right) X^r.$$

THEOREM 4.1.13. If $\langle \mathfrak{F}, \mathfrak{M}, v\rangle$ is pseudocomplete, then $\langle \mathfrak{F}, \mathfrak{M}, v\rangle$ satisfies Hensel's lemma.

Proof: Let $\bar{f} = F = GH$, G, H relatively prime,

$$r = \deg(G), \qquad s = \deg(f) - r,$$

and D be the set of all

$$\langle \lambda, a_0, \ldots, a_r, b_0, \ldots, b_s, m\rangle$$

such that $\lambda = 0$ or λ is a limit ordinal,

$$a_0, \ldots, b_s\colon \lambda \to F,$$

$m\colon \lambda \to \{x \in M \mid x < e\}$ and is strictly decreasing, and

(1) for every $\tau < \lambda$,

$$\overline{a_0(\tau)} + \cdots + \overline{a_r(\tau)}X^r = G \qquad \text{and} \qquad \overline{b_0(\tau)} + \cdots + \overline{b_s(\tau)}X^s = H;$$

(2) if $\kappa \le \lambda$ is a limit ordinal and c is one of $a_0, \ldots, b_s$, then $c \mid \kappa$ is an $m[\{\alpha \mid \alpha < \kappa\}]$-Cauchy κ-sequence, and if $\kappa \le \tau < \lambda$, then $c(\tau)$ is an $m[\{\alpha \mid \alpha < \kappa\}]$-limit for $c \mid \kappa$;

(3) if $\tau < \lambda$ and $v(d) \ge m(\tau)$, then

$$f = (a_0(\tau) + \cdots + a_r(\tau)X^r)(b_0(\tau) + \cdots + b_s(\tau)X_s) \in dR[X].$$

Note that D is partially ordered by $\prec$, where

$$\langle \lambda, a_0, \ldots, m\rangle \prec \langle \lambda', \ldots, m'\rangle$$

iff $\lambda \subset \lambda'$ and $a_0 \subset a_0'$, and $\cdots$ and $m \subset m'$. Clearly if $C \subset D$ is a chain under $\prec$, C is bounded in D by the $1 + (r + 1) + (s + 1) + 1$-tuple, each coordinate of which is the union of the corresponding coordinate of the elements of C, so D has maximal elements. From now on, let $\langle \lambda, a_0, \ldots, m\rangle$ denote such an element, and, provided that $\lambda > 0$, let $a_i(\lambda)$, $b_j(\lambda)$ denote $\mathscr{R}(m)$-limits of a_i, b_j respectively. We also set

$$g_\tau = a_0(\tau) + \cdots + a_r(\tau)X^r, \qquad h_\tau = b_0(\tau) + \cdots + b_s(\tau)X^s$$

for $\tau \le \lambda$.

We show that $f = g_\lambda h_\lambda$. For otherwise, let d_0 be a coefficient of $f = g_\lambda h_\lambda$ of maximum value. We shall construct sequences $g_{\lambda+1}, g_{\lambda+2}, \ldots, h_{\lambda+1}, h_{\lambda+2}, \ldots$ of polynomials of degrees r and s respectively such that if we set

$$g_{\lambda+n} = a_0(\lambda + n) + \cdots + a_r(\lambda + n)X^r,$$

$$h_{\lambda+n} = b_0(\lambda + n) + \cdots + b_s(\lambda + n)X^s,$$

then the above definitions extend $a_0, \ldots, b_s$ to $\lambda + \omega$-sequences, and if

$$m(\lambda + n) = \max\{v(a_0(\lambda + n)), \ldots, v(b_s(\lambda + n))\},$$

then $\langle \lambda + \omega, a_0, \ldots, m \rangle \in D$, a contradiction. In this construction, we use the fact that since G, H are relatively prime, polynomials $j_q, k_q \in R_{\mathfrak{F}}[X]$ exist for $q = 0, \ldots, \deg(f)$ such that

$$\deg(k_q) \le s, \qquad \deg(j_q) \le r, \qquad \text{and} \qquad G\bar{k}_q + H\bar{j}_q = X^q$$

(see Problem 4.1.12). Thus there is a $d \in \mathfrak{F}$ such that $v(d) < e$ and for $0 \le q \le \deg(f)$,

$$X^q - g_{\lambda+n}k_q - h_{\lambda+n}j_q \in dR_{\mathfrak{F}}[X]$$

(in fact, since

$$\overline{X^q - g_{\lambda+n}k_q - h_{\lambda+n}j_q} = 0,$$

$v(c) < e$ for each coefficient c of

$$X^q - g_{\lambda+n}k_q - h_{\lambda+n}j_q \qquad \text{for each} \quad q,$$

and d may be taken to be a coefficient of maximum value among those that appear in all of the $X^q - g_{\lambda+n}k_q - h_{\lambda+n}j_q$). Write, as we may,

$$f - g_{\lambda+n}h_{\lambda+n} = p_0 + \cdots + p_{r+s}X^{r+s} \in d_nR_{\mathfrak{F}}[X],$$

and let

$$g_{\lambda+n+1} = g_{\lambda+n} + p_0j_0 + \cdots + p_{r+s}j_{r+s},$$
$$h_{\lambda+n+1} = h_{\lambda+n} + \cdots + p_{r+s}k_{r+s}.$$

Then

$$g_{\lambda+n+1} - g_{\lambda+n} = p_0j_0 + \cdots + p_{r+s}j_{r+s} \subset d_nR_{\mathfrak{F}}[X],$$

similarly

$$h_{\lambda+n+1} - h_{\lambda+n} \in d_nR_{\mathfrak{F}}[X],$$

and

$$\deg(g_{\lambda+n+1}) \le \max\{\deg(g_{\lambda+n}), \ldots, \deg(j_{r+s})\} \le r, \quad \deg(h_{\lambda+n+1}) \le s.$$

Also

$$\begin{aligned}
f - g_{\lambda+n+1}h_{\lambda+n+1} &= f - (g_{\lambda+n} + \cdots + p_{r+s}j_{r+s})(h_{\lambda+n} + \cdots + p_{r+s}k_{r+s}) \\
&= (f - g_{\lambda+n}h_{\lambda+n}) - g_{\lambda+n}(p_0k_0 + \cdots + p_{r+s}k_{r+s}) \\
&\quad - h_{\lambda+n}(p_0j_0 + \cdots + p_{r+s}j_{r+s}) - \sum_{q,q'=0}^{r+s} (p_qj_qp_{q'}k_{q'}) \\
&= p_0 + \cdots + p_{r+s}X^{r+s} - p_0(g_{\lambda+n}k_0 + h_{\lambda+n}j_0) - \cdots \\
&\quad - p_{r+s}(g_{\lambda+n}k_{r+s} + h_{\lambda+n}j_{r+s}) - \sum_{q,q'=0}^{r+s} (p_qp_{q'})(j_qk_{q'}) \\
&= [p_0(1 - g_{\lambda+n}k_0 - h_{\lambda+n}j_0) + \cdots \\
&\quad + p_{r+s}(X^{r+s} - g_{\lambda+n}k_{r+s} - h_{\lambda+n}j_{r+s})] \\
&\quad - \sum_{q,q'=0}^{r+s} (p_qp_{q'})(j_qk_{q'}) \in dd_nR_{\mathfrak{F}}[X] + d_n^2R_{\mathfrak{F}}[X],
\end{aligned}$$

and since $v(d)$, $v(d_n) < e$,

$$v(dd_n),\ v(d_n^2) < v(d_n),$$

so if d_{n+1} is any element of $\mathfrak{F}$ such that

$$v(d_{n+1}) = \max\{v(d_n^2),\ v(dd_n)\},$$

$$f - g_{\lambda+n+1}h_{\lambda+n+1} \in d_{n+1}R_{\mathfrak{F}}[X].$$

Now for $n < \omega$, we define

$$m(\lambda + n) = \max\{v(a_0(\lambda + n)), \ldots, v(b_s(\lambda + n))\},$$

and leave for the reader the now-simple verification of (1) through (3) for $\langle \lambda + \omega, a_0, \ldots, b_s, m\rangle$ as defined above, contradicting the maximality of $\langle \lambda, \ldots, m\rangle$.

If $\lambda = 0$, we can find g_0, h_0 such that $\overline{g_0} = G$, $\overline{h_0} = H$,

$$\deg(g_0) = \deg(G), \qquad \deg(h_0) = \deg(H) \leq \deg(f) - \deg(g_0),$$

and if $f \neq g_0h_0$, we proceed in the construction of $\langle \omega, a_0, \ldots, m\rangle$ in the same manner as above, beginning with g_0, h_0 in place of g_λ, h_λ, again contradicting the maximality of $\langle \lambda, \ldots, m\rangle$.

Problems

‡4.1.1 (a) Prove Corollary 4.1.2 (a).

(b) Let $\mathfrak{F}$ be the field if quotients of the integral domain $\mathfrak{R}$, and let I be a prime ideal in $\mathfrak{R}$. For ideals $J, K \subset R$, let

$$JK = \{a_1b_1 + \cdots + a_nb_n \mid n \in \omega, a_1, \ldots, a_n \in J, b_1, \ldots, b_n \in K\},$$

and for any ideal J, set

$$J^0 = R, \qquad J^{n+1} = J^nJ.$$

Show JK to be an ideal. Now assume that $\bigcap_{n\in\omega} I^n = \{0\}$.

For $a \in R \sim \{0\}$, set $v_I(a) = -n$, where $n = \max\{m \mid a \in I^m\}$, and for $r \in F$, let $r = a/b$ and set

$$v_I(r) = v_I(a) - v_I(b).$$

Show that v_I is a valuation on $\mathfrak{F}$ (i.e., $\langle \mathfrak{F}, \mathbb{Z}, v_I\rangle$ is a valued field).

Show that if $\langle \mathfrak{F}, \mathbb{Z}, v\rangle$ is a valued field then it is of the form described above.

(c) Prove Corollary 4.1.2 (b) and (c).

‡4.1.2 Write axioms for the concept of valued field. Also show that a mapping f from a valued field $\mathfrak{A}$ into another $\mathfrak{A}'$ (actually f maps the disjoint union of F and M into that of F' and M') is an isomorphism of the

structures suggested following Corollary 4.1.2 iff $f \mid F: \mathfrak{F} \cong \mathfrak{F}'$, $f \mid M: \mathfrak{M} \cong \mathfrak{M}'$, and for every $a \in F$, $f(v(a)) = v'(f(a))$.

Thus we call an isomorphism $f: \mathfrak{F} \cong \mathfrak{F}'$ together with an isomorphism (for which we use the same name) $f: \mathfrak{M} \cong \mathfrak{M}'$ such that $f(v(a)) = v'(f(a))$ an isomorphism of valued fields (provided that $\langle \mathfrak{F}, \mathfrak{M}, v \rangle$, $\langle \mathfrak{F}', \mathfrak{M}', v' \rangle$ are valued fields).

4.1.3 Provide an example of a valued field with $^-: \mathfrak{H} \not\cong \overline{\mathfrak{F}}_{\{e\}}$.

‡4.1.4 (a) Show that if $\text{char}(\mathfrak{F}) = p \neq 0$, then $\text{char}(\overline{\mathfrak{F}}) = p$.
(b) Show that $\text{char}(\mathbb{Q}_p) = 0$, but $\overline{\mathbb{Q}}_p$ is isomorphic to the integers modulo p.
(c) If $\text{char}(\overline{\mathfrak{F}}) = 0$, then $\text{char}(\mathfrak{F}) = 0$.

‡4.1.5 Let $L \subset R_{\mathfrak{F}}$ be such that $0 \in L$, and if $r \in R_{\mathfrak{F}}$, there is a unique $s \in L$ such that $r - s \in I_{\mathfrak{F}}$. Suppose that $\mathfrak{M} \cong \mathbb{Z}$ and that $\langle \mathfrak{F}, \mathfrak{M}, v \rangle$ is complete, i the smallest positive element of M. If $\{a_j \mid j \in \mathbb{Z}\} \subset F$ is such that for each $j \in \mathbb{Z}$, $v(a_j) = -ji$ show that for each $f \in F$ there is an $n \in \mathbb{Z}$ such that $f = \sum_{j=n}^{\infty} s_j a_j$ with $s_j \in L$ for each j, and this series (and n) is unique. Also show that for every $n \in \mathbb{Z}$, $\{s_n, s_{n+1}, \ldots\} \subset S$, $\sum_{j=n}^{\infty} s_j a_j$ converges to some element of F.

As a special case if $v(a) = -i$, then for each $f \in F$ there is a unique series $\sum_{j=n}^{\infty} s_j a^j$ converging to f.

In particular, each element of $\mathbb{Q}_p$ can be expressed as $\sum_{j=n}^{\infty} a_j p^j$, where $a_j \in \{0, \ldots, p-1\}$ for each j. Each element of $\mathbb{Z}_p((X))$ can be expressed as $\sum_{j=n}^{\infty} a_j X^j$, again with $a_j \in \{0, \ldots, p-1\}$ for each j.

‡4.1.6 Let $\mathfrak{G}$ be an algebraic extension of $\mathfrak{F}$, and suppose that $\langle \mathfrak{F}, \mathfrak{M}, v \rangle \subset \langle \mathfrak{G}, \mathfrak{N}, w \rangle$ (both valued fields). Show that if $y \in N$, then $ny \in M$ for some $n \in \mathbb{Z}$. Next show that there is no nontrivial automorphism of $\mathfrak{N}$ that is trivial on $\mathfrak{M}$. Finally, use this to show that if $\langle \mathfrak{F}, \mathfrak{M}, v \rangle$ satisfies the uniqueness property and $\langle \mathfrak{F}, \mathfrak{M}, v \rangle \subset \langle \mathfrak{G}, \mathfrak{N}, w' \rangle$, then $w = w'$, thus completing the proof of Lemma 4.1.9 (a).

‡4.1.7 Write a set of first-order sentences equivalent to Hensel's lemma.

4.1.8 If $\mathbb{Z} = \mathfrak{M}$, show that the $\langle \mathfrak{F}, d \rangle$ of the comments following Corollary 4.1.12 is complete iff $\langle \mathfrak{F}, \mathfrak{M}, v \rangle$ is pseudocomplete.

4.1.9 The original definition of pseudocompleteness, due to Ostrowski and used by Kaplansky, differs from ours. They use the concept of psuedo-Cauchy λ-sequence: $a: \lambda \to F$ is pseudo-Cauchy iff when $\alpha < \beta < \gamma < \lambda$ then

$$v(a_\beta - a_\gamma) < v(a_\alpha - a_\beta).$$

(a) Define $m_a: \lambda \to M$ by $m_a(\kappa) = v(a_\kappa - a_{\kappa+1})$ for $\kappa < \lambda$. Show that if $a: \lambda \to F$ is pseudo-Cauchy and $\alpha < \beta < \lambda$, then

$$v(a_\alpha - a_\beta) = m_a(\alpha).$$

b is called a pseudo-limit of the pseudo-Cauchy λ-sequence a iff for each $\alpha < \lambda$,

$$v(a_\alpha - b) = m_a(\alpha).$$

$\langle \mathfrak{F}, \mathfrak{M}, v \rangle$ is called λ-pseudocomplete iff each pseudo-Cauchy λ-sequence has a pseudo-limit, and $\langle \mathfrak{F}, \mathfrak{M}, v \rangle$ is pseudo-complete (in the sense of Ostrowski) iff it is λ-pseudo-complete for each limit ordinal λ.

(b) If for every S with $c(S) \leq c(\lambda)$, every S-Cauchy sequence (on any ordinal α) has an S-limit, then $\langle \mathfrak{F}, \mathfrak{M}, v \rangle$ is κ-pseudocomplete for each limit ordinal $\kappa \leq \lambda$. (Thus $\leq\lambda$-pseudocomplete implies κ-pseudocomplete for each limit ordinal $\kappa \leq \lambda$.)

For any $S \subset M$, let co(S) be the least ordinal β such that for some $\varphi: \beta \to S$, φ is monotone decreasing (i.e., if $\alpha < \gamma < \beta$, then $\varphi(\alpha) > \varphi(\gamma)$), and for every $s \in S$, there is a $\gamma < \beta$ such that $\varphi(\gamma) < s$. Also, for $m \in M$, $S \subset M$, define $m < S$ iff $m < s$ for every $s \in S$. (Note that $\text{co}(S) = \text{cf}(\langle S, > | S \rangle)$.)

(c) Let $a: \lambda \to F$ be S-Cauchy and assume that there is a $\kappa < \lambda$ such that if $\kappa < \sigma < \tau < \lambda$, then $v(a_\sigma - a_\tau) < S$. Then if $\kappa < \sigma < \lambda$, a_σ is an S-limit of a.

(d) If $a: \lambda \to F$ is S-Cauchy and no $\kappa < \lambda$ is such that if $\kappa < \sigma < \tau < \lambda$, then $v(a_\sigma - a_\tau) < S$, prove there is a monotone increasing $\psi: \text{co}(S) \to \lambda$ such that $\mathscr{R}\psi$ is cofinal in λ.

(e) Let $\langle \mathfrak{F}, \mathfrak{M}, v \rangle$ be β-psuedocomplete for every limit ordinal $\beta \leq \lambda$. Then $\langle \mathfrak{F}, \mathfrak{M}, v \rangle$ is $\leq\lambda$-pseudocomplete.

(f) Show that $\langle \mathfrak{F}, \mathfrak{M}, v \rangle$ is pseudocomplete in the sense of Ostrowski iff it is pseudocomplete in our sense.

‡4.1.10 Show that if $\mathfrak{G}$ is algebraically closed in $\mathfrak{F}$, $\langle \mathfrak{G}, \mathfrak{N}, w \rangle \subset \langle \mathfrak{F}, \mathfrak{M}, v \rangle$, and $\langle \mathfrak{F}, \mathfrak{M}, v \rangle$ satisfies Hensel's lemma, then so does $\langle \mathfrak{G}, \mathfrak{N}, w \rangle$. (Hint: If $f \in \mathfrak{G}[X]$ can be factored over $\mathfrak{F}$, show the coefficients of some factors (thus of all factors) to be algebraic over $\mathfrak{G}$.)

‡4.1.11 Let $a: \lambda \to F$ be S-Cauchy. Show that either for some $m \in M$ there is an $s \in S$ such that $s \leq m$ and a $\sigma < \lambda$ such that if $\sigma < \tau < \lambda$ then $v(a_\tau) = m$, or 0 is an S-limit of a.

‡4.1.12 Let $\mathfrak{F}$ be a field, $\mathfrak{F}[X]$ its ring of polynomials.

(a) Show the Euclidean algorithm: If $f, g \in \mathfrak{F}[X]$, $f \neq 0$, then $g = fh + r$ for some $h, r \in \mathfrak{F}[X]$ with $r = 0$ or $\deg(r) < \deg(f)$.

(b) If $I \subset \mathfrak{F}[X]$ is an ideal, $f \in I$ of minimal degree, then prove

$$I = f\mathfrak{F}[X] = \{fg \mid g \in \mathfrak{F}[X]\};$$

f is called a generator of I.

The greatest common divisor (f, g) of f and g is defined to be the monic polynomial generating $\{af + bg \mid a, b \in \mathfrak{F}[X]\}$, the least common multiple to be the monic generator of $f\mathfrak{F}[X] \cap g\mathfrak{F}[X]$. f and g are said to be relatively prime if $(f, g) = 1$.

(c) Show that (f, g) is a divisor of f and g and that every divisor of f and g divides (f, g); that $[f, g]$, the least common multiple of f and g is a multiple of f and g and every multiple of f and g is divided by $[f, g]$.

Also show that $(f, g)[f, g] = rfg$ for some $r \in \mathfrak{F}$. (HINT: Write $fg = d[f, g]$, and then show that d is a divisor of f and g divided in turn by every divisor of f and g.) Thus if $(f, g) = 1$, $[f, g] = rfg$ for some $r \in \mathfrak{F}$.

(d) Let f, g be relatively prime, $\deg(f) = m$, $\deg(g) = n$. Show that $\varphi\colon \mathfrak{F}^{n+1} \times \mathfrak{F}^m_{\to}\mathfrak{F}^{m+n+1}$ is an onto map, where

$$\varphi(\langle a_0, \ldots, a_n\rangle, \langle b_0, \ldots, b_{m-1}\rangle) = \langle c_0, \ldots, c_{m+n}\rangle$$

iff

$$(a_0 + \cdots + a_nX^n)f + (b_0 + \cdots + b_{m-1}X^{m-1})g$$
$$= c_0 + \cdots + c_{m+n}X^{m+n}.$$

(HINT: Show φ linear, one–one.)

Note that (d) allows us to write $X^q = G\overline{k_q} + H\overline{j_q}$ as in the proof of Theorem 4.1.13.

4.2 Artin's Conjecture

Consider now the valued fields $\langle \mathbb{Q}_p, \mathbb{Z}, v_p\rangle$ and $\langle \mathbb{Z}_p((X)), \mathbb{Z}, v_x\rangle$ for p a prime. Elements of both of these can be written as similar power series expansions, $\sum_{j=n}^{\infty} a_j p^j$, $\sum_{j=n}^{\infty} b_j X^j$, with each a_j, $b_j \in \{0, \ldots, p-1\}$ (see Problem 4.1.5). Each has the same residue class field (by Problem 4.1.4, $\overline{\mathbb{Q}_p} = \mathbb{Z}_p = \overline{\mathbb{Z}_p((X))}$), each satisfies Hensel's lemma, they are both among the few locally compact topological fields, and throughout the years many other common properties have been discovered, enough to make mathematicians call $\mathbb{Q}_p$ the characteristic 0 analogue of $\mathbb{Z}_p((X))$.

Naturally, there are also differences, the main one the fact that $\mathbb{Z}_p((X))$ is of characteristic p, while the characteristic of $\mathbb{Q}_p$ is 0 (also note that since $\mathbb{Z}_p((X)) \not\cong \mathbb{Q}_p$, addition and multiplication of our infinite series must differ in the two cases).

However, more than enough similarities have remained to encourage conjectures stating that if $\langle \mathbb{Z}_p((X)), \mathbb{Z}, v_x\rangle$ has a certain property, then $\langle \mathbb{Q}_p, \mathbb{Z}, v_p\rangle$ must have that property as well (and conversely). One of the best-known of these, due to E. Artin [1], states:

Let f be a form of degree d in $n > d^2$ variables over $\mathbb{Q}_p$. Then f has a nontrivial root in $\mathbb{Q}_p$, where:

DEFINITION 4.2.1. f is a form of degree d over $\mathfrak{F}$ iff

$$f \in \mathfrak{F}[X_1, \ldots, X_n] \qquad \text{for some} \quad X_1, \ldots, X_n,$$

and

$$f = \sum_{i_1 + \cdots + i_n = d} a_{i_1 \cdots i_n} X_1^{i_1} \cdots X_n^{i_n}$$

(i.e., each term of f is of degree d). A root is an element $\langle r_1, \ldots, r_n \rangle$ of $\mathfrak{F}^n$ such that

$$f(r_1, \ldots, r_n) = \sum_{i_1 + \cdots + i_n = d} a_{i_1 \cdots i_n} r_1^{i_1} \cdots r_n^{i_n} = 0,$$

and it is nontrivial iff some $r_i \neq 0$.

Examples: $2XY + X^2 + Y^2$ is a form of degree 2 (in two variables) over $\mathbb{R}$, but $2 + X^2 + Y^2$ is not a form, since 2 is not of the same degree as X^2.

Artin, of course, made his conjecture knowing that it held with $\mathbb{Z}_p((X))$ substituted for $\mathbb{Q}_p$. Ax and Kochen provided the following solution to Artin's conjecture:

For each integer d, there is a finite set $A(d) \subset P$ (P, from now on, will denote the set of primes) such that if $p \notin A(d)$, then every form f of degree d in $n > d^2$ variables over $\mathbb{Q}_p$ has a nontrivial root in $\mathbb{Q}_p$. Subsequent counterexamples to the full conjecture have been found and one is discussed in Problem 4.2.8.

The above results from the following, more general theorem:

Let $F \in \Sigma^t$, t the type of valued fields. Then there is a finite set $A(F) \subset P$ such that if $p \notin A(F)$, then

$$\mathfrak{A}_p = \langle \mathbb{Q}_p, \mathbb{Z}, v_p \rangle \models F \quad \text{iff} \quad \mathfrak{B}_p = \langle \mathbb{Z}_p((X)), \mathbb{Z}, v_X \rangle \models F.$$

The strategy of the Ax-Kochen proof is as follows. The continuum hypothesis is used to show that for any nonprincipal ultrafilter D on P,

$$\prod_P \mathfrak{B}_p/D \cong \prod_P \mathfrak{A}_p/D.$$

If $F \in \Sigma^t$ were such that $\{p \mid \text{not } (\mathfrak{A}_p \models F \text{ iff } \mathfrak{B}_p \models F)\}$ were infinite, then for some infinite $A \subset P$,

$$\mathfrak{A}_p \models F \quad \text{and} \quad \mathfrak{B}_p \not\models F \quad \text{for every} \quad p \in A,$$

or for some infinite $A \subset P$,

$$\mathfrak{A}_p \not\models F \quad \text{and} \quad \mathfrak{B}_p \models F \quad \text{for every} \quad p \in A.$$

In either case, there is a nonprincipal ultrafilter D on P with $A \in D$. For this D,

$$\prod_P \mathfrak{A}_p/D \not\cong \prod_P \mathfrak{B}_p/D,$$

contradicting the fact that they are isomorphic. (We have seen results similar to this in Section 2.2.)

Techniques in Section 2.3 help motivate this proof, because they show that, the continuum hypothesis assumed, isomorphism between $\prod_P \mathfrak{A}_p/D$

and $\prod_P \mathfrak{B}_p/D$ would hold for every nonprincipal D iff for every $F \in \Sigma^t$ we could find a finite $A(F) \subset P$ such that for $p \notin A(F)$, $\mathfrak{A}_p \models F$ iff $\mathfrak{B}_p \models F$.

With results from the latter part of Chapter 2, an alternative proof of this result of Ax and Kochen that avoids the continuum hypothesis can be developed. (Well-known set-theoretic facts proven in Gödel [1] make possible an elimination of the axiom of choice, but this work is beyond the scope of our text.)

We now proceed to the study of concepts used in the proof that

$$\prod_P \mathfrak{A}_p/D \cong \prod_P \mathfrak{B}_p/D.$$

First, some obvious properties of our ultraproducts:

LEMMA 4.2.2. Let $\{\mathfrak{A}_\mathbf{i} = \langle \mathfrak{F}_\mathbf{i}, \mathfrak{M}_\mathbf{i}, v_\mathbf{i}\rangle \mid \mathbf{i} \in \mathbf{I}\}$ be a set of valued fields, D an ultrafilter on $\mathbf{I}$, $\mathfrak{A} = \langle \mathfrak{F}, \mathfrak{M}, v\rangle = \prod_\mathbf{I} \mathfrak{A}_\mathbf{i}/D$.

(a) $\mathfrak{A}$ is a valued field.

(b) $\mathfrak{R}_\mathfrak{F} \cong \prod_\mathbf{I} \mathfrak{R}_{\mathfrak{F}_\mathbf{i}}/D$.

(c) $I_\mathfrak{F} \cong \prod_\mathbf{I} I_{\mathfrak{F}_\mathbf{i}}/D$.

(d) Let $\{\mathfrak{S}_\mathbf{i} \mid \mathbf{i} \in \mathbf{I}\}$ be a set of rings, and for each $\mathbf{i}$ let $J_\mathbf{i} \subset S_\mathbf{i}$ be an ideal in $\mathfrak{S}_\mathbf{i}$. Then

$$\Big(\prod_\mathbf{I} \mathfrak{S}_\mathbf{i}/D\Big)\Big/\Big(\prod_\mathbf{I} J_\mathbf{i}/D\Big) \cong \prod_\mathbf{I} (\mathfrak{S}_\mathbf{i}/J_\mathbf{i})/D.$$

(Thus $\overline{\mathfrak{F}} \cong \prod_\mathbf{I} \overline{\mathfrak{F}}_\mathbf{i}/D$.)

(e) Both $\prod_P \mathfrak{A}_p/D$ and $\prod_P \mathfrak{B}_p/D$ are fields of characteristic 0 and cardinality 2^ω, and $\overline{\prod_P \mathbb{Q}_p/D} \cong \overline{\prod_P Z_p((X))/D}$, both of which are also fields of characteristic 0, all provided that D is nonprincipal.

(f) If $\{\mathbf{i} \mid \mathfrak{A}_\mathbf{i}$ satisfies Hensel's lemma$\} \in D$, then $\prod_\mathbf{I} \mathfrak{A}_\mathbf{i}/D$ satisfies Hensel's lemma. (In particular, $\prod_P \mathfrak{A}_p/D$, $\prod_P \mathfrak{B}_p/D$ both satisfy Hensel's lemma.)

Proof: (a), (b), (c), and (f) are immediate from Łos' theorem (Theorem 2.1.13), while (e) follows from Łos' theorem and the cardinality results in Section 2.2, particularly Corollary 2.2.2 (also see Problem 4.2.1).

For (d), set

$$\varphi\colon \prod_\mathbf{I} \mathfrak{S}_\mathbf{i}/D \to \prod_\mathbf{I} (\mathfrak{S}_\mathbf{i}/J_\mathbf{i})/D \qquad \text{by} \qquad \varphi(f/D) = g/D,$$

where $f(\mathbf{i}) + J_\mathbf{i} = g(\mathbf{i})$. Note that $g/D = 0/D$ iff $\{\mathbf{i} \mid g(\mathbf{i}) = 0\} \in D$, iff $\{\mathbf{i} \mid f(\mathbf{i}) \in J_\mathbf{i}\} \in D$ iff $f/D \in \prod_\mathbf{I} J_\mathbf{i}/D$. Thus there is a one-one onto

$$\psi\colon \Big(\prod_\mathbf{I} \mathfrak{S}_\mathbf{i}/D\Big)\Big/\Big(\prod_\mathbf{I} J_\mathbf{i}/D\Big) \to \prod_\mathbf{I} (\mathfrak{S}_\mathbf{i}/J_\mathbf{i})/D,$$

defined by

$$\psi\Big(f/D + \prod_\mathbf{I} J_\mathbf{i}/D\Big) = \varphi(f/D),$$

and it is simple to check that this is an isomorphism.

DEFINITION 4.2.3. A $\mathbb{Z}$-group $\mathfrak{M} = \langle M, +, e, <, \imath\rangle$ is an ordered Abelian group $\langle M, +, e, <\rangle$ together with a distinguished element $\imath$, which is the smallest element of $\{x \in M \mid x > e\}$, and such that if $0 < n \in \omega$, $y \in M$, then there is a $z \in M$, $k \in \mathbb{Z}$ such that $0 \leq k < n$ and $y = nz + k\imath$.

Our second condition, essentially the division algorithm, assures us that $\langle \mathbb{Z}, +, 0, <, 1\rangle$ is a $\mathbb{Z}$-group, and, as we shall see, that all $\mathbb{Z}$-groups are much like it.

DEFINITION 4.2.4. Let $\mathfrak{M}$ be an Abelian group (or ordered Abelian, or $\mathbb{Z}$-group). Then $\mathfrak{N}$ (or its universe, N) is a pure subgroup of $\mathfrak{M}$ iff $\mathfrak{N}$ is a subgroup of $\mathfrak{M}$ and for every integer $r \neq 0$, every $x \in M$, if $rx \in N$ then $x \in N$.

LEMMA 4.2.5. Let $\{\mathfrak{M}_{\mathbf{i}} \mid \mathbf{i} \in \mathbf{I}\}$ be a set of $\mathbb{Z}$-groups, D an ultrafilter on $\mathbf{I}$, $\mathfrak{M}$ a $\mathbb{Z}$-group.

(a) $\prod_{\mathbf{I}} \mathfrak{M}_{\mathbf{i}}/D$ is a $\mathbb{Z}$-group.

(b) If for each $\mathbf{i} \in \mathbf{I}$, $c(\mathfrak{M}_{\mathbf{i}}) \leq 2^{\omega}$, $c(\mathbf{I}) = \omega$, and D is nonprincipal, then

$$c\Big(\prod_{\mathbf{I}} \mathfrak{M}_{\mathbf{i}}/D\Big) = 2^{\omega}.$$

(c) If N is a pure subgroup of $\mathfrak{M}$ and $\imath \in N$, then $\mathfrak{M} \mid N$ is a $\mathbb{Z}$-group.

Proof: (a) and (b) are clear from Łos' theorem and Corollary 2.2.2. For (c), clearly $\mathfrak{M} \mid N$ is an ordered Abelian group together with smallest positive element $\imath$. Now let r be an integer, $x \in N$. Then for some $y \in M$, $k \in \mathbb{Z}$ with $0 \leq k < r$, $x = ry + k\imath$. However, since $\imath \in N$, $k\imath \in N$, so $ry = x - k\imath \in N$, and since N is pure, $y \in N$.

DEFINITION 4.2.6. A Hensel field is a structure $\mathfrak{A} = \langle \mathfrak{F}, \mathfrak{M}, v, \imath, \rho\rangle$ such that $\langle \mathfrak{F}, \mathfrak{M}, v\rangle$ is a valued field, and

(a) $\langle M, +, e, <, \imath\rangle$ is a $\mathbb{Z}$-group, where $\mathfrak{M} = \langle M, +, e, <\rangle$;
(b) $\rho \in F$, and $v(\rho) = \imath$;
(c) $\langle \mathfrak{F}, \mathfrak{M}, v\rangle$ satisfies Hensel's lemma.

Note that as a result of 4.1.10(b) and 4.2.5(b), if $\langle \mathfrak{F}, \mathfrak{M}, v, \imath, \rho\rangle$ is a Hensel field, $\mathfrak{H}$ a maximal subfield of $\mathfrak{R}_{\mathfrak{F}}$, and $\bar{\mathfrak{H}} = \mathfrak{H}(A)$ an algebraic closure of $\mathfrak{H}$, then $\mathfrak{F}(A, \{\rho^{1/k} \mid k = 1, 2, \ldots\})$ is an algebraic closure of $\mathfrak{F}$, provided that $\mathfrak{H} \neq \{0\}$ and $\mathrm{char}(\mathfrak{H}) = 0$, where $\rho^{1/k}$ denotes an arbitrary kth root of ρ.

LEMMA 4.2.7. (a) Any ultraproduct of Hensel fields is a Hensel field.

(b) If $\mathfrak{G}$ is relatively algebraically closed in $\mathfrak{F}$, $^{-}[G] = {}^{-}[F]$, $\langle \mathfrak{F}, \mathfrak{M}, v, \imath, \rho \rangle$ a Hensel field with $\overline{\mathfrak{F}}$ of characteristic 0 and $\rho \in G$, then $\langle \mathfrak{G}, \mathfrak{M} \mid v[G], v \mid G, \imath, \rho \rangle$ is a Hensel field.

Proof: (a) is immediate from Łos' theorem (and Problem 4.2.1).

(b) By Problem 4.1.10, $\langle \mathfrak{G}, \mathfrak{M} \mid v[G], v \mid G \rangle$ satisfies Hensel's lemma, clearly $\rho \in G$, $v(\rho) = \imath$, so $\imath \in v[G]$. We now check that

$$\langle v[G], + \upharpoonright v[G], e, < \upharpoonright v[G], \imath \rangle$$

is a $\mathbb{Z}$-group. It will do by Lemma 4.2.5(c) to show that $v[G]$ is a pure subgroup of $\mathfrak{M}$. Let $x \in M$, $n \in \mathbb{Z}$, $0 < n$, $nx \in v[G]$. Let $a \in G$ be such that $v(a) = nx$, $b \in F$ such that $v(b) = x$. Thus

$$a = a(b^{-n}b^{n}) = (ab^{-n})b^{n}, \qquad \text{and} \qquad v(ab^{-n}) = e,$$

so we can find $c \in H$ ($\mathfrak{H}$ a maximal subfield of $\mathfrak{R}_{\mathfrak{F}}$) $\subset G$ such that $v(ab^{-n} - c) < e$ (by Problem 4.2.6, $\overline{\mathfrak{H}} = \overline{\mathfrak{F}} = \overline{\mathfrak{G}}$), so

$$v(c^{-1}ab^{-n} - 1) = v(c^{-1}) + v(ab^{-n} - c) = v(ab^{-n} - c) < e.$$

Let $d = c^{-1}ab^{-n}$. By Lemma 4.1.9(a), $X^n - d$ has a root in F (because $v((X^n - d)(1)) < e$), and if r, r' are roots of $X^n - d$, then $r' = r\xi$ for some root ξ of $X^n - 1$, so if $r \neq r'$

$$w(r - r') = w(r(1 - \xi)) = w(r) + w(1 - \xi) = e,$$

for $nw(r) = w(d) = e$, and $1 - \xi$ is in an algebraic extension of $\mathfrak{H}$, so $w(1 - \xi) = e$ as in the proof of 4.1.6(a). Let $r^n = d$, $r \in F$. Then $br^{-1} \in G$ (since $\mathfrak{G}$ is algebraically closed in $\mathfrak{F}$), and

$$v(br^{-1}) = v(b) - v(r) = x.$$

Let $a\colon \lambda \to F$, $\sigma < \lambda$, and set

$$S_{a,\sigma} = \{x \in M \mid \text{if } \sigma < \kappa < \lambda \text{ then } v(a_\sigma - a_\kappa) \leq x\},$$

$$S_a = \bigcup_{\sigma < \lambda} \Big(\bigcap_{\sigma \leq \tau < \lambda} S_{a,\tau} \Big), \qquad T_a = \bigcup_{\sigma < \lambda} S_{a,\sigma}.$$

Clearly if a is S_a-Cauchy, then S_a has no least element.

LEMMA 4.2.8. (a) If a is S-Cauchy then $S \subset T_a$, and if in addition for no $\sigma < \lambda$ is a_σ an S-limit for a, then S is cofinal in $\langle T_a, > \upharpoonright T_a \rangle$.

(b) Let $x_1, \ldots, x_n \in M$, $t_1, \ldots, t_n \in \omega$, $t_1 < \cdots < t_n$. If $S \subset M$ has no least element, then for some $s \in S$ there is an $i \leq n$ such that if $j \neq i$, $s' < s$, and $s' \in S$, then

$$x_j + t_j s' < x_i + t_i s'.$$

(c) Let $a\colon \lambda \to F$ be T_a-Cauchy with T_a-limit b. Then if $\deg(f) \geq 1$ and for no $i \leq n = \deg(f)$ is 0 an $S_{f^{(i)} \circ a}$-limit for $f^{(i)} \circ a$, then $f \circ a$ is $S_{f \circ a}$-Cauchy. Furthermore, $f(b)$ is an $S_{f \circ a}$-limit of $f \circ a$. (Here $f^{(i)}$ denotes the ith formal derivative of the polynomial f.)

Proof: (a)Suppose a is S-Cauchy, $x \in S$. Then for some $\tau < \lambda$, if $\tau < \mu < \kappa < \lambda$, then $v(a_\mu - a_\kappa) < x$. Thus $x \in S_{a,\mu} \subset T_a$. If in addition a_σ is never an S-limit of a, let $y \in T_a$. Then for some $\tau < \lambda$, if $\tau < \kappa < \lambda$, then $v(a_\sigma - a_\kappa) \leq y$. $y < S$ would assure us that a_σ is an S-limit, contradicting our hypothesis.

(b) This is obvious if $n = 1$. Now suppose it holds for $n - 1$ and we have $x_1, \ldots, t_n$, S as above. Then for some $i \leq n - 1$, there is an $s \in S$ such that if $j \leq n - 1$, $j \neq i$, $s' \in S$, $s' < s$,

$$x_j + t_j s' < x_i + t_i s'.$$

Note now that

$$x_n + t_n s'' < x_i + t_i s'' \qquad \text{iff} \quad (t_n - t_i)s'' < x_i - x_n.$$

Either for some $s'' \in S$ this inequality holds, or for every $s'' \in S$,

$$(t_n - t_i)s'' > x_i - x_n$$

(for if $(t_n - t_i)s'' = x_i - x_n$, then for $s''' \in S$, $s''' < s''$,

$$(t_n - t_i)s''' < x_i - x_n).$$

In the first case, select s'' and note that for $s''' < \min\{s, s''\}$,

$$x_j + t_j s''' < x_i + t_i s''' \qquad \text{for} \quad j \leq n, \qquad j \neq i.$$

In the second case, for $s''' < s, j \neq n$,

$$x_j + t_j s''' \leq x_i + t_i s''' < x_n + t_n s'''.$$

(c) If $\deg(f) = n \geq 1$ then

$$f(r) - f(s) = (r - s)f'(s) + \cdots + (1/n!)(r - s)^n f^{(n)}(s)$$

(by Taylor's expansion valid in any field of characteristic 0 with a similar expansion holding for other fields (see Problem 4.2.5)). Since 0 is not an $S_{f^{(i)} \circ a}$-limit of $f^{(i)} \circ a$ for $1 \leq i \leq n$, by Problem 4.1.11 we can find a $\sigma < \lambda$ such that if $\sigma < \tau < \kappa < \lambda$, then for each i,

$$v(f^{(i)}(a_\tau)/i!) = v(f^{(i)}(a_\kappa)/i!).$$

Now let $x \in S_{f \circ a}$ and choose σ' such that $x \in \bigcap_{\sigma' \leq \tau < \lambda} S_{f \circ a, \tau}$; thus if $\sigma' \leq \tau < \kappa < \lambda$, then

$$v(f(a_\tau) - f(a_\kappa)) \leq x.$$

By (b) find $i \in \{1, \ldots, n\}$, $s \in T_a$ such that if $\sigma < \mu < \nu < \lambda$ and $v(a_\mu - a_\nu) < s$, then

$$iv(a_\mu - a_\nu) + v((1/i!)f^{(i)}(a_\nu)) > jv(a_\mu - a_\nu) + v((1/j!)f^{(j)}(a_\nu)) \quad \text{for} \quad j \neq i, \quad 1 \leq j \leq n.$$

If $\max\{\sigma, \sigma', \sigma_s\} < \mu < \nu < \lambda$† then

$$x \geq iv(a_\mu - a_\nu) + v((1/i!)f^{(i)}(a_\nu)),$$

so

$$x - v((1/i!)f^{(i)}(a_\nu)) \geq iv(a_\mu - a_\nu), \qquad v(a_\mu - a_\nu) \in T_a.$$

Choose σ'' so that if $\sigma'' < \mu' < \nu' < \lambda$, then

$$v(a_{\mu'} - a_{\nu'}) < v(a_\mu - a_\nu)$$

(possible since a is T_a-Cauchy), and if $\max\{\sigma, \sigma', \sigma_s, \sigma''\} < \mu' < \nu' < \lambda$, then

$$\begin{aligned} x &\geq iv(a_\mu - a_\nu) + v((1/i!)f^{(i)}(a_\nu)) \\ &> iv(a_{\mu'} - a_{\nu'}) + v((1/i!)f^{(i)}(a_{\nu'})) \\ &= v(f(a_{\mu'}) - f(a_{\nu'})). \end{aligned}$$

The above shows that $f \circ a$ is $S_{f \circ a}$-Cauchy; if b is a T_a-limit for a we may assume inductively that when $\deg(g) < n$ then $g(b)$ is an $S_{g \circ a}$-limit for $g \circ a$ (thus this holds for $f^{(j)}$, $1 \leq j \leq n$). Let $s, x, \sigma, \sigma_s, \sigma', \sigma'', \nu, \mu$ be as above; the reader can easily check that if $\max\{\sigma, \sigma_s, \sigma', \sigma''\} < \nu' < \lambda$ then

$$v(f^{(j)}(a_{\nu'})/j!) = v(f^{(j)}(b)/j!) \qquad \text{for} \quad 1 \leq j \leq n;$$

if in addition $i \neq j$, then

$$iv(b - a_{\nu'}) + v((1/i!)f^{(i)}(a_{\nu'})) > jv(b - a_{\nu'}) + v((1/j!)f^{(j)}(a_{\nu'})),$$

thus

$$\begin{aligned} x &\geq iv(a_\mu - a_\nu) + v((1/i!)f^{(i)}(a_\nu)) \\ &> iv(b - a_{\nu'}) + v((1/i!)f^{(i)}(a_{\nu'})) \\ &= v(f(b) - f(a_{\nu'})) \end{aligned}$$

(using the Taylor expansion with $r = b$, $s = a_{\nu'}$).

Lemma 4.2.9. (a) Let $a: \lambda \to F$ be S-Cauchy with no S-limit in F, and suppose that for each $f \in \mathfrak{F}[X]$, 0 is not an $S_{f \circ a}$-limit of $f \circ a$. Let $\mathfrak{F}(b)$ be a transcendental extension of $\mathfrak{F}$. Then there is a unique $w: \mathfrak{F}(b) \to \mathfrak{M}$ such that b is an S-limit of a (in $\langle \mathfrak{F}(b), \mathfrak{M}, w\rangle$),

$$\langle \mathfrak{F}, \mathfrak{M}, v\rangle \subset \langle \mathfrak{F}(b), \mathfrak{M}, w\rangle, \qquad \text{and} \qquad \overline{\mathfrak{F}} = \overline{\mathfrak{F}(b)}.$$

† Note: By σ_s, we mean some $\sigma < \lambda$ such that if $\sigma_s < \tau < \kappa < \lambda$, then $v(a_\tau - a_\kappa) < s$—such exists since a is T_a-Cauchy.

(b) Let $a: \lambda \to F$ be S-Cauchy with no S-limit in F. If $f \in \mathfrak{F}[X]$ is a monic polynomial of smallest degree such that 0 is an $S_{f \circ a}$-limit of $f \circ a$, let $\mathfrak{F}(b)$ be an extension of $\mathfrak{F}$ with $f(b) = 0$. Then there is a unique $w: \mathfrak{F}(b) \to \mathfrak{M}$ such that b is an S-limit of a,

$$\langle \mathfrak{F}, \mathfrak{M}, v \rangle \subset \langle \mathfrak{F}(b), \mathfrak{M}, w \rangle \qquad \text{and} \qquad \overline{\mathfrak{F}} = \overline{\mathfrak{F}(b)}.$$

(c) The following are equivalent:

(i) $\langle \mathfrak{F}, \mathfrak{M}, v \rangle$ is pseudocomplete.

(ii) There is no proper extension $\langle \mathfrak{G}, \mathfrak{M}, w \rangle$ of $\langle \mathfrak{F}, \mathfrak{M}, v \rangle$ such that $\overline{\mathfrak{F}} = \overline{\mathfrak{G}}$.

Proof: (a) By Problem 4.1.11, there is always some $x_f \in M$ and some $\sigma < \lambda$ such that if $\sigma < \tau < \lambda$ then $v(f(a_\tau)) = x_f$. Then define

$$w\left(\frac{f(b)}{g(b)}\right) = x_f - x_g \qquad \text{for} \quad f, g \in \mathfrak{F}[X] \sim \{0\}.$$

We now check that w is a valuation over $\mathfrak{F}(b)$.

$$w\left(\left(\frac{f(b)}{g(b)}\right)\left(\frac{f^*(b)}{g^*(b)}\right)\right) = x_{ff^*} - x_{gg^*}.$$

However,

$$v(ff^*(a_\tau)) = v(f(a_\tau)) + v(f^*(a_\tau)),$$

so

$$x_{ff^*} = x_f + x_{f^*}.$$

Similarly,

$$w\left(\frac{f(b)}{g(b)} + \frac{f^*(b)}{g^*(b}\right) \leq \max\left\{w\left(\frac{f(b)}{g(b)}\right), w\left(\frac{f^*(b)}{g^*(b)}\right)\right\}.$$

Also, $v \subset w$, for let $f = r \in F \sim \{0\}$. Then

$$x_f = v(f(a_\tau)) = v(r).$$

Consider now that $f_\tau = X - a_\tau$. Then for some $\sigma < \lambda$,

$$w(f_\tau(b)) = v(a_\kappa - a_\tau) \qquad \text{whenever} \quad \sigma < \kappa < \lambda.$$

Now select for $s \in S$ σ_s such that if $\sigma_s < \mu < v < \lambda$, then $w(a_\mu - a_v) < s$. Thus if $\sigma, \sigma_s < \tau < \kappa < \lambda$,

$$w(b - a_\kappa) \leq \max\{w(a_\kappa - a_\tau), w(b - a_\tau)\} < s,$$

so b is an S-limit of a. No a_σ is an S-limit of a since $a_\sigma \in F$, thus a is T_a-Cauchy by Lemma 4.2.8(a) and Problem 4.2.7.

Let $f(b)/g(b) \in \mathfrak{R}_{\mathfrak{F}(b)}$. To show $\overline{\mathfrak{F}(b)} = \overline{\mathfrak{F}}$, we must find $r \in \mathfrak{R}_{\mathfrak{F}}$ with $w(r - f(b)/g(b)) < e$. $r = 0$ works if $w(f(b)/g(b)) < e$, so assume that

$$w\left(\frac{f(b)}{g(b)}\right) = e = x_f - x_g.$$

However,

$$\begin{aligned} w\left(\frac{f(a_\tau)}{g(a_\tau)} - \frac{f(b)}{g(b)}\right) &= w\left(\frac{(f(a_\tau)g(b) - g(a_\tau)f(b))}{g(a_\tau)g(b)}\right) \\ &= w\left(\frac{f(a_\tau)(g(b) - g(a_\tau)) + g(a_\tau)(f(a_\tau) - f(b))}{g(a_\tau)g(b)}\right) \\ &\leq \max\{w(f(a_\tau)) + w(g(b) - g(a_\tau)), w(g(a_\tau)) \\ &\qquad\qquad + w(f(a_\tau) - f(b))\} \\ &\quad - w(g(a_\tau)) - w(g(b)). \end{aligned}$$

Now select $\sigma < \lambda$ such that if $\sigma < \tau < \lambda$, then

$$w(g(a_\tau)) = w(g(b)), \qquad w(f(a_\tau)) = w(f(b)),$$
$$w(f(a_\tau) - f(b)) < w(f(b)), \qquad \text{and} \qquad w(g(a_\tau) - g(b)) < w(g(b))$$

(thus $w(f(a_\tau)) = w(g(a_\tau))$), all possible by Problem 4.2.8, since $f \circ a$ is $S_{f \circ a}$-Cauchy with $S_{f \circ a}$-limit $f(b)$, and a similar result holds for g. Thus if $\sigma < \tau < \lambda$,

$$w\left(\frac{f(a_\tau)}{g(a_\tau)} - \frac{f(b)}{g(b)}\right) < e \qquad \text{and} \qquad \frac{f(a_\tau)}{g(a_\tau)} \in R_{\mathfrak{F}},$$

so

$$\overline{\mathfrak{F}} = \overline{\mathfrak{F}(b)}.$$

Now suppose that $\langle \mathfrak{F}, \mathfrak{M}, v\rangle \subset \langle \mathfrak{F}(b), \mathfrak{M}, w'\rangle$ and that b is an S-limit of a in $\langle \mathfrak{F}(b), \mathfrak{M}, w'\rangle$. We wish to show that

$$w'\left(\frac{f(b)}{g(b)}\right) = w\left(\frac{f(b)}{g(b)}\right),$$

and for this it will suffice to show that we always have $w'(f(b)) = x_f$. However, since $f(b)$ is an $S_{f \circ a}$-limit of $f \circ a$ and 0 is not such a limit, for some $\sigma' < \lambda$, if $\sigma' < \tau < \lambda$, then $w'(f(b)) = v(f(a_\tau))$, and therefore if $\max\{\sigma, \sigma'\} < \tau < \lambda$,

$$w'(f(b)) = v(f(a_\tau)) = w(f(b)).$$

(b) We proceed here in a manner similar to that used in (a), defining now

$$w(g(b)) = x_g \qquad \text{for} \quad \deg(g) < \deg(f) = n.$$

There are only two changes from the proof of (a). First, in order to show that b is an S-limit of a, we must show $n > 1$ (and then continue as in (a))—thus insuring that $X - a_\tau = g$ always has an x_g. However, since a has no S-limit in F, this is clear, for 0 is an S-limit of $r - a$ (where $(r - a)_\sigma = r - a_\sigma$) iff r is an S-limit of a.

Next, the proof that

$$w(g(b)h(b)) = w(g(b)) + w(h(b))$$

must be altered. Let $gh = kf + j$, with $\deg(j)$, $\deg(k) < n$. Then

$$g(a_\tau)h(a_\tau) - j(a_\tau) = k(a_\tau)f(a_\tau),$$

and since $f(b) = 0$, 0 is an $S_{f \circ a}$-limit of $f \circ a$. Thus select $\sigma < \lambda$ such that if $\sigma < \tau$, $\kappa < \lambda$, then

$$v(g(a_\tau)) = v(g(a_\kappa)), \qquad v(h(a_\tau)) = v(h(a_\kappa)),$$

$$v(j(a_\tau)) = v(j(a_\kappa)), \qquad \text{and} \qquad v(k(a_\tau)) = v(k(a_\kappa)).$$

Assume now, by way of contradiction, that for $\sigma < \tau < \lambda$,

$$v(j(a_\tau)) \neq v(f(a_\tau)) + v(g(a_\tau)),$$

Then for $\sigma < \tau < \lambda$,
$v(f(a_\tau)) = \max\{v(j(a_\tau)) - v(k(a_\tau)), v(f(a_\tau)) + v(g(a_\tau)) - v(k(a_\tau))\} = z.$
Thus if $\sigma < \tau < \kappa < \lambda$,

$$v(f(a_\tau) - f(a_\kappa)) \leq \max\{v(f(a_\tau)), v(f(a_\kappa))\} \leq z,$$

so $z \in S_{f \circ a}$. Thus for some $\sigma' < \lambda$, if $\sigma' < \tau' < \lambda$,

$$v(f(a_{\tau'}) - f(b)) < z,$$

and since $f(b) = 0$,

$$v(f(a_{\tau'})) < z,$$

a contradiction.

(c) Assume (i) and let $\langle \mathfrak{F}, \mathfrak{M}, v\rangle \subset \langle \mathfrak{G}, \mathfrak{M}, w\rangle$, $r \in G \sim F$, $S = \{v(r - q) \mid q \in F\}$. S cannot have a least element, for if x were such, then for some $q \in F$, $v(r - q) = x$, so let $c \in F$ with $v(c) = x$. Then

$$v(r/c - q/c) = e,$$

so for some $p \in F$, $v(r/c - q/c - p) < e$ (since $\overline{\mathfrak{F}} = \overline{\mathfrak{G}}$), so

$$v(r - (q + pc)) < v(c) = x,$$

a contradiction. Let $\psi\colon \lambda \to S$ be decreasing and cofinal, and choose $a\colon \lambda \to F$ such that $v(a_\sigma - r) = \psi(\sigma)$. Thus the λ-sequence a is S-Cauchy with S-limit r. If r is the only S-limit of a, then by (i), $r \in F$, a contradiction. However, if $r_1 \in F$ were another S-limit of a, then $v(r - r_1) < S$. But this is impossible by the definition of S, since $v(r - r_1) \in S$, a contradiction establishing (ii).

Conversely, if (ii) holds, then by (a) and (b), for every $S \subset M$, and every limit ordinal λ, every S-Cauchy λ-sequence has an S-limit in F.

For the remainder of this section we assume $\mathrm{char}(\overline{\mathfrak{F}}) = 0$ (thus $\mathfrak{F}$ is also of characteristic 0, and $\mathfrak{H} \neq \{0\}$ for a maximal subfield $\mathfrak{H}$ of $\mathfrak{R}_{\mathfrak{F}}$).

LEMMA 4.2.10. (a) Let a be T_a-Cauchy and assume that 0 is not an $S_{f^{(i)} \circ a}$-limit for $f^{(i)} \circ a$ when $1 \leq i \leq n = \deg(f)$. If $1 \leq i < j \leq n$, then for some $s \in T_a$, if $v(a_\tau - b) < s$ where b is a T_a-limit of a,

$$v(f^{(i)}(b)) > (j - i)v(a_\tau - b) + v(f^{(j)}(b)).$$

(b) Let $a\colon \lambda \to F$ be T_a-Cauchy. If 0 is an $S_{f \circ a}$-limit for $f \circ a$ but not an $S_{f^{(i)} \circ a}$-limit for $f^{(i)} \circ a$ with $1 \leq i \leq n = \deg(f)$, and if $\langle \mathfrak{F}, \mathfrak{M}, v\rangle$ is pseudocomplete, then f has a root in F that is a T_a-limit of a.

Proof: (a) Assume that this has been shown for $j > i > i_0$ and that we wish to show it for $j > i \geq i_0$. For some $\tau < \lambda$

$$v(f^{(i_0)}(a_\tau) - f^{(i_0)}(b)) < v(f^{(i_0)}(b)),$$

thus $v(f^{(i_0)}(a_\tau)) = v(f^{(i_0)}(b))$ (τ exists since $f^{(i_0)} \circ a$ is $S_{f^{(i_0)} \circ a}$-Cauchy by Lemma 4.2.8(c) and 0 is not an $S_{f^{(i_0)} \circ a}$-limit of $f^{(i_0)} \circ a$). Then

$$\begin{aligned} v(f^{(i_0)}(b)) &= v(f^{(i_0)}(a_\tau)) \\ &= v(f^{(i_0)}(b) + \cdots + (a_\tau - b)^{n - i_0} f^{(n)}(b)(1/(n - i_0)!)). \end{aligned}$$

For $i_0 < i < j \leq n$, select s_{ij} such that if $v(a_\tau - b) < s_{ij}$, then

$$v(f^{(i)}(b)) > (j - i)v(a_\tau - b) + v(f^{(j)}(b)).$$

Thus if

$$s' < \min\{s_{ij} \mid i_0 < i < j \leq n\} \cup \{v(f^{(i_0)}(b)\},$$

then

$$\begin{aligned} v(a_\tau - b) + v(f^{(i_0+1)}(b)) &> 2v(a_\tau - b) + v(f^{(i_0+2)}(b)) > \cdots \\ &> (n - i_0)v(a_\tau - b) + v(f^{(n)}(b)) \end{aligned}$$

(since $\mathrm{char}(\overline{\mathfrak{F}}) = 0$, $v(1/k!) = e$). Now let $v(a_\tau - b) < s'$, and assume by way of contradiction that

$$v(f^{(i_0)}(b)) < v(f^{(i_0+1)}(b)) + v(a_\tau - b).$$

Then

$$\begin{aligned} v(f^{(i_0)}(b)) &= v(f^{(i_0)}(b) + \cdots + (a_\tau - b)^{n - i_0}(1/(n - i_0)!)f^{(n)}(b)) \\ &= v(a_\tau - b) + v(f^{(i_0+1)}(b)), \end{aligned}$$

a contradiction. Clearly, if $v(a_\pi - b) < v(a_\tau - b)$, then

$$v(a_\pi - b) + v(f^{(io+1)}(b)) < v(a_\tau - b) + v(f^{(io+1)}(b)) \le v(f^{(io)}(b)),$$

and the remaining inequalities follow from this one.

(b) Let r_0 be a T_a-limit of a. By Taylor's expansion,

$$f\left(r_0 - \frac{f(r_0)}{f'(r_0)}\right) = f(r_0) + \left(\frac{-f(r_0)}{f'(r_0)}\right) f'(r_0) + \cdots + \frac{1}{n!}\left(\frac{-f(r_0)}{f'(r_0)}\right)^n f^{(n)}(r_0)$$

$$= f(r_0) - f(r_0) + \left(\frac{-f(r_0)}{f'(r_0)}\right)^2 \frac{1}{2} f''(r_0) + \cdots$$

$$+ \left(\frac{-f(r_0)}{f'(r_0)}\right)^n \frac{1}{n!} f^{(n)}(r_0)$$

$$= f(r_0)\left[\left(\frac{f(r_0)}{(-f'(r_0))^2}\right)^2 \frac{1}{2} f''(r_0) + \cdots + \frac{1}{n!}\left(\frac{f(r_0)^{n-1}}{(-f'(r_0))^n}\right)^n f^{(n)}(r_0)\right].$$

Thus

$$v\left(f\left(r_0 - \frac{f(r_0)}{f'(r_0)}\right)\right) \le v(f(r_0)) + \max\{(i-1)v(f(r_0)) - iv(f'(r_0)) + v(f^{(i)}(r_0)) \mid i = 2, \ldots, n\}.$$

However, by (a), for each $i \in \{2, \ldots, n\}$,

(*) $$v(f'(r_0)) > (i-1)x + v(f^{(i)}(r_0)) \quad \text{if} \quad x < T_a$$

(Problem 4.1.9 defines this). Since 0 is an $S_{f \circ a}$-limit of $f \circ a$ for $\tau < \lambda$,

$$v(f(r_0)) < v(f(a_\tau)),$$

so

$$v(f(r_0)) < v(f(a_\tau) - f(r_0)) = v(a_\tau - r_0) + v(f'(r_0)),$$

thus

$$v(f(r_0)) - v(f'(r_0)) < v(a_\tau - r_0) \qquad \text{for every} \quad \tau < \lambda,$$

and since r_0 is a T_a-limit for a,

$$v(f(r_0)) - v(f'(r_0)) < T_a.$$

Combining our last inequality with (*), we find that

$$v(f'(r_0)) > (i-1)(v(f(r_0)) - v(f'(r_0))) + v(f^{(i)}(r_0)),$$

so

$$v(f(r_0))(i-1) - iv(f'(r_0)) + v(f^{(i)}(r_0)) < e \quad \text{for each } i \in \{2, \ldots, n\}.$$

Thus

$$v\left(f\left(r_0 - \frac{f(r_0)}{f'(r_0)}\right)\right) < v(f(r_0)).$$

Consider now the set of all sequences on ordinals of the form r such that r_0 is a T_a-limit of a,

$$r_{\sigma+1} = r_\sigma - \frac{f(r_\sigma)}{f'(r_\sigma)},$$

for limit ordinals κ, r_κ is $T_{r|\kappa}$-limit of $r \mid \kappa$ (we leave it for the reader to check that $r \mid \kappa$ is actually $T_{r|\kappa}$-Cauchy) and $f(r_\sigma) \neq 0$.

The above set is partially ordered by $\subset$, so let r^* with $\mathscr{D}r^* = \lambda^*$ be a maximal element (our set is clearly closed under ascending unions). If λ^* is a limit ordinal it is simple to check that r^* is T_{r^*}-Cauchy; thus let b be a T_{r^*}-limit. However, then

$$r^* \subset r^* \cup \{\langle \lambda^*, b\rangle\},$$

which will contradict the maximality or r^* unless $f(b) = 0$. If, however, $\mathscr{D}r^*$ is not a limit ordinal, let $\lambda^* = \kappa + 1$. Then

$$r^* \subset r^* \cup \{\langle \kappa + 1, r_\kappa - f(r_\kappa)/f'(r_\kappa)\rangle\},$$

again a contradiction to the maximality of r^* unless

$$f(r_\kappa - f(r_\kappa)/f'(r_\kappa)) = 0.$$

In either case, we have found a root for f in F. The fact that our root is a T_a-limit for a can be checked by showing inductively that each r_σ is a T_a-limit for a.

DEFINITION 4.2.11. $\langle \mathfrak{G}, \mathfrak{M}, w\rangle$ is called a pseudocompletion of $\langle \mathfrak{F}, \mathfrak{M}, v\rangle$ iff

(i) $\langle \mathfrak{F}, \mathfrak{M}, v\rangle \subset \langle \mathfrak{G}, \mathfrak{M}, w\rangle$;
(ii) $\langle \mathfrak{G}, \mathfrak{M}, w\rangle$ is pseudocomplete; and
(iii) $\overline{\mathfrak{G}} = \overline{\mathfrak{F}}$.

By Lemma 4.2.9(c), there is no pseudocomplete valued field, other than the trivial one such that

$$\langle \mathfrak{F}, \mathfrak{M}, v\rangle \subset \langle \mathfrak{F}', \mathfrak{M}, v'\rangle \subset \langle \mathfrak{G}, \mathfrak{M}, w\rangle.$$

Extensions $\langle \mathfrak{F}', \mathfrak{M}', v'\rangle$ of a valued field are called immediate iff $\mathfrak{M} = \mathfrak{M}'$ and $\overline{\mathfrak{F}} = \overline{\mathfrak{F}'}$. It is clear (though of no use in our treatment) that a pseudocompletion of $\langle \mathfrak{F}, \mathfrak{M}, v\rangle$ is precisely a maximal immediate extension of $\langle \mathfrak{F}, \mathfrak{M}, v\rangle$.

We do not now show the existence of pseudocompletions; however, for the moment we assume that we have a pseudocompletion for $\langle \mathfrak{F}, \mathfrak{M}, v\rangle$:

PROPOSITION 4.2.12 (Kaplansky). Let $\varphi\colon \langle \mathfrak{F}, \mathfrak{M}, v\rangle \cong \langle \mathfrak{F}', \mathfrak{M}', v'\rangle$, $\langle \mathfrak{G}, \mathfrak{M}, w\rangle$ be a pseudocompletion of $\langle \mathfrak{F}, \mathfrak{M}, v\rangle$ and $\langle \mathfrak{G}', \mathfrak{M}', w'\rangle$ one of $\langle \mathfrak{F}', \mathfrak{M}', v'\rangle$. Then there is a

$$\psi\colon \langle \mathfrak{G}, \mathfrak{M}, w\rangle \cong \langle \mathfrak{G}', \mathfrak{M}', w'\rangle$$

such that $\varphi \subset \psi$.

Proof: Let

$$\begin{aligned} D = \{\pi\colon \langle \mathfrak{K}, \mathfrak{M}, u\rangle \cong \langle \mathfrak{K}', \mathfrak{M}', u'\rangle \\ \mid \varphi \subset \pi, \langle \mathfrak{F}, \mathfrak{M}, v\rangle \subset \langle \mathfrak{K}, \mathfrak{M}, u\rangle \subset \langle \mathfrak{G}, \mathfrak{M}, w\rangle, \text{ and} \\ \langle \mathfrak{F}', \mathfrak{M}', v'\rangle \subset \langle \mathfrak{K}', \mathfrak{M}', u'\rangle \subset \langle \mathfrak{G}', \mathfrak{M}', w'\rangle. \end{aligned}$$

D is clearly partially ordered by $\subset$ and each chain in D is bounded by its union, thus let ψ be a maximal element. We are through if we can show $\mathscr{D}\psi = G$ and $\mathscr{R}\psi = G'$. Thus assume by way of contradiction that $\mathscr{D}\psi = K \neq G$. Then $\langle \mathfrak{K}, \mathfrak{M}, u\rangle$ is not pseudocomplete, so let $a\colon \lambda \to K$ be an S-Cauchy sequence ($S \subset M$) with no S-limit in K. There are now two cases to consider:

(1) For no $f \in \mathfrak{K}[X]$ is 0 an $S_{f\circ a}$-limit for $f \circ a$.
(2) For some $f \in \mathfrak{K}[X]$, 0 is an $S_{f\circ a}$-limit for $f \circ a$.

In Case (1), let $b \in G$ be an S-limit for a. Note that since ψ is an isomorphism of valued fields, $\psi \circ a$ is a $\psi[S]$-Cauchy sequence in K' with no $\psi[S]$-limit in K'; and note further that for no $f' \in \mathfrak{K}'[X]$ is 0 an $S_{f'\circ a}$-limit of $f' \circ a$. Thus let b' be a $\psi[S]$-limit of $\psi \circ a$. Note that $\mathfrak{K}(b)$ and $\mathfrak{K}'(b')$ are transcendental extensions of $\mathfrak{K}$ and $\mathfrak{K}'$ respectively, for if $f \in \mathfrak{K}[X]$, for example, there is a $\sigma < \lambda$ such that if $\sigma < \tau < \lambda$ then $v(f(a_\tau))$ becomes a constant, and this constant must be $v(f(b))$, so $f(b) \neq 0$. Now by the uniqueness part of Lemma 4.2.9(a), ψ can be extended to an isomorphism from $\langle \mathfrak{K}(b), \mathfrak{M}, w \mid K(b)\rangle$ onto

$$\langle \mathfrak{K}'(b'), \mathfrak{M}', w' \mid K'(b')\rangle,$$

contradicting the maximality of ψ. In Case (2), we proceed as in Case (1), this time using Lemma 4.2.10(b) to find roots for appropriate polynomials in $\mathfrak{G}$, $\mathfrak{G}'$ before applying the uniqueness assertion of Lemma 4.2.9(b). Thus, since ψ is maximal we must have $\mathscr{D}\psi = G$. Similarly, $\mathscr{R}\psi = G'$.

We need a rather technical lemma at this point.

LEMMA 4.2.13. (a) Let $\langle \mathfrak{F}, \mathfrak{M}, v, \imath, \rho\rangle$ be a Hensel field, h algebraic over $\mathfrak{H}$ with minimal polynomial f of degree n, k a positive integer, and b a kth root of ρ. Then if $a \in \mathfrak{F}(h, b)$, a is of the form

$$\sum_{\substack{0 \le j < k \\ 0 \le i < n}} r_{ij}h^i b^j \qquad (\text{with } r_{ij} \in F),$$

and

$$v(a) = \max\{v(r_{ij}h^i b^j) \mid 0 \le i < n, 0 \le j < k\}.$$

(b) If $\mathfrak{H}(\rho) \subset \mathfrak{F} \subset \mathfrak{G}$, $\mathfrak{F}$ algebraically closed in $\mathfrak{G}$, $y \in G$, and $r \in \tilde{\mathfrak{F}}$, then for some $s \in F$,

$$v(y - s) \le v(y - r).$$

Proof: (a) $\mathfrak{F}(h, b) = (\mathfrak{F}(h))(b)$, so

$$a = \sum_{0 \le j < k} s_j b^j = \sum_{0 \le j < k} \left(\sum_{0 \le i < n} r_{ij}h^i\right) b^j = \sum_{\substack{0 \le i < n \\ 0 \le j < k}} r_{ij}h^i b^j.$$

Now let

$$x = \max\{v(r_{ij}h^i b^j) \mid 0 \le i < n, 0 \le j < k\},$$

and let $\{r_{i_1 j_1}h^{i_1}b^{j_1}, \ldots, r_{i_m j_m}h^{i_m}b^{j_m}\}$ be those summands with

$$v(r_{ij}h^i b^j) = x.$$

We must show that

$$v\left(\sum_{p=1}^{m} r_{i_p j_p}h^{i_p}b^{j_p}\right) = x,$$

that is, that

$$e = v\left(\sum_{p=1}^{m} r_{i_p j_p}h^{i_p}b^{j_p}\right) - v(r_{i_1 j_1}h^{i_1}b^{j_1}) = v(1 + \cdots + s_m h^{i'_m}b^{j'_m}),$$

where

$$s_p = \frac{r_{i_p j_p}}{r_{i_1 j_1}}, \qquad i'_p = i_p - i_1, \qquad \text{and} \qquad j'_p = j_p - j_1.$$

Since

$$v(s_p h^{i'_p} b^{j'_p}) = v(1) = e \qquad \text{and} \qquad v(h) = e,$$

$$v(s_p) = -j'_p v(b) = \frac{-j'_p}{k} v(\rho) = \frac{-j'_p}{k} \imath.$$

But

$$v(s_p) \ge e \qquad \text{or} \qquad -\imath \ge v(s_p), \qquad \text{while} \qquad 0 \le \frac{j'_p}{k} < 1,$$

so

$$v(s_p) = e = \frac{-j'_p}{k} \imath, \qquad \text{thus } j'_p = 0.$$

Thus it will do to show that

$$v(1 + \cdots + s_m h^{i'm}) = e.$$

Since

$$v(s_2) = \cdots = v(s_m) = e \qquad \text{and} \qquad \bar{\mathfrak{H}} = \bar{\mathfrak{F}},$$

we can find

$$g_2, \ldots, g_m \in H \qquad \text{with} \qquad v(s_p - g_p) < e.$$

Since v is trivial on $\mathfrak{H}$, it is trivial on any algebraic extension of $\mathfrak{H}$, so

$$\begin{aligned} e &= v(1 + \cdots + g_m h^{i'm}) \\ &\le \max\{v(1 + \cdots + s_m h^{i'm}), v((g_2 - s_2)h^{i'2}), \ldots, v((g_m - s_m)h^{i'm})\} \\ &= v(1 + \cdots + s_m h^{i'm}) \le \max\{v(1), \ldots, v(s_m h^{i'm})\} \\ &= e. \end{aligned}$$

(b) By comments following the definition of Hensel field, we can find an integer k and $h \in \tilde{\mathfrak{H}}$ such that

$$r \in \mathfrak{G}(b, h) \qquad \text{and} \qquad b^k = \rho.$$

Let m be the degree of the minimal polynomial of h, and write

$$r = \sum_{0 \le i < k}^{0 \le j < m} r_{ij} b^i h^j \qquad \text{with} \qquad r_{ij} \in \mathfrak{F}$$

(see Problem 4.2.2). Let d_{ij} be 1 if $i = j = 0$ and 0 otherwise. Then

$$r - y = \sum_{0 \le i < k}^{0 \le j < m} (r_{ij} - d_{ij} y) b^i h^j$$

and

$$v(r - y) = \max\{v((r_{ij} - d_{ij}y)b^i h^j)\} \ge v(r_{00} - d_{00}y) = v(r_{00} - y),$$

so $s = r_{00}$ satisfies the required conditions.

PROPOSITION 4.2.14. Let $\langle \mathfrak{F}, \mathfrak{M}, v \rangle$ be ω-pseudocomplete,† $\langle \mathfrak{G}, \mathfrak{N}, w \rangle \subset \langle \mathfrak{F}, \mathfrak{M}, v \rangle$ with $\bar{\mathfrak{G}} = \bar{\mathfrak{F}}$, $\mathfrak{N}$ countable and pure in $\mathfrak{M}$, and $\mathfrak{G}$ maximal with respect to the property that $v[G] \subset N$. Then $\mathfrak{G}$ is algebraically closed in $\mathfrak{F}$ and $\langle \mathfrak{G}, \mathfrak{N}, w \rangle$ is pseudocomplete.

Proof: Let

$$a_0 + \cdots + a_n X^n \in \mathfrak{G}[X], \qquad r \in F \text{ a root.}$$

† Since ω is the smallest limit ordinal, from now on we replace the notation $\le \omega$-pseudocomplete with ω-pseudocomplete.

Suppose $v(a_j r^j)$ is maximal among the $v(a_i r^i)$. Since

$$a_0 + \cdots + a_n r^n = 0,$$

we must have

$$v(a_k) + kv(r) = v(a_j) + jv(r) \qquad \text{for some} \quad k \neq j,$$

so

$$(k - j)v(r) = v\left(\frac{a_j}{a_k}\right) \in N.$$

Since $\mathfrak{N}$ is pure, $v(r) \in N$.

If $r' \in \mathfrak{G}(r)$, then r' is the root of some polynomial over $\mathfrak{G}$, so as above, $v(r') \in N$. Thus $v[\mathfrak{G}(r)] \subset N$, a contradiction to the maximality of $\mathfrak{G}$ unless $r \in G$.

Now let $a: \lambda \to G$ be S-Cauchy ($S \subset N$) with no S-limit in G. Since S is countable, a has an S-limit $b \in F$. If for some $c \in G$, $v(b - c) < x$ for every $x \in S$, then $b - c \in J_S$, so c is an S-limit of a in $\mathfrak{G}$, thus we may assume that for every $c \in G$,

$$v(b - c) \geq x \qquad \text{for} \quad \text{some } x \in S.$$

We now show that $v[\mathfrak{G}(b)] \subset N$, contradicting the maximality of $\mathfrak{G}$. Let $f \in \mathfrak{G}[X]$, thus

$$f = (X - d_1)\cdots(X - d_n) \qquad \text{for some} \quad d_1, \ldots, d_n \in \tilde{\mathfrak{G}}.$$

If $b \in \mathfrak{F} \sim \mathfrak{G}$, we can, by 4.3.13(b), find $r_1, \ldots, r_n \in G$ such that for each i,

$$v(b - r_i) \leq v(b - d_i).$$

Thus

$$v(b - d_i) \geq x_i \qquad \text{for some} \quad x_i \in S.$$

Thus if $v(b - a_\tau) < x_i$,

$$v(a_\tau - d_i) = v(b - d_i).$$

Thus we can find $\sigma < \lambda$ such that if $\sigma < \tau < \lambda$, then for each i,

$$v(a_\tau - d_i) = v(b - d_i),$$

and for such τ,

$$v(f(b)) = \sum_{i=1}^{n} v(b - d_i) = \sum_{i=1}^{n} v(a_\tau - d_i) = v(f(a_\tau)) \in N,$$

and it is now clear that for $f, g \in \mathfrak{G}[X] \sim \{0\}$,

$$v\left(\frac{f(b)}{g(b)}\right) \in N,$$

completing the proof of our assertion.

Problems

‡4.2.1 Check that all concepts mentioned in Lemmas 4.2.2 (a) through (c) and (f), 4.2.5 (a) and (b), and 4.2.7 (a) are first-order, thus entitling us to use Łos' theorem.

‡4.2.2 Let $\mathfrak{K}$, $\mathfrak{K}'$ be fields. We shall denote by $[\mathfrak{K}': \mathfrak{K}]$ the dimension of $\mathfrak{K}'$ over $\mathfrak{K}$ as a vector space, provided $\mathfrak{K} \subset \mathfrak{K}'$. Note that if a is algebraic over $\mathfrak{K}$, $[\mathfrak{K}(a): \mathfrak{K}]$ is the degree of the minimal polynomial of a over $\mathfrak{K}$.

(a) If $\mathfrak{F} \subset \mathfrak{G} \subset \mathfrak{H}$, then show $[\mathfrak{H}: \mathfrak{G}][\mathfrak{G}: \mathfrak{F}] = [\mathfrak{H}: \mathfrak{F}]$.

Now let $\mathfrak{F}$, $\mathfrak{G}$ be fields, $\mathfrak{F} \subset \mathfrak{G}$, $\mathfrak{F}$ algebraically closed in $\mathfrak{G}$, and suppose that $\mathfrak{G}(b)$ is algebraic over $\mathfrak{G}$. Then

(b) Show $[\mathfrak{F}(b): \mathfrak{F}] = [\mathfrak{G}(b): \mathfrak{G}]$ (HINTS: Clearly

$$[\mathfrak{F}(b): \mathfrak{F}] \geq [\mathfrak{G}(b): \mathfrak{G}];$$

now divide the minimal polynomial over $\mathfrak{F}$ for b into factors over $\mathfrak{G}$ and look at the coefficients of these factors).

(c) Show that $\mathfrak{F}(b)$ is algebraically closed in $\mathfrak{G}(b)$. (We must show that

$$\text{if} \quad [\mathfrak{G}(b)(c): \mathfrak{G}(b)] = 1, \qquad \text{then} \quad [\mathfrak{F}(b)(c): \mathfrak{F}(b)] = 1).$$

Thus if $c \in \tilde{\mathfrak{F}} \cap \mathfrak{G}(b, h)$, then $c \in \mathfrak{F}(b, h)$, a fact used in the proof of Lemma 4.2.13.

4.2.3 Let $f_1, \ldots, f_r \in \mathbb{Z}[X_1, \ldots, X_n]$. Then prove that there is a finite $A \subset P$ such that if $p \in P \sim A$ and

$$\overline{f_1}(s_1, \ldots, s_n) = \cdots = \overline{f_r}(s_1, \ldots, s_n) = 0 \qquad \text{in } \mathbb{Z}_p,$$

we can find $r_1, \ldots, r_n \in R_{\mathbb{Q}_p}$ such that

$$f_1(r_1, \ldots, r_n) = \cdots = f_r(r_1, \ldots, r_n) = 0$$

and

$$\overline{r_1} = s_1, \ldots, \overline{r_n} = s_n.$$

(HINT: Show that $\prod_P \mathbb{Z}_p/D$ can be imbedded in $\prod_P R_{\mathbb{Q}_p}/D$ for non-principal D.)

The above result was used by Ax and Kochen [1] to prove a 1960 conjecture by S. Lang, which was shown earlier (unbeknownst to them) by N. Greenleaf.

‡4.2.4 Let $\mathfrak{M}$, $\mathfrak{N}$ be groups, $\mathfrak{M} < \mathfrak{N}$. Show that $\mathfrak{M}$ is pure in $\mathfrak{N}$. Now show, using ultraproducts, that if $\mathfrak{M}$ is countable, then $\langle \mathfrak{F}, \mathfrak{M}, v \rangle$ always has at least one pseudocompletion. Is there an analogous proof for arbitrary $\mathfrak{M}$? (Krull originally showed the existence of pseudocompletions.)

‡4.2.5 Let $\mathfrak{F}$ be any field, $f \in \mathfrak{F}[X]$ of degree n. Show that there are polynomials $g_1, \ldots, g_n \in \mathfrak{F}[X]$ such that for each $a, b \in F$,

$$f(b) = f(a) + (b - a)g_1(a) + \cdots + (b - a)^n g_n(a),$$

and such that for each k, if $1 \leq k \leq n$, $k!\, g_n = f^{(n)}$. (The g_k can obviously be used in place of the $f^{(k)}/k!$ of the text; however, under certain conditions the expression

$$v(g_k(b)) = v(f^{(k)}(b)) - v(k!)$$

is clearly meaningless for fields of characteristic $\neq 0$.)

‡4.2.6 Show that $H \subset G$ in Lemma 4.2.7. (HINT: $^-[G \cap H]$ is algebraically closed in $\mathfrak{F}$.

‡4.2.7 Let $T \subset S \subset M$, T cofinal in $\langle S, > \restriction S\rangle$, $a\colon \lambda \to F$. Then a is S-Cauchy iff a is T-Cauchy, a has S-limit b iff a has T-limit b.

4.2.8 In this problem we study a counterexample to Artin's conjecture due to G. Terjanian.

(a) Let

$$n(X, Y, Z) = X^2YZ + Y^2XZ + Z^2XY + X^2Y^2 + X^2Z^2 + Y^2Z^2 - X^4 - Y^4 - Z^4.$$

If X, Y, and Z are all even, then $n(X, Y, Z) \equiv 0 \pmod 4$; otherwise $n(X, Y, Z) \equiv 3 \pmod 4$. Now let

$$f(X_1, \ldots, X_9) = n(X_1, X_2, X_3) + n(X_4, X_5, X_6) + n(X_7, X_8, X_9).$$

Show that $f(X_1, \ldots, X_9) \equiv 0 \pmod 4$ iff $X_1, \ldots, X_9$ are all even ($X_1, \ldots, X_9 \in \mathbb{Z}$). Show the same for

$$g(X_1, \ldots, X_{18}) = f(X_1, \ldots, X_9) + 4f(X_{10}, \ldots, X_{18}).$$

(b) Let $h \in \mathfrak{F}[X_1, \ldots, X_n]$ be a form of degree d. Show that

$$h(\langle rr_1, \ldots, rr_n\rangle) = r^d h(\langle r_1, \ldots, r_n\rangle);$$

thus if $\mathfrak{F}$ is valued and h has a nontrivial root in $\mathfrak{F}^n$, h has a root in $(R_{\mathfrak{F}})^n$ such that for at least one j, $v(r_j) = e$, where the root is $\langle r_1, \ldots, r_n\rangle$.

(c) Thus if g has nontrivial roots in $\mathbb{Q}_2$, let

$$\langle r_1, \ldots, r_{18}\rangle \in (R_{\mathbb{Q}_2})^{18}$$

be such a root with $v(r_j) = 0$. Then if $\hat{}\colon R_{\mathbb{Q}_2} \to R_{\mathbb{Q}_2}/(I_{\mathbb{Q}_2})^2$,

$$\langle \hat{r}_1, \ldots, \hat{r}_{18}\rangle \in (R_{\mathbb{Q}_2}/(I_{\mathbb{Q}_2})^2)^{18}$$

is a root for $\hat{g} = g$. However

$$R_{\mathbb{Q}_2}/(I_{\mathbb{Q}_2})^2 \cong \mathbb{Z}_4$$

in such a way that

$$\hat{r}_j \equiv 1 \text{ or } 3 \pmod 4,$$

contradicting (a).

Thus g is a form of degree 4 in $18 > 4^2$ variables with no nontrivial root in $\mathbb{Q}_2$, contradicting Artin's conjecture.

4.3 The Basic Ax-Kochen Results

DEFINITION 4.3.1. Let $\langle \mathfrak{F}, \mathfrak{M}, v, \imath, \rho \rangle$ be a Hensel field. Then a cross section for $\langle \mathfrak{F}, \mathfrak{M}, v, \imath, \rho \rangle$ is an injection $\varphi: \langle M, +, e \rangle \to \langle F, \cdot, 1 \rangle$ such that $\varphi(\imath) = \rho$ and $v \circ \varphi$ is the identity map on M.

Clearly if $\mathfrak{M} = \langle \mathbb{Z}, +, 0, < \rangle$, then the map $\varphi: \langle \mathbb{Z}, +, 0 \rangle \to \langle F, \cdot, 1 \rangle$ defined by $\varphi(n) = \rho^n$ is a cross section. Also ultraproducts of Hensel fields with cross sections have cross sections. In particular, $\prod_P \mathfrak{A}_p/D$, $\prod_P \mathfrak{B}_p/D$ possess cross sections.

DEFINITION 4.3.2. Let $\mathfrak{M}$ be an Abelian group or a $\mathbb{Z}$-group. Then if X is a subset of M, $(X_{\mathfrak{M}})$ is the smallest pure subgroup of $\mathfrak{M}$ containing X. If $\mathfrak{N}$ is a subgroup of $\mathfrak{M}$, $(\mathfrak{N}_{\mathfrak{M}}) = (N_{\mathfrak{M}})$.

If $\mathbb{Z}\imath \subset v[F]$ and $\bar{\mathfrak{F}} = \bar{\mathfrak{G}}$, $\mathfrak{F} \subset \mathfrak{G}$, and $\mathfrak{A} = \langle \mathfrak{G}, \mathfrak{M}, v, \imath, \rho \rangle$ is a Hensel field, then $\langle \mathfrak{F}_{\mathfrak{A}} \rangle$ denotes any subfield of $\mathfrak{G}$ maximal with respect to the property $v[\langle \mathfrak{F}_{\mathfrak{A}} \rangle] \subset (v[\mathfrak{F}]_{\mathfrak{M}})$.

Note that by Proposition 4.2.14, if $\mathfrak{A}$ is ω-pseudocomplete, then

$$\langle \langle \mathfrak{F}_{\mathfrak{A}} \rangle, \mathfrak{M} \mid v[\langle \mathfrak{F}_{\mathfrak{A}} \rangle], v \mid \langle \mathfrak{F}_{\mathfrak{A}} \rangle, \imath, \rho \rangle$$

is pseudocomplete, provided that $c(v[F]) = \omega$.

Also note that if $\mathfrak{N}$ is a subgroup of $\mathfrak{M}$,

$$(N_{\mathfrak{M}}) = \{x \mid \text{for some } n \in \mathbb{Z} \sim \{0\}, nx \in N\}.$$

The latter set is (the universe of) a pure subgroup; for let nx, $my \in N$, then

$$mn(x + y) = m(nx) + n(my) \in N, \qquad \text{and} \qquad n(-x) = -(nx) \in N,$$

if rq is in our set, $r \in \mathbb{Z} \sim \{0\}$; then for some $n \in \mathbb{Z} \sim \{0\}$,

$$(nr)q = n(rq) \in N,$$

so q is in our set. Thus

$$(N_{\mathfrak{M}}) \subset \{x \mid \text{for some } n \in \mathbb{Z} \sim \{0\}, nx \in N\},$$

and we leave the reverse inclusion to the reader. Thus if $x \in (N_{\mathfrak{M}})$, then for some nonzero $r \in Z$, $rx \in N$.

PROPOSITION 4.3.3. Let $\mathfrak{A} = \langle \mathfrak{G}, \mathfrak{M}, v, \imath, \rho \rangle$, $\mathfrak{A}' = \langle \mathfrak{G}', \mathfrak{M}', v', \imath', \rho' \rangle$ be ω-pseudocomplete Hensel fields, and suppose that $\mu: \mathfrak{M} \cong \mathfrak{M}'$ (clearly $\mu(\imath) = \imath'$) and $\nu: \bar{\mathfrak{G}} \cong \bar{\mathfrak{G}}'$. Assume also that $\mathfrak{A}$, $\mathfrak{A}'$ have cross sections π, π', that $\bar{\mathfrak{F}} = \bar{\mathfrak{G}}$, $\bar{\mathfrak{F}}' = \bar{\mathfrak{G}}'$, and

$$\mathfrak{B} = \langle \mathfrak{F}, \mathfrak{M} \mid v[F], v \mid F, \imath, \rho \rangle, \qquad \mathfrak{B}' = \langle \mathfrak{F}', \mathfrak{M}' \mid v'[F'], v' \mid F', \imath', \rho' \rangle$$

are pseudocomplete with $\mathfrak{M} \mid v[F]$, $\mathfrak{M}' \mid v'[F']$ pure countable subgroups of $\mathfrak{M}$, $\mathfrak{M}'$. Suppose also that every subvalued field of $\mathfrak{A}$ has a unique pseudocompletion, up to isomorphism, and that $\bar{\mathfrak{F}}$ is of characteristic 0.

If $\psi\colon \mathfrak{B} \cong \mathfrak{B}'$ is such that $\psi \mid M \subset \mu$, ${}^{-\prime} \circ \psi \subset \nu \circ {}^{-}$, and $x \in G \sim F$, then for some extension ψ_0 of ψ,

$$\psi_0\colon \mathfrak{C} \cong \mathfrak{C}' \qquad \text{for some} \quad \mathfrak{C}' \subset \mathfrak{B}',$$

where

$$\mathfrak{C} = \langle\langle\mathfrak{F}(x)_{\mathfrak{A}}\rangle, \mathfrak{M} \mid v[\langle\mathfrak{F}(x)_{\mathfrak{A}}\rangle], v \mid \langle\mathfrak{F}(x)_{\mathfrak{A}}\rangle, \imath, \rho\rangle.$$

Also

$$\psi_0 \mid M \subset \mu, \qquad {}^{-\prime} \circ \psi_0 \subset \nu \circ {}^{-},$$

and

$$v[\langle\mathfrak{F}(x)_{\mathfrak{A}}\rangle] = (v[\mathfrak{F}(x)]_{\mathfrak{M}}).$$

(Note that $\mathrm{char}(\bar{\mathfrak{F}}) = 0$ is used below only to invoke Lemma 4.2.13. We later extend that Lemma and thus this Proposition.)

Proof: Since $\mathfrak{B}$ is pseudocomplete and $\bar{\mathfrak{F}} = \bar{\mathfrak{G}}$,

$$v[\mathfrak{F}(x)] \neq v[F].$$

Thus for some $f \in \mathfrak{F}[X]$, $v(f(x)) \notin v[F]$. Since $\mathfrak{M} \mid v[F]$ is pure in $\mathfrak{M}$, $v(f(x)) \notin v[\tilde{\mathfrak{F}}]$. Factoring f over $\tilde{\mathfrak{F}}$, we find a $b \in \tilde{\mathfrak{F}}$ with $v(x - b) \notin v[\tilde{\mathfrak{F}}]$, thus $v(x) \notin v[\tilde{\mathfrak{F}}]$. By Lemma 4.2.13, for some $c \in F$, $v(x - c) \leq v(x - b)$. But if $v(x - c) < v(x - b)$, then

$$v(c - b) = v(x - b) \notin v[\tilde{\mathfrak{F}}],$$

contradicting $c - b \in \tilde{\mathfrak{F}}$. Thus

$$v(x - c) = v(x - b) \in M \sim v[F].$$

Let $y = x - c$, $m = v(y)$. Since $v(y\pi(-m)) = e$ and $\bar{\mathfrak{F}} = \bar{\mathfrak{G}}$, for some $h \in F$,

$$v(hy\pi(-m) - 1) < e.$$

Let $a = hy$, so $v(a\pi(-m) - 1) < e$. Now set $a' = \pi'(\mu(m))$. Then $\mathfrak{F}(x) = \mathfrak{F}(a)$, and there is an extension ψ_1 of ψ with

$$\psi_1\colon \langle\mathfrak{F}(a), \mathfrak{M} \mid v[\mathfrak{F}(a)], v \mid \mathfrak{F}(a), \imath, \rho\rangle$$
$$\cong \langle\mathfrak{F}'(a'), \mathfrak{F}' \mid v'[\mathfrak{F}'(a')], v' \mid \mathfrak{F}'(a'), \imath', \rho'\rangle.$$

This is due to the fact that since $m \notin v[F]$ and $\mathfrak{M} \mid v[F] = (v[F]_{\mathfrak{M}})$, both a and a' are transcendental over $\mathfrak{F}$, $\mathfrak{F}'$, so

$$\psi_1(r_0 + \cdots + r_n a^n) = \psi(r_0) + \cdots + \psi(r_n)a'^n$$

induces a field isomorphism from $\mathfrak{F}(a)$ to $\mathfrak{F}'(a')$. Also, if

$$f = r_0 + \cdots + r_n X^n \in \mathfrak{F}[X],$$

then

$$\begin{aligned}\mu(v(f(a))) &= \mu(\max\{v(r_j) + jm \mid 0 \leq j \leq n\}) \\ &\qquad \text{(because no two of the } v(r_j) + jm \text{ are equal)} \\ &= \max\{v'(\psi(r_j)) + j\mu(m)) \mid 0 \leq j \leq n\} \\ &= v'(\psi_1(f(a))),\end{aligned}$$

so we set

$$\psi_1(m_0) = \mu(m_0) \qquad \text{for} \quad m_0 \in v[F(a)],$$

making ψ_1 an isomorphism of valued fields (Problem 4.1.2), which by our definition satisfies

$$\psi_1 \mid M \subset \mu \circ {}^{-\prime} \cdot \psi_1 \subset \nu \circ {}^{-}$$

for if $z \in \mathfrak{F}(x)$, since $\overline{\mathfrak{F}} = \overline{\mathfrak{G}}$, we can choose $q \in F$ such that $v(z - q) < e$, so

$$v'(\psi_1(z) - \psi_1(q)) = v'(\psi_1(z - q)) = \psi_1(v(z - q)) < e',$$

thus

$${}^{-\prime} \circ \psi_1(z) = {}^{-\prime} \circ \psi_1(q) = \nu \circ {}^{-}(q) = \nu \circ {}^{-}(z).$$

Since $\mathfrak{M}$ is a $\mathbb{Z}$-group, for all $n \in \mathbb{Z} \sim \{0\}$, we can find $m_n \in M$, $r_n \in \mathbb{Z}$ such that

$$m = nm_n + r_n\iota, \qquad \text{and} \qquad 0 \leq r_n < |n|.$$

Set

$$y_n = a\pi(-r_n\iota) = a\rho^{-r_n} \in \mathfrak{F}(a), a'\pi'(-r_n\iota') = a'\rho'^{-r_n} = \psi_1(a\rho^{-r_n}) \in \mathfrak{F}'(a').$$

Thus

$$v(y_n(\pi(-m_n)^n) - 1) = v(a\pi(-m) - 1) < e,$$

and by Corollary 4.1.9, $y_n(\pi(-m_n)^n) - X^n = 0$ has a root in G so $y_n(\pi(-m_n)^n)$ and therefore y_n have nth roots in G. Let z_n be such a root for y_n. Clearly

$$z_n \in \langle \mathfrak{F}(x)_{\mathfrak{A}} \rangle, \qquad \mathfrak{F}(x) \subset \mathfrak{F}(z_n),$$

and if q is another nth root of y_n, then $q^n = z_n^n$,

$$\text{so} \quad \left(\frac{z_n}{q}\right)^n = 1, \qquad \text{thus} \quad \frac{z_n}{q} = \xi \qquad \text{with} \quad \xi^n = 1.$$

However, then $\xi \in \mathfrak{F}$ for $\mathfrak{F}$ is algebraically closed in $\mathfrak{G}$. Thus

$$\mathfrak{F}(z_n) = \mathfrak{F}(q) \subset \langle \mathfrak{F}(x)_{\mathfrak{A}} \rangle.$$

$z'_n \in G'$ is found similarly. Note that $v(z_n) = m_n$.

We now show that for each positive integer n we can find an isomorphism $\psi_n: \mathfrak{B}_n \cong \mathfrak{B}'_n$, where

$$\mathfrak{B}_n = \langle \mathfrak{F}(z_n), \mathfrak{M} \mid v[\mathfrak{F}(z_n)], v \mid \mathfrak{F}(z_n), \imath, \rho \rangle,$$
$$\mathfrak{B}'_n = \langle \mathfrak{F}'(z'_n), \mathfrak{M}' \mid v'[\mathfrak{F}'(z'_n)], v' \mid \mathfrak{F}'(z'_n), \imath', \rho' \rangle$$

such that $\psi_1 \subset \psi_n$. First note that $X^n - y_n$ is irreducible over $\mathfrak{F}(x)$. For this, it will suffice to show that if $0 < j < n$, then $jm_n \notin v[\mathfrak{F}(x)]$. But let $r \in \mathbb{Z}$, $k \in v[F]$ be such that

$$jm_n = rm + k \in v[\mathfrak{F}(x)].$$

Then

$$jm_n = r(nm_n + r_n\imath) + k = rnm_n + r_nr\imath + k,$$

so

$$(j - rn)m_n = k + r_nr\imath \in v[F].$$

Thus

$$(j - rn)m = (j - rn)(nm_n + r_n\imath) = n(j - rn)m_n + (j - rn)r_n\imath \in v[F],$$

and since $0 < j < n$, $m \in (v[F]_{\mathfrak{M}})$, a contradiction. A similar proof shows $X^n - y'_n$ irreducible in $\mathfrak{F}'(x')[X]$. Thus we can find that

$$\psi_n: \mathfrak{F}(z_n) = (\mathfrak{F}(x))(z_n) \cong (\mathfrak{F}'(x'))(z'_n) = \mathfrak{F}'(z'_n).$$

It is also simple to check, using the above, that for

$$f = a_0 + \cdots + a_{n-1}X^{n-1} \in \mathfrak{F}[X],$$
$$\mu(v(f(z_n))) = v'(\psi_n(f(z_n))),$$

so if we set

$$\psi_n(m_0) = \mu(m_0) \qquad \text{for} \quad m_0 \in v(\mathfrak{F}(z_n)),$$

then ψ_n becomes our isomorphism of valued fields.

We now show that there is an isomorphism

$$\begin{aligned}\psi_\omega: \langle \mathfrak{F}(x, z_2, z_3, \ldots), \mathfrak{M} \mid v[\mathfrak{F}(x, z_2, \ldots)], v \mid \mathfrak{F}(x, z_2, z_3, \ldots), \imath, \rho\rangle \\ = \mathfrak{B}_\omega \cong \mathfrak{B}'_\omega \\ = \langle \mathfrak{F}'(x', z'_2, \ldots), \mathfrak{M}' \mid v'[\mathfrak{F}'(x', z'_2, \ldots)], v' \mid [\mathfrak{F}'(x', z'_2, \ldots)], \imath', \rho'\rangle.\end{aligned}$$

We first produce an ascending chain of maps $\varphi_n: \mathfrak{B}_{n!} \cong \mathfrak{B}'_{n!}$ as follows: Assume that we have $\varphi_1 = \psi_1$. Note that φ_1 can be extended to any $\mathfrak{B}_{n!}$. If we have $\varphi_1 \subset \cdots \subset \varphi_n$, φ_n such that for $r > n$ there is always a $\psi_{r!}$ extending φ_n, since there are at most $(n + 1)!$ maps of the form $\psi_{(n+1)!}$ (by Galois theory), let $\{\psi^{(1)}_{(n+1)!}, \ldots, \psi^{(s)}_{(n+1)!}\}$ be those that extend φ_n. Since for each $r > n$ there is a $\psi_{r!}$ extending φ_n, this must hold for at least one of the $\psi^{(j)}_{(n+1)!}$ (why?), and we let one doing this be φ_{n+1}. Clearly, $\varphi = \bigcup_{n<\omega} \varphi_n$ is our isomorphism.

Note now that

$$v[\mathfrak{F}(x, z_2, z_3, \ldots)] = \bigcup_{n=2}^{\infty} v[\mathfrak{F}(z_n)],$$

so

$$\mathfrak{M} \mid v[\mathfrak{F}(x, z_2, \ldots)] \subset (v[\mathfrak{F}(x)]_{\mathfrak{M}}).$$

However, let $t \in (v[\mathfrak{F}(x)]_{\mathfrak{A}})$. Then for some positive integer p, $pt \in v[F(x)]$, so

$$pt = sm + k, \qquad k \in v[F], \qquad s \in \mathbb{Z}.$$

Now let $k_1 \in \mathfrak{M}$, $r_1 \in \mathbb{Z}$ be such that

$$k = pk_1 + r_1 \imath, \qquad 0 \leq r_1 < p.$$

Since $v[F]$ is pure in $\mathfrak{M}$ and $k - r_1 \imath \in v[F]$, $k_1 \in v[F]$. Thus

$$\begin{aligned} pt &= pk_1 + r_1 \imath + sm \\ &= pk_1 + r_1 \imath + s(pm_p + r_p \imath) \\ &= p(sm_p + k_1) + (r_1 + r_p s)\imath. \end{aligned}$$

$p(t - sm_p - k_1) = (r_1 + r_p s)\imath$, thus $p \mid (r_1 + r_p s)$ (see Problem 4.4.4), so

$$t = k_1 + sm_p + \left(\frac{r_1 + r_p s}{p}\right) \imath.$$

Thus $t \in v[\mathfrak{F}(x, z_2, \ldots)]$ since $\imath, k_1 \in v[F]$, $m_p = v(z_p)$, so

$$\mathfrak{M} \mid v[\mathfrak{F}(x, z_2, \ldots)] = (v[\mathfrak{F}(x)]_{\mathfrak{M}}).$$

Now choose ψ_0 by the uniqueness of pseudocompletion for $\mathfrak{B}_\omega$. The remaining assertions about ψ_0 may be verified first by checking them for ψ_1 (as we have done), then for φ_n for each n, and then for ψ_ω, and finally by applying the uniqueness of pseudocompletions for subvalued fields of $\mathfrak{A}$.

THEOREM 4.3.4. Let $\mathfrak{A}$, $\mathfrak{A}'$ be ω-pseudocomplete Hensel fields of cardinality ω^+, and let $\mathfrak{M} \cong \mathfrak{M}'$, $\mathfrak{H} \cong \mathfrak{H}' \neq \{0\}$, $\mathfrak{H}$ of characteristic 0. If $\mathfrak{A}$ and $\mathfrak{A}'$ both possess cross sections π, π', then $\mathfrak{A} \cong \mathfrak{A}'$.

Proof: Choose transcendence bases B, B' for $\mathfrak{G}$ over $\mathfrak{H}(\rho)$ and $\mathfrak{G}'$ over $\mathfrak{H}'(\rho')$ (see Section 1.6). Since $c(\mathfrak{M}) = \omega^+$ and $c(v[\mathfrak{H}(\rho)]) = \omega$,

$$c(B) = \omega^+ \qquad \text{and similarly} \qquad c(B') = \omega^+.$$

Thus let

$$B = \{x_\alpha \mid \alpha < \omega^+\}, \qquad B' = \{x'_\alpha \mid \alpha < \omega^+\}.$$

For $\lambda < \omega^+$, we now define $\mathfrak{A}_\lambda$, φ_λ, and $\mathfrak{A}'_\lambda$ such that $\mathfrak{A}_\lambda$, $\mathfrak{A}'_\lambda$ are pseudocomplete; $\mathfrak{M}_\lambda$, $\mathfrak{M}'_\lambda$ are pure, countable subgroups of $\mathfrak{M}$, $\mathfrak{M}'$; and $\varphi_\lambda\colon \mathfrak{A}_\lambda \cong \mathfrak{A}'_\lambda$; and further, that if $\lambda < \tau < \omega^+$, then

$$\mathfrak{A}_\lambda \subset \mathfrak{A}_\tau, \qquad \mathfrak{A}'_\lambda \subset \mathfrak{A}'_\tau, \qquad \text{and} \qquad \varphi_\lambda \subset \varphi_\tau.$$

Let

$$\mathfrak{A}_1 = \langle \mathfrak{F}, \mathfrak{M} \mid \mathbb{Z}\imath, v \mid \mathfrak{F}, \imath, \rho\rangle, \qquad \mathfrak{A}'_1 = \langle \mathfrak{F}', \mathfrak{M}' \mid \mathbb{Z}\imath', v' \mid \mathfrak{F}', \imath', \rho'\rangle,$$

where $\mathfrak{F}$, $\mathfrak{F}'$ are subfields of $\mathfrak{G}$, $\mathfrak{G}'$ maximal with respect to $v[F] \subset \mathbb{Z}\imath$, $v[F'] \subset \mathbb{Z}\imath'$. By Proposition 4.2.14, $\mathfrak{A}_1$, $\mathfrak{A}'_1$ are pseudocomplete, and by Proposition 4.2.12 there is an isomorphism between them extending the isomorphism from $\mathfrak{H}(\rho)$ to $\mathfrak{H}'(\rho')$; note that its restriction to M is contained in our map from $\mathfrak{M}$ to $\mathfrak{M}'$.

If $\lambda = \kappa + 2n$ for κ a limit ordinal, $n < \omega$, then assume that we have $x_\tau \notin F_\lambda$ for some, thus some smallest $\tau < \omega^+$. Now let

$$\mathfrak{A}_{\lambda+1} = \langle\langle \mathfrak{F}_\lambda(x_\tau)_{\mathfrak{G}}\rangle, \mathfrak{M} \mid v[\langle \mathfrak{F}_\lambda(x_\tau)_{\mathfrak{G}}\rangle], v \mid \langle \mathfrak{F}_\lambda(x_\tau)_{\mathfrak{G}}\rangle, \imath, \rho\rangle.$$

By Proposition 4.3.3, we can find $\mathfrak{C}'$, ψ satisfying the conditions above, so let

$$\mathfrak{C}' = \mathfrak{A}'_{\lambda+1}, \qquad \psi = \varphi_{\lambda+1}.$$

If $\lambda = \kappa + 2n + 1$, find $\mathfrak{A}'_{\lambda+1}$ in the manner in which $\mathfrak{A}_{\lambda+1}$ was found above, and use Proposition 4.3.3 with the roles of $\mathfrak{A}$, $\mathfrak{A}'$ and φ_λ, φ_λ^{-1} reversed to find $\mathfrak{A}_{\lambda+1}$.

For limit ordinals, let $\mathfrak{A}_\lambda$ be a pseudocompletion (see Proposition 4.2.4) for $\bigcup_{\tau<\lambda} \mathfrak{A}_\tau$, $\mathfrak{A}'_\lambda$ a pseudocompletion for $\bigcup_{\tau<\lambda} \mathfrak{A}'_\tau$, $\varphi_\lambda \supset \bigcup_{\tau<\lambda} \varphi_\tau$ the map given by Proposition 4.2.12.

Note now that

$$\mathfrak{A} = \bigcup_{\lambda<\omega^+} \mathfrak{A}_\lambda, \qquad \mathfrak{A}' = \bigcup_{\lambda<\omega^+} \mathfrak{A}'_\lambda,$$

because

$$B \subset \bigcup_{\lambda<\omega^+} \mathfrak{A}_\lambda, \qquad B' \subset \bigcup_{\lambda<\omega^+} \mathfrak{A}'_\lambda,$$

so no element is transcendental over either of these unions. However, each $\mathfrak{A}_\lambda$ is algebraically closed in $\mathfrak{A}$, thus so is $\bigcup_{\lambda<\omega^+} \mathfrak{A}_\lambda$, so it must equal $\mathfrak{A}$. Similarly, $\mathfrak{A}'$ is the other union, and $\varphi = \bigcup_{\lambda<\omega^+} \varphi_\lambda$ is our isomorphism. (We have only shown that the domain and range of φ contain the fields of $\mathfrak{A}$ and $\mathfrak{A}'$; why must they also contain their groups?)

PROPOSITION 4.3.5. Let $\{\mathfrak{A}_\mathbf{i} = \langle \mathfrak{F}_\mathbf{i}, \mathfrak{M}_\mathbf{i}, v_\mathbf{i}\rangle \mid \mathbf{i} \in \mathbf{I}\}$ be a countable set of valued fields, D a nonprincipal ultrafilter on $\mathbf{I}$. Then $\prod_\mathbf{I} \mathfrak{A}_\mathbf{i}/D$ is ω-pseudocomplete.

Proof: We know, by Theorem 2.3.10, that both these ultraproducts are ω^+-saturated. Thus it will do to show that if $\mathfrak{A}$ is an $\mathfrak{a}^+$-saturated valued field, then $\mathfrak{A}$ is $\leq \mathfrak{a}$-pseudocomplete. Thus let $\{a_\sigma \mid \sigma < \lambda\}$ be an S-Cauchy λ-sequence, $c(S) \leq \mathfrak{a}$, and for $s \in S$ let σ_s be such that if $\sigma_s \leq \kappa$, $\tau < \lambda$, then $v(a_\tau - a_\kappa) < s$. Let

$$H = \{v(c_{a_{\sigma_s}} - v_0) < c_s \mid s \in S\}.$$

Then $c(H) = c(S) < \mathfrak{a}^+$ and H is finitely satisfiable, for if $s_1, \ldots, s_n \in S$, let

$$\sigma = \max\{\sigma_{s_1}, \ldots, \sigma_{s_n}\}.$$

Then if $\tau \geq \sigma$,

$$v(a_{\sigma_{s_r}} - a_\tau) < s_r \qquad \text{if} \quad r = 1, \ldots, n,$$

so a_τ satisfies

$$\{v(a_{\sigma_{s_1}} - v_0) < c_{s_1}, \ldots, v(a_{\sigma_{s_n}} - v_0) < c_{s_n}\}.$$

Thus some b satisfies H, and this b is an S-limit of a, for if $s \in S$ and $\kappa \geq \sigma_s$,

$$v(a_\kappa - b) \leq \max\{v(a_{\sigma_s} - a_\kappa), v(a_{\sigma_s} - b)\} < s.$$

Corollary 4.3.6. If $\omega^+ = 2^\omega$, then

$$\prod_P \mathfrak{A}_p/D \cong \prod_P \mathfrak{B}_p/D$$

for every nonprincipal ultrafilter D on P.

Proof: Theorem 4.3.4 can be used, where Lemmas 4.2.1(e), (f), and 4.2.7(a) guarantee that we have Hensel fields with isomorphic residue class fields of characteristic 0, Proposition 4.2.8(a) guarantees they are ω-pseudocomplete, and our opening discussion of this section assures us of the existence of cross sections.

Corollary 4.3.7. (a) Let $F \in \Sigma^t$, t the type of valued fields. Then there is a finite set $A(F)$ of primes such that if $p \notin A(F)$, then $\mathfrak{A}_p \models F$ iff $\mathfrak{B}_p \models F$.

(b) For each integer d there is a finite set $A(d)$ of primes such that if $p \notin A(d)$, then every form f of degree d in $n > d^2$ variables over $\mathbb{Q}_p$ has a nontrivial root in $\mathbb{Q}_p$.

Proof: (a) is immediate from Corollary 4.3.6, while (b) results from (a) and the fact (see Ax) that every such form has roots in $\mathbb{Z}_p((X))$.

Elimination of the continuum hypothesis can be accomplished by replacing $\prod_P \mathfrak{A}_p/D$ and $\prod_P \mathfrak{B}_p/D$ with special models of equal cardinality containing them, and replacing "ω" by "any infinite cardinal α" in several of the facts shown in Sections 4.2 and 4.3. Proofs similar to ours are valid, as well as the results in Corollary 4.3.7. (Special models are treated in Section 2.8.)

Problems

‡4.3.1 Let t be the type of valued fields. Write a sentence $F \in \sum^t$ that is satisfied by precisely those fields having nontrivial roots for all forms of degree d in $n > d^2$ variables (given d).

4.3.2 Verify the comments on elimination of the continuum hypothesis by making appropriate changes in the statements and proofs of 4.2.14, 4.3.3, 4.3.4, and 4.3.6, and in the comments following Definition 4.3.1.

‡4.3.3 Check that ψ_0 satisfies the remaining assertions of Proposition 4.3.3, namely: $\psi_0 \mid M \subset \mu$, $^{-\prime} \cdot \psi_0 \subset \nu \cdot {}^{-}$.

‡4.3.4 If $rx = s\imath$ with $r, s \in \mathbb{Z}$, $x \in M$, then $r \mid s$. (HINT: In desperation only, see Lemma 4.4.1 (a).)

4.4 Further Results of Ax and Kochen

The principal results discussed below can be found in Ax and Kochen [2] and [3]. Once again we occasionally assume the continuum hypothesis, but it may be eliminated as in Section 4.3.

We recall that to show that $\prod_P \mathfrak{A}_p/D \cong \prod_P \mathfrak{B}_p/D$ we first had to show the existence of cross sections for these Hensel fields. In order to obtain some of our new results, we first need the fact that if D is a nontrivial ultrafilter on ω, then a cross section always exists.

LEMMA 4.4.1. Let $\mathfrak{M}$ be a $\mathbb{Z}$-group.

(a) Let $e \leq x \leq y$, $y \in \mathbb{Z}\imath$. Then $x \in \mathbb{Z}\imath$.

Let A be a collection of pure subgroups of $\mathfrak{M}$ and suppose that for every $N \in A$, N is divisible or $\mathbb{Z}\imath \subset N$.

(b) $N_A = \{n_1 + \cdots + n_r \mid r < \omega$ and for $0 < j \leq r$, $n_j \in N_j$ for some $N_j \in A\}$ is a pure subgroup of $\mathfrak{M}$ (this subgroup is also known as $\sum A$).

(c) If A is a chain under $\subset$, then $\bigcup A$ is a pure subgroup of $\mathfrak{M}$.

Proof: (a) Let $y = r\imath$. We show (a) by induction on r. If $r = 0$, then $x = e$. If we have (a) for $r = k$ and wish to show it for $r = k + 1$, let $e \leq x \leq y = (k + 1)\imath$. Then if $e \leq x \leq k\imath$, $x \in \mathbb{Z}\imath$, and otherwise $k\imath < x \leq y$, so $e < x - k\imath \leq \imath$, thus $x - k\imath = \imath$, so $x = y \in \mathbb{Z}\imath$.

(b) Let $x \in M$, $sx = n_1 + \cdots + n_r \in N_A$, $s > 0$. Then let $n_j = sm_j + s_j \imath$ for $0 \leq s_j < s$, and $0 = s_j$ if N_j is divisible. Then

$$sm_j = n_j - s_j \imath \in N_j, \qquad \text{so} \qquad m_j \in N_j.$$

Thus

$$sx = s(m_1 + \cdots + m_r) + (s_1 + \cdots + s_r)\imath,$$

so

$$s(x - m_1 - \cdots - m_r) = (s_1 + \cdots + s_r)\imath.$$

Therefore

$$e \leq x - \cdots - m_r \leq (s_1 + \cdots + s_r)\imath,$$

and by (a)

$$x - \cdots - m_r \in \mathbb{Z}\imath, \qquad \text{thus} \qquad s \text{ divides } (s_1 + \cdots + s_r).$$

Set $st = s_1 + \cdots + s_r$. Thus

$$sx = s(m_1 + \cdots + m_r) + st\imath,$$

so

$$x = m_1 + \cdots + m_r + t\imath.$$

If each of the N_j is divisible, then $t = 0$, so $x \in N_A$, and if $\mathbb{Z}\imath \subset N_k$ then

$$x = m_1 + \cdots + (m_k + t\imath) + \cdots + m_r \in N_A.$$

(c) In this case it is simple to show that $N_A = \bigcup A$.

PROPOSITION 4.4.2. (a) If $\mathfrak{M}$ is a $\mathbb{Z}$-group, then $\mathfrak{M}/\mathbb{Z}\imath$ is an ordered divisible Abelian group under the order:

$$x + \mathbb{Z}\imath \leq' y + \mathbb{Z}\imath \qquad \text{iff} \quad x \leq y + z \qquad \text{for some} \quad x \in \mathbb{Z}\imath.$$

(b) Let $\{\mathfrak{M}_n \mid n < \omega\}$ be a set of $\mathbb{Z}$-groups and let D be a nonprincipal ultrafilter on ω. Then if $x \in \prod_\omega M_n/D$, there is a y of the form $x + z$ with

$$z \in \prod_\omega (\mathbb{Z}\imath_n)/D \qquad \text{such that} \qquad y/r \in \prod_\omega M_n/D$$

for every nonzero integer r.

Proof: (a) Let $\varphi: \mathfrak{M} \to \mathfrak{M}/\mathbb{Z}\imath$ be the canonical homomorphism, and let $y = \varphi(x)$, $y \in M/\mathbb{Z}\imath$. If n is a nonzero integer, then for some x_n,

$$x = nx_n + p\imath \qquad \text{where} \quad 0 \leq p < |n|.$$

Thus

$$\begin{aligned} y &= \varphi(x) \\ &= \varphi(nx_n + p\imath) \\ &= \varphi(nx_n) + \varphi(p\imath) \\ &= n\varphi(x_n) + \varphi(p\imath) \\ &= n\varphi(x_n), \end{aligned}$$

so

$$y = nz \qquad \text{for some} \quad z \in M/\mathbb{Z}\imath,$$

thus $M/\mathbb{Z}\imath$ is divisible. Clearly the relation defined above is transitive and reflexive, so suppose that $x, y \in M$, $\varphi(x) \leq' \varphi(y)$, and $\varphi(y) \leq' \varphi(x)$. Then $x \leq y + z$ and $y \leq x + z'$ for some $z, z' \in \mathbb{Z}\imath$,

$$\text{so} \quad -z' \leq x - y \leq z, \qquad \text{so} \quad e \leq x - y + z' \leq z + z',$$

$$\text{thus} \quad x - y + z' \in \mathbb{Z}\imath, \qquad \text{so} \quad x - y \in \mathbb{Z}\imath.$$

Therefore

$$\varphi(x) = \varphi(y).$$

Finally if $\varphi(x) \leq' \varphi(x')$ and $\varphi(y) \leq' \varphi(y')$, then

$$\begin{aligned} \varphi(x) + \varphi(y) &= \varphi(x + y) \leq' \varphi(x' + y') \\ &= \varphi(x') + \varphi(y'). \end{aligned}$$

(b) Consider the structures

$$\langle M_n \cup M_n/\mathbb{Z}\imath_n, M_n, +_n, e_n, \imath_n, <_n, M_n/\mathbb{Z}\imath_n, +'_n, e'_n, \varphi_n \rangle$$

$$(\varphi_n\colon M_n \to M_n/\mathbb{Z}\imath_n \text{ the canonical homomorphism})$$

and their ultraproduct. This is ω^+-saturated (Definition 2.7.1). Let

$$x \in M = \prod_\omega M_n/D$$

and consider the set of formulas

$$S = \{(\exists v_1)((rv_1 = v_0) \wedge (\varphi(v_0) = \varphi(x))) \mid 0 < r \in \mathbb{Z}\}.$$

Any finite subset of S is satisfiable, for consider

$$\{(\exists v_1)((r_1 v_1 = v_0) \wedge (\varphi(v_0) = \varphi(x))), \ldots,$$
$$(\exists v_1)((r_k v_1 = v_0) \wedge (\varphi(v_0) = \varphi(x)))\}.$$

There is a $y \in M$ such that

$$x = (r_1 \cdots r_k)y + s\imath \qquad \text{with} \quad 0 \leq s < r_1 \cdots r_k.$$

Then

$$\varphi(r_1 \cdots r_k y) = \varphi(x)$$

and

$$(r_1 \cdots r_k)y = r_1(r_2 \cdots r_k y) = \cdots = r_k(r_1 \cdots r_{k-1} y),$$

so $(r_1 \cdots r_k)y$ satisfies our k formulas. Thus S is satisfiable, and if y satisfies S, $\varphi(y) = \varphi(x)$, and $y = rq$ for some $q \in M$ holds for every positive integer r. Note that

$$\varphi(x - y) = e', \qquad \text{so} \qquad x - y \in \prod_\omega (\mathbb{Z}\imath_n)/D.$$

THEOREM 4.4.3. Let $\{\mathfrak{A}_n \mid n < \omega\}$ be a set of Hensel fields, D a non-principal ultrafilter on ω. Then $\prod_\omega \mathfrak{A}_n/D$ has a cross section.

Proof: Let

$$\mathfrak{A}_n = \langle \mathfrak{F}_n, \mathfrak{M}_n, v_n, \imath_n, \rho_n \rangle, \qquad \mathfrak{A} = \langle \mathfrak{F}, \mathfrak{M}, v, \imath, \rho \rangle = \prod_\omega \mathfrak{A}_n/D.$$

Consider now

$$\begin{aligned} C = \{\psi \subset M \times F \mid \psi &\text{ is a homomorphism} \\ &\text{from } \langle \mathscr{D}\psi, +\restriction \mathscr{D}\psi, e\rangle \text{ into } \langle F, \cdot, 1\rangle, \psi(\imath) = \rho, \\ &\mathscr{D}\psi \text{ is a pure subgroup of } \mathfrak{M}, \textstyle\prod \mathbb{Z}\imath_n/D \subset \mathscr{D}\psi, \\ &\text{and } v \circ \psi \text{ is the identity map on } \mathscr{D}\psi\}. \end{aligned}$$

First note that $C \neq \phi$, for $\prod_\omega (\mathbb{Z}\imath_n)/D$ is a pure subgroup of $\mathfrak{M}$ (because $\mathbb{Z}\imath_n$ is always pure in $\mathfrak{M}_n$), and since $\psi_n\colon \mathbb{Z}\imath_n \to F_n$ by $\psi_n(r\imath_n) = \rho_n^r$ is always such a homomorphism for each $\mathfrak{A}_n$, $\psi = \prod_\omega \psi_n/D$ is such a homomorphism for $\mathfrak{A}$ and

$$\mathscr{D}\psi = \prod_\omega \mathscr{D}\psi_n/D = \prod_\omega (\mathbb{Z}\imath_n)/D.$$

Let E be a maximal chain in C. $N = \bigcup \{\mathscr{D}\psi \mid \psi \in E\}$ is a pure subgroup of $\mathfrak{M}$ by Lemma 4.4.1(c), and it is simple to verify that $\bigcup E\colon N \to F$ is a homomorphism, $\bigcup E(\imath) = \rho$, and $v \circ \bigcup E$ is the identity on N.

Thus C contains maximal elements, so let $\psi \in C$ be such an element. If $\mathscr{D}\psi \neq M$, let $x \in M \sim \mathscr{D}\psi$, and let y be such that

$$y - x \in \prod_\omega (\mathbb{Z}\imath_n)/D \qquad \text{and} \qquad y/r \in M$$

for each positive integer r. Then

$$N_x = \{(r/s)y + z \mid z \in \mathscr{D}\psi, r \in \mathbb{Z}, s \text{ a positive integer}\}$$

is a pure subgroup of $\mathfrak{M}$ by 4.4.1(b). Note also that if

$$w = \frac{r}{s}y + z = \frac{r'}{s'}y + z' \in N_x,$$

then

$$z = z' \qquad \text{and} \qquad \frac{r}{s} = \frac{r'}{s'}.$$

For otherwise, if $(r/s - r'/s')y = z' - z$, then

$$(rs' - sr')y = ss'(z' - z) \in \mathscr{D}\psi,$$

so since $\mathscr{D}\psi$ is pure, $y \in \mathscr{D}\psi$. But $y = x + u$ for some $u \in \prod_\omega (\mathbb{Z}\imath_n)/D \subset \mathscr{D}\psi$, so $x = y - u$, and $y, u \in \mathscr{D}\psi$, so $x \in \mathscr{D}\psi$, a contradiction.

Now let

$$S = \{(\exists v_1)((v_1^r = v_0) \wedge (v(v_0) = y)) \mid r \text{ a positive integer}\}.$$

S is finitely satisfiable, for

$$\{(\exists v_1)((v_1^{r_1} = v_0) \wedge (v(v_0) = y)), \ldots, (\exists v_1)((v_1^{r_k} = v_0) \wedge (v(v_0) = y))\}$$

can be satisfied by $a^{r_1 \cdots r_k}$, where

$$v(a) = \frac{1}{r_1 \cdots r_k} y.$$

Thus select $b \in F$ satisfying S. We now choose a sequence $b_1 = b$, b_2, $b_3, \ldots$ as follows: Assume that we have $b_1, \ldots, b_k$ such that for $1 \leq j \leq k$, $b_j^j = b_{j-1}$, and such that b_k has roots of all orders. Let

$$S_k = \{(\exists v_1)((v_1^s = v_0) \wedge (v_0^{k+1} = b_k)) \mid s \text{ is an integer} \geq 2\}.$$

S_k is finitely satisfiable, for if we have

$$\{(\exists v_1)((v_1^{s_1} = v_0) \wedge (v_0^{k+1} = b_k)), \ldots, (\exists v_1)((v_0^{s_t} = v_0) \wedge (v_0^{k+1} = b_k))\},$$

then select $c \in F$ with $c^{s_1 \cdots s_t(k+1)} = b_k$, and $c^{s_1 \cdots s_t}$ will satisfy this finite set of formulas. Now select b_{k+1} from the elements satisfying S_k. Thus we obtain a sequence $b_1 = b, b_2, \ldots$ with the property that for each r, $b_r^r = b_{r-1}$. Let $r/s \in \mathbb{Q}$ with $s > 0$ and define $\psi' \colon N_x \to F$ by

$$\psi'\left(\frac{r}{s} y + z\right) = b_s^{(s-1)!r} \psi(z).$$

ψ' is a mapping as our notation asserts, for

$$\psi'\left(\frac{r'}{s'} y + z'\right) = b_{s'}^{(s'-1)!r'} \psi(z'),$$

and if

$$\frac{r}{s} y + z = \frac{r'}{s'} y + z',$$

then

$$z = z' \qquad \text{and} \qquad rs' = sr',$$

so we are in possession of a map if we can show that under these conditions

$$b_{s'}^{(s'-1)!r'} = b_s^{(s-1)!r}.$$

However, let $s' > s$. Then $b_s = b_{s'}^{s'(s'-1) \cdots (s+1)}$, so

$$b_s^{(s-1)!r} = b_{s'}^{s'((s'-1)!/s)r} = b_{s'}^{s((s'-1)!/s)r'} = b_{s'}^{(s'-1)!r'}.$$

It is not difficult to show that ψ' is a homomorphism (intuitively we can look upon $b_s^{(s-1)!r}$ as $b^{r/s}$), and we leave this for the reader. Also,

$$v \circ \psi'\left(\frac{r}{s}y + z\right) = v(b_s^{(s-1)!r}\psi(z)) = v(b_s^{(s-1)!r}) + z$$

$$= (s - 1)!\, rv(b_s) + z$$

$$= (s - 1)!\, r\left(\frac{1}{(s!)}\right) v(b) + z$$

$$= \frac{r}{s} y + z,$$

so $\mathscr{D}\psi \neq M$ contradicts the maximality of ψ, so ψ is a cross section.

Assuming the continuum hypothesis, we now proceed to show that for any two $\mathbb{Z}$-groups $\mathfrak{M}$, $\mathfrak{N}$ of cardinality $\leq 2^\omega$ and any nonprincipal ultrafilter D on ω, $\mathfrak{M}^\omega/D \cong \mathfrak{N}^\omega/D$. This, under these circumstances, is equivalent to the statement that the theory of $\mathbb{Z}$-groups is complete.

Let $0 \leq k < r \in \mathbb{Z}$, $m \in M$, $\mathfrak{M}$ a $\mathbb{Z}$-group. By $m \equiv k \pmod r$ we mean that for some $x \in M$, $m = rx + k\imath$. Clearly if $0 \leq k$, $k' < r$, and $m \equiv k \pmod r$, $m \equiv k' \pmod r$, then $k = k'$; also our axioms for $\mathbb{Z}$-groups assure us that if $m \in M$, then for some k, $0 \leq k < r$, and $m \equiv k \pmod r$.

LEMMA 4.4.4. (a) Let

$$r_1, \ldots, r_n, k_1, \ldots, k_n, p_1, \ldots, p_n \in \mathbb{Z},$$
$$0 \leq k_1 < r_1, \ldots, \qquad 0 \leq k_n < r_n,$$

$\mathfrak{M}$ a $\mathbb{Z}$-group. Then the following are equivalent:

(i) For some $x \in M$, $p_1x \equiv k_1 \pmod{r_1}, \ldots, p_nx \equiv k_n \pmod{r_n}$.
(ii) If $y \in M$, there is an $s \in \mathbb{Z}$ such that

$$p_1(y + s\imath) \equiv k_1 \pmod{r_1}, \ldots, p_n(y + s\imath) \equiv k_n \pmod{r_n}.$$

(b) Let $\mathbb{Z}\imath \subset N \subset M$, $\mathbb{Z}\imath' \subset N' \subset M'$, N, N' be pure, countable subgroups of the ω^+-saturated $\mathbb{Z}$-groups $\mathfrak{M}$, $\mathfrak{M}'$, $\varphi\colon \mathfrak{N} \cong \mathfrak{N}'$. Then for some $\psi \supset \varphi$, $\mathfrak{N}^{*\prime}$, $\psi\colon \mathfrak{N}^* \cong \mathfrak{N}^{*\prime}$, where $\mathfrak{N}^* = (N \cup \{x\}_{\mathfrak{M}})$, $\mathfrak{N}^{*\prime}$ a pure, countable subgroup of $\mathfrak{M}'$. (Note that this also assures us that $\mathfrak{N}^*$ is countable; it is by definition pure in $\mathfrak{M}$. By isomorphism here we, of course, mean order-preserving group isomorphism.)

Proof: (a) Clearly (ii) -> (i) if we take $x = y + s\imath$. Conversely, we have

$$x - y = r_1 \cdots r_n m + s\imath \qquad \text{for some} \quad m \in M,\ s \in \mathbb{Z}$$

(why?). Now let $1 \leq j \leq n$; then for some $z_j \in M$,

$$p_j x = r_j z_j + k_j \imath,$$

so

$$\begin{aligned} p_j(y + s\imath) &= p_j x - p_j(x - (y + s\imath)) \\ &= r_j z_j + k_j \imath - p_j(r_1 \cdots r_n m) \\ &= r_j(z_j - p_j r_1 \cdots r_{j-1} r_{j+1} \cdots r_n m) + k_j \imath, \end{aligned}$$

so

$$p_j(y + s\imath) \equiv k_j \pmod{r_j}.$$

(b) This is clear if $x \in N$, thus we assume that $x \notin N$. Consider the structures

$$\mathfrak{A} = \langle M, +, e, \imath, <, m\rangle_{m \in \mathscr{D}\varphi}, \qquad \mathfrak{B} = \langle M', +', e', \imath', <', \varphi(m)\rangle_{m \in \mathscr{D}\varphi}$$

and the set of formulas

$$\begin{aligned} S = \{\neg(\exists v_1)(nv_1 = pv_0 + qc_\imath) \mid n, p, q \in \mathbb{Z} \\ \text{and for no } m \in M \text{ is } nm = px + q\imath\} \\ \cup \{nc_m < pv_0 + qc_\imath \mid n, p, q \in \mathbb{Z}, nm < px + q\imath\} \\ \cup \{(\exists v_1)(nv_1 = pv_0 + qc_\imath) \mid n, p, q \in \mathbb{Z} \\ \text{and for some } m \in M, nm = px + q\imath\}. \end{aligned}$$

We are interested in S because if $y \in M'$ satisfies S, let

$$\begin{aligned} N^{*\prime} &= (N' \cup \{y\}_{\mathfrak{M}'}) \\ &= \left\{z +' \left(\frac{py +' q\imath'}{r}\right) \mid z \in N', p, q, r \in \mathbb{Z}, \right. \\ &\qquad \left. r \neq 0 \text{ and } \frac{py +' q\imath'}{r} \text{ exists}\right\} \quad \text{(by 4.4.1(b))} \\ &= \left\{z +' \left(\frac{py +' q\imath'}{r}\right) \mid a \in N', p, q, r \in \mathbb{Z}, \right. \\ &\qquad \left. r \neq 0 \text{ and } \frac{px + q\imath}{r} \text{ exists}\right\} \quad \text{(by our definition of } S). \end{aligned}$$

Now suppose that

$$z + \left(\frac{px + q\imath}{r}\right) < z_1 + \left(\frac{p_1 x + q_1 \imath}{r_1}\right),$$

where $z, z_1 \in \mathscr{D}\varphi$, and $(px + q\imath)/r$, $(p_1 x + q_1 \imath)/r_1$ both exist. Then

$$z - z_1 < \left(\frac{p_1 x + q_1 \imath}{r_1}\right) - \left(\frac{px + q\imath}{r}\right) = \frac{(rp_1 - r_1 p)x + (rq_1 - q_1 r)\imath}{rr_1},$$

thus $rr_1(z - z_1) < (rp_1 - r_1p)x + (rq_1 - r_1q)\iota$, so

$$(rr_1c_{z-z_1} < (rp_1 - r_1p)v_0 + (rq_1 - r_1q)c_\iota) \in S,$$

thus

$$rr_1\varphi(z - z_1) <' (rp_1 - r_1p)y +' (rq_1 - r_1q)\iota',$$

so

$$\varphi(z) +' \left(\frac{py +' q\iota'}{r}\right) <' \varphi(z_1) +' \left(\frac{p_1y +' q_1\iota'}{r_1}\right).$$

Therefore

$$\psi = \left\{\left\langle m + \left(\frac{px + q\iota}{r}\right), \varphi(m) +' \left(\frac{py +' q\iota'}{r}\right)\right\rangle \mid m \in \mathscr{D}\varphi, p, q, r \in \mathbb{Z}, \right.$$
$$\left. r \neq 0, \left(\frac{px + q\iota}{r}\right) \text{ exists}\right\}$$

is strictly order-preserving, thus a one-one function; also clearly a group homomorphism,

$$\mathscr{D}\psi = (N \cup \{x\}_{\mathfrak{M}}), \qquad \mathscr{R}\psi = (N' \cup \{y\}_{\mathfrak{M}'}),$$

thus

$$\psi: (N \cup \{x\}_{\mathfrak{M}}) \cong (N' \cup \{y\}_{\mathfrak{M}'}),$$

establishing our result.

Thus it remains to show our S satisfiable in $\mathfrak{M}'$, and since S is countable, $\mathfrak{M}'$ ω^+-saturated, it will do to show S finitely satisfiable. Let

$$\begin{aligned} S_0 = \{&\neg(\exists v_1)(n_1v_1 = p_1v_0 + q_1c_\iota), \ldots, \\ &\neg(\exists v_1)(n_sv_1 = p_sv_0 + q_sc_\iota), \\ &(\exists v_1)(n_{s+1}v_1 = p_{s+1}v_0 + q_{s+1}c_\iota), \ldots, \\ &(\exists v_1)(n_tv_1 = p_tv_0 + q_tc_\iota), \\ &(n_{t+1}c_{m_1} < p_{t+1}v_0 + q_{t+1}c_\iota), \ldots, \\ &(n_{t+u}c_{m_u} < p_{t+u}v_0 + q_{t+u}c_\iota)\} \end{aligned}$$

with

$$p_{t+1}, \ldots, p_{t+w} > 0, \qquad p_{t+w+1}, \ldots, p_{t+u} < 0$$

(we may assume that $p_{t+1}, \ldots, p_{t+u} \neq 0$, since if $p_{t+k} = 0$,

$$n_{t+k}m_k < q_{t+k}\iota, \qquad \text{so} \qquad n_{t+k}\varphi(m_k) <' q_{t+k}\iota',$$

thus

$$(n_{t+k}c_{m_k} < p_{t+k}v_0 + q_{t+k}c_i)$$

is automatically satisfied by every $y \in M'$). The inequalities in S_0 are equivalent to

$$c_{d_1} < pv_0, \ldots, c_{d_w} < pv_0, \qquad pv_0 < c_{d_{w+1}}, \ldots, pv_0 < c_{d_u},$$

where $p = |p_{t+1} \cdots p_{t+u}|$ and for $1 \leq j \leq u$,

$$d_j = \frac{p}{p_{t+j}} (n_{t+j} m_j - q_{t+j} \imath).$$

Now choose $1 \leq j \leq w < k \leq u$ such that

$$d_j = \max\{d_1, \ldots, d_w\}, \qquad d_k = \min\{d_{w+1}, \ldots, d_u\}.$$

Then all our inequalities are equivalent to $c_{d_j} < pv_0 < c_{d_k}$. For some $b \in \mathbb{Z}$,

$$m' = \frac{d_j + d_k + b\imath}{2p}$$

exists and is in N since N is pure and $\mathbb{Z}\imath \subset N$. In addition by (a), for some $a \in \mathbb{Z}$, $m = m' + a\imath$ has the property that for $1 \leq g \leq t$,

$$p_g m \equiv r_g \pmod{n_g}, \qquad \text{where} \quad p_g x \equiv r_g \pmod{n_g},$$

and by definition of S,

$$r_g \neq -q_g \quad \text{if} \quad g \leq s, \qquad r_g = -q_g \quad \text{for} \quad g > s.$$

m satisfies S_0 because

$$2pm = 2p(m' + a\imath) = d_j + d_k + (b + 2pa)\imath,$$

thus $2d_j < 2pm < 2d_k$ (for this, note that since $x \notin N$, and x satisfies the above inequalities, if $h_1, h_2 \in \mathbb{Z}$,

$$b_j + h_1\imath < x < b_k + h_2\imath,$$

thus in particular

$$d_j < d_k + (b + 2pa)\imath, \qquad d_j + (b + 2pa)\imath < d_k),$$

so $d_j < pm < d_k$, and the remaining statements of S_0 are satisfied by the previous sentence. (A slightly different selection of m is required for the cases $w = 0$ and $w = u$. What is required in the case of $w = 0$ is an m such that $pm < d_k + h\imath$ for every $h \in \mathbb{Z}$; we leave the reader to treat these two cases.)

THEOREM 4.4.5. Assume the continuum hypothesis and let $\mathfrak{M}$, $\mathfrak{N}$ be $\mathbb{Z}$-groups of cardinality $\leq 2^\omega$, D a nonprincipal ultrafilter on ω. Then

$$\mathfrak{M}^\omega/D \cong \mathfrak{N}^\omega/D.$$

(NOTE: We must show these isomorphic as *ordered* groups.)

Proof: Let $M = \{x_\alpha \mid \alpha < \omega^+\}$, $M' = \{y_\alpha \mid \alpha < \omega^+\}$. For $\alpha \le \omega^+$ we define φ_α such that

(i) $\mathscr{D}\varphi_\alpha$, $\mathscr{R}\varphi_\alpha$ are pure in $\mathfrak{M}$, $\mathfrak{M}'$, and if $\alpha < \omega^+$ they are countable;

(ii) $\{x_\beta \mid \beta < \alpha\} \cup \mathbb{Z}\imath \subset \mathscr{D}\varphi_\alpha$, $\{y_\beta \mid \beta < \alpha\} \cup \mathbb{Z}\imath' \subset \mathscr{R}\varphi_\alpha$;

(iii) $\varphi_\alpha\colon \mathfrak{M} \mid \mathscr{D}\varphi_\alpha \cong \mathfrak{M}' \mid \mathscr{R}\varphi_\alpha$;

(iv) if $\alpha \le \gamma \le \omega^+$, $\varphi_\alpha \subset \varphi_\gamma$,

by induction as follows: Let $\varphi_0 = \{\langle n\imath, n\imath'\rangle \mid n \in \mathbb{Z}\}$, (i) through (iv) are clearly satisfied; if we have $\{\varphi_\gamma \mid \gamma \le \alpha\}$, $\alpha < \omega^+$, then

$$\varphi_\alpha^{-1}\colon \mathfrak{M}' \mid \mathscr{R}\varphi_\alpha \cong \mathfrak{M} \mid \mathscr{D}\varphi_\alpha,$$

so by 4.4.4(b) there is a $\psi \supset \varphi_\alpha^{-1}$ such that $\mathscr{D}\psi$, $\mathscr{R}\psi$ are pure countable subgroups of $\mathfrak{M}'$, $\mathfrak{M}$ respectively, and $y_\alpha \in \mathscr{D}\psi$, and a second application gives us

$$\varphi_{\alpha+1} \supset \psi^{-1} \supset (\varphi_\alpha^{-1})^{-1} = \varphi_\alpha$$

with

$$x_\alpha \in \mathscr{D}\varphi_{\alpha+1}, \qquad \varphi_{\alpha+1}\colon \mathfrak{M} \mid \mathscr{D}\varphi_{\alpha+1} \cong \mathfrak{M}' \mid \mathscr{R}\varphi_{\alpha+1}.$$

Since $y_\alpha \in \mathscr{D}\psi \subset \mathscr{R}\varphi_{\alpha+1}$, (ii) is satisfied as the other three conditions are. If $\alpha \le \omega^+$ is a limit ordinal, $\varphi_\alpha = \bigcup_{\gamma<\alpha} \varphi_\gamma$ satisfies (i) by 4.4.1(c) and our remaining conditions trivially. Clearly

$$\varphi_{\omega^+}\colon \mathfrak{M} \cong \mathfrak{M}'.$$

THEOREM 4.4.6. Let $\mathfrak{A} = \langle \mathfrak{F}, \mathfrak{M}, v, \imath, \rho\rangle$, $\mathfrak{A}' = \langle \mathfrak{F}', \mathfrak{M}', v', \imath', \rho'\rangle$ be Hensel fields, and let the characteristic of $\overline{\mathfrak{F}}$ be 0. If (in the appropriate language) $\overline{\mathfrak{F}} \equiv \overline{\mathfrak{F}}'$, then $\mathfrak{A} \equiv \mathfrak{A}'$.

Proof: Let $\mathfrak{A} \equiv \mathfrak{B} = \langle \mathfrak{G}, \ldots\rangle$, $\mathfrak{A}' \equiv \mathfrak{B}' = \langle \mathfrak{G}', \ldots\rangle$, with $\mathfrak{B}$, $\mathfrak{B}'$ countable, and $\overline{\mathfrak{F}} \equiv \overline{\mathfrak{G}} \equiv \overline{\mathfrak{G}}'$. Then $\mathfrak{B}$, $\mathfrak{B}'$ are Hensel fields, $\overline{\mathfrak{G}}$ is of characteristic 0. Thus $\mathfrak{B}^\omega/D$, $\mathfrak{B}'^\omega/D$ have isomorphic residue class fields ($\overline{\mathfrak{G}}^\omega/D \cong \overline{\mathfrak{G}}'^\omega/D$) and by Theorem 4.4.5, isomorphic value groups. By Theorem 4.4.3 they have cross sections as well, so by Theorem 4.3.4 (and Lemma 4.2.1) $\mathfrak{B}^\omega/D \cong \mathfrak{B}'^\omega/D$. Thus

$$\mathfrak{A} \equiv \mathfrak{B} \equiv \mathfrak{B}' \equiv \mathfrak{A}'.$$

By "the appropriate language" in the statement of Theorem 4.4.6, we, of course, have in mind the language of fields. For the immediate future, we will indicate by t the type of valued fields, and by t' the type of fields (and rings with unit).

THEOREM 4.4.7. Let $\mathfrak{F}$, $\mathfrak{F}'$ be two fields of characteristic 0. Then the following are equivalent:

(i) $\mathfrak{F} \equiv \mathfrak{F}'$.

(ii) $\langle \mathfrak{F}((X)), \mathbb{Z}, v, 1, X\rangle \equiv \langle \mathfrak{F}'((X')), \mathbb{Z}, v', 1, X'\rangle$, where if $a_n \neq 0$, then $v(\sum_n^\infty a_j X^j) = n$, v' defined similarly, ($\mathfrak{F}((X))$ defined in comments following 4.1.12).

(iii) $\mathfrak{F}[[X]] \equiv \mathfrak{F}'[[X']]$ (where

$$\mathfrak{F}[[X]] = \mathfrak{F}((X)) \mid \{y \in F((X)) \mid v(y) \geq 0\}).$$

Proof: Theorem 4.4.6 shows that (i) implies (ii). If (ii) holds and $F \in \Sigma^{t'}$, then $\mathfrak{F}[[X]] \models F$ iff $\mathfrak{F}((X)) \models F_{\mathfrak{F}[[X]]}$ iff $\mathfrak{F}'((X')) \models F_{\mathfrak{F}[[X']]}$ iff $\mathfrak{F}[[X']] \models F$ (see Problem 1.2.11).

Finally, assume that $\mathfrak{F}[[X]] \equiv \mathfrak{F}'[[X']]$. For $F \in \Sigma^{t'}$, define F_- inductively as follows: If $F = (x_1 = x_2)$, then

$$F_- = \neg(\exists v_0)(v_0(x_1 - x_2) = 1);$$

if $F = P_i(x_1, \ldots, x_{t'(i)})$, then

$$F_- = (\exists v_1)\cdots(\exists v_{t'(i)})(P_i(v_1, \ldots, v_{t'(i)}) \wedge (v_1 = x_1)_- \wedge \cdots \wedge (v_{t'(i)} = x_{t'(i)})_-),$$

$$(F \vee G)_- = F_- \vee G_-,$$

$$(\neg F)_- = \neg(F_-),$$

and

$$(\exists v_j)F_- = (\exists v_j)(F_-).$$

Then (see Problem 1.2.12), $\mathfrak{A} \models F$ iff $\mathfrak{F}[[X]] \models F_-$ iff $\mathfrak{F}'[[X']] \models F_-$ iff $\mathfrak{A}' \models F$.

Corollary 4.4.8. Let S be a set of axioms for $T(\mathfrak{F})$, $\mathfrak{F}$ a field of characteristic 0. Then $\{F_- \mid F \in S\} \cup T$ is the set of axioms for a complete theory, where T is a set of axioms for Hensel fields.

Definition 4.4.9. Let $R \subset P$ be infinite. Then

$$Q(R) = \{F \in \Sigma^t \mid \{p \in R \mid \mathfrak{A}_p \not\models F\} \text{ is finite}\},$$

$$S(R) = \{F \in \Sigma^t \mid \{p \in R \mid \mathfrak{B}_p \not\models F\} \text{ is finite}\},$$

and

$$T(R) = \{F \in \Sigma^{t'} \mid \{p \in R \mid \mathbb{Z}_p \not\models F\} \text{ is finite}\}.$$

By Corollary 4.3.7(a), $Q(R) = S(R)$ for every infinite $R \subset P$. Furthermore, both are complete theories. We also have:

Proposition 4.4.10. Let $F \in Q(R)$. Then for some $G \in T(R)$, $\{G'\} \cup T \models F$, where T is the set of axioms for Hensel fields, and $G' = (G_{\{x \mid v(x) \leq e\}})_-$.

Proof: As in Problems 1.2.11 and 1.2.12, $\langle \mathfrak{F}, \mathfrak{M}, v, \iota, \rho \rangle \models G'$ iff $\bar{\mathfrak{F}} \models G$. Now let

$$\mathfrak{A} = \langle \mathfrak{F}, \mathfrak{M}, v, \iota, \rho \rangle \models \{G' \mid G \in T(R)\} \cup T, \quad c(\mathfrak{A}) \leq 2^{\omega}.$$

Then $\bar{\mathfrak{F}} \models T(R)$, so for every nonprincipal ultrafilter D on R,

$$\bar{\mathfrak{F}}^R/D \cong \prod_R \mathbb{Z}_p/D.$$

$\mathfrak{A}^R/D$ has a cross section by Theorem 4.4.3, and by 4.4.5, its valuation group is isomorphic to $\mathbb{Z}^R/D$ ($\cong \mathbb{Z}^{\omega}/E$ for any nonprincipal E), so

$$\mathfrak{A}^R/D \cong \prod_R \mathfrak{A}_p/D, \qquad \text{thus} \qquad \mathfrak{A} \equiv \prod_R \mathfrak{A}_p/D.$$

Thus $\mathfrak{A} \models Q(R)$, so

$$T \cup \{G' \mid G \in T(R)\} \models Q(R),$$

so if $F \in Q(R)$,

$$T \cup \{G'_1, \ldots, G'_n\} \models F \qquad \text{for some} \quad G'_1, \ldots, G'_n \in T(R).$$

But then so does $T \cup \{G'_1 \wedge \cdots \wedge G'_n\}$, but

$$G'_1 \wedge \cdots \wedge G'_n = (G_1 \wedge \cdots \wedge G_n)' \in T(R).$$

Finally, we study the extension by Ax and Kochen of the result in Corollary 4.4.8 to certain fields of characteristic $\neq 0$. Suppose now that $\langle \mathfrak{F}, \mathfrak{M}, v, \iota, \rho \rangle$ is a Hensel field and for every $n \in \mathbb{Z} \subset F$, $v(n) \in \mathbb{Z}\iota \subset M$. Note that the class of Hensel fields satisfying this condition is no longer an elementary class, but it is elementarily closed. We have, corresponding to Lemma 4.2.10(b) and Proposition 4.2.12, essentially the same statements with the understanding that the assumption made in that part of the text, that $\bar{\mathfrak{F}}$ is of characteristic 0, no longer holds. We shall need statements equivalent to these because we are aiming for results like those in Section 4.3 and early in this section. Their proofs are very similar as well, as our new 4.2.12 depends on our new 4.2.10(b), which in turn depends on a new 4.2.10(a), which is Lemma 4.4.11(b) below (we do not rewrite the statements or proofs of the lemmas mentioned when they are almost identical to the earlier statements).

Lemma 4.4.11. (a) Let $S \subset M$ have no least element, $j > 0$, $j, k \in \mathbb{Z}$, $t, t' \in M$, and $s \in S$ such that if $s' < s$ and $s' \in S$ then $js' + t < ks' + t'$.

If $n_1, \ldots, n_r \in \mathbb{Z}\iota$, then there is an $s^* \in S$ such that if $s' < s^*$ and $s' \in S$, then for $1 \leq m \leq r$,

$$js' + t + n_m < ks' + t'.$$

(b) Let $\langle \mathfrak{F}, \mathfrak{M}, v, \imath, \rho \rangle$ be a Hensel field and let $v[\mathbb{Z}] \subset \mathbb{Z}\imath$. Let a be T_a-Cauchy with T_a-limit b, and assume that 0 is not an $S_{f(i) \circ a}$-limit for $f^{(i)} \circ a$ if $1 \leq i \leq n = \deg(f)$. If $1 \leq i < j \leq n$, then for some $\sigma < \lambda$, if $\sigma < \tau < \lambda$, then

$$v((1/i!)f^{(i)}(b)) > (j - i)v(a_\tau - b) + v(1/j!)f^{(j)}(b)).$$

Proof: (a) We leave this for the reader with the hint that if $s \in S$, $z \in \mathbb{Z}\imath$, then for some $s' \in S$, $s' < s - z$.

(b) Assume that this has been shown for $j > i > i_0$ and we wish to show it for $j > i \geq i_0$. Select a σ such that if $\sigma < \tau < \lambda$, then

$$v(f^{(io)}(b)) > v(f^{(io)}(a_\tau) - f^{(io)}(b)),$$

a selection possible since 0 is not an $S_{f(io) \circ a}$-limit of $f^{(io)} \circ a$. Thus for $\sigma < \tau < \lambda$,

$$v(f^{(io)}(b)) = v(f^{(io)}(a_\tau)) = v\left(f^{(io)}(b) + \cdots + \frac{(a_\tau - b)^{n-io} f^{(n)}(b)}{(n - i_0)!}\right).$$

For $i_0 < i < j \leq n$, select $\sigma_{ij} < \lambda$ such that if $\sigma_{ij} < \tau < \lambda$, then

$$v\left(\frac{f^{(i)}(b)}{i!}\right) > (j - i)v(a_\tau - b) + v\left(\frac{f^{(j)}(b)}{j!}\right),$$

a selection possible by induction hypothesis.

Since $v[\mathbb{Z}] \subset \mathbb{Z}\imath$, by (a) we can find $\sigma'_{ij} < \lambda$ such that if $\sigma'_{ij} < \tau < \lambda$, then

$$v(f^{(i)}(b)) > (j - i)v(a_\tau - b) + v\left(\frac{f^{(j)}(b)}{(j - i_0)!}\right).$$

If s' is such that $\sigma_{s'} > \max\{\sigma_{ij}, \sigma'_{ij}\}$, then for $\sigma_{s'} < \tau < \lambda$,

$$v(a_\tau - b) + v\left(\frac{f^{(io+1)}(b)}{(i_0 + 1)!}\right) > \cdots > (n - i_0)v(a_\tau - b) + v\left(\frac{f^{(n)}(b)}{n!}\right).$$

Also,

$$v(f^{(io)}(b)) \geq v(a_\tau - b) + v(f^{(io+1)}(b)),$$

for if

$$v(f^{(io)}(b)) < v(a_\tau - b) + v(f^{(io+1)}(b)),$$

then

$$v(f^{(io)}(b)) = v\left(f^{(io)}(b) + \cdots + \frac{(a_\tau - b)^{n-io} f^{(n)}(b)}{(n - i_0)!}\right)$$
$$= v(a_\tau - b) + v(f^{(io+1)}(b)),$$

a contradiction. Now let $\sigma'' = \max\{\sigma_{s'}, \sigma_{v(a_\tau - b)}\}$. If $\sigma'' < \tau' < \lambda$, then

$$v(a_{\tau'} - b) + v(f^{(io+1)}(b)) < v(a_\tau - b) + v(f^{(io+1)}(b)) \leq v(f^{(io)}(b)),$$

and again by (a) we can choose $s \in T_a$ sufficiently small so that if $\sigma^* = \max\{\sigma'', \sigma_s\}$, then for $\sigma^* < \tau' < \lambda$,

$$v(a_{\tau'} - b) + v\left(\frac{f^{(i_0+1)}(b)}{(i_0 + 1)!}\right) < v\left(\frac{f^{(i_0)}(b)}{i_0!}\right),$$

completing the proof.

A second obstacle in our path is the need to replace 4.2.13 so we can establish 4.2.14 under these more general conditions.

LEMMA 4.4.12. (a) Let $\langle \mathfrak{F}, \mathfrak{M}, w\rangle \subset \langle \mathfrak{F}(a), \mathfrak{N}, v\rangle$ and let a have minimal polynomial of degree n over $\mathfrak{F}$. If a has minimal polynomial over $\bar{\mathfrak{F}}$ of degree n or if $c(\mathfrak{N}/\mathfrak{M}) = n$ and $\mathfrak{N}$ is generated by $M \cup \{v(a)\}$, then

$$v\left(\sum_{j=0}^{n-1} r_j a^j\right) = \max\{v(r_j a^j) \mid 0 \leq j < n\} \quad \text{when} \quad r_0, \ldots, r_{n-1} \in F.$$

(b) Let $\langle \mathfrak{F}, \mathfrak{M}, v\rangle \subset \langle \mathfrak{F}(b, c), \mathfrak{N}, w\rangle$ such that

$$n = [\mathfrak{F}(b): \mathfrak{F}] = [\bar{\mathfrak{F}}(\bar{b}): \bar{\mathfrak{F}}] \quad \text{and} \quad k = [\mathfrak{F}(b)(c): \mathfrak{F}(b)] = c(\mathfrak{N}/\mathfrak{M}),$$

$\mathfrak{N}$ generated by $M \cup \{v(c)\}$. Then

$$v\left(\sum_{\substack{0 \leq j < k \\ 0 \leq i < n}} r_{ij} b^i c^j\right) = \max\{v(r_{ij} b^i c^j) \mid 0 \leq j < k, 0 \leq i < n\} \quad \text{for } r_{ij} \in F.$$

Also

$$[\mathfrak{F}(b, c): \mathfrak{F}] = [\bar{\mathfrak{F}}(\bar{b}): \bar{\mathfrak{F}}] \cdot c(\mathfrak{N}/\mathfrak{M}).$$

(c) Let $\langle \mathfrak{F}, \mathfrak{M}, v\rangle$ be $\langle \mathbb{Q}_p, \mathbb{Z}, v_p\rangle$ or $\langle R_p, \mathbb{Z}, v_p\rangle$, where R_p is the algebraic closure of $\mathbb{Q}$ in $\mathbb{Q}_p$. If a is algebraic over $\mathfrak{F}$, then

$$\mathfrak{F}(a) = \mathfrak{F}(b, c) \quad \text{for some} \quad b, c \in \mathfrak{F}(a)$$

such that

$$[\mathfrak{F}(b): \mathfrak{F}] = [\bar{\mathfrak{F}}(\bar{b}): \bar{\mathfrak{F}}] \quad \text{and} \quad [\mathfrak{F}(b)(c): \mathfrak{F}(b)] = c(\mathfrak{N}/\mathfrak{M}).$$

Proof: (a) Let

$$r_0, \ldots, r_{n-1} \in F, \qquad x = \max\{v(r_i a^i) \mid 0 \leq i < n\} = v(r_j a^j).$$

Then

$$v(r_0 + \cdots + r_{n-1}a^{n-1}) = v(r_j a^j) + v(s_0 a^{-j} + \cdots + s_{n-1}a^{n-1-j}),$$

where $s_i = r_i/r_j$, so it will do to show

$$v(s_0 a^{-j} + \cdots + s_{n-1}a^{n-1-j}) = e.$$

If $\bar{a}$ has minimal polynomial over $\bar{\mathfrak{F}}$ of degree n, then $v(a) = e$ (for $v(a) \leq e$ in order that $\bar{a}$ may exist, and if $v(a) < e$, then $\bar{a} = \bar{0} \in \bar{\mathfrak{F}}$), and if

$$v(s_0 a^{-j} + \cdots + s_{n-1} a^{n-1-j}) < e,$$

then

$$\bar{s}_0 \bar{a}^{-j} + \cdots + \bar{s}_{n-1} \bar{a}^{n-1-j} = \bar{0},$$

so

$$\bar{s}_0 + \cdots + \bar{s}_{n-1} \bar{a}^{n-1} = \bar{a}^j (\bar{s}_0 \bar{a}^{-j} + \cdots + \bar{s}_{n-1} \bar{a}^{n-1-j}) = \bar{0},$$

a contradiction.

In the second case, if $e = v(s_k a^{k-j})$, then

$$e = v(s_k) + (k - j) v(a),$$

so $(j - k) v(a) \in M$, which is impossible if $j \neq k$, for $0 \leq j, k < n$, and $sv(a) \in M$ iff $n \mid s$. Thus if $k \neq j$,

$$v(s_k a^k) < e, \qquad \text{so} \quad v(s_0 a^{-j} + \cdots + s_{n-1} a^{n-1-j}) = e.$$

(b) Our first assertion is shown by (a) if we can show $v[F(b)] \subset M$, for if so,

$$\langle \mathfrak{F}, \mathfrak{M}, v \rangle \subset \langle \mathfrak{F}(b), \mathfrak{M}, v' \rangle \subset \langle \mathfrak{F}(b)(c), \mathfrak{N}, w \rangle,$$

and the first case of (a) applies to

$$\langle \mathfrak{F}, \mathfrak{M}, v \rangle \subset \langle \mathfrak{F}(b), \mathfrak{M}, v' \rangle,$$

the second to

$$\langle \mathfrak{F}(b), \mathfrak{M}, v' \rangle \subset \langle \mathfrak{F}(b)(c), \mathfrak{N}, w \rangle.$$

However if

$$v'(r_0 + \cdots + r_{n-1} b^{n-1}) \notin M,$$

then

$$v'(r_0 + \cdots + r_{n-1} b^{n-1}) \neq \max\{v(r_i) + iv'(b) \mid 0 \leq i < n\},$$

since $v'(b) = e$, contradicting (a). The next assertion follows from Problem 4.2.2 (or a text on fields), since

$$[\mathfrak{F}(b)(c) \colon \mathfrak{F}] = [\mathfrak{F}(b) \colon \mathfrak{F}][\mathfrak{F}(b)(c) \colon \mathfrak{F}(b)] = c(\mathfrak{N}/\mathfrak{M}) \cdot [\bar{\mathfrak{F}}(\bar{b}); \bar{\mathfrak{F}}].$$

(c) By (b), if $b, c \in \mathfrak{F}(a)$ are as in (b), then

$$[\mathfrak{F}(a) \colon \mathfrak{F}] \geq [\mathfrak{F}(b, c) \colon \mathfrak{F}] = c(\mathfrak{N}'/\mathfrak{M}) \cdot [\bar{\mathfrak{F}}(\bar{b}) \colon \bar{\mathfrak{F}}],$$

with $\mathfrak{N}'$ generated by $M \cup \{v(c)\}$, so $c(\mathfrak{N}/\mathfrak{M})$, $[\bar{\mathfrak{F}}(\bar{a}) \colon \bar{\mathfrak{F}}]$ are both finite (why?), and so we may choose $\bar{b} \in \overline{\mathfrak{F}(a)}$, $c \in \mathfrak{F}(a)$ with $v(c)$ the smallest positive element of $\mathfrak{N}$ and $\overline{\mathfrak{F}(a)} = \bar{\mathfrak{F}}(\bar{b})$, and let $v(p) = 1$, s the smallest positive integer such that $sv(c) \in \mathbb{Z}$. By Problem 4.1.5 if $\langle \mathfrak{F}, \mathfrak{M}, v \rangle = \langle \mathbb{Q}_p, \mathbb{Z}, v_p \rangle$, since each element of $\overline{\mathfrak{F}(a)}$ is (uniquely) of the form

$$\overline{r_0} + \cdots + \overline{r_{n-1}} (\bar{b})^{n-1}, \qquad r_0, \ldots, r_{n-1} \in \{0, \ldots, p - 1\},$$

where $[\bar{\mathfrak{F}}(\bar{b}): \bar{\mathfrak{F}}] = n$ and

$$N = \{jv(p) + kv(c) \mid j \in \mathbb{Z}, k = 0, \ldots, n-1\},$$

each element $d \in \mathfrak{F}(a)$ may be written as

$$\begin{aligned} d &= \sum_{j=q}^{\infty} \sum_{k=0}^{s-1} (r_0^{(j,k)} + \cdots + r_{n-1}^{(j,k)} b^{n-1}) c^k p^j \\ &= \sum_{k=0}^{s-1} \left(\left(\sum_{j=q}^{\infty} r_0^{(k,j)} p^j \right) + \cdots + \left(\sum_{j=q}^{\infty} r_{n-1}^{(k,j)} p^j \right) b^{n-1} \right) c^k. \end{aligned}$$

For $0 \le i < n$, let

$$r_{ik} = \sum_{j=q}^{\infty} r_i^{(j,k)} p^j \in \mathbb{Q}_p.$$

Thus

$$d = \sum_{k=0}^{s-1} (r_{0k} + \cdots + r_{n-1k} b^{n-1}) c^k = \sum_{k=0}^{s-1} \sum_{m=0}^{n-1} r_{mk} b^m c^k$$

establishing our lemma in this case. However, by Problem 4.2.2, if a is algebraic over R_p, then

$$[R_p(a): R_p] = [\mathbb{Q}_p(a): \mathbb{Q}_p] = [\mathbb{Z}_p(b): \mathbb{Z}_p] \cdot c(\mathfrak{N}/\mathfrak{M}),$$

where

$$\mathfrak{N} = M \cup \{v(c)\} = [R_p(b, c): R_p],$$

thus

$$R_p(a) = R_p(b, c),$$

and the lemma follows in this case.

DEFINITION 4.4.13. A formally p-adic field is a Hensel field $\langle \mathfrak{F}, \mathfrak{M}, v, \imath, \rho \rangle$ with $\mathfrak{F}$ of characteristic 0, $\bar{\mathfrak{F}} = \mathbb{Z}_p$, and $\rho = p$.

In Lemma 4.4.14, we show that $\langle R_p, \mathbb{Z}, v_p, 1, p \rangle \subset \mathfrak{A}$ for any formally p-adic field $\mathfrak{A}$. By using this, it is simple to check that we have a lemma very similar to 4.2.13(b), if $\mathfrak{F}$ is algebraically closed in $\mathfrak{G}$, $y \in G$, and $r \in \tilde{\mathfrak{F}}$, then for some $s \in F$,

$$v(y - s) \le v(y - r).$$

Since $R_p \subset \mathfrak{F}$, we may write

$$r - y = \sum_{\substack{0 \le i < n \\ 0 \le j < k}} (r_{ij} - d_{ij} y) b^i c^j$$

b, c as in 4.4.12(b) and (c) and use comments similar to those following Definition 4.2.6. Thus

$$v(r_{00} - y) \le v(r - y).$$

Thus, when our imbedding of R_p is done, 4.2.14 holds, and we use it below.

LEMMA 4.4.14. Let $\mathfrak{A} = \langle \mathfrak{F}, \mathfrak{M}, v, \imath, p \rangle$ be formally p-adic. Then $\langle R_p, \mathbb{Z}, v_p, 1, p \rangle$ can be imbedded in $\mathfrak{A}$, and if $\mathfrak{A}$ is ω-pseudocomplete, $\mathfrak{A}_p$ can be imbedded in $\mathfrak{A}$.

Proof: Let $\mathfrak{B} = \langle \mathfrak{G}, \mathbb{Z}\imath, v, \imath, p \rangle \subset \mathfrak{A}$, $\mathfrak{G}$ maximal such that $v[G] \subset \mathbb{Z}\imath$. Then the completion of $\mathfrak{B}$ is isomorphic to $\mathfrak{A}_p$ (use the expansion developed in Problem 4.1.5). Thus $\mathfrak{B}$ can be isomorphically imbedded in $\mathfrak{A}_p$, let the image of that isomorphism be called $\mathfrak{B}'$. Now suppose $a \in \mathbb{Q}_p$ is algebraic over $\mathbb{Q}$, $f \in \mathbb{Q}[X]$ monic and irreducible with a among its roots and each coefficient of f of value ≤ 0. Thus since $\mathbb{Q}$ is a subfield in dense the field of $\mathfrak{B}'$, we can find $r \in \mathbb{Q}$ such that $v(f(r)) < v(D(f))$, (why?) thus a is in the field of $\mathfrak{B}'$ by 4.1.9(a). For any b algebraic over $\mathbb{Q}$, $b = (1/p^n)(p^n b)$ for some n such that $p^n b$ is the root of some monic polynomial in $R_{\mathbb{Q}}[X]$ (thus $p^n b$, therefore b is in the field of $\mathfrak{B}'$). In fact, if $r_0 + \cdots + r_m b^m = 0$, let

$$-n = \max\{v(r_j) - v(r_m) \mid 0 \leq j \leq m\} \cup \{0\},$$

thus

$$\frac{r_0(p^n)^m}{r_m} + \cdots + (p^n b)^m = \frac{(p^n)^m}{r_m} r_0 + \cdots + r_m \left(\frac{1}{p^n}\right)^m (p^n b)^m = 0,$$

and

$$v\left(\frac{r_j(p^n)^m}{r_m}\right) \leq 0.$$

By the above and 4.2.14, we know that if $\mathfrak{G}$ is maximal with $v[G] \subset \mathbb{Z}\imath$ and $\mathfrak{A}$ is ω-pseudocomplete, then $\langle \mathfrak{G}, \mathbb{Z}\imath, v \rangle$ is (pseudo)complete, so as above, $\langle \mathfrak{G}, \mathbb{Z}\imath, v, \imath, p \rangle \cong \mathfrak{A}_p$.

THEOREM 4.4.15. The theory of formally p-adic fields is complete.

Proof: Let $\mathfrak{A}$, $\mathfrak{B}$ be two such and let $c(\mathfrak{A}), c(\mathfrak{B}) \leq 2^\omega$. If D is a nonprincipal ultrafilter on ω, let

$$\langle \mathbb{Q}_p'', \mathbb{Z}'', v_p, 1'', p'' \rangle \subset \mathfrak{A}^\omega/D, \qquad \langle \mathbb{Q}_p', \mathbb{Z}', v_p, 1', p' \rangle \subset \mathfrak{B}^\omega/D.$$

Now choose transcendence bases A, B for $\mathfrak{F}$ and $\mathfrak{G}$ over $\mathbb{Q}_p''$ and $\mathbb{Q}_p'$, and complete the proof as in Theorem 4.3.4, using 4.3.3 via Lemmas 4.4.11, 4.4.12, and 4.4.14.

Problems

4.4.1 Show, using the continuum hypothesis, that if $c(\mathfrak{A}) = \omega$, $c(\mathfrak{B}) \leq 2^\omega$, and $c(t) \leq \omega$, then $\varphi: \mathfrak{A} <' \mathfrak{B}$ iff for every nonprincipal ultrafilter D on ω there is a ψ such that

$$\psi: \mathfrak{A}^\omega/D \cong \mathfrak{B}^\omega/D \quad \text{and} \quad \psi \circ j_{\mathfrak{A}} = j_{\mathfrak{B}} \circ \varphi.$$

4.4.2 Let $T \subset L^{\langle 2,0 \rangle}$ be the theory of linear ordering with first but no last element and every element but the first with an immediate predecessor and every element with an immediate successor. Here is a set of axioms for T:

$$(\forall v_1)((0 < v_1) \vee (0 = v_1));$$

$$(\forall v_1)(\exists v_2)((v_1 < v_2) \wedge (\forall v_3)((v_3 < v_1) \vee (v_3 = v_1) \vee (v_2 = v_3) \vee (v_2 < v_3));$$

$$(\forall v_1)(\exists v_2)((v_1 = 0) \vee ((v_2 < v_1) \wedge (\forall v_3)((v_3 < v_2) \vee (v_3 = v_2) \vee (v_1 = v_3) \vee (v_1 < v_3)));$$

plus the axioms for a strict total ordering.

Using methods developed in Chapter 2 and this section, together with Problem 4.4.1, show T to be complete but not model-complete.

4.4.3 Show that the class of $\mathbb{Z}$-groups is model-complete (result due to Robinson and Zakon).

4.4.4 Show that for each p the class of formally p-adic fields is model-complete. (The above result is due to Ax and Kochen.)

4.4.5 Show that the axioms for ordered divisible Abelian groups are complete and model-complete (a result originally due to A. Robinson [1]).

4.4.6 Let $\langle \mathfrak{F}, \mathfrak{M}, v \rangle$ be a valued field, with $\mathfrak{F}$ algebraically closed. Show that $\langle \mathfrak{F}, \mathfrak{M}, v \rangle$ satisfies Hensel's lemma and $\mathfrak{M}$ is an ordered divisible Abelian group. Also show that $\overline{\mathfrak{F}}$ is algebraically closed.

Show the following results, due originally to A. Robinson:

The theory of algebraically closed valued fields of characteristic 0 with residue class fields of characteristic 0 is complete.

For any prime p, the theory of algebraically closed valued fields of characteristic 0 with residue class fields of characteristic p is complete.

For any prime p, the theory of algebraically closed valued fields of characteristic p is complete.

The theory of algebraically closed valued fields is model-complete, but not complete.

4.4.7 Use Theorem 1.6.18 to give an alternate proof of Proposition 4.4.10 (this proof will use Corollary 4.4.8).

5

Applications to Analysis

5.1 Ultrapowers of the Reals

The purpose of this chapter is to use the theory of ultraproducts and ultrapowers to study analysis.

Suppose for the moment we consider $\mathbb{R}^\omega/D$, D a nonprincipal ultrafilter on ω. We note that we are studying sequences $a = \langle a_0, a_1, \ldots\rangle$ of real numbers modulo an equivalence relation. A sequence a approaches 0 (in the usual sense) iff for every positive $r \in \mathbb{R}$, $\{n \mid |a_n| > r\}$ is finite, thus iff for every nonprincipal ultrafilter D and every $r > 0$,

$$\mathbb{R}^\omega/D \models (|v_0| \leq c_r)[a/D].$$

Thus not only are we studying sequences of reals, but it seems not too difficult to formulate appropriate conditions for convergence. Below we consider a construction based on this example.

Throughout this chapter we shall use the following conventions: $\mathfrak{F} = \langle F, +, \cdot, 0, 1, <\rangle$ will denote an Archimedean ordered field, $\mathbf{I}$ an infinite set, and D a countably incomplete ultrafilter on $\mathbf{I}$ (recall that all nonprincipal ultrafilters on ω and all regular ultrafilters are countably incomplete). $\mathfrak{F}^* = \mathfrak{F}^\mathbf{I}/D$; if $S \subset F^n$ for some positive integer n, then $S^* = S^\mathbf{I}/D$; if $r \in F$, then $r^* = j_\mathfrak{F}(r) = f_r/D$, where $f_r\colon \mathbf{I} \to F$ is defined by $f_r(\mathbf{i}) = r$. For certain basic ordered field relations and operations we find it convenient to drop the $*$; in particular we often use $0, 1, +, <, |\ |$ when we really mean $0^*, 1^*, +^*, <^*, |\ |^*$, and we do this for a few other common relations as well.

Note that $\mathfrak{F}^*$ is by comments following 2.7.1 ω^+-saturated, thus non-Archimedean (consider

$$\langle F^*, +, \cdot, 0, 1, <, 2^*, 3^*, \ldots \rangle \qquad \text{and} \qquad \{c_n < v_0 \mid n \in \omega\}).$$

We now define $st \subset F^* \times F$ by

$$st = \{\langle a, b\rangle \mid a \in F^*, b \in F \text{ and for each positive integer } n, \quad |a - b^*| < 1/n^*\}.$$

PROPOSITION 5.1.1. (a) st is a function and

$$\mathscr{D}st = \{a \mid \text{for some } b \in F, |a - b^*| < 1/n^* \text{ for each positive integer } n\}.$$

Thus in the future we write $st(a) = b$ for $\langle a, b\rangle \in st$.

(b) $st(x) = r$ iff for each $q \in \mathbb{Q}$ if $0 < q$ then $|x - r^*| < q^*$, iff for each $a \in F$, if $0 < a$ then $|x - r^*| < a^*$.

(c) If $a, b \in \mathscr{D}st$, then

$$st(a + b) = st(a) + st(b), \qquad st(ab) = st(a)st(b);$$

if $st(a) \neq 0$, then $st(1/a) = 1/st(a)$ (thus under these conditions $a + b$, ab, $1/a \in \mathscr{D}st$); if $a \leq b$, then $st(a) \leq st(b)$. If $r \in F$, then $st(r^*) = r$; if $S \subset F$, then $S \subset st[S^*]$.

For $a, b \in F^*$, we write $a =_1 b$ iff $st(a - b) = 0$. (NOTE: This requires neither a nor b in $\mathscr{D}st$.)

(d) $=_1$ is an equivalence relation on F^*.

Proof: (a) Let $\langle a, b\rangle, \langle a, c\rangle \in st$, n a positive integer. Then $|a - b^*|$, $|a - c^*| < (1/2n)^*$, so

$$|(b - c)^*| = |b^* - c^*| \leq |b^* - a| + |a - c^*| < 1/n^*$$

(note that $\langle b, c, d\rangle \in -$ iff $\langle b^*, c^*, d^*\rangle \in -$ and since $|x - y| \leq |x - z| + |z - y|$ in $\mathfrak{F}$, this holds in $\mathfrak{F}^*$, all by Łos' Theorem or the definition of ultraproducts). Since n is arbitrary here, $|b - c| < 1/n$ for each positive integer n and since $\mathfrak{F}$ is Archimedean, $b = c$.

The remainder of the proof is clear or done by similar methods, and we leave it for the reader.

Another relation we often find useful is

$$m(r) = \{x \mid st(x) = r\} \qquad \text{for} \quad r \in F.$$

We leave it for the reader to show that $\mathfrak{F}^* \mid \mathscr{D}st$ is an integral domain with maximal ideal $m(0)$, and that for each $r \in F$,

$$m(r) = r^* + m(0) = \{r^* + h \mid h \in m(0)\}.$$

THEOREM 5.1.2. The following are equivalent:

$$\mathfrak{F} \cong \mathbb{R},$$

$$\mathscr{D}st = \{a \in F^* \mid \text{for some positive integer } n,\ |a| < n^*\}.$$

Proof: We show our second assertion equivalent to the least upper bound axiom (that every nonempty set bounded above has a least upper bound) that only holds for ordered fields isomorphic to the real numbers. It is clear that $\mathscr{D}st \subset M$, where

$$M = \{a \in F^* \mid \text{for some positive integer } n,\ |a| < n^*\},$$

for if $a \in \mathscr{D}st$ let $st(a) = b$,

$$|b| + 1 < m \in \omega.$$

Then

$$|a| = |a - b^* + b^*| \leq |a - b^*| + |b^*| < 1 + |b^*| < m^*.$$

Now assume that $\mathfrak{F} \cong \mathbb{R}$, $|a| < n^*$, and let

$$A = \{x \in \mathfrak{F} \mid x^* \leq a\}.$$

Then n is an upper bound for A, for if $x \in A$, then $x^* \leq a < n^*$, so $x < n$ and $-n \in A$, so $A \neq \phi$. Let $b = \text{lub } A$ and consider $|b^* - a|$. If $b^* - a > 1/m^*$, then $a < (b - 1/m)^*$ so $b - 1/m$ is an upper bound for A (since

$$\text{if} \quad x^* \leq a < (b - 1/m)^* \qquad \text{then} \quad x < b - 1/m),$$

a contradiction, and

$$\text{if} \quad a - b^* > 1/m^*, \qquad \text{then} \quad (b + 1/m)^* < a,$$

so b is not an upper bound for A, another contradiction, thus $|b^* - a| \leq 1/m^*$ for an arbitrary positive integer m, so $st(a) = b$, thus $M \subset \mathscr{D}st$, thus $M = \mathscr{D}st$.

Conversely, if $M = \mathscr{D}st$, let $B \neq \phi$ have an upper bound. Then consider the structure

$$\mathfrak{A} = \langle F, +, \cdot, 0, 1, \leq, B, \tfrac{1}{2}, \tfrac{1}{3}, \tfrac{1}{4}, \ldots \rangle$$

and the set of formulas

$$S = \{G_p \mid 0 < p \in \omega\},$$

where

$$G_p = (\forall v_1)(P_B(v_1) \rightarrow v_1 \leq v_0) \wedge (\exists v_1)(P_B(v_1) \wedge v_0 \leq v_1 + c_{1/p}).$$

We now find for each positive integer p an a_p in F satisfying G_p (and thus $G_1, \ldots, G_{p-1}$ as well); let a_1 be the least integral upper bound for B; if we have a_p, either

$$a_p - \frac{1}{p+1} < b \qquad \text{for some} \quad b \in B$$

in which case $a_{p+1} = a_p$ satisfies G_{p+1}, or

$$a_{p+1} = a_p - \frac{1}{p+1} \geq b \qquad \text{for each} \quad b \in B$$

in which case

$$a_{p+1} - \frac{1}{p+1} \leq a_p - \frac{1}{p} < b \qquad \text{for some} \quad b \in B.$$

Thus for each positive integer p, a_p^* satisfies $G_1, \ldots, G_p$ in $\mathfrak{A}^*$, so in the ω^+-saturated structure $\mathfrak{A}^*$ there is an a satisfying S. $a \in \mathscr{D}st$ since for some $b \in B$,

$$b^* \leq a \leq (b+1)^*$$

so

$$|a| \leq \max\{|b^*|, |b^* + 1|\} \leq n^* \qquad \text{for some} \quad n \in \omega.$$

Since a is an upper bound for B^*, if $b \in B$, then $b^* \in B^*$, so $b^* \leq a$; thus

$$b = st(b^*) \leq st(a)$$

so $st(a)$ is an upper bound for B; if c is an upper bound for B, then $st(a) - 1/p \leq c$ for each positive integer p [since $st(a) - 1/p$ is not an upper bound for B] thus $st(a) \leq c$, so $st(a)$ is a least upper bound for B.

Thus analysis on the reals can in principle be studied—though we have no idea yet how difficult this study might be—through a study of ultrapowers and these other operations. It is reasonable to ask whether a study of the ultrapower operation alone—applied to $\mathbb{R}$, for example—will give us the complete information we wish on $\mathbb{R}$. However, if the continuum hypothesis holds, we know that for any real-closed $\mathfrak{F}$ of cardinality $\leq 2^\omega$,

$$\mathfrak{F}^\omega/D \cong \mathbb{R}^\omega/D$$

when D is nonprincipal. Those readers who skipped Section 1.8 may equally well note that there is a countable ordered field elementarily equivalent to $\mathbb{R}$ (by downward Löwenheim-Skolem), and that once again the continuum hypothesis assures us that

$$\mathbb{R}^\omega/D \cong \mathfrak{F}^\omega/D,$$

where D is nonprincipal, $\mathfrak{F}$ this field.

Thus the ultrapower $\mathbb{R}^\omega/D$ alone cannot be expected to give us all the information we wish on the analysis of real-valued functions. It turns out to be most convenient to begin with the real numbers $\mathbb{R}$ and a nonprincipal ultrafilter D on ω. We devote the remainder of this section to informal comments on $\mathbb{R}^\omega/D$, which motivate some of the more formal work to be done in following sections.

Since $\mathbb{R}^\omega/D$ is non-Archimedean, not every bounded subset of it has a least upper bound. However, as shown in Section 2.2, every nonempty set of the form S^* with an upper bound has a least upper bound.

We can extend the usual definition of openness to sets in any ordered field, and let $\mathcal{O} \subset \mathbb{R}$ be open. If

$$F = (\forall v_0)(\exists v_1)(v_0 \in \mathcal{O} \to (c_0 < v_1) \wedge (\forall v_2)(|v_0 - v_2| < v_1 \to v_2 \in \mathcal{O})))$$

[where "$v_0 \in \mathcal{O}$" abbreviates "$P_\mathcal{O}(v_0)$"], then

$$(\mathbb{R}, \mathcal{O}) \models F, \qquad \text{so} \qquad (\mathbb{R}^\omega/D, \mathcal{O}^*) \models F,$$

thus $\mathcal{O}^*$ is open; in fact, $\mathcal{O}$ is open iff $\mathcal{O}^*$ is open. But we can do better—$\mathcal{O}$ is open iff for each $x \in \mathcal{O}$,

$$m(x) = x^* + m(0) \subset \mathcal{O}^*,$$

for let $m(x) \subset \mathcal{O}^*$ for each $x \in \mathcal{O}$; if $0 < y \in m(0)$ and $|x^* - z| < y$, then $z \in \mathcal{O}^*$. Thus for each $x \in \mathcal{O}$,

$$(\mathbb{R}^\omega/D, \mathcal{O}^*) \models (\forall v_2)(|v_0 - v_2| < v_1 \to v_2 \in \mathcal{O})[x^*, y],$$

thus

$$(\mathbb{R}, \mathcal{O}) \models (\exists v_1)(\forall v_2)((c_0 < v_1) \wedge |v_0 - v_2| < v_1 \to v_2 \in \mathcal{O})[x] \qquad \text{for every} \quad x \in \mathcal{O},$$

thus $(\mathbb{R}, \mathcal{O}) \models F$, therefore, so does $(\mathbb{R}^\omega/D, \mathcal{O}^*)$, so $\mathcal{O}^*$ is open. Conversely, if $\mathcal{O}^*$ is open, then $\mathcal{O}$ is open, so if $x \in \mathcal{O}$, then $(x - r, x + r) \subset \mathcal{O}$ for some $r > 0$. Thus $(x - r, x + r)^* \subset \mathcal{O}^*$ (why?), so

$$x^* + m(0) \subset (x - r, x + r)^* \subset \mathcal{O}^*.$$

Later we shall *define* $\mathcal{O}$ to be open iff for each $x \in \mathcal{O}$, $m(x) \subset \mathcal{O}^*$.

To see why the above definition is in a sense natural, let $S \subset \mathbb{R}$, and consider $st[S^*] \subset \mathbb{R}$. We now show $st[S^*] = S^-$, the closure of S. Let $x \in S^-$, then $x = \lim s$ for some sequence

$$s = \langle s_0, s_1, \ldots \rangle \in S^\omega.$$

However, then $|x^* - s/D| < r$ for every positive rational r (since the finite set

$$\{n \mid |x - s_n| \geq r\} \notin D).$$

Thus

$$x = st(x^*) = st(s/D) \in st[S^*].$$

However, if $x \in st[S^*]$, let $x = st(s/D)$, $\mathscr{R}s \subset S$. Thus for each $r > 0$, $r \in \mathbb{Q}$,

$$\{n \mid |x - s_n| \geq r\} \notin D,$$

so for each number $1/n$ we can find an $s_{n'}$ with $|x - s_{n'}| < 1/n$. Now consider s' constructed by the rule $s'_n = s_{n'}$. Then for each r, $r \geq 1/n$ for some n, so

$$\{n \mid |x - s'_n| \geq r\} \supset \{s'_1, \ldots, s'_{n-1}\},$$

so $\lim s' = x$, and $\mathscr{R}s' \subset S$. Thus $x \in S^-$. This is a particularly satisfying use of the operations st and ω/D.

The above also reinforces our eventual choice of definition for openness (discussed above), for $\mathcal{O}$ is open iff $st[(\mathbb{R} \sim \mathcal{O})^*] = \mathbb{R} \sim \mathcal{O}$, i.e., iff

$$st[(\mathbb{R}^* \sim \mathcal{O}^*)] = st[(\mathbb{R} \sim \mathcal{O})^*] \subset \mathbb{R} \sim \mathcal{O}.$$

Thus $\mathcal{O}$ is open iff for every $x \in \mathcal{O}$, $m(x) \subset \mathcal{O}^*$.

Suppose now we have a function $f\colon U \to V$, $U, V \subset \mathbb{R}$. Considering f as a binary relation on $\mathbb{R}$, we can form $f^* = f^\omega/D$. Since

$$(\mathbb{R}, U, V, f) <' (\mathbb{R}^*, U^*, V^*, f^*),$$

$f^*\colon U^* \to V^*$. Also if f is continuous at x, f^* is continuous at x^*. However, once again we find a more appropriate definition for continuity of f at x in terms of f^*, namely: f is continuous at x iff

$$f(x) = st(f^*(x^* + h)) \qquad \text{for every} \quad h \in m(0).$$

We shall check this definition in Section 5.2.

Recalling the fact that $j_{\mathbb{R}}\colon \mathbb{R} \ll' \mathbb{R}^\omega/D$, we can (and in future sections shall) study properties of relations on $\mathbb{R}$ in terms of their extensions to $\mathbb{R}^\omega/D$.

However, we are sometimes interested not in relations on $\mathbb{R}$, but in relations among many relations on $\mathbb{R}$. For example, one often needs the fact that the union of any set of open subsets of $\mathbb{R}$ is open. This cannot be put into a first-order language. In fact, if $(\mathbb{R}, \langle \mathcal{O} \mid \mathcal{O} \in \mathscr{T} \rangle)$ is the real numbers together with all the open sets, then $(\mathbb{R}^\omega/D, \langle \mathcal{O}^* \mid \mathcal{O} \in \mathscr{T} \rangle)$ does not have the property that $\{\mathcal{O}^* \mid \mathcal{O} \in \mathscr{T}\}$ is closed under arbitrary unions (see Problem 5.1.1). Thus the fact that the union of any collection of open sets is open is not a first-order property.

Our problem is solved in part by assuming that we have a model $\langle A, \in \rangle$ of the axioms of set theory, and we are considering the real numbers (and their relations) as elements of the universe of this model.

Then $\langle A, \in\rangle^{\omega}/D$ will contain a structure $\mathbb{R}^* = \mathbb{R}^{\omega}/D$ as an element, as well as $\mathscr{T}^*$, $\mathscr{T}$ the topology on $\mathbb{R}$. We may write

$$F = (\forall v_0)(v_0 \subset \mathscr{T} \rightarrow \bigcup v_0 \in \mathscr{T})$$

(which can easily be put in terms of $\in$, thus making it a first-order formula). Since $\langle A, \in, \mathbb{R}, \mathscr{T}\rangle \models F$, so does $\langle A^*, \in^*, \mathbb{R}^*, \mathscr{T}^*\rangle$, thus here the union of any collection of open sets is open.

The apparent paradox between the two previous situations is resolved by noting that in the first case, by "collection" of open sets, we mean set in the sense of $\langle A, \in\rangle$, our original model of set theory, whereas in the second case we mean it in the sense of $\langle A, \in\rangle^{\omega}/D$. Thus we must take care when working with structures of this sort.

Problems

5.1.1 (a) Show that $(0, 1)^* \cup (2, 3)^* \cup (4, 5)^* \cup \cdots$ is not of the form $\mathcal{O}^*$ for any open $\mathcal{O} \subset \mathbb{R}$.

(b) If A is a collection of open sets and $\bigcup \{\mathcal{O}^* \mid \mathcal{O} \in A\}$ is of the form S^*, then $\bigcup \{\mathcal{O}^* \mid \mathcal{O} \in A\}$ is of the form $\mathcal{O}^*$ for some open $\mathcal{O}$.

5.1.2 Let $\langle M, d\rangle$ be a metric space (consider in your work the structure $\langle M \cup \mathbb{R}, M, d, \mathbb{R}, +, \cdot, 0, 1, <\ \rangle$, where $M \cup \mathbb{R}$ is assumed disjoint). Show that the relation $\sim$ defined on M^{ω}/D by $\langle a, b\rangle \in \sim$ iff

$$d^{\omega}/D(a, b) < r \qquad \text{for every} \quad r \in \mathbb{Q}$$

is an equivalence relation, and that

$$\langle (M^{\omega}/D)/\sim, (d^{\omega}/D)/\sim\ \rangle$$

is a complete metric space with subspace isomorphic to $\langle M, d\rangle$.

‡5.1.3 Complete the proof of Proposition 5.1.1.

‡5.1.4 Prove the assertions following Proposition 5.1.1.

5.2 Nonstandard Analysis on the Reals

Our account of nonstandard analysis in the following sections is designed to use model theory and in general clarify the connections between it and analysis. Our interest is in techniques, rather than results, particularly in this section, thus we do not study any topic in depth.

An extremely well-written account by Luxemburg [1], available through the California Institute of Technology (and which has influenced this section) would best suit the needs of those who wish to avoid logic. Robinson's [3] account emphasizes logic perhaps more than ours and in a different way.

The designation *st* for the map introduced in Section 5.1 is an abbreviation for "standard part of." The reason for the use of "standard" here and "nonstandard" in the title of this section is that the real numbers are considered to be the "standard" or usual model for the theory of the reals (as the integers, rationals, and so forth, are the standard models for their theories) and its elements are also referred to as "standard." $\mathbb{R}^*$ is a different or "nonstandard" model and its elements are also called "nonstandard." The map *st* gives us standard real numbers, in fact, for $x \in \mathscr{D}st$, $st(x)$ is essentially the standard real number nearest to x, thus suggesting the name and notation for this map.

We also use the term "finite" to denote elements of $\mathscr{D}st$ in $\mathbb{R}^*$ and "infinitesimal" for those of $m(0)$.

PROPOSITION 5.2.1. Let $\{T_i \mid i \in I\}$ be a set of relations on and distinguished elements from $\mathbb{R}$, and let

$$\langle \mathbb{R}, T_i \rangle_{i \in I} \in M^t, \qquad F \in L^t.$$

(a) $\langle \mathbb{R}, T_i \rangle_{i \in I} \models F[a]$ iff $\langle \mathbb{R}^*, T_i^* \rangle_{i \in I} \models F[* \circ a]$ for $a \in \mathbb{R}^\omega$.

(b) If $\{T_i \mid i \in I\} \subset \mathscr{P}\mathbb{R}^m$, $m, n \in \omega$, and $i_1, \ldots, i_n \in I$, then

$$(T_{i_1} \cup \cdots \cup T_{i_n})^* = T_{i_1}^* \cup \cdots \cup T_{i_n}^*,$$

$$(T_{i_1} \cap \cdots \cap T_{i_n})^* = T_{i_1}^* \cap \cdots \cap T_{i_n}^*;$$

if $i, j \in I$, then

$$(T_i \sim T_j)^* = T_i^* \sim T_j^*,$$

$$T_i \subset T_j; \qquad \text{iff} \quad T_i^* \subset T_j^*,$$

$$\bigcup \{T_i^* \mid i \in I\} \subset (\bigcup \{T_i \mid i \in I\})^*,$$

$$(\bigcap \{T_i \mid i \in I\})^* \subset \bigcap \{T_i^* \mid i \in I\},$$

$$(T_{i_1} \times \cdots \times T_{i_n})^* = T_{i_1}^* \times \cdots \times T_{i_n}^*;$$

and in addition if $n = 2$, $S \subset \mathbb{R}$, then

$$(T_i \circ T_j)^* = T_i^* \circ T_j^*, \qquad (T_i[S])^* = T_i^*[S^*],$$

$$(\mathscr{D}T_i)^* = \mathscr{D}(T_i^*), \qquad \text{and} \qquad (\mathscr{R}T_i)^* = \mathscr{R}(T_i^*).$$

(c) If $S \subset \mathbb{R}^m$, then

$$*[S] = S^* \cap *[\mathbb{R}^m] \subset S^*,$$

and

$$*[S] = S^* \qquad \text{iff} \quad S \text{ is finite}$$

(thus $\{x^*\} = \{x\}^*$). (Recall that since $*$ is a function, $*[S] = \{s^* \mid s \in S\}$.)

(d) $T \subset \mathbb{R}$ is bounded iff $T^* \subset \mathscr{D}st$.

Proof: (a) is a restatement of Corollary 2.1.19 and (b) results directly from (a). For example

$$\langle \mathbb{R}, T_i, T_j, T_i \circ T_j \rangle \models F,$$

where

$$F = (\forall v_1)(\forall v_3)(P_{ij}(v_1, v_3) <\!-\!> (\exists v_2)(P_j(v_1, v_2) \wedge P_i(v_2, v_3)),$$

thus

$$\langle \mathbb{R}^*, T_i^*, T_j^*, (T_i \circ T_j)^* \rangle \models F,$$

but F defines composition so

$$(T_i \circ T_j)^* = T_i^* \circ T_j^*.$$

(c) If $\langle r_1, \ldots, r_m \rangle \in \mathbb{R}^m$,

$$\langle \mathbb{R}, S \rangle \models P_s(v_1, \ldots, v_m)[r_1, \ldots, r_m]$$

$$\text{iff} \quad \langle r_1, \ldots, r_m \rangle \in S \qquad \text{iff} \quad \langle r_1^*, \ldots, r_m^* \rangle \in {}^*[S],$$

thus

$${}^*[S] = S^* \cap {}^*[\mathbb{R}^m] \; (= S^* \cap {}^*[\mathbb{R}]^m).$$

If

$$S = \{\langle r_1^1, \ldots, r_m^1 \rangle, \ldots, \langle r_1^n, \ldots, r_m^n \rangle\}$$

then

$$\langle \mathbb{R}, S, r_{1_1}, \ldots, r_{m_n} \rangle \vdash (\forall v_1) \cdots (\forall v_m)(P_S(v_1, \ldots, v_m)$$

$$<\!-\!> (v_1 = c_{r_1} \wedge \cdots \wedge v_m = c_{r_{m1}}) \vee \cdots \vee (v_1 = c_{r_{1_n}} \wedge \cdots \wedge v_m = c_{r_{m_n}})),$$

thus so does

$$\langle \mathbb{R}^*, S^*, r_{1_1}, \ldots, r_{m_n} \rangle,$$

so

$${}^*[S] = S^*.$$

If S is infinite, however, let

$$S_1 = \{\langle r_{11}, \ldots, r_{m1} \rangle, \ldots\}$$

be a countable subset of S with

$$\langle r_{1i}, \ldots, r_{mi} \rangle \neq \langle r_{1j}, \ldots, r_{mj} \rangle \qquad \text{if} \quad i \neq j.$$

Thus each finite subset of

$$\{P_s(v_1, \ldots, v_m) \wedge (v_1 \neq c_{r_{1i}} \vee \cdots \vee v_m \neq c_{r_{mi}}) \mid i \in \omega\}$$

is satisfiable in $\langle \mathbb{R}, S_1, r_{11}, \ldots \rangle$, so the whole set is satisfiable in

$$\langle \mathbb{R}^*, S_1^*, r_{11}^*, \ldots \rangle,$$

thus

$${}^*[S_1] \neq S_1^*.$$

But

$$*[S] = *[S_1] \cup *[S \sim S_1] \subsetneqq S_1^* \cup (S \sim S_1)^* = S^*.$$

(d) If T is bounded, then for some $r \in \mathbb{R}$,

$$\langle \mathbb{R}, T \rangle \models (\forall v_0)(P_T(v_0) \rightarrow |v_0| < v_1)[r],$$

so

$$\langle \mathbb{R}^*, T^* \rangle \models (\forall v_0)(P_T(v_0) \rightarrow |v_0| < v_1)[r^*],$$

so by Theorem 5.1.2, $T^* \subset \mathscr{D}st$. Conversely, if T is unbounded, then

$$\langle \mathbb{R}, T \rangle \models (\forall v_1)(\exists v_0)(P_T(v_0) \wedge v_1 < |v_0|),$$

thus so does $\langle \mathbb{R}^*, T^* \rangle$, so T^* is unbounded in $\mathbb{R}^*$. However, since $\mathbb{R}^*$ is non-Archimedean, $\mathscr{D}st$ is bounded, so $T^* \not\subset \mathscr{D}st$.

The above proposition thus asserts (among other things) that * preserves finite Boolean operations $\bigcup$, $\bigcap$, $\sim$; and that it preserves $\subset$, composition, domain, range, and finite Cartesian products.

DEFINITION 5.2.2. The closure of S, $S^- = st[S^*]$ (note that it is not necessary that $S^* \subset \mathscr{D}st$). S is closed iff $S = st[S^*] = S^-$, S is open iff for every $x \in S$, if $x^* =_1 y$ then $y \in S^*$.

The above definition was justified in Section 5.1. The following properties of it are clear.

COROLLARY 5.2.3. (a) $(A \cap B)^- \subset A^- \cap B^-$, $A \subset A^-$, $(A \cup B)^- = A^- \cup B^-$, and $\phi^- = \phi$.

(b) Let $\mathscr{C}$ denote the collection of closed sets. Then if $A, B \in \mathscr{C}$, $A \cup B \in \mathscr{C}$, $\mathbb{R} \in \mathscr{C}$; if A is finite, then $A \in \mathscr{C}$; and if $\mathscr{C}' \subset \mathscr{C}$, then $\bigcap \mathscr{C}' \in \mathscr{C}$.

Proof: We select one assertion from each of (a), (b) and leave the rest to the reader.

(a) $st[A^*] \cup st[B^*] = st[A^* \cup B^*] = st[(A \cup B)^*]$.

(b) By 5.2.1(b), $(\bigcap \mathscr{C}')^* \subset \bigcap \{C^* \mid C \in \mathscr{C}'\}$. Thus

$$st[(\bigcap \mathscr{C}')^*] \subset st[\bigcap \{C^* \mid C \in \mathscr{C}'\}] \subset \bigcap \{st[C^*] \mid C \in \mathscr{C}'\} = \bigcap \mathscr{C}'.$$

Thus $(\bigcap \mathscr{C}')^- \subset \bigcap \mathscr{C}'$, but by (a),

$$\bigcap \mathscr{C}' \subset (\bigcap \mathscr{C}')^-, \quad \text{so} \quad \bigcap \mathscr{C}' \in \mathscr{C}.$$

COROLLARY 5.2.4. (a) Let $\mathscr{T}$ denote the set of open sets. Then $\mathbb{R}, \phi \in \mathscr{T}$; if $A, B \in \mathscr{T}$, then $A \cap B \in \mathscr{T}$; and if $\mathscr{T}' \subset \mathscr{T}$, then $\bigcup \mathscr{T}' \in \mathscr{T}$.
(b) $A \in \mathscr{T}$ iff $\mathbb{R} \sim A \in \mathscr{C}$.

Proof: Once again we prove one assertion from each of (a), (b).
(a) Let $A, B \in \mathscr{T}$, $x \in A \cap B$. Then

$$m(x) \subset A^* \cap B^* = (A \cap B)^*,$$

so $A \cap B \in \mathscr{T}$.
(b) If $A \in \mathscr{T}$, $x \in st[(\mathbb{R} \sim A)^*]$, then

$$x = st(y) \qquad \text{for some} \quad y \in (\mathbb{R} \sim A)^* = \mathbb{R}^* \sim A^*.$$

But $x = st(x^*)$, so

$$x^* =_1 y \qquad \text{for some} \quad y \notin A^*.$$

Thus $x \notin A$, so

$$(\mathbb{R} \sim A)^- = \mathbb{R} \sim A.$$

Conversely, if $(\mathbb{R} \sim A)^- = \mathbb{R} \sim A$, $x \in A$, $x^* =_1 y$, then $y \in A^*$; for otherwise, $y \in \mathbb{R}^* \sim A^* = (\mathbb{R} \sim A)^*$, so

$$x \in st[(\mathbb{R} \sim A)^*] = \mathbb{R} \sim A,$$

a contradiction.

THEOREM 5.2.5 (Bolzano-Weierstrass). If S is bounded and infinite, then for some a, $a \in (S \sim \{a\})^-$.

Proof: $S^* \sim {}^*[S] \neq \phi$ and $S^* \subset \mathscr{D}st$. If $y \in S^* \sim {}^*[S]$, then

$$st(y) \in S^- \qquad \text{and} \qquad y \neq st(y)^*,$$

so

$$y \in S^* \sim \{st(y)^*\} = S^* \sim \{st(y)\}^* = (S \sim \{st(y)\})^*$$

so

$$st(y) \in st[(S \sim \{st(y)\})^*] = (S \sim \{st(y)\})^-.$$

Recall that a set C is called compact iff when $C \subset \bigcup \mathscr{T}'$ for some $\mathscr{T}' \subset \mathscr{T}$, then

$$C \subset A_1 \cup \cdots \cup A_n \qquad \text{for some} \quad A_1, \ldots, A_n \in \mathscr{T}'.$$

THEOREM 5.2.6 (Heine-Borel). X is compact iff X is closed and bounded.

Proof: Let X be compact. $X \subset \bigcup_{n=1}^{\infty} (-n, n)$ so X is bounded. If $x \in X^- \sim X$, then

$$X \subset \bigcup_{n=1}^{\infty} \left(\mathbb{R} \sim \left[x - \frac{1}{n}, x + \frac{1}{n}\right]\right)$$

and

$$X \not\subset \left(\mathbb{R} \sim \left[x - \frac{1}{n}, x + \frac{1}{n}\right]\right)$$

for any n, for otherwise

$$X^- \subset \mathbb{R} \sim \left(x - \frac{1}{n}, x + \frac{1}{n}\right),$$

contradiction.

Conversely, let $X \subset \bigcup \{\mathcal{O}_\lambda \mid \lambda \in \Lambda\}$ and suppose that for no finite $F \subset \Lambda$ does $X \subset \bigcup \{\mathcal{O}_\lambda \mid \lambda \in F\}$. We assume, as we may, that D is regular on $\mathbf{I}$, $c(\Lambda) \leq c(\mathbf{I})$. Then by our finite satisfaction property we can find

$$y \in X^* \sim \bigcup_{\lambda \in \Lambda} (\mathcal{O}_\lambda^*).$$

But since $y \in X^*$, X closed and bounded, $y \in \mathcal{D}st$ and $st(y) \in st[X^*] = X$, and since $\mathcal{O}_\lambda$ is open, $st(y) \notin \mathcal{O}_\lambda$ for any $\lambda \in \Lambda$, so

$$st(y) \in X \sim \bigcup_{\lambda \in \Lambda} \mathcal{O}_\lambda.$$

In this and the following sections, it often appears that we are "proving" definitions. We only mean, of course, to prove our definitions equivalent to the usual ones.

Definition 5.2.7. Let $f\colon X \to \mathbb{R}$, $x \in X \subset \mathbb{R}$. Then f is continuous at x iff $f^*(y) =_1 (f(x))^*$ for every $y =_1 x^*$, $y \in X^*$ (that is, iff $f^*[m(x)] \subset m(f(x))$).

Proof: Let f be continuous at x, $y =_1 x^*$. Then for each $n > 0$, we can find an $m > 0$ such that

$$\langle \mathbb{R}, f, x, 1/m, 1/n\rangle \models (\forall v_0)(|v_0 - c_x| < c_{1/m} \to |f(v_0) - f(c_x)| < c_{1/n}),$$

thus so does $\langle \mathbb{R}^*, f^*, x^*, 1/m^*, 1/n^*\rangle$. However, if $y =_1 x^*$, then

$$|y - x^*| < 1/m \qquad \text{for each} \quad m,$$

so

$$|f^*(y) - (f(x))^*| < 1/n^* \qquad \text{for each} \quad n,$$

so

$$f^*(y) =_1 (f(x))^*.$$

Conversely, if f is not continuous at x, let

$$\lim(y_n) = x \qquad \text{and not} \qquad \lim(f(y_n)) = f(x).$$

For some infinite collection of the y_n and some $m > 0$,

$$|f(y_n) - f(x)| \geq 1/m,$$

and in fact, if $n > 0$,

$$\langle \mathbb{R}, f, x, 1/m, 1/n \rangle \models (\exists v_1)(|v_1 - c_x| < c_{1/n} \wedge |f(v_1) - f(c_x)| \geq c_{1/m}).$$

If $y \in \mathbb{R}^*$ satisfies

$$(|v_1 - c_x| < c_{1/n} \wedge |f(v_1) - f(c_x)| \geq c_{1/m})$$

for every positive integer n (and such a y exists by our definition of *), then $y =_1 x^*$, but $f^*(y) \neq_1 (f(x))^*$, so our condtiion also fails.

Corollary 5.2.8. Let f, g be continuous at x; h continuous at $f(x)$. Then $f + g$, fg, $1/g$ (if $g(x) \neq 0$), and $h \circ f$ are continuous at x.

Proof: If $y =_1 x^*$,

$$g^*(y) =_1 (g(x))^* \neq_1 0,$$

by 5.1.1(c),

$$(1/g)^*(y) = 1/(g^*(y)) =_1 1/(g(x))^* = (1/g(x))^*,$$

and the proofs of the remaining facts are similar.

Proposition 5.2.9. Let $f: S \to \mathbb{R}$. Then f is continuous (i.e., continuous at every $x \in S$) iff $f^{-1}[\mathcal{O}]$ is open in S for every $\mathcal{O} \in \mathcal{T}$.

Proof: Let f be continuous, $\mathcal{O} \in \mathcal{T}$, $x \in f^{-1}[\mathcal{O}]$, $y \in S^*$, $y =_1 x^*$. Then $f^*(y) =_1 (f(x))^*$, and since $f(x) \in \mathcal{O}$, $f^*(y) \in \mathcal{O}^*$, so

$$y \in f^{*-1}[\mathcal{O}^*] = (f^{-1}[\mathcal{O}])^*.$$

Thus $f^{-1}[\mathcal{O}]$ is open in S.

Conversely if $f^{-1}[\mathcal{O}]$ is open for every $\mathcal{O} \in \mathcal{T}$, let $y =_1 x^*$. Then

$$y \in \bigcap \{(f^{-1}[\mathcal{O}])^* \mid f(x) \in \mathcal{O}\} = \bigcap \{f^{*-1}[\mathcal{O}^*] \mid f(x) \in \mathcal{O}\}$$

so

$$f^*(y) \in \bigcap \{\mathcal{O}^* \mid f(x) \in \mathcal{O}\}$$

thus

$$f^*(y) =_1 (f(x))^*$$

(see Problem 5.2.2(b)).

Proposition 5.2.10. If X is compact and f continuous, then $f[X]$ is compact.

Proof: To show $f[X]$ compact, we first show $f[X] \subset \mathcal{D}st$. $f[X]^* = f^*[X^*]$; and if $x \in X^*$,

$$x \in \mathcal{D}st \quad \text{and} \quad st(x) \in X;$$

and since f is continuous,

$$f^*(x) =_1 (f(st(x)))^* \qquad \text{so} \qquad f^*(x) \in \mathscr{D}st,$$

thus

$$f^*[X^*] \subset \mathscr{D}st.$$

$f[X]$ is closed: If $y \in st[f[X]^*] = st[f^*[X^*]]$, let $y = st(f^*(x))$, $x \in X^*$. Then

$$f^*(x) =_1 (f(st(x)))^*$$

so

$$st(f^*(x)) = st(f(st(x))^*) = f(st(x)) \in f[X].$$

The following are easily established (see Problem 5.2.4(a)).

Definition 5.2.11. $X \subset \mathbb{R}$ is connected iff whenever $\phi \neq A \subsetneq X$, then

$$\phi \neq (A^* \cap (\bigcup \{m(x) \mid x \in X \sim A\})) \cup ((X \sim A)^* \cap (\bigcup \{m(x) \mid x \in A\})).$$

Lemma 5.2.12. X is connected iff X is an interval.

Proposition 5.2.13. If f is continuous and X connected, then $f[X]$ is connected. Thus if X is an interval and f is continuous, then $f[X]$ is an interval. (This is the intermediate value theorem.)

Recall that if $X \subset \mathbb{R}$, $f: X \to \mathbb{R}$ is said to be uniformly continuous iff for every $\varepsilon > 0$ we can find a $\delta > 0$ such that if $|x - y| < \delta$ then $|f(x) - f(y)| < \varepsilon$.

Definition 5.2.14. $f: X \to \mathbb{R}$ is uniformly continuous iff whenever $x, y \in X^*$, and $x =_1 y$ then $f^*(x) =_1 f^*(y)$.

Proof: Let f be uniformly continuous, n a positive integer. Then we can find a positive integer m such that

$$\text{if} \quad |x - y| < 1/m \qquad \text{then} \quad |f(x) - f(y)| < 1/n.$$

Thus if $x =_1 y$, then

$$|f^*(x) - f^*(y)| < (1/n)^* \qquad \text{for each} \quad n,$$

so

$$f^*(x) =_1 f^*(y).$$

If f is not uniformly continuous, find such an m such that for every positive integer n there are $x, y \in X$ such that

$$|x - y| < 1/n \qquad \text{but} \qquad |f(x) - f(y)| \geq 1/m.$$

This shows that

$$\{(\exists v_1)(\exists v_2)(P_X(v_1) \wedge P_X(v_2) \wedge |v_1 - v_2| < c_{1/n} \wedge P_\omega(c_n) \wedge |f(v_1) - f(v_2)| \geq c_{1/m}) \mid n \in \omega\}$$

is finitely satisfiable in $\langle \mathbb{R}, X, f, \omega, 1/m, 1, 2, \ldots \rangle$, thus satisfiable in $\langle \mathbb{R}^*, X^*, f^*, \omega^*, 1/m^*, 1^*, \ldots \rangle$; thus for some $x, y \in X^*$,

$$x =_1 y \qquad \text{and} \qquad |f^*(x) - f^*(y)| \geq 1/m^*,$$

so

$$f^*(x) \neq_1 f^*(y).$$

PROPOSITION 5.2.15. If $f: X \to \mathbb{R}$ is continuous and X is compact then f is uniformly continuous.

Proof: Let $x, y \in X^*$, $x =_1 y$. Then since $X^* \subset \mathscr{D}st$, $st(x)^* =_1 x$ (since $st(st(x)^*) = st(x)$), and $st(x) \in X^- = X$. Thus

$$f^*(x) =_1 (f(st(x)))^* =_1 f^*(y), \qquad \text{so} \qquad f^*(x) =_1 f^*(y).$$

PROPOSITION 5.2.16. If $f: X \to \mathbb{R}$ is uniformly continuous, there is a (uniformly) continuous $g: X^- \to \mathbb{R}$ such that $g \mid X = f$.

Proof: For $x \in X^* \cap \mathscr{D}st$, we wish to define $g(st(x)) = st(f^*(x))$, but we must first show that if $x \in X^* \cap \mathscr{D}st$, then $f^*(x) \in \mathscr{D}st$ (with this established, g must be a function with domain X^-, for if $x, y \in X^* \cap \mathscr{D}st$ and $st(x) = st(y)$, then $x =_1 y$ so $f^*(x) =_1 f^*(y)$, thus

$$g(st(x)) = st(f^*(x)) = st(f^*(y)) = g(st(y))).$$

If, however,

$$x \in X^* \cap \mathscr{D}st \qquad \text{and} \qquad |f^*(x)| > q^* \qquad \text{for every} \quad q \in \mathbb{Q}$$

then

$$\{P_X(v_0) \wedge (|v_0 - c_x| < c_{1/n^*}) \wedge (|f(v_0)| < |c_{f^*(x)}| - 1) \mid 0 < n \in \omega\}$$

is finitely satisfiable in $\langle \mathbb{R}^*, X^*, f^*, \omega^*, ||, f^*(x), <, x, 1, \frac{1}{2}^*, \ldots \rangle$ (why?) thus satisfiable there, but it must be satisfied by a y such that $y =_1 x$ and $f^*(y) \neq_1 f^*(x)$. Our definition also shows g to be continuous, and we leave proof of its uniform continuity for the reader (see Problem 5.2.10).

DEFINITION 5.2.17. f is differentiable at x with derivative $f'(x)$ iff for every $h =_1 0$ such that $h \neq 0$ and $x^* + h \in X^*$,

$$\frac{f^*(x^* + h) - (f(x))^*}{h} =_1 (f'(x))^*, \qquad \text{and} \qquad x \in X \cap (X \sim \{x\})^-.$$

(The proof is similar to those of Definitions 5.2.7 and 5.2.14.)

PROPOSITION 5.2.18. If f, g are differentiable at x with derivatives $f'(x)$, $g'(x)$, then $f + g$, fg, and if $g(x) \neq 0$, $1/g$ are differentiable at x with derivatives

$$f'(x) + g'(x), \qquad f(x)g'(x) + f'(x)g(x), \qquad \text{and} \qquad \frac{-g'(x)}{g(x)^2}.$$

PROPOSITION 5.2.19. If f is differentiable at x with derivative $f'(x)$, and at $f(x)$, g has derivative $g'(f(x))$, then $g \circ f$ is differentiable at x with derivative $g'(f(x))f'(x)$.

PROPOSITION 5.2.20. If f is differentiable at x, then f is continuous at x.

Proof: For appropriate h,

$$\frac{f^*(x^* + h) - (f(x))^*}{h} =_1 (f'(x))^*,$$

so

$$hf'(x)^* =_1 f^*(x^* + h) - f(x)^* \qquad \text{and} \qquad hf'(x)^* =_1 0,$$

thus $(f(x))^* =_1 f^*(x^* + h)$ when $h =_1 0$, $x^* + h \in \mathscr{D}f^*$, thus if $y \in \mathscr{D}f^*$, $y =_1 x^*$, then

$$f^*(y) =_1 (f(x))^*.$$

DEFINITION 5.2.21. f reaches a relative minimum at x iff for every $y =_1 x^*$, $(f(x))^* \leq f^*(y)$.

Proof: If f reaches a relative minimum at x, then for some integer n,

$$\langle \mathbb{R}, f, x, |\ |, 1/n \rangle \models (\forall v_0)(|v_0 - c_x| < c_{1/n} \rightarrow P_f(c_x) \leq P_f(v_0)),$$

thus so does $\langle \mathbb{R}, f, x, |\ |, 1/n \rangle^*$, and if $y =_1 x^*$, then

$$|y - x^*| < 1/n^*, \qquad \text{so} \qquad (f(x))^* \leq f^*(y).$$

Conversely, if

$$\langle \mathbb{R}^*, f^*, x^*, |\ |, <, 0\rangle \models (\exists v_2)(\forall v_1)((v_2 > c_0) \wedge (|v_1 - c_x| < v_2 \rightarrow f(c_x) \le f(v_1)))$$

(as it will under our condition by taking any positive infinitesimal for v_2), then so does $\langle \mathbb{R}, f, x, |\ |, <, 0\rangle$, so f reaches a minimum at x.

COROLLARY 5.2.22. If f reaches a relative maximum or minimum at $x \in \mathcal{O} \subset \mathcal{D}f$ and is differentiable at x, then $f'(x) = 0$.

Proof: Assume that f reaches a relative minimum at x. If $x^* < y$, $x^* =_1 y$, $y \in \mathcal{D}f^*$, then

$$\frac{f^*(y) - (f(x))^*}{y - x^*} \ge 0,$$

and if $z < x^*$, $x^* =_1 z \in \mathcal{D}f^*$ then

$$\frac{f^*(z) - (f(x))^*}{z - x^*} \le 0.$$

But for such y, z,

$$\frac{f^*(z) - (f(x))^*}{z - x^*} =_1 (f'(x))^* =_1 \frac{f^*(y) - (f(x))^*}{y - x^*},$$

so $f'(x) = 0$. For maxima the corollary can be proved using $-f$ or arguments similar to those above.

COROLLARY 5.2.23 (Rolle). If $a < b$, f is continuous on $[a, b]$ and differentiable on (a, b), and if $f(a) = f(b)$, then for some $c \in (a, b)$, $f'(c) = 0$.

The proof that is simplest is also the usual one. From the above we obtain a form of the mean value theorem.

PROPOSITION 5.2.24. If f is continuous on $[a, b]$ and $M \in \mathbb{R}$ is such that for every $x \in (a, b)$, $f'(x)$ always exists and $|f'(x)| \le M$, then for each $y, z \in [a, b]$,

$$|f(y) - f(z)| \le M|y - z|.$$

An interesting proof of the mean value theorem not involving an application of Proposition 5.2.10 may be found in Luxemburg [1]. Before passing, for the time, from the theory of differential calculus, we note that in nonstandard analysis the high school teacher's idea that *dy* and dx are really infinitesimally small numbers whose quotient is the derivative dy/dx takes on meaning and some degree of truth.

Also interesting is the fact that we have succeeded in establishing a theory of continuity, one of differentiability, and even one of the topology of the reals without introducing or using the idea of limit within our theory. This was possible because the elements $y \in \mathbb{R}^*$ with $y =_1 x^*$ served in our treatment as the sequences with limit x. However, our treatment would be incomplete unless we could arrive at a usable definition for the concept of limit. Recall that a sequence may be regarded as a function $a\colon \omega \to \mathbb{R}$.

Definition 5.2.25. Let $a\colon \omega \to \mathbb{R}$, $x \in \mathbb{R}$. Then a has limit x (often written $\lim_{n \to \infty} a_n = x$ or $\lim a = x$) iff for every $m \in \omega' = \omega^* \sim {}^*[\omega]$ (which we shall refer to as the set of infinite natural numbers),

$$a_m^* \ (= a^*(m)) =_1 x^*.$$

Proof: Let a have limit x, $0 < \varepsilon \in \mathbb{Q}$. Then for some $n \in \omega$,

$$\langle \mathbb{R}, a, \omega, n, x, \varepsilon \rangle \models (\forall v_1)(P_\omega(v_1) \wedge (v_1 > c_n) \to |a_{v_1} - c_x| < c_\varepsilon),$$

thus so does $\langle \mathbb{R}^*, a^*, \omega^*, n^*, x^*, \varepsilon^* \rangle$; if $m \in \omega'$, $n^* < m$ (why?) and so $|a_m^* - x^*| < \varepsilon$ but this holds for each $\varepsilon > 0$, $\varepsilon \in \mathbb{Q}$, our condition.

Conversely, if our condition holds, then for each $\varepsilon \in \mathbb{Q}$, if $\varepsilon > 0$ then

$$\langle \mathbb{R}^*, a^*, \omega^*, x^*, \varepsilon^* \rangle \models (\exists v_1)(\forall v_2)((v_1 < v_2) \wedge P_\omega(v_2) \to |a_{v_2} - c_x| < c_\varepsilon),$$

since any $m \in \omega'$ works for v_1, thus so does $\langle \mathbb{R}, a, \omega, x, \varepsilon \rangle$, making x a limit of a.

Corollary 5.2.26. Limits are unique.

The following definition is established similarly.

Definition 5.2.27. Let $a\colon \omega \to \mathbb{R}$. Then a is Cauchy iff for every m, $m' \in \omega'$,

$$a_m^* =_1 a_{m'}^*.$$

Proposition 5.2.28. (a) Let $a\colon \omega \to \mathbb{R}$. Then a is Cauchy iff a has a limit.

(b) Let $\lim a = x$, $\lim b = y$. Then

$$\lim(a + b) = x + y, \qquad \lim(ab) = xy,$$

and if $x \neq 0$, $\lim(1/a) = 1/x$. Thus if a, b are Cauchy, so are $a + b$, ab, and if $\lim a \neq 0$, $1/a$.

Proof: (a) If $\lim a = x$ then for $m, m' \in \omega'$,

$$a_m^* =_1 x^* =_1 a_{m'}^*, \qquad \text{so} \qquad a_m^* =_1 a_{m'}^*,$$

thus a is Cauchy.

Conversely, let a be Cauchy. $\mathscr{R}a^* \subset \mathscr{D}st$, for otherwise

$$\langle \mathbb{R}, \omega, a, |\ |, >, +, 1\rangle \vDash F,$$

where

$$F = (\forall v_1)(\exists v_2)(P_\omega(v_1) \to (v_1 < v_2) \wedge (P_\omega(v_2)) \wedge (|a_{v_2}| > |a_{v_1}| + 1)),$$

thus

$$\langle \mathbb{R}^*, \omega^*, a^*, |\ |, >, +, 1\rangle \vDash F,$$

thus if $m \in \omega'$, we can find $m' > m$, $m' \in \omega^*$ (thus $m' \in \omega'$) such that $|a_{m'}^*| > |a_m^*| + 1$, contradicting the Cauchy condition of 5.2.27. Now let $m, m' \in \omega'$. Then $a_m^* \in \mathscr{D}st$, so

$$(st(a_m^*))^* =_1 a_m^* =_1 a_{m'}^*,$$

thus $st(a_m^*)$ is the limit of a.

(b) Here we show only that $\lim(1/a) = 1/x$. If $m \in \omega'$, then

$$\left(\frac{1}{x}\right)^* - \left(\frac{1}{a_m^*}\right) = \left(\frac{1}{x^* a_m^*}\right)(a_m^* - x^*)$$

$$=_1 \left(\frac{1}{x^{*2}}\right)(a_m^* - x^*)$$

$$=_1 \left(\frac{1}{x^{*2}}\right)0$$

$$= 0,$$

so

$$\frac{1}{a_m^*} =_1 \frac{1}{x^*}.$$

PROPOSITION 5.2.29. If a is monotone increasing, and for each $n \in \omega$, $a_n \leq r$, then $\lim a$ exists and $\lim a \leq r$.

Proof: $\mathscr{R}a \subset [a_0, r]$ so $\mathscr{R}a^* \subset [a_0^*, r^*] \subset \mathscr{D}st$. If $m \in \omega'$, $n \in \omega$, then

$$a_n \leq st(a_m^*),$$

thus (supplying the appropriate formula) if $m, m' \in \omega'$,

$$a_{m'}^* \leq (st(a_m^*))^*, \qquad \text{so} \qquad st(a_m^*) \leq st(a_{m'}^*).$$

Reversing the roles of m and m', we see

$$st(a_m^*) = st(a_{m'}^*), \qquad \text{so} \qquad (st(a_m^*))^* =_1 a_{m'}^*,$$

thus

$$\lim a = st(a_m^*) \in [a_0, r] \qquad \text{for} \quad m \in \omega'.$$

Earlier theorems implied 5.2.28 and 5.2.29 but we chose to do the theory of limits independently of our earlier work.

The following well-known facts about infinite series have simple nonstandard proofs.

PROPOSITION 5.2.30. (a) $\sum_{n=0}^{\infty} a_n = x$ iff for every $m \in \omega'$, $\sum_{n=0}^{m} a_n^* =_1 x^*$.

(b) $\sum_{n=0}^{\infty} a_n$ exists iff for each $m, m' \in \omega'$, $\sum_{n=0}^{m} a_n^* =_1 \sum_{n=0}^{m'} a_n^*$.

(c) If $\sum_{n=0}^{\infty} a_n$ exists, then $\lim_{n \to \omega} a_n^* = 0$.

In (d), (e) we assume $a_n, b_n \geq 0$.

(d) $\sum_{n=0}^{\infty} a_n$ exists iff $\sum_{n=0}^{m'} a_n^* \in \mathscr{D}st$ for some $m \in \omega'$ (iff $\{\sum_{n=0}^{k} a_n \mid k \in \omega\}$ is bounded) and fails to exist iff for some $m \in \omega'$,

$$\sum_{n=0}^{m} a_n^* \notin \mathscr{D}st.$$

(e) If $b_n \leq a_n$ and $\sum_{n=0}^{\infty} a_n$ exists, then so does $\sum_{n=0}^{\infty} b_n$.

(f) If $\sum_{n=0}^{\infty} |a_n|$ exists, then so does $\sum_{n=0}^{\infty} a_n$, and if $\varphi: \omega \to \omega$ is a permutation, then

$$\sum_{n=0}^{\infty} a_n = \sum_{n=0}^{\infty} a_{\varphi(n)}.$$

The proofs are all straightforward and left for the reader (however, see Problem 5.2.4). The main question is as to the meaning of $\sum_{n=0}^{m} a_n$ for $m \in \omega'$. However, it is simple to define $s_k = \sum_{n=0}^{k} a_n$ so we have a function $s: \omega \to \mathbb{R}$ such that

$$s_0 = a_0 \qquad \text{and} \qquad s_{k+1} = s_k + a_{k+1}.$$

Thus $s^*: \omega^* \to \mathbb{R}^*$ exists with the same properties. Another such question might be asked about $\max\{a_0, \ldots, a_m\}$, $m \in \omega'$, and it receives a similar answer.

Now let $\sum_{n=0}^{\infty} a_n$, $\sum_{n=0}^{\infty} b_n$ be series. Then since for each $m \in \omega$,

$$\left(\sum_{n=0}^{m} a_n\right)\left(\sum_{n=0}^{m} b_n\right) = \sum_{k=0}^{2m} \left(\sum_{n=\max\{0,k-m\}}^{\min\{k,m\}} a_n b_{k-n}\right)$$

we also have for each $m \in \omega^*$,

$$\left(\sum_{n=0}^{m} a_n^*\right)\left(\sum_{n=0}^{m} b_n^*\right) = \sum_{k=0}^{2m}\left(\sum_{n=max\{0,k-m\}}^{min\{k,m\}} a_n^* b_{k-n}^*\right)$$
$$= \sum_{k=0}^{m}\left(\sum_{n=0}^{k} a_n^* b_{k-n}^*\right) + \sum_{k=m+1}^{2m}\left(\sum_{n=k-m}^{m} a_n^* b_{k-n}^*\right).$$

Thus if $\sum_{n=0}^{\infty} a_n$, $\sum_{n=0}^{\infty} b_n$ exist,

$$\left(\sum_{n=0}^{\infty} a_n\right)\left(\sum_{n=0}^{\infty} b_n\right) = st\left(\left(\sum_{n=0}^{m} a_n^*\right)\left(\sum_{n=0}^{m} b_n^*\right)\right)$$
$$= st\left(\sum_{k=0}^{m}\left(\sum_{n=0}^{k} a_n^* b_{k-n}^*\right)\right)$$
$$+ st\left(\sum_{k=m+1}^{2m}\left(\sum_{n=k-m}^{m} a_n^* b_{k-n}^*\right)\right)$$
$$= \sum_{k=0}^{\infty}\left(\sum_{n=0}^{k} a_n b_{k-n}\right) + st\left(\sum_{k=m+1}^{2m}\left(\sum_{n=k-m}^{m} a_n^* b_{k-n}^*\right)\right),$$

provided all these terms exist and $m \in \omega'$. If $\sum_{n=0}^{\infty} a_n$, $\sum_{n=0}^{\infty} b_n$ exist and we can show that

$$st\left(\sum_{k=m+1}^{2m}\left(\sum_{n=k-m}^{m} a_n^* b_{k-n}^*\right)\right) = 0,$$

then all the other terms will exist and we will have shown that

$$\left(\sum_{n=0}^{\infty} a_n\right)\left(\sum_{n=0}^{\infty} b_n\right) = \sum_{k=0}^{\infty}\left(\sum_{n=0}^{k} a_n b_{k-n}\right).$$

PROPOSITION 5.2.31. If $\sum_{n=0}^{\infty} b_n$ exists and $\sum_{n=0}^{\infty} |a_n|$ exists, then

$$\left(\sum_{n=0}^{\infty} a_n\right)\left(\sum_{n=0}^{\infty} b_n\right) = \sum_{k=0}^{\infty}\left(\sum_{n=0}^{k} a_n b_{k-n}\right)$$

(and all terms mentioned exist).

Proof: If $m \in \omega'$ then for some $m' \in \omega'$, $m - m' \in \omega'$, for in fact $m/2 = m'$ works if m is even, $(m + 1)/2 = m'$ works if m is odd.

$$\sum_{k=m+1}^{2m}\left(\sum_{n=k-m}^{m} a_n^* b_{k-n}^*\right) = \sum_{n=1}^{m}\left(\sum_{k=m+1}^{m+n} a_n^* b_{k-n}^*\right)$$
$$= \sum_{n=1}^{m}\left(a_n^* \sum_{k=m+1}^{m+n} b_{k-n}^*\right)$$
$$= \sum_{n=1}^{m'}\left(a_n^* \sum_{k=m+1}^{m+n} b_{k-n}^*\right)$$
$$+ \sum_{n=m'+1}^{m}\left(a_n^* \sum_{k=m+1}^{m+n} b_{k-n}^*\right).$$

Thus

$$\left|\sum_{k=m+1}^{2m}\left(\sum_{n=k-m}^{m} a_n^* b_{k-n}^*\right)\right|$$

$$\leq \left|\sum_{n=1}^{m'}\left(a_n^* \sum_{k=m+1}^{m+n} b_{k-n}^*\right)\right| + \left|\sum_{n=m'+1}^{m}\left(a_n^* \sum_{k=m+1}^{m+n} b_{k-n}^*\right)\right|$$

$$\leq \sum_{n=1}^{m'}\left|a_n^* \sum_{k=m+1}^{m+n} b_{k-n}^*\right| + \sum_{n=m'+1}^{m}\left|a_n^* \sum_{k=m+1}^{m+n} b_{k-n}^*\right|$$

$$\leq \sum_{n=1}^{m'}|a_n^*|\left|\sum_{k=m+1}^{m+n} b_{k-n}^*\right| + \sum_{n=m'+1}^{m}|a_n^*|\left|\sum_{k=m+1}^{m+n} b_{k-n}^*\right|$$

$$\leq \sum_{n=1}^{m'}|a_n^*|\left(\max\left\{\left|\sum_{k=m+1}^{m+n} b_{k-n}^*\right| \mid n = 1,\ldots,m'\right\}\right)$$

$$+\left(\sum_{n=m'+1}^{m}|a_n^*|\right)\left(\max\left\{\left|\sum_{k=m+1}^{m+n} b_{k-n}^*\right| \mid n = m'+1,\ldots,m\right\}\right)$$

$$=_1 \left(\sum_{n=1}|a_n|\right)^* 0 + 0\, M = 0$$

(M, the max in the previous equation is bounded because if

$$\left|\sum_{j=1}^{\infty} b_j - \sum_{j=1}^{s'} b_j\right| < \delta \qquad \text{for each} \quad s' \geq s$$

then

$$M \leq \max\left\{\left(\left|\sum_{j=p}^{\infty} b_j\right| + \delta\right)^* \mid p = 1,\ldots,s\right\}\right).$$

A sequence $f_n\colon X \to \mathbb{R}$ of functions converges uniformly to f iff for each $\varepsilon > 0$ there is an $m \in \omega$ such that if $m < n \in \omega$, then $|f_n(x) - f(x)| < \varepsilon$ for each $x \in X$. It is said to converge pointwise to f iff for each $x \in X$, $f(x) = \lim_{n\to\infty} f_n(x)$. We regard our sequence as a ternary relation F on $\mathbb{R}$ with $F(n, x, y)$ iff $f_n(x) = y$.

Definition 5.2.32. Let $f_n\colon X \to \mathbb{R}$, $n \in \omega$, $f\colon X \to \mathbb{R}$. Then $f_n \to f$ uniformly iff for each $m \in \omega'$, $x \in X^*$, $f_m^*(x) =_1 f^*(x)$. $f_n \to f$ pointwise iff for each $m \in \omega'$, $x \in X$, $f_m^*(x^*) =_1 (f(x))^*$.

Proof: Let $\varepsilon > 0$, $\varepsilon \in \mathbb{Q}$ and let

$$G_n = (\forall v_1)(\forall v_2)(P_\omega(v_1) \wedge (c_n < v_1) \wedge P_X(v_2) \to |f_{v_1}(v_2) - f(v_2)| < c_\varepsilon).$$

If $f_n \to f$ for some n,

$$\langle \mathbb{R}, \omega, X, F, f, \varepsilon, 1, \ldots, n, \ldots\rangle \vDash G_n \qquad (\text{where } F(n, x) = f_n(x))$$

so

$$\langle \mathbb{R}^*, \omega^*, X^*, F^*, f^*, \varepsilon^*, 1, \ldots, n^*, \ldots \rangle \models G_n,$$

so if $m \in \omega'$, $x \in X^*$,

$$|f_m^*(x) - f^*(x)| < \varepsilon \qquad \text{for each} \quad 0 < \varepsilon \in \mathbb{Q}$$

so

$$f_m^*(x) =_1 f^*(x).$$

The converse and the second assertion, as well as the formation of Cauchy criteria are left for the reader (see Problem 5.2.7).

Corollary 5.2.33. Let $f_n: X \to \mathbb{R}$ converge uniformly to $f: X \to \mathbb{R}$, f_n continuous. Then f is continuous.

Proof: If $x \in X$ and $y \in m(x) \cap X^*$ then

$$f^*(y) =_1 f_m^*(y) =_1 f_m^*(x^*) =_1 (f(x))^* \qquad \text{for} \quad m \in \omega'.$$

We leave for the reader the determination of the standard equivalent to the following nonstandard:

Definition 5.2.34. The sequence $f_n: X \to \mathbb{R}$ of functions converges to $f: X \to \mathbb{R}$ uniformly at $x \in X$ iff for each $m \in \omega'$, $y \in X^*$, if $y =_1 x^*$ then $f^*(y) =_1 f_m^*(y)$.

Proposition 5.2.35. If X is compact and $f_n \to f$ uniformly at each $x \in X$, then $f_n \to f$ uniformly.

Proof: If $y \in X^*$, then $y =_1 (st(y))^*$, $st(y) \in X$. Thus $f^*(y) =_1 f_m^*(y)$. (Note that the converse holds as well.)

We now comment briefly on Riemann integration. Let $f: [a, b] \to \mathbb{R}$ be bounded. Then f is Riemann integrable on $[a, b]$ iff for some $r \in \mathbb{R}$ it is true that if $0 < \varepsilon \in \mathbb{Q}$ there is a $\delta \in \mathbb{Q}$ such that $\delta > 0$ and if

$$a = x_1 \leq t_1 \leq \cdots \leq x_n = b \quad \text{and} \quad \max\{x_{j+1} - x_j \mid 1 \leq j < n\} < \delta,$$

then

$$\left| \sum_{j=1}^{n-1} f(t_j)(x_{j+1} - x_j) - r \right| < \varepsilon.$$

In this case r is called the Riemann integral of f on $[a, b]$, denoted $\int_a^b f(t)\,dt$.

DEFINITION 5.2.36. $f\colon [a, b] \to \mathbb{R}$ is Riemann integrable on $[a, b]$ with Riemann integral r iff whenever $a^* = x_1 \le t_1 \le \cdots \le t_{n-1} \le x_n = b^*$ and $\max\{x_{j+1} - x_j \mid 1 \le j < n\} =_1 0$ then

$$\sum_{j=1}^{n-1} f^*(t_j)(x_{j+1} - x_j) =_1 r^*.$$

THEOREM 5.2.37. Let $f\colon [a, b] \to \mathbb{R}$ be continuous. Then f is Riemann integrable on $[a, x]$ for each $x \in [a, b]$ and if $F\colon [a, b] \to \mathbb{R}$ is defined by $F(z) = \int_a^z f(t)\,dt$ then for each $z \in [a, b]$, $F'(z) = f(z)$.

Proof: Let $f[[a, z]] \subset [m, M]$, $m, M \in \mathbb{R}$,

$$a^* = x_1 \le t_1 \le \cdots \le x_n = z^*, \qquad a^* = x_1' \le t_1' \le \cdots \le x_{n'}' = z^*,$$

$$\max\{x_{j+1} - x_j \mid 1 \le j < n\} =_1 \max\{x_{k+1}' - x_k' \mid 1 \le k < n'\} =_1 0.$$

Below our proofs are for $x_1, \ldots, t_{n-1}, x_n$ but they clearly hold for $x_1', \ldots, t_{n'-1}', x_{n'}'$, as well, a fact we use.

$$m^*(z^* - a^*) = \sum_{j=1}^{n-1} m^*(x_{j+1} - x_j) \le \sum_{j=1}^{n-1} f^*(t_j)(x_{j+1} - x_j)$$
$$\le \sum_{j=1}^{n-1} M^*(x_{j+1} - x_j) = M^*(z^* - a^*),$$

so these sums are in $\mathscr{D}st$. Let

$$\{w_1, \ldots, w_p\} = \{x_1, \ldots, x_n\} \cup \{x_1', \ldots, x_{n'}'\},$$
$$a^* = w_1 \le s_1 \le \cdots \le w_p = z^*.$$

We show

$$\sum_{j=1}^{n-1} f^*(t_j)(x_{j+1} - x_j) =_1 \sum_{i=1}^{p-1} f^*(s_i)(w_{i+1} - w_i).$$

First note that for $i = 1, \ldots, p - 1$ we may choose j_i such that $x_{j_i} = w_i \le w_{i+1} \le x_{j_{i+1}}$, and if we do then

$$\sum_{j=1}^{n-1} f^*(t_j)(x_{j+1} - x_j) = \sum_{i=1}^{p-1} f^*(t_{j_i})(w_{i+1} - w_i),$$

so

$$\left|\sum_{i=1}^{p-1} f^*(s_i)(w_{i+1} - w_i) - \sum_{j=1}^{n-1} f^*(t_j)(x_{j+1} - x_j)\right|$$
$$= \left|\sum_{i=1}^{p-1} (f^*(s_i) - f^*(t_{j_i}))(w_{i+1} - w_i)\right|$$
$$\le \sum_{j=1}^{p-1} |f^*(s_i) - f^*(t_{j_i})|\,|w_{i+1} - w_i|.$$

$s_i, t_{j_i} \in [x_{j_i}, x_{j_i+1}]$ thus $s_i =_1 t_{j_i}$ and since f is continuous on $[a, b]$, it is uniformly continuous so $f^*(s_i) =_1 f^*(t_{j_i})$, thus if

$$K = \max\{|f^*(s_i) - f^*(t_{j_i})| \mid 1 \leq i < p\},$$

then $K =_1 0$. Thus

$$\left|\sum_{i=1}^{p-1} f^*(s_i)(w_{i+1} - w_i) - \sum_{j=1}^{n-1} f^*(t_j)(x_{j+1} - x_j)\right| \leq \sum_{i=1}^{p-1} K(w_{i+1} - w_i) = K(z^* - a^*) =_1 0.$$

Therefore

$$\int_a^z f(t)\,dt = st\left(\sum_{j=1}^{n-1} f^*(t_j)(x_{j+1} - x_j)\right).$$

By Definition 5.2.36 if they exist, and $c \leq d \leq e$ then

$$\int_c^d g(t)\,dt + \int_d^e g(t)\,dt = \int_c^e g(t)\,dt$$

and with the above this shows that if $x \leq y$, $f[[x, y]] \subset [m, M]$, then

$$m \leq \frac{\int_x^y f(t)\,dt}{y - x} = \frac{F(y) - F(x)}{y - x} \leq M,$$

thus the same holds for F^*. Thus if $y \in m(z) \sim \{z^*\}$ then

$$\frac{F^*(y) - F(z)^*}{y - z^*} =_1 f(z)^*, \qquad \text{so} \qquad F'(z) = f(z).$$

The second assertion of 5.2.37 assures us of the "change of variables" rule:

$$\int_a^b f \circ g(x) g'(x)\,dx = \int_{g(a)}^{g(b)} f(x)\,dx$$

for f continuous on $g[[a, b]]$, g' continuous on $[a, b]$, since if

$$F'(x) = f(x) \qquad \text{for} \quad x \in g[[a, b]],$$

by 5.2.37 and the mean value theorem, both of the above integrals are given by $F(g(b)) - F(g(a))$.

Problems

5.2.1 (a) Let $f: X \to \mathbb{R}$, $a \in X^-$. Give a nonstandard definition for $\lim_{x \to a} f(x)$ and a condition for the existence of such a limit. Show the usual rules for addition, etc., of limits. Also define $\lim_{x \to \infty} f(x)$ and "$\lim_{x \to a} f(x) = \infty$" and establish the usual rules for their existence and operations with them.

(b) Show that $\lim_{x \to a} f(x) = r$ iff for each sequence $x_n \to a$ in $\mathscr{D}f$, $\lim_{n \to \infty} f(x_n) = r$. Now let f be continuous. Show that $f \cup \{\langle a, r \rangle\}$ is continuous iff for every sequence $x_n \to a$ in $\mathscr{D}f$, $\lim_{n \to \infty} f(x_n) = r$.

‡5.2.2 (a) If $A \subset B \subset \mathbb{R}$, show that A is dense in B iff for each $b \in B$, $b^* =_1 a$ for some $a \in A^*$ (also iff for each $b \in B^*$ there is an $a \in A^*$ such that $a =_1 b$). Thus show that A^- is always closed.

(b) Show that $m(x) = \bigcap \{\mathscr{O}^* \mid x \in \mathscr{O} \in \mathscr{T}\}$ for use in the proof of Proposition 5.2.9.

(c) Show that all elements in ω' are infinite—i.e., if $n \in \omega$, $m \in \omega'$, then $n^* < m$. (HINT: How many elements $k \in \omega^*$ satisfy $0 \leq k \leq n^*$?)

5.2.3 Elementary calculus can be done by nonstandard means. For practice, use our definitions to:

(a) Verify that x^2 is continuous at each point (uniformly continuous on each bounded set, but not on all of $\mathbb{R}$);

(b) Show that

$$\sum_{n=1}^{\infty} \left(\frac{1}{(n(n+1))}\right) = 1;$$

(c) Find $(\sqrt{x})'$ (use nonstandard "Δ-process");

(d) Prove that if $|r| < 1$, then

$$\sum_{n=0}^{\infty} ar^n = \frac{a}{(1-r)};$$

(e) Show the integral test: Let $f\colon [1, \infty) \to [0, \infty)$ be continuous and nonincreasing. Then $\sum_{n=1}^{\infty} f(n)$ exist iff $\int_1^{\infty} f(x)\, dx$ exists.

(f) Show that $\sum_{n=1}^{\infty} 1/(n^p)$ converges iff $p > 1$.

‡5.2.4 Show Definition 5.2.11, Lemma 5.2.12, and Proposition 5.2.13.

(b) Give nonstandard proofs of Corollary 5.2.26 and Definition 5.2.27.

(c) Prove Proposition 5.2.30, particularly the last assertion of (f).

5.2.5 Prove that every continuous homomorphism $f\colon \langle \mathbb{R}, +, 0 \rangle \to \langle \mathbb{R}, +, 0 \rangle$ has the property that for some $a \in \mathbb{R}$, $f(x) = ax$ for every $x \in \mathbb{R}$, and every such homomorphism bounded on some interval is continuous (thus is multiplication by some $a \in \mathbb{R}$).

5.2.6 Let $f\colon X \to \mathbb{R}$, $x \in X$. If f^* reaches a minimum (or maximum) on $X^* \cap m(x)$ then this value is achieved at x^*.

5.2.7 A sequence f_n of functions defined on X is called uniformly Cauchy iff for each $\varepsilon > 0$ there is an $N \in \omega$ such that if $N \leq m, n \in \omega$, then for every $x \in X$,

$$|f_n(x) - f_m(x)| < \varepsilon.$$

Show that f_n is uniformly Cauchy iff for every $m, m' \in \omega'$,

$$f_m^*(y) =_1 f_{m'}^*(y) \qquad \text{for every} \quad y \in X^*.$$

Using this, show that every uniformly Cauchy sequence of functions approaches some function uniformly.

5.2.8 (a) A sequence f_n of functions on X is called equicontinuous on X iff for each $\varepsilon > 0$, $x \in X$, there is a $\delta > 0$ such that if $n \in \omega$, $y \in X$, and $|x - y| < \delta$, then $|f_n(x) - f_n(y)| < \varepsilon$. Find an equivalent nonstandard definition.

(b) If f_n is a uniformly Cauchy sequence of continuous functions on X then f_n is equicontinuous on X.

(c) If f_n is a sequence of continuous functions that converges pointwise to f, then f_n converges to f uniformly iff f_n is equicontinuous on X.

5.2.9 (a) We generalize the concept of uniform Cauchyness: Let $S, T \subset \mathbb{R}$, $F: S \times T \to \mathbb{R}$ (think of $F(x, t) = f_x(t)$). Then $\lim_{x \to s} F(x, t)$ exists uniformly in t iff for each $\varepsilon > 0$ there is a $\delta > 0$ such that if $|x - s| < \delta$, $|y - s| < \delta$, $x, y \in S$, $t \in T$, then

$$|F(x, t) - F(y, t)| < \varepsilon.$$

Develop and prove a nonstandard definition for this concept.

(b) Show that for $f: [a, b] \to \mathbb{R}$, f' is continuous on $[a, b]$ iff for

$$F(x, y) = \frac{f(y) - f(x)}{y - x}, \quad F(x, x) = f'(x),$$

$\lim_{x \to y} F(x, y)$ exists uniformly in y.

‡5.2.10 Show g of Proposition 5.2.16 to be uniformly continuous. (HINT: Show that

$$\text{if } \quad |st(x) - st(y)| < \delta, \qquad \text{then } \quad |f^*(x) - f^*(y)| < \varepsilon,$$

thus

$$|g(st(x)) - g(st(y))| \le \varepsilon.)$$

5.2.11 Show for $X \subset \mathbb{R}$ that X is compact iff for every collection $\{C_\gamma \mid \gamma \in \Gamma\}$ of sets closed in X, $\langle X, C_\gamma \rangle_{\gamma \in \Gamma}$ has the finite satisfaction property for sets of positive formulas.

The above characterization of compactness falls within the realm of model theory but not within the realm of nonstandard analysis.

5.2.12 (a) Let $z: \omega \to \omega'$ be a sequence. Then for some $m \in \omega'$, if $n \in \omega$ then $m < z_n$. (HINT: For $n \in \omega$ let $F_n = (c_n < v_0 \wedge v_0 < c_{z_n})$.)

(b) Let $a \in (SEQ)^*$, where $SEQ = \{a: \omega \to \mathbb{R}\}$. If $^*[\omega] \subset \{i \mid a_i =_1 0\}$ then for some $k \in \omega'$ if $n < k$, $a_n =_1 0$. (HINT: For $p \in \omega$, consider $\{i \mid |a_i| \ge (1/p)^*\}$.)

5.2.13 (a) Let $a: \omega \times \omega \to \mathbb{R}$ (i.e., a is a double sequence). Show that $\lim_{m,n \to \infty} a_{mn} = x$ iff for every $m, n \in \omega'$, $a^*_{mn} =_1 x^*$; show that a is Cauchy iff $a^*_{mn} =_1 a^*_{m'n'}$ for every $m, n, m', n' \in \omega'$.

Below it will be convenient to write $\lim_{n \to \omega} b_n = x$ when $\mathscr{D}b$ is a cofinite subset of ω (that is, $\omega \sim \mathscr{D}b$ is finite) and for some (thus for every) $c: \omega \to \mathbb{R}$ such that $b \subset c$, $\lim_{n \to \infty} c_n = x$.

(b) If $x = \lim_{m,n \to \omega} a_{mn}$, then for each sequence k in ω' there is an $m_0 \in \omega$ such that if $m_0 < m \in \omega$ then $st(a^*_{mk_m})$ exists and $x = \lim_{m \to \infty} st(a^*_{mk_m})$ (and a similar result holds for $a^*_{k_n n}$).

(c) Let $\lim_{m,n\to\infty} a_{mn} = x$ and assume that for some $n_0 \in \omega$ if $n_0 < n \in \omega$ then $\lim_{m\to\infty} a_{mn}$ exists. Then $\lim_{n\to\infty}(\lim_{m\to\infty} a_{mn})$ exists and is x.

(d) If a is a double sequence then $\lim_{m\to\infty} a_{mn}$ exists uniformly in n iff for each $m, n, m' \in \omega'$, $a^*_{mn} =_1 a^*_{m'n}$. Find the standard equivalent.

(e) $\lim_{m,n\to\infty} a_{mn} = \lim_{m\to\infty}(\lim_{n\to\infty} a_{mn})$ iff

(i) $\lim_{m\to\infty} a_{mn}$ exists uniformly in n, and

(ii) for some $m_0 \in \omega$, if $m_0 < m \in \omega$ then $\lim_{n\to\infty} a_{mn}$ exists.

A similar condition holds with the role of m, n reversed. (HINT: Use Problem 5.2.12 (b) to show that if $n, n' \in \omega'$ then for some $m'' \in \omega'$, $a^*_{m''n} =_1 a_{m''n'}$.)

(f) Let $a: \omega \to \mathbb{R}$, and show that $\{st(a^*_m) \mid m \in \omega'\}$ is closed. Thus $\underline{\lim}\, a$ and $\overline{\lim}\, a$ are both of the form $st(a^*_m)$ for some $m \in \omega'$, if a is bounded.

(g) If a is a Cauchy double sequence then

$$\lim_{m,n\to\infty} a_{mn} = \overline{\lim_{m\to\infty}}\left(\overline{\lim_{n\to\infty}}\, a_{mn}\right) = \overline{\lim_{m\to\infty}}\left(\underline{\lim_{n\to\infty}}\, a_{mn}\right)$$

$$= \cdots = \underline{\lim_{n\to\infty}}\left(\underline{\lim_{m\to\infty}}\, a_{mn}\right).$$

5.3 Functions of Several Real Variables; Complex Numbers

We first study the topology of $\mathbb{R}^n$, the vector space of ordered n-tuples of real numbers under the usual operations and the usual norm:

$$\|\langle a_1, \ldots, a_n\rangle\| = \sqrt{a_1^2 + \cdots + a_n^2}.$$

Proposition 5.2.1 tells us that $(\mathbb{R}^n)^* = (\mathbb{R}^*)^n$ and gives us $+^*$, $\cdot^*$, 0^*, $\|\ \|^*$ (which we shall henceforth refer to as $+$, $\cdot$, etc.). Note that for $a_1, \ldots, a_n \in \mathbb{R}^*$,

$$\|\langle a_1, \ldots, a_n\rangle\| =_1 0 \qquad \text{iff} \quad a_1 =_1 \cdots =_1 a_n =_1 0,$$

and that

$$\|\langle a_1, \ldots, a_n\rangle\| \in \mathscr{D}st \qquad \text{iff} \quad a_1, \ldots, a_n \in \mathscr{D}st.$$

Since $\mathbb{R}^n$ is a vector space over $\mathbb{R}$, $\mathbb{R}^{n*}$ is one over $\mathbb{R}^*$ and thus over $\mathbb{R}$ (where $\cdot: \mathbb{R}\times\mathbb{R}^{*n} \to \mathbb{R}^{*n}$ is defined by

$$r\langle a_1, \ldots, a_n\rangle = \langle r^*a_1, \ldots, r^*a_n\rangle).$$

LEMMA 5.3.1. (a)

$$Z^n = \{x \in \mathbb{R}^{*n} \mid \|x\| =_1 0\} \subset D^n = \{x \in \mathbb{R}^{*n} \mid \|x\| \in \mathscr{D}st\}$$

are both $\mathbb{R}$-subspaces (but not $\mathbb{R}^*$-subspaces) of $\mathbb{R}^{*n}$.

(b) The map $St\colon D^n \to \mathbb{R}^n$ defined by

$$St(\langle a_1, \ldots, a_n\rangle) = \langle st(a_1), \ldots, st(a_n)\rangle$$

is $\mathbb{R}$-linear with kernel Z^n. Thus:

(i) if $x, y \in D^n$, $St(x + y) = St(x) + St(y)$;
(ii) if $x \in D^n$, $r \in \mathbb{R}$, $St(rx) = rSt(x)$ (in fact, if $s \in \mathscr{D}st$, then $St(sx) = st(s)St(x)$);
(iii) $St(x) = 0$ iff $x \in Z^n$; and also
(iv) if $x \in \mathbb{R}^n$, $St(x^*) = x$, where for $x = \langle a_1, \ldots, a_n\rangle$, $x^* = \langle a_1^*, \ldots, a_n^*\rangle$;
(v) $st(\|x\|) = \|St(x)\|$ for $x \in D^n$.
If we define $(\ ,\ )\colon (\mathbb{R}^n)^2 \to \mathbb{R}$ by

$$(\langle a_1, \ldots, a_n\rangle, \langle b_1, \ldots, b_n\rangle) = a_1b_1 + \cdots + a_nb_n,$$

then we obtain $(\ ,\ )^* = (\ ,\ )\colon (\mathbb{R}^{*n})^2 \to \mathbb{R}^*$, and
(vi) if $x, y \in D^n$, $(St(x), St(y)) = st((x, y))$.

We leave proof of the above for the reader. The following theorems can be derived from corresponding facts shown in Section 5.2 or from proofs there and we leave details for the reader to work out. For $x \in \mathbb{R}^n$,

$$m(x) = \{y \in \mathbb{R}^{n*} \mid St(y) = x\}.$$

THEOREM 5.3.2. (a) If $X, \mathcal{O} \subset \mathbb{R}^n$, then $X^- = St[X^*]$; X is closed iff $X = X^-$; $\mathcal{O}$ is open iff when $x \in \mathcal{O}$ and $y =_1 x^*$ (i.e., $St(y - x^*) = 0$, $y \in m(x)$, or equivalently $\|y - x^*\| =_1 0$) then $y \in \mathcal{O}^*$. Furthermore, all results of Corollaries 5.2.3 and 5.2.4 hold here with $\mathbb{R}^n$ replacing $\mathbb{R}$ in their statements.
(b) If X is bounded and infinite, then for some x, $x \in (X \sim \{x\})^-$.
(c) $X \subset \mathbb{R}^n$ is compact iff any one (thus all) of these hold:
(i) $X^* \subset \mathscr{D}st$ $(= D^n)$ and $X = St[X^*]$;
(ii) $\langle X, C_i\rangle_{i \in I}$ has the finite satisfaction property for positive formulas for any collection $\{C_i \mid i \in I\}$ of closed sets in X (see Problem 5.2.11);
(iii) X is closed and bounded.

THEOREM 5.3.3. Let $X \subset \mathbb{R}^n$. (a) $f\colon X \to \mathbb{R}^m$ is continuous at $x \in X$ iff $f^*(y) =_1 (f(x))^*$ whenever $x^* =_1 y \in X^*$.
(b) If $f, g\colon X \to \mathbb{R}^m$ are continuous at x, then so is $f + g$. If $h\colon X \to \mathbb{R}$ is also continuous at x, then so is hf, and if $t\colon Y \to \mathbb{R}^p$, $f(x) \in Y \subset \mathbb{R}^m$, and t is continuous at $f(x)$, then $t \circ f$ is continuous at x.
(c) $f\colon X \to \mathbb{R}^m$ is continuous (on X) iff $f^{-1}[\mathcal{O}]$ is open in X for each $\mathcal{O}$ open in $\mathbb{R}^m$.

(d) If $f\colon X \to \mathbb{R}^m$ is continuous, and X compact (or connected), then so is $f[X]$.

(e) $f\colon X \to \mathbb{R}^m$ is uniformly continuous (on X), iff for each $x, y \in X^*$ such that $x =_1 y$ we have $f^*(x) =_1 f^*(y)$.

(f) If f is continuous on X, X compact, then f is uniformly continuous on X.

(g) If $f\colon X \to \mathbb{R}^m$ is uniformly continuous on X, then there is a uniformly continuous $g\colon X^- \to \mathbb{R}^m$ with $f \subset g$.

THEOREM 5.3.4. (a) Let $a\colon \omega \to \mathbb{R}^n$, $x \in \mathbb{R}^n$. Then $\lim_{n\to\infty} a_n = x$ iff for every $m \in \omega'$, $a_m^* =_1 x^*$; a is Cauchy iff $a_m^* =_1 a_{m'}^*$, whenever $m, m' \in \omega'$.

(b) a has a limit iff a is Cauchy, and if a is Cauchy, a is bounded.

(c) If $a, b\colon \omega \to \mathbb{R}^n$, $c\colon \omega \to \mathbb{R}$, $\lim_{n\to\infty} a_n = x$, $\lim_{n\to\infty} b_n = y$, and $\lim_{n\to\infty} c_n = q$, then

$$\lim_{n\to\infty} a_n + c_n b_n = x + qy.$$

Before we study differential calculus we need more information on our norms and on linear transformations. For example, in order to show a function continuous at each point of differentiability, we must first show that linear maps from $\mathbb{R}^n$ into $\mathbb{R}^m$ are continuous.

LEMMA 5.3.5. A pseudo-norm on $\mathbb{R}^n$ is a map $\|\ \|'\colon \mathbb{R}^n \to \mathbb{R}$ such that for every $x, y \in \mathbb{R}^n$, $r \in \mathbb{R}$,

$$\|rx\|' = |r|\,\|x\|' \qquad \text{and} \qquad \|x + y\|' \leq \|x\|' + \|y\|'$$

(thus $0 \leq \|x\|'$). If $\|\ \|'$ is a pseudo-norm, then

$$K^n = \{x \in \mathbb{R}^{*n} \mid \|x\|'^* =_1 0\} \supset Z^n,$$

and if $\|\ \|'$ is a norm (a pseudo-norm for which if $\|x\| = 0$ then $x = 0$), then $Z^n = K^n$.

Proof: We show both facts by induction on n. If $n = 1$, then

$$\|\langle a_1\rangle\|' = |a_1|\,\|\langle 1\rangle\|', \qquad \text{so} \qquad Z^1 \subset K^1.$$

Assume the first assertion now for $k < n$. If $a_1 =_1 \cdots =_1 a_n =_1 0$, then

$$\|\langle a_1, \ldots, a_n\rangle\|'^* \leq \|\langle a_1, \ldots, a_{n-1}, 0\rangle\|'^* + \|\langle 0, \ldots, 0, a_n\rangle\|'^*.$$

However,

$$\|\langle b_1, \ldots, b_{n-1}\rangle\|'' = \|\langle b_1, \ldots, b_{n-1}, 0\rangle\|'$$

and

$$\|\langle b_n\rangle\|''' = \|\langle 0, \ldots, 0, b_n\rangle\|'$$

are pseudo-norms on $\mathbb{R}^{n-1}$ and $\mathbb{R}^1$ respectively, so by induction hypothesis,

$$a_1 =_1 \cdots =_1 a_{n-1} =_1 0 =_1 a_n,$$

thus

$$\|\langle a_1, \ldots, a_{n-1}, 0\rangle\|'^* =_1 0 =_1 \|\langle 0, \ldots, 0, a_n\rangle\|'^*,$$

so

$$\|\langle a_1, \ldots, a_n\rangle\|'^* =_1 0, \qquad \text{showing} \quad Z^n \subset K^n.$$

If $\| \ \|'$ is a norm, $n = 1$, $a_1 \neq_1 0$, then for some $r \in \mathbb{R}$,

$$0 < r^* < |a_1| \qquad \text{so} \qquad 0 < 1/|a_1| < 1/r^*,$$

thus

$$0 \neq_1 |r^*| \, \|\langle 1\rangle\|'^* = \frac{|r^*|}{|a_1|} \|\langle a_1\rangle\|'^* < \frac{|r^*|}{|r^*|} \|\langle a_1\rangle\|'^* = \|\langle a_1\rangle\|'^*,$$

thus

$$K^1 \subset Z^1.$$

If we have this for $k < n$, then $\| \ \|_1 \colon \mathbb{R}^{n-1} \to \mathbb{R}$, $\| \ \|_2 \colon \mathbb{R}^1 \to \mathbb{R}$ defined by

$$\|\langle a_1, \ldots, a_{n-1}\rangle\|_1 = \inf\{\|\langle a_1, \ldots, a_{n-1}, a_n\rangle\|' \mid a_n \in \mathbb{R}\},$$
$$\|\langle a_n\rangle\|_2 = \inf\{\|\langle a_1, \ldots, a_{n-1}, a_n\rangle\|' \mid a_1, \ldots, a_{n-1} \in \mathbb{R}\}$$

are norms (see Problem 5.3.1). Thus by induction, if

$$\|\langle a_1, \ldots, a_{n-1}\rangle\|_1^* =_1 0 \qquad \text{and} \qquad \|\langle a_n\rangle\|_2^* =_1 0$$

then

$$a_1 =_1 \cdots =_1 0 =_1 a_n,$$

but

$$\|\langle a_1, \ldots, a_{n-1}\rangle\|_1^*, \|\langle a_n\rangle\|_2^* \leq \|\langle a_1, \ldots, a_n\rangle\|'^*,$$

so

$$K^n \subset Z^n.$$

PROPOSITION 5.3.6. (a) (Uniqueness of Norm) If $\| \ \|' \colon \mathbb{R}^n \to \mathbb{R}$ is a norm then for some $a, b \in \mathbb{R}$ we have

$$\|x\| \leq a\|x\|', \qquad \|x\|' \leq b\|x\| \qquad \text{for every} \quad x \in \mathbb{R}^n.$$

(b) If $T\colon \mathbb{R}^n \to \mathbb{R}^m$ is a linear transformation, then T is continuous at $0 \in \mathbb{R}^n$.

Proof: (a) Assume that for each $m \in \omega$ we can find an $x_m \in \mathbb{R}^n$ such that

$$\|x_m\|' > m\|x_m\|.$$

Then $\{\|v_0\|' > c_m\|v_0\| \mid m \in \omega\}$ is finitely satisfiable in

$$\langle \mathbb{R}^n \cup \mathbb{R}, \| \ \|', \| \ \|, 1, \ldots, m, \ldots\rangle,$$

thus satisfiable in

$$\langle \mathbb{R}^{*n} \cup \mathbb{R}^*, \|\ \|'^*, \|\ \|, 1, \ldots, m^*, \ldots \rangle.$$

Then let $x \in \mathbb{R}^{*n}$ be such that $\|x\|'^* > m^*\|x\|$ for every $m \in \omega$, and let $y = x/\|x\|'^*$. Then

$$\|y\|'^* = \left\| \frac{x}{\|x\|'^*} \right\|'^* = 1, \qquad \|y\| = \left\| \frac{x}{\|x\|'^*} \right\| = \frac{1}{\|x\|'^*} \|x\| < \frac{1}{m^*}$$

for each $m \in \omega$. Then $y \in Z^n \sim K^n$, a contradiction (even if $\|\ \|'$ is merely a pseudo-norm) which gives us b, and a is found similarly using the fact that $K^n \subset Z^n$.

(b) $\|\ \|' \colon \mathbb{R}^n \to \mathbb{R}$ defined by $\|x\|' = \|T(x)\|$ is a pseudo-norm, so $Z^n \subset K^n$, i.e., if $\|x\| =_1 0$, then $\|T(x)\| =_1 0$, or equivalently, if $x =_1 0$, then $T(x) =_1 0$.

Lemma 5.3.7. The following are equivalent (thus all hold) for $T\colon \mathbb{R}^n \to \mathbb{R}^m$ linear:

(i) T is uniformly continuous;
(ii) T is continuous (at every point $x \in \mathbb{R}^n$);
(iii) T is continuous at 0;
(iv) T is bounded (i.e., $\{\|T(x)\|/\|x\| \mid x \in \mathbb{R}^n \sim \{0\}\}$ is bounded).

Proof: Clearly (i) -> (ii) -> (iii). For (iii) -> (iv), first note that

$$1 = \frac{\|T(x)\|}{\|T(x)\|} = \left\| \frac{1}{\|T(x)\|} T(x) \right\| = \left\| T\left(\frac{x}{\|T(x)\|} \right) \right\| \qquad \text{for} \quad T(x) \neq 0.$$

Thus if (iv) fails, for each $n \in \omega$ there is a y with $\|y\| < 1/n$, $\|T(y)\| = 1$, so

$$S = \{\|v_0\| < c_{1/n} \wedge \|P_T(v_0)\| = c_1 \mid n \in \omega\}$$

is finitely satisfiable in $\langle \mathbb{R}^n \cup \mathbb{R}^m \cup \mathbb{R}, T, \|\ \|, <, 1, \ldots, n, \ldots \rangle$, thus satisfiable in $\langle \mathbb{R}^{*n} \cup \mathbb{R}^{*m} \cup \mathbb{R}^*, T^*, \|\ \|, <, 1, \ldots, n^*, \ldots \rangle$. If y satisfies S, then

$$\|y\| =_1 0 \qquad \text{and} \qquad \|T(y)\| \neq_1 0$$

so (iii) fails. For (iv) -> (i), let $x, y \in \mathbb{R}^{*n}$, $x =_1 y$. Then

$$T^*(y) = T^*(x) + T^*(y - x).$$

But for some $r \in \mathbb{R}$,

$$\|T^*(y - x)\| \leq r^*\|y - x\| =_1 0, \qquad \text{so} \qquad T^*(y) =_1 T^*(x).$$

DEFINITION 5.3.8. $H(\mathbb{R}^n, \mathbb{R}^m) = \{T: \mathbb{R}^n \to \mathbb{R}^m \mid T \text{ linear}\}$. For $T \in H(\mathbb{R}^n, \mathbb{R}^m)$,

$$\|T\| = \text{lub}\left\{\frac{\|T(x)\|}{\|x\|} \mid x \in \mathbb{R}^n \sim \{0\}\right\}.$$

LEMMA 5.3.9. (a) $H(\mathbb{R}^n, \mathbb{R}^m)$ is a vector space over $\mathbb{R}$ (under $(T + U)(x) = T(x) + U(x)$, $(rT)(x) = r(T(x))$, $\| \ \|$ a norm on $H(\mathbb{R}^n, \mathbb{R}^m)$.

(b) If $T \in H(\mathbb{R}^n, \mathbb{R}^m)$, $U \in H(\mathbb{R}^m, \mathbb{R}^p)$, then $\|U \circ T\| \leq \|U\| \, \|T\|$.

(c) $H(\mathbb{R}^n, \mathbb{R}^n)$ is an algebra under composition and the operations mentioned in (a). (A vector space V with an associative, distributive multiplication such that if $x, y \in V$, $r \in \mathscr{F}$, then $r(xy) = (rx)y = x(ry)$.)

(d) The set $U(\mathbb{R}^n)$ of invertible maps in $H(\mathbb{R}^n, \mathbb{R}^n)$ is open (under the $\| \ \|$-topology) and $^{-1}: U(\mathbb{R}^n) \to U(\mathbb{R}^n)$ is continuous.

(e) If $U \in U(\mathbb{R}^n)$, then $\|U \circ T\| \geq \|U^{-1}\|^{-1}\|T\|$.

Proof: (a) through (c) are routine (and algebraic) and (e) results from (c).

For (d) we first show that if $\|I - T\| < 1$ then $T \in U(\mathbb{R}^n)$. Thus let $T = I - U$, $\|U\| < 1$. For $m \in \omega$,

$$(I - U)(I + U + \cdots + U^m) = I - U^{m+1},$$

and for $m \in \omega'$ by (b),

$$\|U^{*m}\| \leq \|U^*\|^m =_1 0;$$

and if $m, m' \in \omega'$, $m < m'$,

$$\begin{aligned}\|(I + \cdots + U^{*m'}) - (I + \cdots + U^{*m})\| &= \|U^{*m+1} + \cdots + U^{*m'}\| \leq \|U^*\|^{m+1} + \cdots + \|U^*\|^{m'} \\ &= \frac{\|U^*\|^{m+1}(1 - \|U^*\|^{m'-m})}{1 - \|U^*\|} =_1 0.\end{aligned}$$

Thus $\sum_{n=0}^{\infty} U^n$ converges and

$$(I - U)\left(\sum_{n=0}^{\infty} U^n\right) = I; \qquad \text{in fact} \qquad \sum_{n=0}^{\infty} U^n = (I - U)^{-1}.$$

If $W \in U(\mathbb{R}^n)$, $W^* =_1 X \in H(\mathbb{R}^n, \mathbb{R}^n)^*$, then set $Y = W^* - X$, so

$$\|W^{*-1}Y\| \leq \|W^{*-1}\| \, \|Y\| =_1 0 \qquad \text{and} \qquad I - W^{*-1}Y \in U(\mathbb{R}^n)^*,$$

so $X = W^*(I - W^{*-1}Y) \in U(\mathbb{R}^n)^*$.

For continuity, first note that the formula derived in the preceding paragraph assures us that if $\|U\| < 1$, then

$$\|(I - U)^{-1} - I\| \leq \sum_{n=1}^{\infty} \|U\|^n = \frac{\|U\|}{1 - \|U\|},$$

thus if $U =_1 0$,

$$\|(I - U)^{-1} - I\| =_1 0.$$

Now let $T =_1 0$, $V \in U(\mathbb{R}^n)$. Then

$$\begin{aligned}\|(V^* - T)^{-1} - V^{*-1}\| &\le \|V^{*-1}\|\,\|V^*(V^* - T)^{-1} - I\|\\ &= \|V^{*-1}\|\,\|(I - TV^{*-1})^{-1} - I\|\\ &=_1 \|V^{*-1}\|0\\ &= 0,\end{aligned}$$

since

$$\|TV^{*-1}\| =_1 0\|V^{*-1}\| = 0.$$

We would now like to proceed to a theory of differentiation for functions of several variables. Usually $f\colon X \to \mathbb{R}^m$, $X \subset \mathbb{R}^n$ is called differentiable at $x \in X$, X open (with derivative $f'(x) \in H(\mathbb{R}^n, \mathbb{R}^m)$) iff

$$f(y) - f(x) = f'(x)(y - x) + \|y - x\|\xi(x, y)$$

and

$$\lim_{\substack{y \in X\\ y \to x}} \xi(x, y) = 0.$$

Definition 5.3.10. Let $f\colon X \to \mathbb{R}^m$, $X \subset \mathbb{R}^n$, $x \in X$, X open. Then f is differentiable at x with derivative $f'(x) \in H(\mathbb{R}^n, \mathbb{R}^m)$ iff for every $y \in X^*$,

$$f^*(y) - (f(x))^* = f'(x)^*(y - x^*) + \|y - x^*\|\xi^*(x^*, y),$$

and

$$\text{if} \quad y =_1 x^* \qquad \text{then} \quad \xi^*(x^*, y) =_1 0.$$

Lemma 5.3.11. (a) The derivative is unique at each x.

(b) If f is differentiable at x, then f is continuous at x.

(c) Let $f, g\colon X \to \mathbb{R}^m$, $h\colon Y \to \mathbb{R}^p$ with $X \subset \mathbb{R}^n$, $Y \subset \mathbb{R}^m$, f, g be differentiable at x, and h be differentiable at $f(x)$. Then

$$(f + g)'(x) = f'(x) + g'(x);$$

$$\text{if} \quad r \in \mathbb{R} \qquad \text{then} \quad (rf)'(x) = r(f'(x));$$

and

$$(h \circ f)'(x) = h'(f(x))f'(x).$$

The proofs are left for the reader. Now for $x, y \in \mathbb{R}^n$, let

$$L'(x, y) = \{ax + by \mid a, b \in [0, 1], a + b = 1\}.$$

THEOREM 5.3.12. Let $f: X \to \mathbb{R}^m$, $L'(x, y) \subset X \subset \mathbb{R}^n$, f be differentiable at each $z \in L'(x, y)$, and for such z, $\|f'(z)\| \leq M$. Then

$$\|f(y) - f(x)\| \leq M\|y - x\|.$$

Proof: Let g: $[0, 1] \to \mathbb{R}^m$ by $g(t) = f((1 - t)x + ty)$. It will then do to show that

$$\|g(1) - g(0)\| \leq M\|y - x\|.$$

However,

$$g = f \circ h, \qquad \text{where} \quad h(t) = (1 - t)x + ty,$$

thus

$$h'(t) = y - x \qquad \text{for each} \quad t \in [0, 1]$$

(i.e., $h'(t)(r) = r(y - x)$). Thus it will do to show for k: $[0, 1] \to \mathbb{R}^m$ that

$$\|k(1) - k(0)\| \leq N$$

for any upper bound N of $\{\|k'(a)\| \mid a \in [0, 1]\}$.

Assume first that $k(0) = 0$ and $\|k'(t)\| < N$ for $t \in [0, 1]$, and consider

$$A = \{t \in [0, 1] \mid \text{if } 0 \leq t' < t \quad \text{then} \quad \|k(t')\| \leq Nt'\}.$$

If w is the least upper bound of A and $t' < w$, then let $t' < t < w$, $t \in A$. Then

$$\|k(t')\| \leq Nt', \qquad \text{so} \qquad w \in A.$$

If $w < 1$, $w^* =_1 u$, $w^* \leq u$, then

$$\begin{aligned}\|k^*(u)\| &= \|(k(w))^* + k'(w)^*(u - w^*) + \|u - w^*\|\xi^*(w^*, u)\| \\ &\leq \|(k(w))^*\| + \|u - w^*\|(\|(k'(w))^*\| + \|\xi^*(w^*, u)\|) \\ &\leq N^*|w^*| + N^*|u - w^*| \\ &= N^*w^*.\end{aligned}$$

Thus w^* is not an upper bound of A^*, a contradiction, so $\|k(1)\| \leq N$ for each such N, so

$$\|k(1)\| \leq \text{lub}\{\|k'(t)\| \mid 0 \leq t \leq 1\}:$$

We may drop the assumption $k(0) = 0$ by working with s defined by $s(t) = k(t) - k(0)$.

We now proceed toward a proof of the inverse function theorem.

LEMMA 5.3.13. (a) Let $X \subset \mathbb{R}^n$ be closed, $f: X \to X$, $k < 1$ such that for every $a, b \in X$,

$$\|f(b) - f(a)\| \leq k\|b - a\|.$$

Then there is a unique $x \in X$ such that $f(x) = x$.

(b) Let $A = \{g \mid g$ a function, $\mathscr{D}g$ is closed, and $\mathscr{D}g, \mathscr{R}g \subset \mathbb{R}^n\}$. If $f \in A^*$ is such that for some $k < 1$,

$$\|f(a) - f(b)\| \leq k^* \|a - b\| \qquad \text{for} \quad a, b \in \mathscr{D}f, \text{and m (x) } (\mathscr{D}f)$$

and $f(x) =_1 x$, there is a unique $y =_1 x$ with $y = f(y)$.

Proof: (a) A nonstandard proof of this well-known fact may be constructed by showing $\{\|v_0 - P_f(v_0)\| < c_{1/n} \mid n \in \omega\}$ finitely satisfiable. Uniqueness may be established in the usual way (i.e., if $a = f(a)$, $b = f(b)$, then

$$\|a - b\| \leq k\|a - b\|, \qquad \text{so} \qquad \|a - b\| = 0).$$

(b) Let $r = \|x - f(x)\| =_1 0$, $X = \{y \mid \|x - y\| \leq \sqrt{r}\}$. Then $f \mid X \colon X \to X$, for if $\|x - y\| \leq \sqrt{r}$, then

$$\begin{aligned}\|x - f(y)\| &\leq \|x - f(x)\| + \|f(x) - f(y)\| \\ &\leq r + k^*\sqrt{r} \\ &= (\sqrt{r} + k)^*\sqrt{r} < 1\sqrt{r} \\ &= \sqrt{r}.\end{aligned}$$

Below, if v_0 is a variable representing an element of A, the symbol "$v_0(v_1)$" simultaneously asserts that v_1 is in the domain of v_0 and denotes the value of v_0 on v_1. Using (a) it is simple to see that if $\langle S, \in\rangle$ is a model of set theory,

$$\begin{aligned}&\langle S, \in, \mathbb{R}^n, A, \mathbb{R}, k, \leq, 0, \|\ \|\rangle \\ &\quad \models (\forall v_0)(\forall v_1)(\forall v_2)([(v_0 \in c_A) \wedge (v_1 \in c_{\mathbb{R}^n}) \wedge (c_0 \leq v_2 \in c_{\mathbb{R}}) \\ &\qquad \wedge (\forall v_3)(\|v_1 - v_3\| \leq v_2 \text{ -> } \|v_1 - v_0(v_3)\| \leq v_2) \\ &\qquad \wedge (\forall v_4)(\forall v_5)((\|v_1 - v_4\| \leq v_2) \\ &\qquad \wedge (\|v_1 - v_5\| \leq v_2) \text{ -> } \|v_0(v_4) - v_0(v_5)\| \\ &\qquad\qquad \leq c_k\|v_4 - v_5\|)] \\ &\quad \text{-> } (\exists v_6)(\forall v_7)((\|v_1 - v_7\| \leq v_2) \wedge (v_0(v_7) = v_7) \text{ <-> } v_6 = v_7)),\end{aligned}$$

thus so does $\langle S^*, \in^*, \mathbb{R}^{*n}, A^*, \mathbb{R}^*, k^*, \leq, \|\ \|\rangle$. However, the above sentence asserts that if $f \in A$ (thus or A^*), $0 \leq r \in \mathbb{R}$ (or $\mathbb{R}^*$), the closed set

$$C = \{y \mid \|y - x\| \leq r\} \subset \mathscr{D}f,$$

$f \mid C \colon C \to C$, and $a, b \in C$ always satisfy

$$\|f(a) - f(b)\| \leq k\|a - b\|,$$

then f has a unique fixed point in C. Thus our f has a fixed point y with $\|y - x\| \leq \sqrt{r} =_1 0$, and the uniqueness of y is shown as in (a).

LEMMA 5.3.14. Let $0 \in \mathcal{O} \subset \mathbb{R}^n$, $f: \mathcal{O} \to \mathbb{R}^n$, $f(0) = 0$, $f'(0) = I$, $f': \mathcal{O} \to H(\mathbb{R}^n, \mathbb{R}^n)$ be continuous. If $y =_1 0$ then $y = f^*(x)$ for some $x =_1 0$.

Proof: By definition of derivative, for $x =_1 0$,

$$f^*(x) = f^*(0) + f'(0)^*(x) + \|x\|\xi^*(0, x) = x + \|x\|\xi^*(0, x)$$

and

$$\xi^*(0, x) =_1 0.$$

Now for $y =_1 0$, define g_y by

$$g_y(x) = x - f^*(x) + y \in A^*$$

(A^* from 5.3.13); note that $g_y(0) = y =_1 0$. Also note that

$$\begin{aligned}
\|g_y(x) - g_y(x')\| &= \|x - f^*(x) - x' + f^*(x')\| \\
&= \|(x - x') - (f^*(x) - f^*(x'))\| \\
&= \|(x - x') - ((f')^*(x')(x - x') + \xi^*(x', x)\|x - x'\|)\| \\
&= \|(I - (f')^*(x'))(x - x') + \xi^*(x', x)\|x - x'\|\,\| \\
&\leq \|I - (f')^*(x')\|\,\|x - x'\| + \|\xi^*(x', x)\|\,\|x - x'\| \\
&= (\|I - (f')^*(x')\| + \|\xi^*(x', x)\|)\|x - x'\| \\
&< k^*\|x - x'\|
\end{aligned}$$

for each $k \in (0, 1)$ if $x, x' =_1 0$. Thus by 5.3.13(b), for some $z =_1 0$, $g_y(z) = z$. However, then

$$z = z - f^*(z) + y, \qquad \text{so} \qquad f^*(z) = y.$$

THEOREM 5.3.15 (Inverse Function Theorem). Let $f: \mathcal{O} \to \mathbb{R}^n$, $x \in \mathcal{O}$ be open in $\mathbb{R}^n$, f' be continuous on $\mathcal{O}$, $f'(x) \in U(\mathbb{R}^n)$. Then for some open $\mathcal{P} \ni x$, $f[\mathcal{P}]$ is open, $f'(z) \in U(\mathbb{R}^n)$ for $z \in \mathcal{P}$, f is one-one on $\mathcal{P}$, and $(f \mid \mathcal{P})^{-1}: f[\mathcal{P}] \to \mathcal{P}$ is continuous with continuous derivative satisfying $f^{-1\prime}(f(z)) = (f'(z))^{-1}$.

Proof: Let $h(z) = (f'(x))^{-1}(f(x + z) - f(x))$. Thus $h(0) = 0$, $h'(0) = I$, so if $y =_1 0$, $y = h^*(z)$ for some $z =_1 0$. If $q =_1 (f(x))^*$, then

$$(f'(x)^{-1})^*(q - (f(x))^*) =_1 0$$

so for some $z =_1 0$,

$$h(z) = (f'(x)^{-1})^*(q - (f(x))^*),$$

so

$$(f'(x)^{-1})^*(f^*(x^* + z) - (f(x))^*) = (f'(x)^{-1})^*(q - (f(x))^*),$$

thus

$$q = f^*(x^* + z) \qquad \text{for some} \quad z =_1 0.$$

Thus if $\mathscr{P}$ is open, $x \in \mathscr{P}$ and $y =_1 (f(x))^*$, then $y \in f^*[\mathscr{P}]$. But this holds for any x with $f'(x) \in U(\mathbb{R}^n)$, so for any open $\mathscr{P}$ such that $f'[\mathscr{P}] \subset U(\mathbb{R}^n)$, $f[\mathscr{P}]$ is open. Next note f one-one on $\{y \mid \|x - y\| < \varepsilon\}$ for some $\varepsilon > 0$ because f^* is one-one on $m(x)$; this in turns holds because if y, $z =_1 x^*$, then

$$f^*(z) = f^*(y) + (f')^*(y)(z - y) + \|z - y\|\xi^*(y, z)$$

with $\xi^*(y, z) =_1 0$ (see Problem 5.3.2). Thus

$$\begin{aligned}\|f^*(z) - f^*(y)\| &\geq \|(f')^*(y)^{-1}\|^{-1}\|z - y\| - \|\xi^*(y, z)\|\,\|z - y\| \\ &= \|z - y\|(\|(f')^*(y)^{-1}\|^{-1} - \|\xi^*(y, z)\|)\end{aligned}$$

and since

$$\|(f')^*(y)^{-1}\|^{-1} \neq_1 0, \qquad \|\xi^*(y, z)\| =_1 0,$$

this is > 0.

We must now show that

$$f^{*-1}(f(x)^* + z) = f^{-1}(f(x))^* + f'(x)^{*-1}(z) + \zeta^*(f(x)^*, z)\|z\|,$$

with

$$\zeta^*((f(x))^*, z) =_1 0 \qquad \text{for} \quad z =_1 0.$$

But for such z,

$$(f(x))^* + z = f^*(x^* + h) \qquad \text{for some} \quad h =_1 0,$$

so

$$z = f^*(x^* + h) - (f(x))^* = (f'(x))^*(h) + \xi^*(x^*, x^* + h)\|h\|$$

and

$$\xi^*(x^*, h + x^*) =_1 0,$$

thus

$$\begin{aligned}\|z\| &= \|(f'(x))^*(h) + \xi^*(x^*, x^* + h)\|h\|\,\| \\ &\geq (\|(f'(x))^{*-1}\|^{-1} - \|\xi^*(x^*, x^* + h)\|)\|h\|\end{aligned}$$

and

$$(f'(x))^{*-1}(z) = h + (f'(x))^{*-1}\xi^*(x^*, x^* + h)\|h\|.$$

Thus setting, as we must

$$\zeta^*((f(x))^*, z) = \frac{f^{*-1}(f(x)^* + z) - f^{-1}(f(x))^* - f'(x)^{*-1}(z)}{\|z\|},$$

we have

$$\|\zeta^*(f(x)^*, z)\| = \left\|\frac{f^{*-1}(f(x)^* + z) - x^* - f'(x)^{*-1}(z)}{\|z\|}\right\|$$
$$\leq \left\|\frac{x^* + h - x^* - (h + f'(x)^{*-1}\xi^*(x^*, x^* + h)\|h\|)}{\|h\|(\|(f'(x))^{*-1}\|^{-1} - \|\xi^*(x^*, x^* + h)\|)}\right\|$$
$$\leq \left\|\frac{\|f'(x)^{*-1}\| \; \|\xi^*(x^*, x^* + h)\| \; \|h\|}{(\|(f'(x))^{*-1}\|^{-1} - \|\xi^*(x^*, x^* + h)\|)\|h\|}\right\|$$
$$=_1 0,$$

since

$$\xi^*(x^*, x^* + h) =_1 0 \qquad \text{and} \qquad \|f'(x)^{-1}\|^{-1} \neq_1 0.$$

f^{-1} is clearly continuously differentiable on $f[\mathscr{P}]$, since if $z = f(y)$, $q =_1 z^*$, then

$$q = f^*(r), \qquad r =_1 y^*,$$

so

$$f^{*-1\prime}(z) = (f'(y))^{*-1} =_1 (f')^*(r)^{-1} = f^{-1*\prime}(q).$$

We now leave our sketchy discussion of functions of several real variables and proceed toward complex analysis. Before introducing the complex numbers, however, we study a concept used in complex analysis that can be defined more generally.

A curve is a continuous function $f\colon [a, b] \to \mathbb{R}^n$ for some $a, b \in \mathbb{R}$, $a < b$. It is called rectifiable iff

$$\operatorname{lub}\left\{\sum_{i=0}^{n} \|f(t_{i+1}) - f(t_i)\| \mid n \in \omega, a = t_0 < \cdots < t_{n+1} = b\right\} < \infty,$$

and if f is rectifiable this least upper bound is called $L(f)$. Let $P = \{t_0, \ldots, t_{n+1}\}$ be such that $t_0 < \cdots < t_{n+1}$. Then

$$|P| = \max\{t_{j+1} - t_j \mid j = 0, \ldots, n\}.$$

Definition 5.3.16. The curve f is rectifiable iff for some $P = \{t_0, \ldots, t_{m+1}\}$,

$$a^* = t_0 < \cdots < t_{m+1} = b^*, \qquad |P| =_1 0$$

and

$$\sum_{k=0}^{m} \|f^*(t_{k+1}) - f^*(t_k)\| \in \mathscr{D}st$$

and for such f, P,

$$L(f) = st\left(\sum_{k=0}^{m} \|f^*(t_{k+1}) - f^*(t_k)\|\right).$$

Proof: To show f rectifiable, it will do to prove that if

$$a = s_0 < \cdots < s_{n+1} = b,$$

then

$$\sum_{j=0}^{n} \|f(s_{j+1}) - f(s_j)\| \leq st \left(\sum_{k=0}^{m} \|f^*(t_{k+1}) - f^*(t_k)\| \right).$$

However, for each j,

$$\|f(s_{j+1}) - f(s_j)\|^* \leq \left(\sum_{k=r_j}^{r'_j} \|f^*(t_{k+1}) - f^*(t_k)\| \right)$$

$$+ \|f^*(t_{r_j}) - (f(s_j))^*\| + \|f^*(t_{r'_j}) - (f(s_{j+1}))^*\|,$$

where r_j is the smallest element of ω^* such that $s_j^* \leq t_{r_j}$, $r'_j \in \omega^*$ the largest such that $t_{r_j'} \leq s_{j+1}^*$. Thus

$$\sum_{j=0}^{n} (\|f(s_{j+1}) - f(s_j)\|)^* \leq \left(\sum_{k=0}^{m} \|f^*(t_{k+1}) - f^*(t_k)\| \right)$$

$$+ \sum_{j=0}^{n} (\|f^*(t_{r_j}) - (f(s_j))^*\| + \|f^*(t_{r'_j}) - (f(s_{j+1}))^*\|).$$

Since $|P| =_1 0$,

$$t_{r_j} - s_j^* \leq t_{r_j} - t_{r_j - 1} =_1 0, \qquad \text{and} \qquad s_{j+1}^* - t_{r'_j} =_1 0,$$

and since f is continuous,

$$\|f^*(t_{r_j}) - (f(s_j))^*\| =_1 0 =_1 \|f^*(t_{r'_j}) - (f(s_{j+1}))^*\|$$

so

$$\sum_{j=0}^{n} (\|f^*(t_{r_j}) - (f(s_j))^*\| + \|f^*(t_{r'_j}) - (f(s_{j+1}))^*\|) =_1 0.$$

Thus

$$\sum_{j=0}^{n} (\|f(s_{j+1}) - f(s_j)\|) \leq st \left(\sum_{k=0}^{m} \|f^*(t_{k+1}) - f^*(t_k)\| \right) \in \mathscr{D}st.$$

We leave for the reader the checking of

$$\sum_{k=0}^{m} \|f^*(t_{k+1}) - f^*(t_k)\| \leq L(f)^*,$$

which, together with the above shows that

$$L(f) = st \left(\sum_{k=0}^{m} \|f^*(t_{k+1}) - f^*(t_k)\| \right).$$

Note that our proof holds for arbitrary P with $|P| =_1 0$.

DEFINITION 5.3.17. Let I, J be intervals, $C: I \to \mathbb{R}^n$, $D: J \to \mathbb{R}^n$. Then D is equivalent to C ($D \equiv C$) iff for some strictly increasing continuous $h: I \to J$ onto, $D = C \circ h$.

$$^{-}C: -I \to \mathbb{R}^n \; (-I = \{-x \mid x \in I\})$$

is defined by $^{-}C(-t) = C(t)$. If $I = [a, b]$, $J = [c, d]$, $C(b) = D(c)$, then $C + D: [a, b + d - c] \to \mathbb{R}^n$ is defined by $C + D \mid [a, b] = C$ and for $t \in [b, b + d - c]$, $(C + D)(t) = D(t + c - b)$.

LEMMA 5.3.18. (a) $\equiv$ is an equivalence relation. Thus we may set $C_{\equiv} = \{D \mid C \equiv D\}$. If $C \equiv D$, then $\mathscr{R}C = \mathscr{R}D$, thus we may define $\mathscr{R}C_{\equiv} = \mathscr{R}C$. If $C \equiv C'$, $D \equiv D'$, and $C + D$ is defined, then so is $C' + D'$ and $C + D \equiv C' + D'$, thus we may define $C_{\equiv} + D_{\equiv} = (C + D)_{\equiv}$. If $C \equiv D$, $C \mid [a, b)$ is one-one, then so is $D \mid [c, d)$; if C is one-one, then so is D; and if C is continuous, then so is D (thus we may refer to $C_{\equiv}$ as having each of these properties if they hold for C).

(b) Let C, D be continuous on $[a, b]$, $[c, d]$ respectively, $C \mid [a, b)$, $D \mid [c, d)$ one-one, $C(a) = D(c)$, $C(b) = D(d)$, $\mathscr{R}C = \mathscr{R}D$. Then $C \equiv D$ or $C \equiv {}^{-}D$.

Proof: (a) is straightforward and left to the reader.

(b) Define $h: [a, b] \to [c, d]$ by $h(x) = D^{-1}(C(x))$ for $x \in (a, b)$. Then that part of h already defined is continuous and monotone on (a, b) and $h[(a, b)] = (c, d)$. If h is increasing, set $h(a) = c$, $h(b) = d$, otherwise $h(a) = d$, $h(b) = c$. The reader should check that h is continuous at its endpoints, establishing (b).

DEFINITION 5.3.19. Let $z, z' \in \mathbb{R}^n$. Then $L(z, z') = C_{\equiv}$, where C is defined on $[0, 1]$ by $C(t) = (1 - t)z + tz'$, and $l(z, z') = (C \mid (0, 1))_{\equiv}$. $L(z, z')$ ($l(z, z')$) is called the closed (open) line from z to z'.

DEFINITION 5.3.20. Let $C: [a, b] \to \mathbb{R}^n$, $a < b$, $a, b \in \mathbb{R}$, C be a rectifiable curve, $f: X \to \mathbb{R}$ where $\mathscr{R}C \subset X \subset \mathbb{R}^n$. Then f is integrable over C with respect to x_i ($i = 1, \ldots, n$) iff there is a real number $\int_C f\, dx_i$ such that if

$$P = \{a^* = t_0 < t_1 < \cdots < t_{m+1} = b^*\}$$

is a partition of $[a^*, b^*]$, $|P| =_1 0$, and for $j = 0, \ldots, m$, $t_j \le t_j' \le t_{j+1}$, then

$$\int_C f\, dx_i = st\left(\sum_{j=0}^{m} (f \circ C)^*(t_j')(c_i^*(t_{j+1}) - c_i^*(t_j))\right),$$

(where $C(t) = (c_1(t), \ldots, c_n(t))$).

C is a contour iff there are

$$a_0 = a < a_1 < \cdots < a_{p+1} = b$$

such that $C \mid [a_j, a_{j+1}]$ is continuously differentiable for $j = 0, \ldots, p$.

While we could, at the expense of more work, do the theory of integration of continuous functions over rectifiable curves, we choose to make the author's work easier (and perhaps the reader's harder) by confining our study to contours here and leaving the more general case to the problems.

PROPOSITION 5.3.21. (a) If C is a contour, then C is rectifiable.

(b) If f is continuous, C continuously differentiable, $\mathscr{D}C = [a, b]$, then

$$\int_C f\, dx_i = \int_a^b (f \circ C)c_i'\, dt$$

(and thus exists).

(c) Every continuously differentiable curve is a contour. If

$$C_k\colon [a_k, b_k] \to \mathbb{R}^n, \qquad k = 1, \ldots, q$$

are contours, and

$$C_k(b_k) = C_{k+1}(a_{k+1}) \qquad \text{for} \quad 1 \le k < q,$$

then $C_1 + \cdots + C_q$ is a contour and $\int_{C_1 + \cdots + C_q} f\, dx_i$ exists and is $\sum_{k=1}^q \int_{C_k} f\, dx_i$, provided that

$$\mathscr{R}(C_1 + \cdots + C_q) \subset \mathscr{D}f \subset \mathbb{R}^n$$

and each of the latter integrals exists. Under these conditions

$$\int_{-C_1} f\, dx_i = -\int_{C_1} f\, dx_i,$$

and thus exists.

(d) If f is continuous and C a contour, then $\int_C f\, dx_i$ exists.

Proof: Let P be as in Definition 5.3.16 or 5.3.20. If

$$M \ge \|C'(t)\| \qquad \text{for each} \quad t \in [a, b] \sim \{a_1, \ldots, a_p\},$$

then

$$\sum_{j=0}^{m} \|C^*(t_{j+1}) - C^*(t_j)\| \le \sum_{j=0}^{m} M^*(t_{j+1} - t_j) = M^*(b^* - a^*)$$

so C is rectifiable by 5.3.16. Note that such an M exists since $(C \mid [a_k, a_{k+1}])'$ is continuous, thus bounded on each of this finite number of intervals, and the largest such bound will serve as our M. This completes the proof of (a).

(b)

$$\int_a^b (f \circ C)c_i' \, dt = st\left(\sum_{j=0}^{m} (f \circ C)^*(t_j')c_i'^*(t_j')(t_{j+1} - t_j)\right)$$

$$= st\left(\sum_{j=0}^{m} (f \circ C)^*(t_j')\,(c_i^*(t_{j+1}) - c_i^*(t_j)) + \sum_{j=0}^{m} (f \circ C)^*(t_j')(c_i'^*(t_j') - c_i'^*(t_j''))(t_{j+1} - t_j)\right)$$

(where t_j'' is selected by the mean value theorem such that $t_j \le t_j'' \le t_{j+1}$ and $c_i^*(t_{j+1}) - c_i^*(t_j) = (c_i'^*(t_j'')(t_{j+1} - t_j))$

$$= \int_C f \, dx_i + st\left(\sum_{j=0}^{m} (f \circ C)^*(t_j')(c_i'^*(t_j') - c_i'^*(t_j''))(t_{j+1} - t_j)\right).$$

But

$$\left|\sum_{j=0}^{m} (f \circ C)^*(t_j')(c_i'^*(t_j') - c_i'^*(t_j''))(t_{j+1} - t_j)\right| \le M(b^* - a^*),$$

where

$$M = \max\{|(f \circ C)^*(t_j')(c_i'^*(t_j') - c_i'^*(t_j''))| \mid j = 0, \ldots, m\},$$

and since f, C, c_i' are continuous and $[a, b]$ is compact, the $(f \circ C)^*(t_j')$ are bounded and the $c_i'^*(t_j') - c_i'^*(t_j'')$ infinitesimal, so each of these terms, thus their max, must be $=_1 0$, thus

$$M(b^* - a^*) =_1 0,$$

completing the proof.

(c) is left for the reader and (d) results immediately from (b), (c).

Note that from Definition 5.3.20 if $a \in \mathbb{R}$, $f, g\colon X \to \mathbb{R}$, C, X, i as in that definition,

$$\int_C (f + ag) \, dx_i = \int_C f \, dx_i + a \int_C g \, dx_i,$$

and from this similar rules result for the integral defined below and complex integral to be defined in Section 5.4.

Definition 5.3.22. Let $C\colon [a, b] \to \mathbb{R}^n$ be rectifiable, $f\colon X \to \mathbb{R}^n$, where $\mathscr{R}C \subset X \subset \mathbb{R}^n$. Then f is integrable over C and

$$\int_C f = \int_C f_1 \, dx_1 + \cdots + \int_C f_n \, dx_n \quad (\text{where } f(x) = (f_1(x), \ldots, f_n(x)))$$

provided that all the integrals on the right-hand side of the equation exist.

PROPOSITION 5.3.23. For each $i = 1, \ldots, n$, let $f_i = \partial g/\partial x_i$ (i.e., $f = g'$), where $g: X \to \mathbb{R}$ ($X = \mathscr{D}f$), C be a contour. Then

$$\int_C f = g(C(b)) - g(C(a)), \qquad \text{where} \quad C: [a, b] \to X.$$

Thus if C is also closed [we call a curve closed if $C(b) = C(a)$], then $\int_C f = 0$.

Proof: Using 5.3.21(c), we may assume C continuously differentiable on $[a, b]$. Then

$$\begin{aligned}\int_C f &= \int_C f_1\, dx_1 + \cdots + \int_C f_n\, dx_n \\ &= \int_a^b (f_1 \circ C)c_1'\, dt + \cdots + \int_a^b (f_n \circ C)c_n'\, dt \\ &= \int_a^b ((f_1 \circ C)c_1' + \cdots + (f_n \circ C)c_n')\, dt \\ &= \int_a^b (g \circ C)'\, dt,\end{aligned}$$

where this step follows from the chain rule, 5.3.11(c). However, by our assumptions on f, C, $(g \circ C)'$ is continuous, so

$$\int_a^b (g \circ C)'\, dt = g \circ C(b) - g \circ C(a) = g(C(b)) - g(C(a)).$$

In the past we have considered the complex numbers to be the only algebraically closed field of characteristic 0 and cardinality 2^ω. Here, however, we are interested in analytic properties of the complex numbers and their relationship to the reals. Thus we study them as a system of the form $\langle \mathbb{R}^2, +, \cdot, 0, 1, |\ |\rangle$, where $+$ is the usual vector space addition and $\langle a, b\rangle \langle c, d\rangle = \langle ac - bd, ad + bc\rangle$. As usual, we denote by 1 the vector $\langle 1, 0\rangle$, and by i the vector $\langle 0, 1\rangle$. Also, $|\ | = \|\ \|$. We assume the trivial well-known results about complex arithmetic and $|\ |$, but for the time have lost the assurance that the complex numbers are algebraically closed. To establish that they are, we first glance at the basics of differentiation theory for functions of a complex variable.

DEFINITION 5.3.24. Let $f: X \to \mathbb{C}$ $(= \mathbb{R}^2)$, $X \subset \mathbb{C}$ be open. Then f is (complex-) differentiable at $x \in X$ iff there is a $p \in \mathbb{C}$ (called $f'(x)$) such that if $y \in X^* \sim \{x^*\}$, $y =_1 x^*$, then

$$p^* =_1 \frac{f^*(y) - f(x)^*}{y - x^*}.$$

COROLLARY 5.3.25. The usual rules for derivatives of sums, products, quotients and compositions of differentiable functions hold (see the statements of 5.2.18 and 5.2.19). If f is differentiable at x, then f is continuous at x.

Let $p \in \mathbb{C}$. Then $p\,\cdot : \mathbb{C} \to \mathbb{C}$ defined by $p \cdot (x) = px$ is clearly a linear transformation. Therefore:

COROLLARY 5.3.26. Let $f: X \to \mathbb{C}$, $X \subset \mathbb{C}$, $x \in X$, X open, f (complex-) differentiable at x with complex-derivative p. Then $p\,\cdot$ is the derivative of f in the sense of Definition 5.3.10. The "converse" also holds (i.e., if f is differentiable in the sense of Definition 5.3.10 and has derivative *of the form* $p\,\cdot$ *for some* $p \in \mathbb{C}$, then f is complex-differentiable at x with complex-derivative p). (Note that this is a statement of the Cauchy-Riemann equations.)

Therefore the following is immediate from 5.3.15:

PROPOSITION 5.3.27. Let $f: \mathcal{O} \to \mathbb{C}$, $x \in \mathcal{O}$ open, $\mathcal{O} \subset \mathbb{C}$, f' be continuous on $\mathcal{O}$, $f'(x) \neq 0$. Then for some open $\mathcal{P} \subset \mathcal{O}$, $x \in \mathcal{P}$, $f[\mathcal{P}]$ is open, f is one-one on $\mathcal{P}$ and for $y \in f[\mathcal{P}]$, $(f^{-1})'(y) = f'(z)^{-1}$, where $y = f(z)$.

LEMMA 5.3.28. Let $\mathfrak{K} = \mathbb{R}$ or $\mathbb{C}$, $Y \subset \mathfrak{K}$ be closed, $f \in \mathfrak{K}[X]$ (the polynomials over $\mathfrak{K}$). Then $f[Y]$ is closed. (NOTE: For $\mathbb{C}$, we let $St = st$.)

Proof: Let $f = a_0 + \cdots + a_n X^n$, $y \in Y^* \sim \mathcal{D}st$. Then

$$f^*(y) = (a_0^* y^{-n} + \cdots + a_n^*)y^n$$

and

$$a_0^* y^{-n} + \cdots + a_n^* =_1 a_n^* \neq_1 0,$$

so $f^*(y) \notin \mathcal{D}st$ (otherwise

$$y^n = \frac{f^*(y)}{a_0^* y^{-n} + \cdots + a_n^*} \in \mathcal{D}st).$$

Now let $z \in st[f[Y]^*]$. Then $z^* =_1 f^*(y)$, $y \in Y^*$, and by the above, $y \in \mathcal{D}st$, so let $y =_1 u^*$. But since Y is closed, $u \in Y$. By the continuity of f, $f^*(y) =_1 f(u)^*$, so $z^* =_1 f(u)^*$, thus $z = f(u) \in f[Y]$.

We now assume the easily established fact that if $X \subset \mathbb{C}$ is finite then $\mathbb{C} \sim X$ is connected.

THEOREM 5.3.29. $\mathbb{C}$ is algebraically closed.

Proof: Let $f \in \mathbb{C}[X]$,

$$S = \mathbb{C} \sim \{x \mid f'(x) = 0\}, \qquad T = \mathbb{C} \sim \{f(x) \mid f'(x) = 0\}.$$

By the inverse function theorem (or 5.3.27), $f[S] \cap T$ is open. But

$$\begin{aligned} f[S] \cap T &= f[\mathbb{C} \sim \{x \mid f'(x) = 0\}] \cap T \\ &\supset (f[\mathbb{C}] \sim \{f(x) \mid f'(x) = 0\}) \cap T \\ &= f[\mathbb{C}] \cap T, \end{aligned}$$

so $f[S] \cap T = f[\mathbb{C}] \cap T$. Thus $f[S] \cap T$ is both open and closed in T, and by the standard definition of connectedness, it remains only to show that $f[S] \cap T \neq \phi$. But if $\deg(f) \geq 1$, $S \neq \phi$, so $f[S] \neq \phi$ and is open. Thus $f[S]$ is infinite so $f[S] \cap T \neq \phi$.

Problems

‡5.3.1 (a) Prove Lemma 5.3.1 and Theorems 5.3.2 through 5.3.4.

(b) Show that $\| \ \|_1$, $\| \ \|_2$ of the second part of the proof of 5.3.5 are norms. (HINT: To show that

$$\inf(\{\| \langle a_1, \ldots, a_n \rangle \| \mid a_n \in \mathbb{R}\}) \neq 0$$

where one of $a_1, \ldots, a_{n-1} \neq 0$, let

$$\| \langle a_1^*, \ldots, a_{n-1}^*, a_n \rangle \| =_1 0, \qquad a_n \in \mathbb{R}^*.$$

If $a_n \in \mathscr{D}st$, then

$$\| \langle a_1^*, \ldots, a_{n-1}^*, a_n \rangle \| =_1 \| \langle a_1, \ldots, a_{n+1}, st(a_n) \rangle \|^*$$

(why?), a contradiction. If $a_n \notin \mathscr{D}st$, consider $(1/a_n)\langle a_1^*, \ldots, a_{n-1}^*, a_n \rangle$.)

‡5.3.2 Show that Theorem 5.3.12 implies that if f is continuously differentiable on some open set containing x, then for $y, z \in m(x)$,

$$f^*(z) - f^*(y) = f'^*(y)(z - y) + \xi^*(y, z - y)\|z - y\|$$

with $\xi^*(y, z - y) =_1 0$. (HINT: Let

$$h(z) = f^*(z) - f^*(y) + f'^*(y)(z - y)$$

and use 5.3.12—why does it apply?)

5.3.3 ‡(a) Show Lemma 5.3.11.

(b) If x is in the interior of $\mathscr{D}f$, then $f'(x)$, if it exists is given by the matrix of partials. That is, if $(y_1, \ldots, y_n) \in \mathbb{R}^n$, then

$$f'(x)((y_1, \ldots, y_n)) = \begin{pmatrix} (\partial f_1/\partial x_1) & \cdots & (\partial f_1/\partial x_n) \\ \cdot & \cdots & \cdot \\ \cdot & \cdots & \cdot \\ \cdot & \cdots & \cdot \\ (\partial f_m/\partial x_1) & \cdots & (\partial f_m/\partial x_n) \end{pmatrix} \begin{pmatrix} y_1 \\ \cdot \\ \cdot \\ \cdot \\ y_n \end{pmatrix}$$

where $\partial f_i/\partial x_j = f'_{ij}$, f_{ij} is a real function of a real variable defined on an open set about x_j (where $x = (x_1, \ldots, x_n)$) by

$$f_{ij}(y) = f_i((x_1, \ldots, x_{j-1}, y, x_{j+1}, \ldots, x_n)),$$

and $f_i(z)$ is the ith coordinate of $f(z)$.

(c) If x is in the interior of $\mathscr{D}f$ and the partials defined above exist and are continuous on some open set containing x, then $f'(x)$ exists and is given by the matrix of partials.

‡5.3.4 (a) Complete the proof of Lemma 5.3.18.
(b) Prove Proposition 5.3.21 (c) and the comment following it.

‡5.3.5 (a) Show Definition 5.3.24 and Corollary 5.3.25.
(b) Establish Corollary 5.3.26.

‡5.3.6 Show the easily established fact that if X is finite then $\mathbb{C} \sim X$ is connected. (HINT: Any two points of $\mathbb{C} \sim X$ are almost connected by a line in that set.)

‡5.3.7 Let $T \in H(\mathbb{R}^n, \mathbb{R}^n)$, $\mathscr{O} \subset \mathbb{R}^n$, $x: \mathscr{O} \to \mathbb{R}^n$. The series $\sum_{n=0}^{\infty} (U - T)^n(x_n)$ is said to have radius of convergence $r > 0$ iff $\sum_{n=0}^{\infty} s^n \|x_n\|$ converges for $0 \le s < r$, and r is the largest number for which this holds.

(a) Let $\sum_{n=0}^{\infty} (U - T)^n(x_n)$ have radius of convergence r and define $f, f_m: B(T, r) \to \mathbb{R}^n$, where

$$B(T, r) = \{U \mid \|U - T\| < r\}$$

by

$$f(U) = \sum_{n=0}^{\infty} (U - T)^n(x_n), \qquad f_m(U) = \sum_{n=0}^{m} (U - T)^n(x_n).$$

Show that f_m approaches f uniformly on

$$B^-(T, s) = \{U \mid \|T - U\|\} \le s \qquad \text{for every} \quad s < r.$$

Thus f is continuous.

(b) If $T - V$ is in the center of $H(\mathbb{R}^n, \mathbb{R}^n)$ (where the center of a ring is composed of those elements that commute with all elements under multiplication), then $\sum_{p=0}^{\infty} (U - V)^p(y_p)$ is a series with radius of convergence at least $r - \|T - V\|$, where

$$y_p = \sum_{n=0}^{\infty} \left(\frac{n!}{p!(n-p)!}\right) (V - T)^{n-p}(x_n).$$

Furthermore when $\|U - V\| < r - \|T - V\|$, $f(U)$ exists and

$$f(U) = \sum_{p=0}^{\infty} (U - V)^p(y_p).$$

(NOTE: You must show that for each n the series for y_n converges, you need the ability to "reshuffle" terms, but 5.2.30 allows this.)

(c) f has derivatives of all orders at T and $f^{(n)}(T) = \cdot n!\, x_n$, where for $y \in \mathbb{R}^n$, $\cdot y \in H(H(\mathbb{R}^n, \mathbb{R}^n), \mathbb{R}^n)$ is defined by $\cdot y(U) = U(y)$. Combining this with (b), we see that f is differentiable at each V with $\|T - V\| < r$, $T - V$ in the center of $H(\mathbb{R}^n, \mathbb{R}^n)$, and that

$$f^{(p)}(V) = \cdot\sum_{n=0}^{\infty} \left(\frac{n!}{(n-p)!}\right)(V - T)^{n-p}(x_n),$$

the result of "differentiating term-by-term" p times.

(d) If $f^*(V) \in {}^*[\mathbb{R}^n]$ for some $V =_1 T^*$ with $V - T^* \in U(\mathbb{R}^n)^*$, then f is constant.

(e) If f is not a constant then $f^*[m(T)] = m(f(T))$.

The above clearly specializes to real and complex power series.

‡5.3.8 Let C, D_n: $[a, b] \to \mathbb{R}^p$ be rectifiable curves. We say $\lim_{n\to\infty} D_n = C$ iff $D_n \to C$ uniformly and $\lim_{n\to\infty} L(D_n) = L(C)$. Let $\mathcal{O} \subset \mathbb{R}^p$ be open.

(a) Let $f\colon \mathcal{O} \to \mathbb{R}$ be continuous, C, D_n: $[a, b] \to \mathcal{O}$ be rectifiable curves, $\lim_{n\to\infty} D_n = C$, and let $\int_{D_n} f\, dx_j$ exist for each n. Then $\int_C f\, dx_j$ exists and is $\lim_{n\to\infty} \int_{D_n} f\, dx_j$.

(b) If C is rectifiable, then $C = \lim_{n\to\infty} C_n$, where C_n: $[a, b] \to \mathbb{R}^n$ is defined by

$$C_n\left(a + \frac{k+t}{n}(b-a)\right) = (1-t)C\left(a + \frac{k}{n}(b-a)\right) + tC\left(a + \frac{k+1}{n}(b-a)\right)$$

$$\text{for } k = 0, \ldots, n-1, \quad t \in [0, 1].$$

Now show that for $f\colon \mathcal{O} \to \mathbb{R}$ continuous, $C\colon [a, b] \to \mathcal{O}$ rectifiable, $\int_C f\, dx_j$ always exists.

(c) If C, $\mathcal{O}$ are as in (b), $f\colon \mathcal{O} \to \mathbb{R}$; is continuous, then $\int_C f$ exists, and if a g exists satisfying the conditions of Proposition 5.3.23 then

$$\int_C f = g(C(b)) - g(C(a)).$$

‡5.3.9 If $\int_C f = 0$ for every rectifiable closed curve C such that $\mathcal{R}C \subset \mathcal{O}$, where $f\colon \mathcal{O} \to \mathbb{R}^n$, $\mathcal{O} \subset \mathbb{R}^n$ open, f continuous, then for some $g\colon \mathcal{O} \to \mathbb{R}$, $\partial g/\partial x_i = f_i$ on $\mathcal{O}$ for $i = 1, \ldots, n$. (PROOF: Let $a \in \mathcal{O}$ and define $g\colon \mathcal{O} \to \mathbb{R}$ by $g(z) = \int_C f$ for some, thus all (why?) rectifiable curves with initial point a and final point z. Now note that

$$\frac{\partial g}{\partial x_i} = st\left(\frac{\int^*_{C^*+L(z,\,z+hi'')} f^* - (\int_C f)^*}{h}\right)$$

for $0 \neq h$, $0 =_1 h \in \mathbb{R}^*$, where $i'' = (0, \ldots, 0, 1, 0, \ldots, 0)$, 1 in the ith place, and from this show that $\partial g/\partial x_i = f_i$.)

‡5.3.10 Let C, C' be rectifiable curves, $C \doteq C'$, $f\colon X \to \mathbb{R}$ continuous, $C \subset X$. Then $\int_C f\, dx_i = \int_{C'} f\, dx_i$ for $i = 1, \ldots, n$.

5.3.11 Write $a + bi$ as

$$\begin{bmatrix} a \\ b \end{bmatrix}.$$

Show that

$$(c + di)(a + bi) = \begin{bmatrix} c & -d \\ d & c \end{bmatrix} \begin{bmatrix} a \\ b \end{bmatrix},$$

thus the matrix of $(c + di) \cdot$ is

$$\begin{bmatrix} c & -d \\ d & c \end{bmatrix}.$$

Use this, Corollary 5.3.26 and Problem 5.3.3 (b) to show a more common statement of the Cauchy-Riemann equations.

Let $f = \operatorname{re} f + i \cdot \operatorname{im} f$, $\mathscr{R} \operatorname{re} f$, $\mathscr{R} \operatorname{im} f \subset \mathbb{R}$. f is complex-differentiable at $z \in \mathbb{C}$ iff f is real-differentiable at z and

$$\frac{\partial \operatorname{re} f}{\partial x} = \frac{\partial \operatorname{im} f}{\partial y}, \qquad \frac{\partial \operatorname{im} f}{\partial x} = -\frac{\partial \operatorname{re} f}{\partial y}.$$

In this case the complex derivative of f is

$$\frac{\partial \operatorname{re} f}{\partial x} + i \frac{\partial \operatorname{im} f}{\partial x}.$$

5.4 Complex Analysis

The bit of complex analysis studied at the end of the previous section was introduced largely as an application of the inverse function theorem. Here we study some of the deeper results of complex analysis. Below

$$\operatorname{re}(a + bi) = a, \qquad \operatorname{im}(a + bi) = b.$$

DEFINITION 5.4.1. $L(w, z)$ is a re-line iff $\operatorname{im}(w) = \operatorname{im}(z)$, and an im-line iff $\operatorname{re}(w) = \operatorname{re}(z)$. Let $z_1, \ldots, z_n \in \mathbb{C}$, $n \geq 2$. Then

$$P(z_1, \ldots, z_n) = L(z_1, z_2) + \cdots + L(z_{n-1}, z_n)$$

and is called a polygon (the polygon with vertices $z_1, \ldots, z_n$ if we wish to be more specific), an HV-gon if each of $L(z_1, z_2), \ldots, L(z_{n-1}, z_n)$ is either a re-line or an im-line.

A curve $C: [a, b] \to \mathbb{C}$ is called closed iff $C(b) = C(a)$, Jordan iff closed and $C \mid [a, b)$ is one-one. Now let $P(z_1, \ldots, z_n) = C_{-}$. Then $P(z_1, \ldots, z_n)$ is called closed or Jordan iff C is (this is a good definition, see 5.3.18).

For closed curves we adopt the following convention: Let $c, d \in [a, b]$. If $c < d$, $f \mid [c, d]$ is defined as usual, but

$$f \mid [d, c] = f \mid [a, c] \cup [d, b], \qquad f[[d, c]] = \mathscr{R} f \mid [d, c],$$

and a similar convention is adopted for (d, c).

LEMMA 5.4.2. If P is a Jordan HV-gon there are two open connected sets $E(P)$, $I(P)$ such that:

(i) $E(P) \cup I(P) \cup \mathscr{R}P = \mathbb{C}$, a disjoint union;
(ii) $E(P)^- = E(P) \cup \mathscr{R}P$, $I(P)^- = I(P) \cup \mathscr{R}P$;
(iii) if $\mathscr{R}P \subset \{x \mid |x| \leq m\}$ $(= B^-(0, m))$, then $I(P) \subset B^-(0, m)$.

Proof: If $P = P(z_1, \ldots, z_4, z_1)$ is a rectangle, we may set $z_1 = a + bi$, $z_2 = a + di$, $z_3 = c + di$, $z_4 = c + bi$ with $a < c$, $b < d$. Then

$$I(P) = \{x + yi \mid a < x < c, b < y < d\},$$
$$E(P) = \{x + yi \mid x < a \text{ or } c < x \text{ or } y < b \text{ or } d < y\}$$

fulfill our conditions.

We proceed by induction on n, where $P = P(z_1, \ldots, z_n, z_1)$. $n > 4$ thus at least three of the lines $L(z_1, z_2), \ldots, L(z_n, z_1)$ are re-lines or three are im-lines. Assume three im-lines $L(z_j, z_{j+1})$, $L(z_{j_1}, z_{j_1+1})$, $L(z_{j_2}, z_{j_2+1})$ [from now on, we count mod n in situations of this sort, so for example $L(z_n, z_1)$ is of this form], and assume that

$$\text{re}(z_{j_1}) \leq \text{re}(z_j) \leq \text{re}(z_{j_2}).$$

Since $\mathscr{R}P = \mathscr{R}P(z_j, \ldots, z_n, z_1, \ldots, z_j)$, we may assume that $j = 1$. We also may assume that for no $k = 1, \ldots, n$ are $L(z_{k-1}, z_k)$, $L(z_k, z_{k+1})$ both im-lines, for otherwise

$$\text{if} \quad P' = P(z_1, \ldots, z_{k-1}, z_{k+1}, \ldots, z_n) \qquad \text{then} \quad \mathscr{R}P' = \mathscr{R}P,$$

so $E(P) = E(P')$, $I(P) = I(P')$ fulfill our conditions, where the latter exist by induction. If $\text{re}(z_{j_q}) = \text{re}(z_1)$ for $q = 1$ or 2, then

$$\{z \mid \text{re}(z) = \text{re}(z_1)\} \cap A \neq \phi, \qquad \text{where} \quad A = \mathscr{R}P \sim \mathscr{R}L(z_1, z_2)$$

if not, by the connectedness of A and the fact that

$$A \cap \{z \mid \text{re}(z) < \text{re}(z_1)\} \neq \phi \neq \{z \mid \text{re}(z) > \text{re}(z_1)\} \cap A,$$

we still have that

$$A \cap \{z \mid \text{re}(z) = \text{re}(z_1)\} \neq \phi.$$

So let $\text{re}(z) = \text{re}(z_1)$, $z \in \mathscr{R}P$, $z \notin \mathscr{R}L(z_1, z_2)$. Of the two similar cases

$$|z - z_1| < |z - z_2|, \qquad |z - z_2| < |z - z_1|$$

we consider only the first. Since $L(z_n, z_1)$ is not an im-line there is a least $t \in (0, 1]$ such that $tz + (1 - t)z_1 \in \mathscr{R}P$; let this point be z_{n+1}. Our assumption $|z - z_1| < |z - z_2|$ and choice of z_{n+1} assure us that

$$P_1 = P(z_1, z_{n+1}, z_{k+1}, \ldots, z_n, z_1), \qquad P_2 = P(z_{n+1}, z_1, \ldots, z_k, z_{n+1})$$

are Jordan HV-gons, where $z_{n+1} \in \mathscr{R}l(z_k, z_{k+1})$ (slight alterations are required if $z_{n+1} \in \{z_1, \ldots, z_n\}$), and since k must be at least 4 and at most

$n - 2$, P_1 has $n - k + 3 < n$ vertices and P_2 has $k + 1 < n$ vertices, so we have $E(P_1)$, $I(P_1)$, $E(P_2)$, $I(P_2)$.

$$Q_1 = \mathscr{R}P_1 \sim \mathscr{R}L(z_1, z_{n+1}), \qquad Q_2 = \mathscr{R}P_2 \sim L(z_1, z_{n+1})$$

are connected sets, and for $j = 1, 2$,

$$Q_j \cap \mathscr{R}P_{3-j} = \phi \quad \text{so} \quad Q_j \subset E(P_{3-j}) \quad \text{or} \quad Q_j \subset I(P_{3-j}).$$

This apparently gives rise to four situations. The following illustrates the three possible cases involved in the induction step of the proof of Lemma 5.4.2.

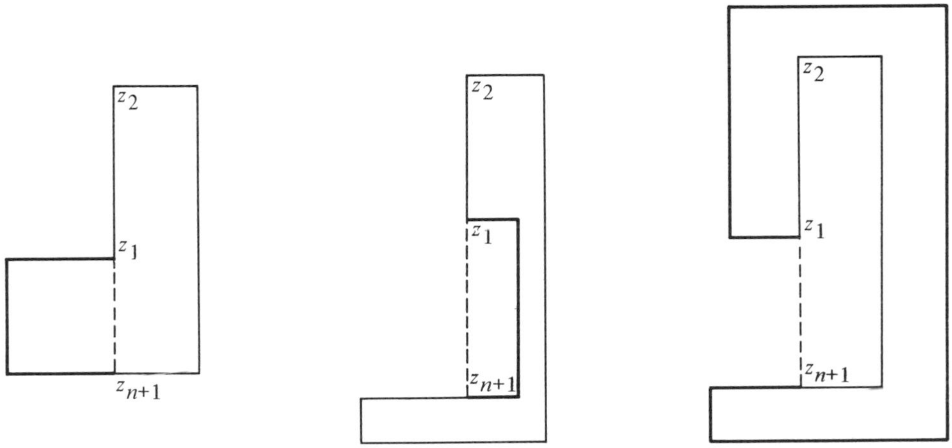

$Q_1 \subset E(P_2)$, $Q_2 \subset E(P_1)$ (in which case $E(P) = E(P_1) \cap E(P_2)$, $I(P) = I(P_1) \cup I(P_2) \cup \mathscr{R}l(z_1, z_{n+1})$ satisfy our conditions);
$Q_1 \subset I(P_2)$, $Q_2 \subset E(P_1)$ (here $E(P) = E(P_2) \cup I(P_1) \cup \mathscr{R}l(z_1, z_{n+1})$, $I(P) = I(P_2) \cap E(P_1)$ work);
$Q_1 \subset E(P_2)$, $Q_2 \subset I(P_1)$ (and $E(P) = E(P_1) \cup I(P_2) \cup \mathscr{R}l(z_1, z_{n+1})$, $I(P) = I(P_1) \cap E(P_2)$ here);

and

$Q_1 \subset I(P_2)$, $Q_2 \subset I(P_1)$ (but this case is impossible since if $Q_1 \subset I(P_2)$ let $z \in Q_1$, then $m(z) \subset I(P_2)^*$, and since $Q_1 \subset E(P_1)^-$, $m(z) \cap E(P_1)^* \neq \phi$, thus $E(P_1) \cap I(P_2) \neq \phi$. If $Q_2 \subset I(P_1)$, then $\mathscr{R}P_2 \cap E(P_1) = \phi$, thus $E(P_1) \subset E(P_2) \cup I(P_2)$, $E(P_1)$ is connected, and

$$E(P_1) \cap I(P_2) \neq \phi, \qquad \text{so} \qquad E(P_1) \subset I(P_2),$$

a contradiction since $E(P_1)$ is unbounded, $I(P_2)$ bounded.)

Clearly some of the details have been left for the reader (see Problem 5.4.1).

It is easy to see that if P is a Jordan HV-gon (or any Jordan curve with an interior and exterior) and $\mathcal{O}$, $\mathcal{P}$ are nonempty open sets such that $\mathcal{O} \cup \mathcal{P} \cup \mathcal{R}P = \mathbb{C}$, a disjoint union, then $\mathcal{O}$, $\mathcal{P}$ are (in some order) $I(P)$ and $E(P)$. Using this, we can show that if $p_1, p_2 \in \mathcal{R}P$ are respectively the initial and final points of a one-one HV-gon Q with

$$\mathcal{R}Q \sim \{p_1, p_2\} \subset I(P), \qquad p_1 = f(t_1), \qquad p_2 = f(t_2), \qquad P = f_{\underline{-}},$$

then

$$Q_1 = Q + (f \mid [t_2, t_1])_{\underline{-}}, \qquad Q_2 = {}^{-}Q + (f \mid [t_1, t_2])_{\underline{-}}$$

are Jordan HV-gons and $I(P) = I(Q_1) \cup I(Q_2) \cup (\mathcal{R}Q \sim \{p_1, p_2\},)$ a disjoint union, and $E(P) = E(Q_1) \cap E(Q_2)$. This last fact is used in our proof of the Jordan separation theorem (5.4.7), and can be shown using only the fact that the interiors and exteriors referred to above exist.

Definition 5.4.3. Let $C: [a, b] \to \mathbb{C}$, $a \leq c < d \leq b$, $\{a, b\} \neq \{c, d\}$. Then

$$C/[c, d] = C \mid [a, c] + C \mid [d, b], \qquad C/ = \bigcup_{n \in \omega} C/(n),$$

where $C/(0) = \{C\}$, $C/(n + 1) = C/(n) \cup \{D/[r, s] \mid D: [e, f] \to \mathbb{C}, D \in C/(n), D(r) = D(s), e \leq r < s \leq f, \{e, f\} \neq \{r, s\}\}$.

Let $A \subset [a, b]$, $C: [a, b] \to \mathbb{C}$. Then C is strongly one-one on A iff for each $t \in A$, $t' \in [a, b]$, if $C(t) = C(t')$ then $t = t'$.

Let $P = P(z_0, \ldots, z_n)$. Then $SP: [0, 1] \to \mathbb{C}$ is defined by

$$SP((k + t)/n) = z_k + t(z_{k+1} - z_k) \quad \text{for } k = 0, \ldots, n - 1, \; t \in [0, 1].$$

For example, if the curve C can be represented by the following picture:

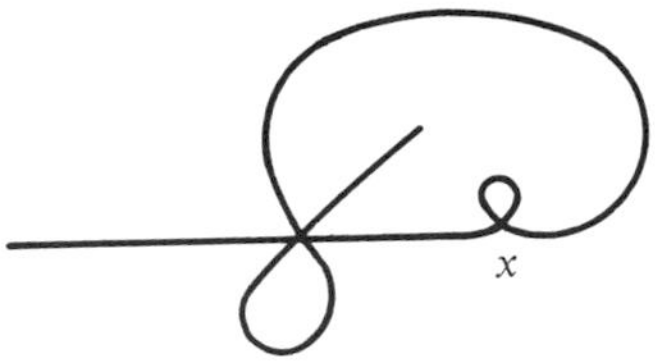

$$x = C(c) = C(d)$$

Then $C/[c, d]$ can be represented by:

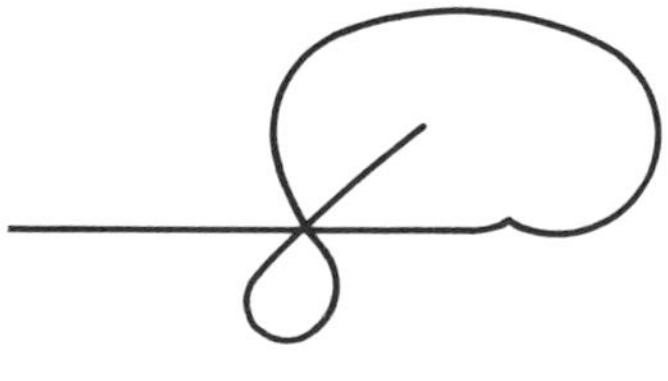

and $C/$ can be represented by:

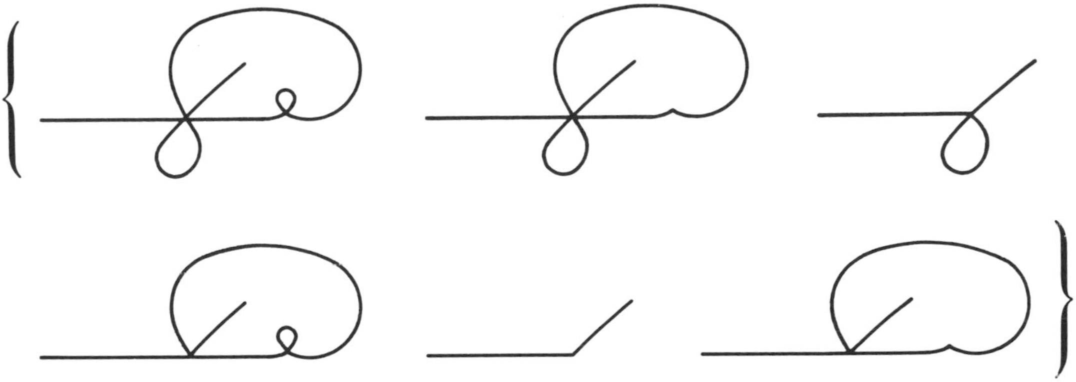

Let $D \in C/$. If C is continuous, so is D and if $C_{\underline{-}} = P(z_1, \ldots, z_n)$, $D \neq C$, then for some $m < n$, $z'_1, \ldots, z'_m$, $D_{\underline{-}} = P(z'_1, \ldots, z'_m)$. If C is an HV-gon then so is D.

$$(SP(z_0, \ldots, z_n))_{\underline{-}} = P(z_0, \ldots, z_n)$$

and if $z_j \neq z_{j+1}$, $SP(z_0, \ldots, z_n) \mid [j/n, (j + 1)/n]$ is one-one.

LEMMA 5.4.4. Let C: $[a, b] \to \mathbb{C}$, $C_{\underline{-}}$ be a polygon.

(a) If $\phi \neq (r, s) \subset [a, b]$, C strongly one-one on $[r, s]$ then for some $D \in C/$, $c, d \in \mathscr{D}D$, $c < d$,

$$C[[r, s]] \subset D[[c, d]] \ (\subset \mathscr{R}C)$$

and either:

(i) $D(c) = C(a)$, $D(d) = C(b)$, $\mathscr{D}D = [c, d]$ and D is one-one, or
(ii) $D \mid [c, d]$ is Jordan.

(b) If $C(a) \neq C(b)$ then for some $D \in C/$,

$$D\colon [c, d] \to \mathbb{C}, \qquad D(c) = C(a), \qquad D(d) = C(b),$$

and $D_{\underline{-}}$ is a one-one polygon.

Proof: (a) It will do to show our result for $SP = SP(z_0, \ldots, z_n)$, which we do by induction on n. Our result is clear if $n = 1$, for then $D = SP(z_0, z_1)$, $c = 0$, $d = 1$. If $n \geq 2$, let

$$\mathscr{M} = \{(w', x') \mid (r, s) \subset (w', x') \subset (a, b) \text{ and } SP \text{ is strongly one-one on } (w', x')\}.$$

$\mathscr{M}$ contains the nonempty interval (r, s) and is closed under ascending unions, thus let $(w, x) \neq \phi$ be maximal in $\mathscr{M}$.

If $[w, x] \neq [0, 1]$, we show that SP is not strongly one-one on $[w, x]$;

by way of contradiction, assume SP strongly one-one on $[w, x] \subsetneq [0, 1]$. Then $w \neq 0$ or $x \neq 1$, so let $0 < w$; let

$$\frac{j}{n} < w \leq \frac{j+1}{n}, \qquad \frac{k}{n} \leq x < \frac{k+1}{n},$$

$$\delta = \inf\{|z - y| \mid z = SP(w), y \in \mathscr{R}P(z_0, \ldots, z_j) \cup \mathscr{R}P(z_k, \ldots, z_n)\} > 0$$

and by continuity choose $0 < \varepsilon \leq w$ such that if $|w - t| < \varepsilon$, then

$$|SP(w) - SP(t)| < \delta.$$

If $t \in (w - \varepsilon, x)$, $t' \in [0, 1]$, and $SP(t) = SP(t')$, then $t = t'$ or $t \in (w - \varepsilon, w)$, thus

$$SP(t) \in \mathscr{R}SP \sim (SP[[w, x]] \cup \mathscr{R}P(z_0, \ldots, z_j) \cup \mathscr{R}P(z_k, \ldots, z_n))$$

and therefore $t', t \in [j/n, (j+1)/n]$, thus $t = t'$ in any case. Thus SP is strongly one-one on $(w - \varepsilon, x)$ contradicting the maximality of (w, x). The case $x < 1$ is similar.

Since SP is not strongly one-one on $[w, x]$ (unless $[w, x] = [0, 1]$, in which case $D = SP$, $w = c = a$, $x = d = b$), either

$$SP(x) = SP(t) \qquad \text{for some} \quad t \neq x,$$

or

$$SP(w) = SP(t) \qquad \text{for some} \quad t \neq w;$$

assume the first. If $x < t$, let $C' = SP/[x, t]$, then C' is strongly one-one on $[r, s]$ and by induction for some $D \in C'/ \subset SP/$, $c, d \in \mathscr{D}D$,

$$SP[[r, s]] = C'[[r, s]] \subset D[[c, d]],$$

and either

$$D(c) = C'(0) = SP(0), \qquad D(d) = C'(1 + x - t) = SP(1),$$

D one-one, $\mathscr{D}D = [c, d]$, or D is Jordan. If $t < x$, then $t \leq w$ (since $SP \mid [w, x]$ is one-one); in this case either $SP \mid [t, x]$ is Jordan (in which case $D = SP$, $c = t$, $d = x$) or for some t', t'', $t \leq t' < t'' \leq w$, $SP(t') = SP(t'')$. In this last case let $C' = SP/[t', t'']$; then C' is strongly one-one on $[r + t' - t'', s + t' - t'']$ and again we find D by induction (the reader may check details). The case $SP(t) = SP(w)$, $t \neq w$ is similar to the case just discussed. This completes the induction step and thus (a).

For (b), let $a' \in [a, b]$ be largest such that $C(a') = C(a)$ (a' exists because $C^{-1}[C[\{a\}]]$ is compact), and if $a' \neq a$, let $C' = C/[a, a']$, then by induction we have a one-one $D \in C'/ \subset C/$ such that

$$D\colon [c, d] \to \mathbb{C}, \qquad D(c) = C'(a) = C(a),$$

$$D(d) = C'(b + a - a') = C(b).$$

Otherwise the reader may check that for some $r \in (a, b]$, C is strongly one-one on $[a, r]$. Then by (a) there is a $D \in C/$ such that

$$D\colon [c, d] \to \mathbb{C}, \qquad D(c) = C(a), \qquad \text{and} \qquad D(d) = C(b)$$

(the other possibility in (a) cannot occur since if $C[[a, r]] \subset D[[c, d]]$, $c = a$, thus $D(d) = C(a)$, which is impossible since $C(x) \neq C(a)$ for $x \in (a, b]$; on this see Problem 5.4.8).

LEMMA 5.4.5. If P is a polygon and $\mathscr{R}P \subset \mathscr{D}st$, then $st[\mathscr{R}P]$ is connected.†

Proof: Let

$$st[\mathscr{R}P] \subset \mathscr{O} \cup \mathscr{P}, \qquad \mathscr{O} \cap \mathscr{P} \cap st[\mathscr{R}P] = \phi,$$
$$\mathscr{O} \cap st[\mathscr{R}P] \neq \phi \neq \mathscr{P} \cap st[\mathscr{R}P],$$

$\mathscr{O}$, $\mathscr{P}$ be open. If $x \in \mathscr{R}P$, $x =_1 (stx)^*$, $stx \in st[\mathscr{R}P]$, so $(stx)^* \in \mathscr{O}^* \cup \mathscr{P}^*$, thus $x \in \mathscr{O}^* \cup \mathscr{P}^*$, therefore $\mathscr{R}P \subset \mathscr{O}^* \cup \mathscr{P}^*$. Let $P = P(z_1, \ldots, z_m)$; if $z_m \in \mathscr{P}^*$, let

$$k = \max\{j \mid \mathscr{R}L(z_{j-1}, z_j) \cap \mathscr{P}^* = \phi\} < m$$

(we leave for the reader the construction of appropriate formulas to show that such a max exists). Thus $z_k \in \mathscr{R}L(z_{k-1}, z_k) \subset \mathscr{O}^*$ so

$$z_k \in \mathscr{O}^*, \qquad \mathscr{R}L(z_k, z_{k+1}) \cap \mathscr{P}^* \neq \phi.$$

Since $z_k \in \mathscr{D}st$, $st(z_k) \in \mathscr{O} \cup \mathscr{P}$ but must be in $\mathscr{O}$ since otherwise $z_k \in \mathscr{P}^*$, a contradiction. Thus $(st(z_k))^* \in \mathscr{O}^*$, but

$$st[\mathscr{R}L(z_k, z_{k+1})] = \mathscr{R}L(st(z_k), st(z_{k+1})),$$
$$(1 - t)st(z_k) + tst(z_{k+1}) \in \mathscr{P}$$

for some $t \in [0, 1]$, so

$$\mathscr{O} \cap \mathscr{R}L(st(z_k), st(z_{k+1})) \neq \phi \neq \mathscr{P} \cap \mathscr{R}L(st(z_k), st(z_{k+1})),$$

a contradiction since lines are connected.

Unbounded polygons and bounded continuous images of intervals need not have the above property.

If $C\colon [a, b] \to \mathbb{C}$ is a Jordan or one-one curve, we call a set of the form $C[(r, s)]$ an open interval in $\mathscr{R}C_-$. Note that $\phi = C[(r, r)]$, $\mathscr{R}C = C[(a - 1, b + 1)]$ are open intervals in $\mathscr{R}C$, and that the above is a good definition, for if $C_- = D_-$ then $\mathscr{R}C = \mathscr{R}D$ is an open interval in both, and $C[(r, s)] = D[(h(r), h(s))]$, where h is defined as in the proof of Lemma 5.3.18(b).

† See Problem 5.4.9 and Proposition 5.2.1 (a).

LEMMA 5.4.6. Let P be a Jordan HV-gon, Q a polygon. Then $I(P) \cap \mathscr{R}Q$ is a finite union of open intervals in $\mathscr{R}Q$. The same holds for $E(P) \cap \mathscr{R}Q$.

Proof: Let $Q = P(z_1, \ldots, z_n)$, we use induction on n. The openness of $I(P)$ $(E(P))$ and the fact that SQ is continuous from $[0, 1]$ to $\mathscr{R}Q$ tell us that $\mathscr{R}Q$ is a disjoint union of open intervals in $\mathscr{R}Q$, and it is clear that their endpoints must be in $\mathscr{R}P \cup \{SQ(0), SQ(1)\}$. But if $P = P(y_1, \ldots, y_m, y_1)$, it is clear that if $n = 2$ at most one of these points comes from each of

$$\mathscr{R}l(y_1, y_2), \ldots, \mathscr{R}l(y_m, y_1), \qquad \{y_1\}, \ldots, \{y_m\}.$$

If $n = 2$, thus there is in this case a finite number of such endpoints, therefore a finite number of such intervals. If $n > 2$,

$$I(P) \cap \mathscr{R}Q = (I(P) \cap \mathscr{R}L(z_1, z_2)) \cup \cdots \cup (I(P) \cap \mathscr{R}L(z_{n-1}, z_n)),$$

a disjoint of open intervals in $\mathscr{R}Q$ (and the same induction step holds for $E(P) \cap \mathscr{R}Q$).

THEOREM 5.4.7 (Jordan Separation Theorem). Let $C: [a, b] \to \mathbb{C}$ be a Jordan curve. Then there are two open, connected sets $E(C)$, $I(C)$ such that

(i) $E(C) \cup I(C) \cup \mathscr{R}C = \mathbb{C}$, a disjoint union;
(ii) $E(C)^- = E(C) \cup \mathscr{R}C$, $I(C)^- = I(C) \cup \mathscr{R}C$;
(iii) $E(C)$ is unbounded, $I(C)$ bounded.

Proof: We assume $a = 0$, $b = 1$ (by replacing C with $C \circ \kappa$, where $\kappa: [0, 1] \to [a, b]$ by $\kappa(t) = a + t(b - a)$). Let $m \in \omega'$, and for $n < m$, let

$$z_{2n} = C^*(n/m), \qquad z_{2n+1} = \mathrm{re}(z_{2n}) + \mathrm{im}(z_{2n+2})i$$

(if $n + 1 = m$, $z_{2n+1} = \mathrm{re}(z_{2n}) + \mathrm{im}(z_0)i$). Clearly $P(z_0, \ldots, z_{2m-1}, z_0)$ is a closed HV-gon. The following is a detail of C^* and $P(z_0, \ldots, z_{m-1}, z_0)$:

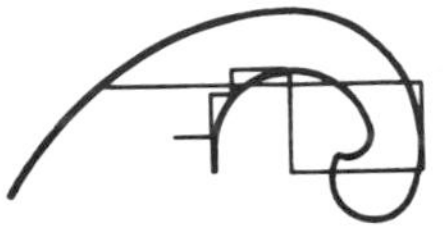

Since C is continuous and $C(0) = C(1)$, $z_j =_1 z_{j+1}$ for $j = 0, \ldots, 2m - 2$, $z_{2m-1} =_1 z_0$, and by this

$$st[\mathscr{R}P(z_0, \ldots, z_{2m-1}, z_0)] \subset \mathscr{R}C,$$

but clearly

$$\mathscr{R}C \subset st[\{z_0, \ldots, z_{2m-1}\}] \subset st[\mathscr{R}P(z_0, \ldots, z_{2m-1}, z_0)],$$

so

$$\mathscr{R}C = st[\{z_0, \ldots, z_{2m-1}\}] = st[\mathscr{R}P(z_0, \ldots, z_{2m-1}, z_0)].$$

Since $z_0 = C(0)^*$, $z_m =_1 C(1/2)^*$, and C is Jordan, $z_0 \neq z_m$. Thus if $P_1 = P(z_0, \ldots, z_m)$ by Lemma 5.4.4(b) there is a D: $[c, d] \to \mathbb{C}$, $D \in SP_1/$ such that $D_{\overline{-}}$ is a one-one HV-gon, $D(c) = z_0$, and $D(d) = z_m$.

$$\mathscr{R}D \subset \mathscr{R}P_1 \subset C[[0, 1/2]]^*$$

so

$$C^{-1}[st[\mathscr{R}D]] \subset C^{-1}[C[0, 1/2]] = [0, 1/2].$$

Since C is continuous and one-one on $[0, 1/2]$, $C \mid [0, 1/2]$ is a homeomorphism (see Problem 5.5.7); thus since $0, 1/2 \in C^{-1}[st[\mathscr{R}D]]$ and $st[\mathscr{R}D]$ is a connected set,

$$C^{-1}[st[\mathscr{R}D]] = [0, 1/2], \qquad \text{so} \qquad st[\mathscr{R}D] = C[0, 1/2].$$

$C[[1/6, 1/3]] \subset st[\mathscr{R}D]$, so we may choose q, $r \in [0, 1]$ such that $D(q) =_1 C(1/6)^*$, $D(r) =_1 C(1/3)^*$ ($q < r$ because if $SP_1(q') =_1 C(1/6)^*$, $SP_1(r') =_1 C(1/3)^*$ then $q' < r'$, see Problem 5.4.9). Let $D' = D + SP(z_m, \ldots, z_{2m-1}, z_0)$, $P_2 = D'_{\overline{-}}$. D' is strongly one-one on $[q, r]$ for if $t \in [q, r]$, $t' \in \mathscr{D}D'$, $D'(t) = \overline{D'}(t')$ then $t' \in [c, d]$ (because otherwise $D(t') \in \mathscr{R}P(z_m, \ldots, z_{2m-1}, z_0)$, thus $D(t') =_1 C(x)^*$ for some $x \in [1/2, 1]$, $D(t) =_1 C(y)^*$ for some $y \in [1/6, 1/3]$, thus $D(t) \neq D(t')$), thus $t = t'$ since $D' \mid [c, d] = D$ and D is one-one. By Lemma 5.4.4(a) we now have a Jordan HV-gon P with $D'[[q, r]] \subset \mathscr{R}P \subset \mathscr{R}D'$ (the other case is impossible since the initial and final points of D' are identical). The following details the part of C^* drawn above and P:

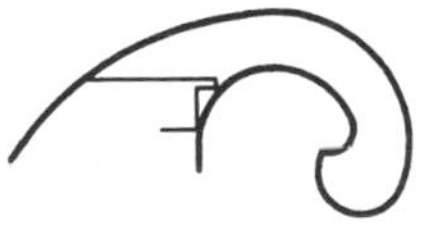

Since P is Jordan there is a subpolygon P_3 of P containing $D'(q)$, $D'(r)$ and no other points of $D'[[q, r]]$. Thus

$$st[\mathscr{R}P_3] \subset st[D'[\mathscr{D}D' \sim (q, r)]] \subset C[[0, 1] \sim (1/6, 1/3)],$$

so by reasoning involving connectedness like that used above, $st[\mathscr{R}P_3] = C[[0, 1] \sim (1/6, 1/3)]$, thus

$$\mathscr{R}C = C[[0, 1/2]] \cup C[[0, 1] \sim (1/6, 1/3)] \subset st[\mathscr{R}P],$$

and since $\mathscr{R}P \subset \mathscr{R}P(z_0, \ldots, z_{2m-1}, z_0)$, the first paragraph of this proof tells us that

$$\mathscr{R}C = st[\mathscr{R}P].$$

We have now constructed a Jordan HV-gon P such that $st[\mathscr{R}P] = \mathscr{R}C$, and we define

$$I(C) = \{x \notin \mathscr{R}C \mid x^* \in I(P)\}, \qquad E(C) = \{x \notin \mathscr{R}C \mid x^* \in E(P)\}.$$

$\mathbb{C} = E(C) \cup I(C) \cup \mathscr{R}C$ disjointly, for if $x \notin \mathscr{R}C = st[\mathscr{R}P]$, then

$$x^* \notin \mathscr{R}P, \qquad \text{thus} \quad x \in I(C) \quad \text{or} \quad x \in E(C).$$

The disjointness of $I(P)$, $E(P)$ assures the disjointness of $E(C)$, $I(C)$ and our definitions assert that

$$E(C) \cap \mathscr{R}C = \phi = I(C) \cap \mathscr{R}C.$$

$E(C)$, $I(C)$ are open, for if $x \in I(C)$ $(E(C))$, then $x \notin \mathscr{R}C$, a compact, thus closed set. Thus for some $r > 0$, if $|x - y| < r$, $y \notin \mathscr{R}C$. Also if $|x - y| < r$, $z \in \mathscr{R}L(x^*, y^*)$, then

$$|x^* - z| \leq s^* \qquad \text{for some} \quad s < r,$$

so

$$z \neq_1 (C(t))^* \qquad \text{for any} \quad t \in [a, b],$$

thus

$$z \notin \mathscr{R}P \qquad \text{so} \qquad \mathscr{R}L(x^*, y^*) \subset I(P)\ (E(P))$$

thus

$$y^* \in I(P)\ (E(P)), \qquad y \notin \mathscr{R}C$$

thus

$$y \in I(C)\ (E(C)).$$

It is clear from (iii) of 5.4.2 that $I(C)$ is bounded, and from this and (i) above it follows that $E(C)$ is unbounded. Thus we are left to show that $I(C)$, $E(C)$ are connected and (ii).

To see (ii), let $z \in \mathscr{R}C$, $0 < r \in \mathbb{R}$ be such that for some $w \in \mathscr{R}C$, $|z - w| > r$. Let S be an HV-square with center z and sides of length r. In Problem 5.4.2 the reader will show that

$$\mathscr{R}S \cap I(C) \neq \phi \neq \mathscr{R}S \cap E(C).$$

This establishes (ii) since r can be arbitrarily small.

To see $I(C)$ connected, let $x, y \in I(C)$, L_1, L_2 be vertical lines through x and y respectively. By the boundedness of $I(C)$, L_1 meets $\mathscr{R}C$ at a lowest point above x, $C(t_1)$ and a highest point below x, $C(t_2)$, and there are similar such points $C(t_3)$, $C(t_4)$ in $\mathscr{R}L_2 \cap \mathscr{R}C$. We may also assume that $t_1 = a$ (if necessary replacing C by $C \mid [t_1, b] + C \mid [a, t_1]$). For $j = 1, \ldots, 4$ either the appropriate line crosses $\mathscr{R}P$ at some closest point $z_j =_1 C(t_j)^*$ or let

$$z'_j \in \mathscr{R}P, \qquad z'_j =_1 C(t_j)^*, \qquad P'_j = P(C(t_j)^*, \operatorname{re} z'_j + \operatorname{im} C(t_j)^* i, z'_j),$$
$$z_j = SP'_j(s_j), \qquad s_j \in [0, 1]^*$$

least such that $SP'_j(s_j) \in \mathscr{R}P$. In the first case set $D^{(j)} = L(z_j, p_j)$, in the second

$$D^{(j)} = ({}^{-}SP'_j \mid [0, s_j] + SL(C(t_j)^*, p_j))_{\underline{-}},$$

where $p_1 = p_2 = x^*$, $p_3 = p_4 = y^*$. Now let

$$D_1 = D^{(1)} + {}^{-}D^{(2)}, \qquad D_2 = D^{(3)} + {}^{-}D^{(4)}.$$

For now assume $\mathscr{R}D_1 \cap \mathscr{R}D_2 = \phi$. Of the six apparently possible orders for t_2, t_3, t_4, $t_4 < t_2 < t_3$, $t_3 < t_2 < t_4$ are impossible, since if $z_1 = SP(r_1)$, $z_2 = SP(r_2)$, then

$$C_1 = D_1 + (SP|[r_2,r_1])_{\underline{-}}, \qquad C_2 = {}^{-}D_1 + (SP|[r_1,r_2])_{\underline{-}}$$

are Jordan HV-gons and

$$I(P) = I(C_1) \cup I(C_2) \cup (\mathscr{R}D_1 \sim \{z_1, z_2\})$$

by comments following the proof of 5.4.2. Then

$$\mathscr{R}D_2 \sim \{z_3, z_4\} \subset I(C_1) \quad \text{or} \quad I(C_2)$$

(since it satisfies the formal properties of connectedness in $\mathbb{C}^*$, is contained in $I(P)$, and is disjoint from $\mathscr{R}(D_1)$, assuring us that z_3, z_4 both lie in the same one of the sets $SP[[r_1, r_2]]$, $SP[[r_2, r_1]]$, thus contradicting the two orders listed above, since they require z_3, z_4 to be in distinct such sets. We now assume $t_2 < t_3 < t_4$ to complete our proof (the other three possibilities lead to identical proofs). The proof of the connectedness of $I(C)$ is motivated by the following diagram:

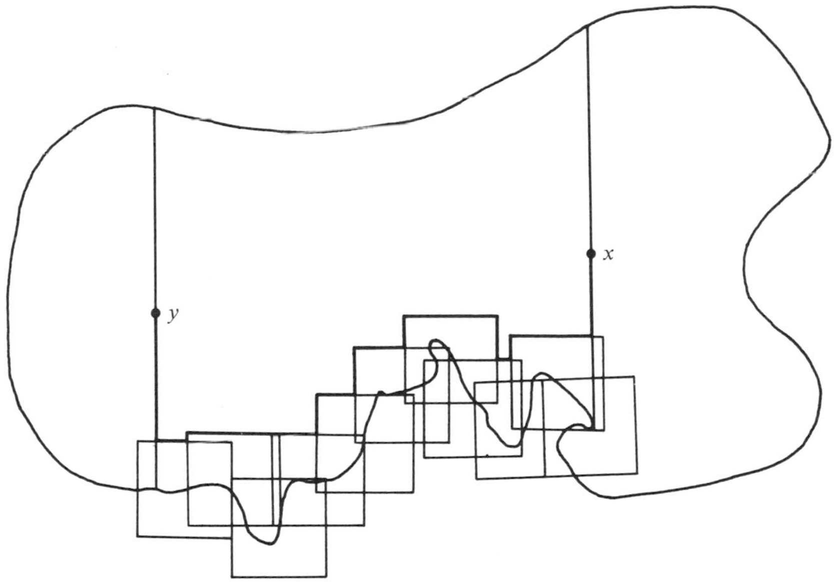

Since $C[[t_2, t_3]]$, $C[[t_4, t_1]]$ are nonintersecting compact sets, there is a positive $p \in \mathbb{R}$ such that if $u \in C[[t_2, t_3]]$ and $v \in C[[t_4, t_1]]$, then $|u - v| > p$. Also $C[[t_2, t_3]]$ can be covered by the interiors of a finite number of HV-squares $B_1, \ldots, B_n$ with sides of length $\leq p/2$. It is easy to see that

$$SP_2'[[0, s_2]] \cup SP[[r_2, r_3]] \cup SP_3'[[0, s_3]]$$

is contained in the unions of the interiors of $B_1^*, \ldots, B_n^*$. We now show that $x, y \in X \subset I(C)$ for some connected X by induction on $m = m_1 + \cdots + m_n$, m_k the number of open intervals in $I(B_k) \cap \mathscr{R}P$. Note first that

$$Q = D_1 + SP \mid [r_2, r_3] + D_2 + SP \mid [r_4, r_1]$$

is a Jordan HV-gon and $I(Q) \subset I(P)$. If $m = 1$,

$$SP[[r_2, r_3]] \subset I(B_1)^* \qquad \text{so} \qquad SP[[r_2, r_3]] \cap \mathscr{R}B_1^* = \phi,$$

and

$$SP[[r_4, r_1]] \cap \mathscr{R}B_1^* = \phi$$

as well by our choice of p. In fact,

$$\mathscr{R}B_1^* \cap \mathscr{R}Q = (\mathscr{R}B_1^* \cap \mathscr{R}L(C(t_1)^*, C(t_2)^*)) \cup (\mathscr{R}B_1^* \cap \mathscr{R}L(C(t_3)^*, C(t_4)^*)).$$

$\mathscr{R}B_1^* \cap L(C(t_1)^*, C(t_2)^*) \neq \phi$ since $C(t_2)^* \in I(B_1^*)$, $C(t_1)^* \in E(B_1^*)$, but it contains at most one point, since $\alpha < \operatorname{re} C(t_2)^* < \beta$ where α, β are the real parts of the im-lines of B_1^* (since $C(t_2)^* \in I(B_1^*)$); similarly

$$\mathscr{R}B_1^* \cap \mathscr{R}L(C(t_3)^*, C(t_4)^*)$$

is a single point; call these points $SB_1(q_1)^*$, $SB_1(q_2)^*$. Then

$$SB_1^*[[q_1^*, q_2^*]] \cap I(Q) \neq \phi \qquad \text{or} \qquad I(Q) \cap SB_1^*[[q_2^*, q_1^*]] \neq \phi,$$

not both, and for the appropriate one, say $SB_1^*[[q_1^*, q_2^*]]$,

$$SB_1^*[[q_1^*, q_2^*]] \sim \{SB_1(q_1)^*, SB_1(q_2)^*\} \subset I(Q).$$

Then

$$X = \mathscr{R}L(x, SB_1(q_1)) \cup \mathscr{R}SB_1 \mid [q_1, q_2] \cup \mathscr{R}L(SB_1(q_2), y)$$

will do, for this X is connected, $X^* \subset I(P)$ and $X \cap \mathscr{R}C = \phi$

$$(X \cap \mathscr{R}C = (\mathscr{R}L(x, SB_1(q_1)) \cap \mathscr{R}C) \cup (SB_1[[q_1, q_2]] \cap \mathscr{R}C) \cup (\mathscr{R}L(SB_1(q_2), y) \cap \mathscr{R}C)$$

and the first of these is empty since

$$\mathscr{R}L(x, SB_1(q_1)) \subset \mathscr{R}1(C(t_1), C(t_2)),$$

the third for a similar reason, and the second because

$$C[[t_2, t_3]] \subset I(B_1), \qquad C[[t_4, t_1]] \subset E(B_1),$$
$$C[(t_1, t_2)] \cup C[(t_3, t_4)] \subset E(Q)).$$

Now assume that we are through for m and $C[[t_2, t_3]]$ is covered by the interiors of $B_1, \ldots, B_n$ with $C(t_2) \in I(B_1)$. Let

$$x' \in I(B_1) \cap I(B_j) \cap I(C), \qquad \text{where} \quad j \neq 1$$

(why do such a point and a j exist?), and let L_2' be a vertical line through x'. Constructing D_1' using L_1' as L_1 was used in the construction of D_1

above, we then construct Q', Q'' using D_1, D_1' and D_1', D_2 respectively. Since our result is assumed to hold for $\leq m$ and inductive hypotheses are easy to check, we obtain X' for x, x', X'' for x', y, obeying the results mentioned above for X, and $Y = X' \cup X''$ can clearly be used as our set. This shows $I(C)$ to be connected. If $\mathscr{R}D_1 \cap \mathscr{R}D_2 \neq \phi$ then re $(x) =$ re (y), so im $(x) \neq$ im (y) (or our result is trivial), thus the above, with vertical replaced by horizontal, re by im, im by re, works.

A similar proof may be used to show $E(C)$ connected (although some details must be changed), or choose $x \in I(C)$ and let

$$\psi: \mathbb{C} \sim \{x\} \to \mathbb{C} \sim \{0\} \qquad \text{by} \qquad \psi(y) = \frac{1}{y - x}.$$

$\psi \circ C$ is a Jordan curve, $I(\psi \circ C) = \psi[E(C)] \cup \{0\}$, and the continuity of ψ^{-1} and connectedness of $I(\psi \circ C)$ assure us of the connectedness of $E(C)$.

We now proceed toward a study of complex integration.

Definition 5.4.8. Let $C: [a, b] \to \mathbb{C}$ be rectifiable, $f: X \to \mathbb{C}$, where $\mathscr{R}C \subset X \subset \mathbb{C}$. Then f is complex-integrable over C iff

$$\int_C (\operatorname{re} f - i \cdot \operatorname{im} f), \qquad \int_C (\operatorname{im} f + i \cdot \operatorname{re} f)$$

both exist (see Definition 5.3.22), and in this case

$$\int_C f\,dz = \int_C (\operatorname{re} f - i \cdot \operatorname{im} f) + i \int_C (\operatorname{im} f + i \cdot \operatorname{re} f).$$

Proposition 5.4.9. (a) If $P = \{a^* = t_0 < \cdots < t_{m+1} = b^*\}$, $|P| =_1 0$, and for $j = 0, \ldots, m$, $t_j \leq t_j' \leq t_{j+1}$, then

$$\int_C f\,dz = st\left(\sum_{j=0}^{m} (f \circ C)^*(t_j')(C^*(t_{j+1}) - C^*(t_j))\right),$$

and either of these exists iff both do.

(b) If $g: X \to \mathbb{C}$, $g'(z) = f(z)$ for every $z \in X$ (here, as well as throughout the remainder of this section by *derivative* we mean *complex*-derivative, unless we specify otherwise), then

$$\int_C f\,dz = g(C(b)) - g(C(a))$$

if C is rectifiable and $\mathscr{R}C \subset X$.

(c) Thus if C is closed and the other conditions of (b) hold, then $\int_C f\,dz = 0$.

Proof: (a)

$$
\begin{aligned}
st&\left(\sum_{j=0}^{m} (f\circ C)^*(t_j')(C^*(t_{j+1}) - C^*(t_j))\right)\\
&= st\Bigg(\sum_{j=0}^{m} \operatorname{re}(f\circ C)^*(t_j')(\operatorname{re} C^*(t_{j+1}) - \operatorname{re} C^*(t_j))\\
&\qquad\qquad - \operatorname{im}(f\circ C)^*(t_j')(\operatorname{im} C^*(t_{j+1}) - \operatorname{im} C^*(t_j))\\
&\qquad\qquad + i\cdot \operatorname{im}(f\circ C)^*(t_j')(\operatorname{re} C^*(t_{j+1}) - \operatorname{re} C^*(t_j))\\
&\qquad\qquad + i\cdot \operatorname{re}(f\circ C)^*(t_j')(\operatorname{im} C^*(t_{j+1}) - \operatorname{im} C^*(t_j))\Bigg)\\
&= st\Bigg(\sum_{j=0}^{m} \operatorname{re}(f\circ C)^*(t_j')(\operatorname{re} C^*(t_{j+1}) - \operatorname{re} C^*(t_j))\\
&\qquad\qquad - \sum_{j=0}^{m} \operatorname{im}(f\circ C)^*(t_j')(\operatorname{im} C^*(t_{j+1}) - \operatorname{im} C^*(t_j))\Bigg)\\
&\quad + i\cdot st\Bigg(\sum_{j=0}^{m} \operatorname{im}(f\circ C)^*(t_j')(\operatorname{re} C^*(t_{j+1}) - \operatorname{re} C^*(t_j))\\
&\qquad\qquad + \sum_{j=0}^{m} \operatorname{re}(f\circ C)^*(t_j')(\operatorname{im} C^*(t_{j+1}) - \operatorname{im} C^*(t_j))\Bigg)\\
&= \int_C (\operatorname{re} f - i\cdot \operatorname{im} f) + i\int_C (\operatorname{im} f + i\cdot \operatorname{re} f)\\
&= \int_C f\, dz.
\end{aligned}
$$

(b) If $g'(z) = f(z)$, then by Problem 5.3.11,

$$\frac{\partial \operatorname{re} g}{\partial x} = \operatorname{re} f, \qquad \frac{\partial \operatorname{re} g}{\partial y} = -\operatorname{im} f,$$

so

$$\int_C (\operatorname{re} f - i\cdot \operatorname{im} f) = \operatorname{re} g(C(b)) - \operatorname{re} g(C(a)),$$

and similarly

$$\int_C (\operatorname{im} f + i\cdot \operatorname{re} f) = \operatorname{im} g(C(b)) - \operatorname{im} g(C(a)),$$

thus

$$
\begin{aligned}
\int_C f\, dz &= (\operatorname{re} g(C(b)) + i\cdot \operatorname{im} g(C(b))) - (\operatorname{re} g(C(a))\\
&\qquad + i\cdot \operatorname{im} g(C(a))) = g(C(b)) - g(C(a)).
\end{aligned}
$$

(c) is clear from (b) and the fact that $C(b) = C(a)$. In the proofs of (b), (c) here we have used facts established for contours in Proposition 5.3.23, but for rectifiable curves only in Problems 5.3.8 and 5.3.9.

Note that from (a) above it follows that for f continuous, C rectifiable,

$$\left|\int_C f\, dz\right| \le ML(C), \qquad \text{where} \quad M = \sup\{|f(z)| \mid z \in \mathscr{R}C\}.$$

(c) assures us that if n is any integer other than -1, $d \notin \mathscr{R}C$, C a closed rectifiable curve, $\int_C (z - d)^n \, dz = 0$.

We now proceed toward our proof of the Cauchy integral theorem.

LEMMA 5.4.10. Let C be a Jordan HV-rectangle, $\mathcal{O}$ open, $\mathscr{R}C \cup I(C) \subset \mathcal{O}$, $f: \mathcal{O} \to \mathbb{C}$ analytic (i.e., complex-differentiable at each point of $\mathcal{O}$). Then $\int_C f \, dz = 0$.

Proof: We first show by induction that for each integer $n \geq 0$ there is a Jordan HV-rectangle C_n such that

$$L(C_n) = \frac{L(C)}{2^n} \qquad \text{and} \qquad 4^{-n}\left|\int_C f \, dz\right| \leq \left|\int_{C_n} f \, dz\right|.$$

Clearly $C = C_0$ works, so assume that we have

$$C_n = L(a_1, a_2) + L(a_2, a_3) + L(a_3, a_4) + L(a_4, a_1).$$

Let

$$\begin{aligned} C_{nj} = {} & L(a_j, \tfrac{1}{2}(a_j + a_{j+1})) + L(\tfrac{1}{2}(a_j + a_{j+1}), \tfrac{1}{4}(a_1 + a_2 + a_3 + a_4)) \\ & + L(\tfrac{1}{4}(a_1 + a_2 + a_3 + a_4), \tfrac{1}{2}(a_{j-1} + a_j)) \\ & + L(\tfrac{1}{2}(a_{j-1} + a_j), a_j), \end{aligned}$$

$j = 1, \ldots, 4$, and $j - 1, j + 1$ are considered mod 4. Since all lines with either endpoint $\frac{1}{4}(a_1 + a_2 + a_3 + a_4)$ are traversed in both directions, Proposition 5.3.21(c) (extended by Problems 5.3.8 and 5.3.9) assures us that

$$\int_{C_n} f \, dz = \sum_{j=1}^{4} \int_{C_{nj}} f \, dz$$

thus let $C_{n+1} = C_{nj}$ for some j such that $|\int_{C_{nj}} f \, dz|$ is a maximum and note that

$$\left|\int_{C_n} f \, dz\right| \leq \sum_{j=1}^{4} \left|\int_{C_{nj}} f \, dz\right| \leq 4\left|\int_{C_{n+1}} f \, dz\right|,$$

so

$$4^{-(n+1)}\left|\int_C f \, dz\right| \leq 4^{-1}\left|\int_{C_n} f \, dz\right| \leq \left|\int_{C_{n+1}} f \, dz\right|,$$

and clearly

$$L(C_{n+1}) = \frac{L(C_n)}{2} = \frac{L(C)}{2^{n+1}}.$$

Note that no use has yet been made of the fact that f is more than continuous on $\mathcal{O}$.

Note that if $n < m$, $\mathscr{R}C_m \cup I(C_m) \subset \mathscr{R}C_n \cup I(C_n)$; thus this extends to the C_m^*. If $n \in \omega$, $m \in \omega'$, $z \in \mathscr{R}C_m^* \cup I(C_m^*)$, then

$$z_0 = st(z)^* =_1 z \in \mathscr{R}C_n^* \cup I(C_n^*),$$

and since $\mathscr{R}C_n \cup I(C_n)$ is closed, $z_0 \in \mathscr{R}C_n^* \cup I(C_n^*)$ for each $n \in \omega$, thus for each $m \in \omega^*$.

Now let $m \in \omega'$.

$$\left|\int_C f\,dz\right|^* \leq 4^{*m}\left|\int_{C_m^*} f^*\,dz\right|$$

$$= 4^{*m}\left|\int_{C_m^*} (f^*(z_0) + f^{*\prime}(z_0)(z - z_0) + \xi^*(z_0, z - z_0)(z - z_0))\,dz\right|$$

$$= 4^{*m}\left|f^*(z_0)\int_{C_m^*} 1\,dz + f^{*\prime}(z_0)\int_{C_m^*}(z - z_0)\,dz + \int_{C_m^*} \xi(z_0, z - z_0)(z - z_0)\,dz\right|$$

$$= 4^{*m}\left|0 + 0 + \int_{C_m^*} \xi(z_0, z - z_0)(z - z_0)\,dz\right|$$

by comments following 5.4.9. However, $\xi(z_0, z - z_0) =_1 0$, so

$$k = \text{lub}\{|\xi^*(z_0, z - z_0)| \mid z \in \mathscr{R}C_m^*\} =_1 0$$

and for $z \in \mathscr{R}C_m^*$, $|z - z_0| \leq L(C_m^*)$. Thus

$$\left|\int_C f\,dz\right|^* \leq 4^{*m}L(C_m^*)(L(C_m^*)k) = 4^{*m}L(C)^*4^{*-m}L(C)^*k =_1 0,$$

so

$$\int_C f\,dz = 0.$$

LEMMA 5.4.11. (a) If $C_{\overline{-}}$ is a Jordan *HV*-gon of more than 4 vertices and if $z_{j+1} \notin \mathscr{R}L(z_j, z_{j+2})$ for $j = 1, \ldots, n$ then there are points $C(t_1)$, $C(t_2)$ such that

$$\mathscr{R}1(C(t_1), C(t_2)) \subset I(C),$$

and

$$C \mid [t_1, t_2]_{\overline{-}} + L(C(t_2), C(t_1)), \qquad C \mid [t_2, t_1]_{\overline{-}} + L(C(t_1), C(t_2))$$

are Jordan *HV*-gons, each with fewer vertices than C.

(b) If C is a Jordan *HV*-gon, $\mathcal{O}$ open, $\mathscr{R}C \cup I(C) \subset \mathcal{O}$, $f: \mathcal{O} \to \mathbb{C}$ analytic, then $\int_C f\,dz = 0$.

Proof: (a) We may let C have ≥ 3 im-lines and let $L(a_j, a_{j+1})$ be one farthest on the right. Let $L(a_k, a_{k+1})$ be an im-line farthest on the right other than $L(a_j, a_{j+1})$ among those with

$$\{\text{im } z \mid z \in \mathscr{R}L(a_j, a_{j+1})\} \cap \{\text{im } z \mid z \in \mathscr{R}L(a_k, a_{k+1})\} \neq \phi.$$

Let

$$b'_p = \text{re } a_k + i \cdot \text{im } a_{j-1+p} \qquad \text{for} \quad p = 1, 2,$$

$$b_1 = b'_1 + t(b'_2 - b'_1) \qquad \text{for the largest} \quad t$$

with

$$SL(b'_1, b'_2)[[0, t]] \subset \mathscr{R}C.$$

(Note that $b'_1, b'_2 \in \mathscr{R}C$ because $L(a_{j+2}, a_{j+3}), L(a_{j-2}, a_{j-1})$ are im-lines, $\text{im } a_{j-1} = \text{im } a_j$ and $\text{im } a_{j+1} = \text{im } a_{j+2}$, so $b'_1 \in \mathscr{R}L(a_{j-1}, a_j)$, $b'_2 \in \mathscr{R}L(a_{j+1}, a_{j+2})$.) $t \neq 1$ for otherwise $\mathscr{R}L(b'_1, b'_2) \subset \mathscr{R}C$, and there is no im-line closer to $L(a_j, a_{j+1})$ and intersecting $L(a_{j+1}, b'_2)$ or $L(a_j, b'_1)$ than $L(b'_1, b'_2)$, thus

$$L(a_j, a_{j+1}) + L(a_{j+1}, b'_2) + L(b'_2, b'_1) + L(b'_1, a_j)$$

is a Jordan HV-rectangle whose range is contained in $\mathscr{R}C$, contrary to our hypotheses. If $b_2 = b_1 + t(b'_2 - b'_1)$ for the least $t > 0$ such that $b_1 + t(b'_2 - b'_1) \in \mathscr{R}C$, then $b_1 \neq b_2$. Also $b_1 = C(t_1)$, $b_2 = C(t_2)$ and clearly as in the argument of Lemma 5.4.2,

$$C \mid [t_1, t_2]_{\equiv} + L(C(t_2), C(t_1)), \qquad C \mid [t_2, t_1]_{\equiv} + L(C(t_1), C(t_2))$$

are Jordan HV-gons. Finally, let $x \in \mathscr{R}1(C(t_1), C(t_2))$, then $x \notin \mathscr{R}C$. Consider the "ray" $\{x + t(y - x) \mid t \geq 0\}$, where $y = \text{re } a_j + i \cdot \text{im } x$ (the point on $L(a_j, a_{j+1})$ opposite x). By our construction of this ray and x, its intersection with $\mathscr{R}C$ is precisely $\{y\}$. By constructing a circle of small radius about y we find that our ray intersects $I(C)$: furthermore

$$\{x + t(y - x) \mid t \geq 1\} \cap I(C) = \phi$$

since otherwise

$$\{x + t(y - x) \mid t > 1\} \subset I(C)$$

by its connectedness and nonintersection with $\mathscr{R}C$, contradicting its unboundedness. Thus

$$x \in \{x + t(y - x) \mid 0 \leq t < 1\} \subset I(C),$$

completing the proof.

(b) Let $C = P(z_1, \ldots, z_n, z_1)$. The case $n = 4$ was Lemma 5.4.10, so assume that $n > 4$ and proceed by induction. If for some $j = 1, \ldots, n$, $z_{j+1} \in \mathscr{R}L(z_j, z_{j+2})$, then

$$SL(z_j, z_{j+2}) \equiv SL(z_j, z_{j+1}) + SL(z_{j+1}, z_{j+2}) \quad \text{or} \quad z_{j+1} \in \{z_j, z_{j+2}\},$$

thus by Problem 5.3.10

$$0 = \int_{P(z_1, \cdots, z_j, z_{j+2}, \cdots, z_n, z_1)} f\, dz = \int_C f\, dz.$$

Otherwise for some $t_1, t_2 \in \mathscr{D}SC$,

$$C_1 = SC \mid [t_1, t_2]_{\equiv} + L(SC(t_2), SC(t_1)),$$

$$C_2 = SC \mid [t_2, t_1]_{\equiv} + L(SC(t_1), SC(t_2))$$

are Jordan HV-gons with fewer than n vertices. Thus

$$\int_C f\,dz = \int_{SC\,|\,[t_1,t_2]} f\,dz + \int_{SC\,|\,[t_2,t_1]} f\,dz + \int_{L(SC(t_2),SC(t_1))} f\,dz$$

$$+ \int_{L(SC(t_1),SC(t_2))} f\,dz$$

$$= \int_{C_1} f\,dz + \int_{C_2} f\,dz$$

$$= 0.$$

DEFINITION 5.4.12. $A \subset \mathbb{C}$ is simply connected iff A is open and A, $\mathbb{C} \sim A$ are both connected.

The reader will find it simple to check that if $\mathcal{O}$ is bounded and simply connected, C a Jordan curve with $\mathcal{R}C \subset \mathcal{O}$, then $I(C) \subset \mathcal{O}$, and that if C is a Jordan curve then $I(C)$ is simply connected (so is $E(C)$, but our use of this fact is somewhat limited since $E(C)$ is not bounded).

LEMMA 5.4.13. (a) Let C be a closed HV-gon, $\mathcal{R}C \subset \mathcal{O}$, $\mathcal{O}$ simply connected and bounded, $f\colon \mathcal{O} \to \mathbb{C}$ analytic. Then $\int_C f\,dz = 0$.

(b) Let $\mathcal{O}$ be simply connected and bounded. If $x, y \in \mathcal{O}$, there is an HV-gon $C\colon [a, b] \to \mathcal{O}$ with $C(a) = x$, $C(b) = y$. Furthermore, if C, C' are two such HV-gons, $\int_C f\,dz = \int_{C'} f\,dz$ for any analytic $f\colon \mathcal{O} \to \mathbb{C}$.

Proof: (a) If C is Jordan we are through by 5.4.12(b). Otherwise let $C(t_1) = C(t_2)$, $t_1 \neq t_2$. Then

$$\int_C f\,dz = \int_{C\,|\,[t_1,t_2]} f\,dz + \int_{C\,|\,[t_2,t_1]} f\,dz = 0$$

if we proceed by induction, since it is clear that $C \mid [t_1, t_2]$, $C \mid [t_2, t_1]$ both have fewer vertices than C does.

(b) For the first assertion, let

$$\mathcal{P}_x = \{y \mid \text{some such } C \text{ exists}\}, \qquad \mathcal{Q}_x = \{y \mid \text{no such } C \text{ exists}\};$$

then $\mathcal{P}_x^*, \mathcal{Q}_x^*$ have the same properties, so if $y \in \mathcal{P}_x$, $z =_1 y^*$, then we have a C^* with initial point x^* and final point y^*, so $C^* + SP(y^*, \text{re } y^* + \text{im } zi, z)$ is an HV-gon with initial point x^* and final point z, thus $z \in \mathcal{P}_x^*$, so $\mathcal{P}_x$ is open. Similarly, $\mathcal{Q}_x$ is open, thus since $\mathcal{O}$ is connected, $x \in \mathcal{P}_x$, $\mathcal{P}_x = \mathcal{O}$.

For the second assertion here note that

$$\int_C f\,dz - \int_{C'} f\,dz = \int_{C+{}^-C'} f\,dz = 0.$$

THEOREM 5.4.14 (Cauchy Integral Theorem I). Let $\mathcal{O}$ be a simply connected set, $f: \mathcal{O} \to \mathbb{C}$ analytic, D a closed rectifiable curve with $\mathscr{R}D \subset \mathcal{O}$. Then $\int_D f\, dz = 0$.

Proof: Let $x \in \mathcal{O}$ and define $g: \mathcal{O} \to \mathbb{C}$ by $g(z) = \int_C f\, dz$ for some [thus by 5.4.13(b), for all] HV-gon with initial point x and final point z. At z,

$$\left(\frac{\partial \operatorname{re} g}{\partial x}\right)^* =_1 \frac{\operatorname{re} \int^*_{C^* + L(z^*, z^* + h)} f^*\, dz - (\operatorname{re} \int_C f\, dz)^*}{h}$$

(where $0 \neq h \in \mathbb{R}^*$, $h =_1 0$)

$$= \frac{\operatorname{re} \int^*_{L(z^*, z^*+h)} f^*\, dz}{h}$$

$$= \frac{\int^*_{L(z^*, z^*+h)} (\operatorname{re} f^* - i \cdot \operatorname{im} f^*)}{h}$$

$$= \frac{\int^*_{L(z^*, z^*+h)} \operatorname{re} f^*\, dx}{h} - \frac{\int^*_{L(z^*, z^*+h)} \operatorname{im} f^*\, dy}{h}$$

$$= \frac{\int_0^{*1} (\operatorname{re} f^* \circ SL(z^*, z^* + h))(\operatorname{re} SL(z^*, z^* + h)')\, dt}{h}$$

$$- \frac{\int_0^{*1} (\operatorname{im} f^* \circ SL(z^*, z^* + h))(\operatorname{im} SL(z^*, z^* + h)')\, dt}{h}$$

[by Proposition 5.3.21(b)]

$$= \frac{\int_0^{*1} \operatorname{re} f^*(z^* + th)h\, dt}{h} - \frac{\int_0^{*1} \operatorname{im} f^*(z^* + th)0\, dt}{h}$$

$$= \int_0^{*1} \operatorname{re} f^*(z^* + th)\, dt =_1 \operatorname{re} f^*(z^*)$$

$$= (\operatorname{re} f(z))^*,$$

where the next-to-last equality is due to the fact that

$$\operatorname{re} f^*(z^* + t_0 h) \leq \int_0^{*1} \operatorname{re} f^*(z^* + th)\, dt \leq \operatorname{re} f^*(z^* + t_1 h) \qquad \text{for some} \quad t_0, t_1 \in [0, 1]^*,$$

but since f is continuous, both of these values are $=_1 (\operatorname{re} f(z))^*$. Similarly it can be shown that

$$\frac{\partial \operatorname{im} g}{\partial x} = \operatorname{im} f = -\frac{\partial \operatorname{re} g}{\partial y}, \qquad \frac{\partial \operatorname{im} g}{\partial y} = \operatorname{re} f,$$

so $g'(z) = f(z)$, and z is an arbitrary point of $\mathcal{O}$. Thus by Proposition 5.4.9(c), $\int_D f\, dz = 0$.

THEOREM 5.4.15 (Cauchy Integral Theorem II). Let $\mathcal{O}$ be any open set, $f: \mathcal{O} \to \mathbb{C}$ analytic, C a rectifiable Jordan curve with $\mathcal{R}C \cup I(C) \subset \mathcal{O}$. Then $\int_C f\, dz = 0$.

Proof: As in the proof of 5.4.7, we construct a Jordan HV-gon P such that $st[\mathcal{R}P] = \mathcal{R}C$; let $P = P(x_1, \ldots, x_r, x_1)$, $G = \{x_1, \ldots, x_r\}$. If $F = \{y_1, \ldots, y_n\} \subset \mathbb{C}$ the function

$$g_F(z) = \min\{|z - y_j| \mid j = 1, \ldots, n\}$$

is continuous, thus for some $z \in \mathcal{R}C$, $g_F(z) \geq g_F(w)$ for each $w \in \mathcal{R}C$, by the compactness of $\mathcal{R}C$. Thus this holds for C^* and G, so let $z \in \mathcal{R}C^*$ be such that $g_G^*(z) \geq g_G^*(w)$ for each $w \in \mathcal{R}C^*$, and note that $st[G] = st[\mathcal{R}P]$. Since $z \in \mathcal{R}C^* \subset \mathcal{D}st$,

$$z =_1 st(z)^* =_1 x_j \qquad \text{for some} \quad j = 1, \ldots, r,$$

so $g_G^*(z) =_1 0$; let $s = g_G^*(z)$. For $j = 1, \ldots, r$, let B_j be an HV-square with center x_j and sides of length $3s$; note that if $w \in \mathcal{R}C^*$, then for some j, $|w - x_j| \leq s$ so $w \in I(B_j)$, also note that

$$st\left[\mathcal{R}P \cup \left(\bigcup_{j=1}^{r} \mathcal{R}B_j\right)\right] = \mathcal{R}C.$$

Below we show the existence of a Jordan HV-gon Q such that

$$\mathcal{R}Q \subset \mathcal{R}P \cup \left(\bigcup_{j=1}^{r} \mathcal{R}B_j\right);$$

$$I(C^*) \subset I(P) \cup \left(\bigcup_{j=1}^{r} I(B_j)\right) \subset I(Q) \subset \mathcal{O}^*.$$

This will establish our theorem, for $I(Q)$ is a bounded simply connected set, so by Theorem 5.4.14

$$\left(\int_C f\, dz\right)^* = \int_{C^*}^{*} f^*\, dz = 0.$$

The existence of Q results from the following more general fact: Let $\{P_j \mid j = 1, \ldots, m\}$ be a finite set of Jordan HV-gons such that if $j \leq m$ then $I(P_j) \cap I(P_m) \neq \phi$. Then for some Jordan HV-gon Q,

$$\mathcal{R}Q \subset \bigcup_{j=1}^{m} \mathcal{R}P_j \qquad \text{and} \qquad \bigcup_{j=1}^{m} I(P_j) \subset I(Q).$$

This can be shown by induction on m; clearly if $m = 1$ then $Q = P_1$ and we are through. Assume that we are through up to m and have $P_1, \ldots, P_{m+1}$; let

$$\mathcal{R}Q_1 \subset \bigcup_{j=2}^{m+1} \mathcal{R}P_j, \qquad \bigcup_{j=2}^{m+1} I(P_j) \subset I(Q_1).$$

We show that for some Q,

$$I(P_1) \cup I(Q_1) \subset I(Q), \qquad \mathcal{R}Q \subset \mathcal{R}P_1 \cup \mathcal{R}Q_1,$$

and we are then through by our induction hypotheses on Q_1. The existence of this Q for P_1 and Q_1 is shown by induction on the number p of nonempty intervals in $\mathscr{R}P_1 \cap E(Q_1)$. If $p = 0$, then

$$E(Q_1) \cap \mathscr{R}P_1 = \phi \qquad \text{so} \qquad E(Q_1) \subset I(P_1) \cup E(P_1)$$

and since $E(Q_1)$ is connected,

$$E(Q_1) \subset I(P_1) \qquad \text{or} \qquad E(Q_1) \subset E(P_1),$$

but the first is impossible since $E(Q_1)$ is unbounded, $I(P_1)$ bounded. Thus $I(P_1) \subset I(Q_1) \cup \mathscr{R}Q_1$, but $I(P_1) \cap \mathscr{R}Q_1 = \phi$, for otherwise

$$I(P_1) \cap E(Q_1) \neq \phi$$

since $E(Q_1)^- \supset \mathscr{R}Q_1$, a contradiction, thus $I(P_1) \subset I(Q_1)$ so $Q = Q_1$ works here. Assume that we are through for $< p$ but have p nonempty intervals, one of which is $SP_1[(s, v)]$; note that since $I(P_1) \cap I(Q_1) \neq \phi$, $s, v \in \mathscr{R}SQ_1$ and $SP_1(s) \neq SP_1(v)$, so we may let

$$SQ_1(s') = SP_1(s), \qquad SQ_1(v') = SP_1(v).$$

Now consider the three HV-gons

$$Q_1 = (SQ_1 \mid [s', v'] + SQ_1 \mid [v', s'])_{\underline{-}},$$
$$Q_2 = (SQ_1 \mid [v', s'] + SP_1 \mid [s, v])_{\underline{-}},$$
$$Q_3 = (SQ_1 \mid [s', v'] + {}^{-}(SP_1 \mid [s, v]))_{\underline{-}}.$$

Reasoning similar to that used near the end of the proof of 5.4.2 tells us that since $SP_1[(s, v)] \subset E(Q_1)$,

$$\text{if} \quad SQ_1[(s', v')] \subset E(Q_2) \qquad \text{then} \quad SQ_1[(v', s')] \subset I(Q_3)$$

and thus assures us that

$$I(Q_1) \cup I(Q_2) \cup SQ_1[(v', s')] = I(Q_3),$$

so

$$I(P_1) \cup I(Q_1) \subset I(P_1) \cup I(Q_3), \qquad \mathscr{R}Q_3 \subset \mathscr{R}P_1 \cup \mathscr{R}Q_1.$$

In addition, $E(Q_3) \cap \mathscr{R}P_1$ has at most $p - 1$ intervals, for $SP_1[(s, v)]$ is not one of its intervals, and if $SP_1[(t, u)]$ is one of its intervals, then

$$SP_1[(t, u)] \subset E(Q_3) = E(Q_1) \cap E(Q_2) \subset E(Q_1)$$

so

$$SP_1[(t, u)] \subset SP_1[(t_1, u_1)],$$

an interval on $E(Q_1) \cap \mathscr{R}P_1$, but

$$SP_1(t), \qquad SP_1(u) \in \mathscr{R}Q_3 \sim SP_1[(s, v)] \subset \mathscr{R}Q_1,$$

so $t = t_1$, $u = u_1$, thus $SP_1[(t, u)]$ is one of the remaining intervals of $\mathscr{R}P_1 \cap E(Q_1)$. Thus we have Q for Q_3, P_1 and it clearly works for Q_1, P_1.

We now show that if Q is constructed from P $(= B_{r+1})$, $B_1, \ldots, B_r$ as above, then $I(Q) \subset \mathcal{O}^*$ to complete proof of our theorem. But

$$st[\mathscr{R}Q] \subset st\left[\mathscr{R}P \cup \left(\bigcup_{j=1}^{r} \mathscr{R}B_j\right)\right] = \mathscr{R}C,$$

and a connectedness argument like that of 5.4.7 shows $st[\mathscr{R}Q] = \mathscr{R}C$. However, under these conditions, we showed in 5.4.7,

$$I(C) = \{x \notin \mathscr{R}C \mid x^* \in I(Q)\}.$$

If $z \in I(Q)$, let $z \in m(y)$, then $y \in I(C) \cup \mathscr{R}C \subset \mathcal{O}$, so $m(y) \subset \mathcal{O}^*$, thus $z \in \mathcal{O}^*$.

Definition 5.4.16. Let C be a Jordan curve that is rectifiable. C is positively oriented iff for every $a \in I(C)$, $\int_C (z - a)^{-1}\, dz = 2\pi i$. Let $r > 0$, $a \in \mathbb{C}$. Then $SC(a, r)$: $[0, 2\pi] \to \mathbb{C}$ by

$$SC(a, r)(t) = a + r(\cos t + i \sin t), \qquad C(a, r) = SC(a, r)_{\underline{-}}.$$

(SC is thus a parametrization of a positively sensed circle with radius r and center a, and C is the positively sensed circle.)

Now let C be a rectifiable Jordan curve, $a \in I(C)$, $I(C) \cup \mathscr{R}C \subset \mathcal{O} \cup \{a\}$, $f\colon \mathcal{O} \to \mathbb{C}$ be analytic, $b \neq a$, $0 < r =_1 0$. Let $C(t_1)^*$, $C(t_2)^*$, $SC(a^*, r)(s_1)$, $SC(a^*, r)(s_2)$ be the points on $\mathscr{R}C^*$, $\mathscr{R}C(a^*, r)$ of the form $a^* + t(b^* - a^*)$ for the smallest positive and largest negative t's respectively. Let

$$D_1 = SL(C(t_2)^*, SC(a^*, r)(s_2)) + SC(a^*, r) \mid [s_2, s_1] + SL(SC(a^*, r)(s_1), C(t_1)^*),$$

then

$$C_1 = D_1 + (C \mid [t_1, t_2])^*, \qquad C_2 = {}^-D_1 + (C \mid [t_2, t_1])^*$$

are clearly rectifiable Jordan curves and

$$\left(\int_C f\, dz\right)^* = \int_{C_1}^* f^*\, dz + \int_{C_2}^* f^*\, dz.$$

By comments following 5.4.2,

$$I(C)^* = I(C_1) \cup I(C_2) \cup (\mathscr{R}D_1 \sim \{C(t_1)^*, C(t_2)^*\})$$

disjointly, so $a^* \in I(C_1)$ or $I(C_2)$, not both. If $a^* \in I(C_1)$, then

$$\int_{C_2}^* f^*\, dz = 0$$

since f^* is analytic on $\mathcal{O}^*$ and $I(C_2) \cup \mathscr{R}C_2 \subset \mathcal{O}^*$,

$$\text{so} \qquad \left(\int_C^* f\, dz\right)^* = \int_{C_1}^* f^*\, dz.$$

Now let

$$D_2 = {}^{-}(C(a^*, r) \mid [s_1, s_2]),$$

$$M = (\mathscr{R}D_2 \sim \{C(a^*, r)(s_1), C(a^*, r)(s_2)\}) \cup I(C(a^*, r)).$$

$M \cap \mathscr{R}C_1 = \phi$, $a^* \in M \cap I(C_1)$, and M is connected, so

$$\mathscr{R}D_2 \sim \{C(a^*, r)(s_1), C(a^*, r)(s_2)\} \subset M \subset I(C_1),$$

thus if

$$C_3 = (C \mid [t_2, t_1])^* + SL(C(t_1)^*, C(a^*, r)(s_1)) + SC(a^*, r) \mid [s_1, s_2] + SL(C(a^*, r)(s_2), C(t_2)^*),$$

$$\int_{C_1}^* f^*\, dz = \int_{C_3}^* f^*\, dz + \int_{C(a^*,r)}^* f^*\, dz,$$

but $a^* \in I(C(a^*, r))$ so $a^* \notin I(C_3)$, thus

$$\left(\int_C f\, dz\right)^* = \int_{C(a^*,r)}^* f^*\, dz,$$

and if $a^* \in I(C_2)$, it can similarly be shown that

$$\left(\int_C f\, dz\right)^* = \int_{C_2}^* f^*\, dz = \int_{-C(a^*,r)}^* f^*\, dz = -\int_{C(a^*,r)}^* f^*\, dz.$$

In either case,

$$\left(\int_C f\, dz\right)^* \in \left\{\pm \int_{C(a^*,r)}^* f^*\, dz\right\}.$$

THEOREM 5.4.17. (a) For any $a \in \mathbb{C}$, $r > 0$,

$$\int_{C(a,r)} (z - a)^{-1}\, dz = 2\pi i.$$

(b) If C is a rectifiable Jordan curve, C or ${}^{-}C$ is positively oriented.

(c) C is positively oriented iff for every $a_1, \ldots, a_n \in I(C)$, $f\colon \mathcal{O} \to \mathbb{C}$ analytic, if $I(C) \cup \mathscr{R}C \subset \mathcal{O} \cup \{a_1, \ldots, a_n\}$, then for any $r > 0$, $r =_1 0$,

$$\left(\int_C f\, dz\right)^* = \sum_{j=1}^{n} \int_{C(a^*,r)}^* f^*\, dz.$$

Proof: A straightforward calculation using Proposition 5.3.21(b) and Definition 5.3.22 (and left for the reader) establishes (a).

(b) For $a \in I(C)$, let

$$N_C(a) = \left(\frac{1}{2\pi i}\right) \int_C (z - a)^{-1} \, dz.$$

By (a) and comments following Definition 5.4.16, $N_C(a) \in \{1, -1\}$. However, N_C is continuous, for if $b =_1 a^*$,

$$\begin{aligned}(N_C(a))^* - N_C^*(b) &= \left(\frac{1}{2\pi i}\right)^* \left(\left(\int_C (z - a)^{-1} \, dz\right)^* - \int_{C^*}^* (z - b)^{-1} \, dz\right) \\ &= \left(\frac{1}{2\pi i}\right)^* \left(\int_{C^*}^* \frac{a^* - b}{(z - a^*)(z - b)} \, dz\right) \\ &=_1 0\end{aligned}$$

(since

$$\sup\left\{\left|\frac{a^* - b}{(z - a^*)(z - b)}\right| \mid z \in \mathscr{R}C^*\right\} =_1 0)$$

and this, together with the connectedness of $I(C)$ shows N_C to be constant since $\{1\}$, $\{-1\}$ are the only nonempty connected subsets of its range. If $N_C(a) = 1$ always, then C is positively oriented, otherwise $N_{-C}(a) = -N_C(a) = 1$, so ^-C is positively oriented.

(c) Our condition implies positive orientation, for if $a \in I(C)$,

$$(z - a)^{-1} \colon (\mathbb{C} \sim \{a\}) \to \mathbb{C} \qquad \text{analytically},$$

$$I(C) \cup \mathscr{R}C \subset (\mathbb{C} \sim \{a\}) \cup \{a\},$$

thus

$$\left(\int_C (z - a)^{-1} \, dz\right)^* = \int_{C(a^*,r)}^* (z - a^*)^{-1} \, dz = (2\pi i)^*,$$

so for each $a \in I(C)$,

$$\left(\frac{1}{2\pi i}\right) \int_C (z - a)^{-1} \, dz = 1.$$

For the converse, our comments following Definition 5.4.16 established the case $n = 1$, so assume for general n. If $a_1, \ldots, a_{n+1} \in I(C)$, let $b \neq a_1$ be such that

$$\{a_1 + t(b - a_1) \mid t \in \mathbb{R}\} \cap \{a_2, \ldots, a_{n+1}\} = \phi,$$

and construct D_1, D_2, C_1, C_2, C_3 as in those comments. Since $a_1^*, \ldots, a_{n+1}^* \notin \mathscr{R}D_1, \mathscr{R}D_2$;

$$a_1^*, \ldots, a_{n+1}^* \in I(C_1) \cup I(C_2),$$

and since C is positively oriented, $a_1^* \in I(C_1)$. Note that C_1, C_2, C_3 are positively oriented: In general if C is a positively oriented Jordan curve,

$$D\colon [c, d] \to I(C) \cup \mathscr{R}C, \qquad D[(c, d)] \subset I(C),$$

$$D(c) = C(t_1), \qquad D(d) = C(t_2),$$

and D is rectifiable and one-one, then $D' = C \mid [t_2, t_1] + D$ is a rectifiable Jordan curve, and so is $D'' = C \mid [t_1, t_2] + {}^{-}D$; both are positively oriented, for if $a \in I(D')$, for example,

$$2\pi i = \int_C (z - a)^{-1}\, dz = \int_{D'} (z - a)^{-1}\, dz + \int_{D''} (z - a)^{-1}\, dz$$

$$= \int_{D'} (z - a)^{-1}\, dz.$$

If not all of the a_j^* are in $I(C_1)$, then by induction

$$\left(\int_C f\, dz\right)^* = \int_{C_1}^* f^*\, dz + \int_{C_2}^* f^*\, dz = \sum_{j=1}^{n+1} \int_{C(a_j^*, r)} f^*\, dz,$$

but if all are in $I(C_1)$, then

$$\left(\int_C f\, dz\right)^* = \int_{C_1}^* f^*\, dz = \int_{C_3}^* f^*\, dz + \int_{C(a_1^*, r)}^* f^*\, dz$$

$$= \sum_{j=1}^{n+1} \int_{C(a_j^*, r)}^* f^*\, dz.$$

THEOREM 5.4.18 (Cauchy Integral Formula). If $f\colon \mathcal{O} \to \mathbb{C}$ is analytic, $I(C) \cup \mathscr{R}C \subset \mathcal{O}$, C a positively oriented Jordan curve, $a \in I(C)$, then

$$\left(\frac{1}{2\pi i}\right) \int_C f(z)(z - a)^{-1}\, dz = f(a).$$

Proof: Since

$$\frac{f^*(z) - (f(a))^*}{z - a^*} = f'(a)^* + \xi(a^*, z - a^*),$$

$$\int_{C(a^*, r)}^* f'(a)^*\, dz = 0$$

and

$$\sup\{|\xi(a^*, z - a^*)| \mid z \in \mathscr{R}C(a^*, r)\} =_1 0,$$

by 5.4.17(c) and (a)

$$\left(\int_C f(z)(z-a)^{-1}\,dz\right)^* = \int^*_{C(a^*,r)} f^*(z)(z-a^*)^{-1}\,dz$$

$$= f(a)^* \int^*_{C(a^*,r)} (z-a^*)^{-1}\,dz$$

$$+ \int^*_{C(a^*,r)} (f^*(z) - f(a)^*)(z-a^*)^{-1}\,dz$$

$$=_1 (2\pi i f(a))^*.$$

If $f_n \mid \mathscr{R}C \to f \mid \mathscr{R}C$ uniformly, then $\int_C f_n\,dz \to \int_C f\,dz$, for if $m \in \omega'$,

$$\left|\int^*_{C^*} f^*\,dz - \int^*_{C^*} f^*_m\,dz\right| = \left|\int^*_{C^*} (f^* - f^*_m)\,dz\right| \le ML(C) =_1 0$$

since

$$M = \sup\{|f^*(z) - f^*_m(z)| \mid z \in \mathscr{R}C^*\} =_1 0.$$

Thus if $f = \sum_{n=0}^{\infty} g_n$ uniformly on $\mathscr{R}C$,

$$\int_C f\,dz = \sum_{n=0}^{\infty} \int_C g_n\,dz.$$

THEOREM 5.4.19. (a) (Taylor Expansion) Let $f\colon \mathcal{O} \to \mathbb{C}$ be analytic, $\mathcal{O}$ open, $\{z \mid |z-a| \le r\} \subset \mathcal{O}$ for some $r > 0$. If $|b-a| < r$, then

$$f(b) = \sum_{n=0}^{\infty} a_n(b-a)^n,$$

a series with radius of convergence $\ge r$, where

$$a_n = \left(\frac{1}{2\pi i}\right) \int_{C(a,r)} f(z)((z-a)^{-n-1})\,dz.$$

(b) If f, a, $\mathcal{O}$ are as in (a) and C is any positively oriented Jordan curve such that $a \in I(C)$, $I(C) \cup \mathscr{R}C \subset \mathcal{O}$, then f has derivatives of all orders at a and

$$f^{(n)}(a) = \left(\frac{n!}{2\pi i}\right) \int_C f(z)((z-a)^{-n-1})\,dz.$$

(c) (Laurent Expansion) Let f, a be as in (a), $\mathcal{O}$ open,

$$\{z \mid r \le |z-a| \le R\} \subset \mathcal{O}.$$

If $r < |b - a| < R$, then

$$f(b) = \sum_{n=-\infty}^{\infty} a_n(b - a)^n,$$

a series converging for $r < |b - a| < R$. Here

$$a_n = \left(\frac{1}{2\pi i}\right) \int_{C(a,R)} f(z)((z - a)^{-n-1})\, dz, \qquad \text{for} \quad n \geq 0,$$

and

$$a_n = \left(\frac{1}{2\pi i}\right) \int_{C(a,r)} f(z)(z - a)^{n-1}\, dz, \qquad \text{for} \quad n < 0.$$

Proof: (a)

$$f(b) = \left(\frac{1}{2\pi i}\right) \int_{C(a,r)} f(z)(z - b)^{-1}\, dz$$

$$= \left(\frac{1}{2\pi i}\right) \int_{C(a,r)} f(z)(z - a)^{-1} \left(1 - \frac{b - a}{z - a}\right)^{-1} dz$$

$$= \left(\frac{1}{2\pi i}\right) \int_{C(a,r)} f(z)(z - a)^{-1} \left(\sum_{n=0}^{\infty} \left(\frac{b - a}{z - a}\right)^n\right) dz.$$

Note that

$$\sum_{n=0}^{\infty} \left(\frac{b - a}{z - a}\right)^n$$

converges since

$$\left|\frac{b - a}{z - a}\right| < 1$$

$$= \left(\frac{1}{2\pi i}\right) \int_{C(a,r)} \sum_{n=0}^{\infty} f(z)(b - a)^n(z - a)^{-n-1}\, dz$$

$$= \sum_{n=0}^{\infty} \left(\frac{1}{2\pi i}\right) \int_{C(a,r)} (b - a)^n f(z)(z - a)^{-n-1}\, dz$$

$$= \sum_{n=0}^{\infty} (b - a)^n \left(\frac{1}{2\pi i}\right) \int_{C(a,r)} f(z)(z - a)^{-n-1}\, dz.$$

(b) Results immediately from (a) and Problem 5.3.7.

(c) By drawing two lines from $\mathscr{R}C(a, r)$ to $\mathscr{R}C(a, R)$ not meeting b, we can show that

$$\begin{aligned}
f(b) &= \left(\frac{1}{2\pi i}\right) \int_{C(a,R)} f(z)(z - b)^{-1}\, dz - \left(\frac{1}{2\pi i}\right) \int_{C(a,r)} f(z)(z - b)^{-1} dz \\
&= \sum_{n=0}^{\infty} (b - a)^n \left(\left(\frac{1}{2\pi i}\right) \int_{C(a,R)} f(z)(z - a)^{-n-1}\, dz\right) \\
&\quad + \left(\frac{1}{2\pi i}\right) \int_{C(a,r)} f(z)(b - z)^{-1}\, dz \\
&= \sum_{n=0}^{\infty} a_n(b - a)^n + \left(\frac{1}{2\pi i}\right) \int_{C(a,r)} f(z)((b - a) - (z - a))^{-1}\, dz \\
&= \sum_{n=0}^{\infty} a_n(b - a)^n + \sum_{p=0}^{\infty} (b - a)^{-p-1} \left(\frac{1}{2\pi i}\right) \int_{C(a,r)} f(z)(z - a)^p\, dz \\
&= \sum_{n=-\infty}^{\infty} a_n(b - a)^n.
\end{aligned}$$

THEOREM 5.4.20. Let $f\colon \mathcal{O} \to \mathbb{C}$ be analytic and nonconstant, $\mathcal{O}$ open and connected. Then there is no point of $\mathcal{O}$ at which $|f|$ is at a maximum.

Proof: If a were a maximum for $|f|$, then a^* would be one for $|f^*|$. But by 5.4.19(a), f can be expanded in a power series $\sum_{j=0}^{\infty} a_j(b - a)^j$ valid in a disc of positive radius about a. Let $n \geq 1$ be the least such with $a_n \neq 0$, and note that $|f|$ reaches a maximum at a iff $|f/a_n|$ reaches a maximum at a so we may assume that $a_n = 1$. Let $a_0 = re^{it}$, $r \geq 0$; $t = 0$ if $a_0 = 0$; and let $b = a^* + s(e^{it/n})^*$, where $s =_1 0$, $s > 0$. Then

$$\begin{aligned}
|f(b)^*| &= \left|\sum_{j \in \omega^*} a_j^*(s(e^{it/n})^*)^j\right| \\
&= \left|a_0^* + s^n(e^{it})^* + s^n(e^{it})^* \sum_{1 \leq j \in \omega^*} a_{j+n}^*(s(e^{it/n})^*)^j\right| \\
&= |(e^{it})^*|\left(\left|r^* + s^n + s^n \sum_{1 \leq j \in \omega^*} a_{j+n}^*(s(e^{it/n})^*)^j\right|\right) \\
&\geq |(e^{it})^*|\left(r^* + s^n\left(1 - \left|\sum_{1 \leq j \in \omega^*} a_{j+n}^*(s(e^{it/n})^*)^j\right|\right)\right) \\
&> |(e^{it})^* r^*| \\
&= |a_0^*| \\
&= |f(a)^*|,
\end{aligned}$$

contradicting the existence of a least such n, thus any such n. Thus f is constant in a neighborhood of a. The proof is completed by the following lemma:

LEMMA 5.4.21. Let $f, g: \mathcal{O} \to \mathbb{C}$, $\mathcal{O}$ open, connected, f, g analytic, $a \in \mathcal{O}$, $b \neq a^*$, $b =_1 a^*$. If $f^*(b) = g^*(b)$, then $f = g$.

Proof: It will do to show that if $h: \mathcal{O} \to \mathbb{C}$ is analytic and $h^*(b) = 0$, then $h = 0$, for we may let $h = f - g$. However, for such h let

$$\mathcal{P} = \{p \mid \text{for some open } \mathcal{Q}, p \in \mathcal{Q} \subset \mathcal{O} \text{ and if } q \in \mathcal{Q} \text{ then } h(q) = 0\},$$

a set which is clearly open. However, $\mathcal{P}$ is closed in $\mathcal{O}$ as well, for if $c \in \mathcal{P}^-$, then $h^*(d) = 0$ for some $d =_1 c^*$, and since h can be expanded in a power series valid in some neighborhood of c, Problem 5.3.7 assures us that h is 0 in a neighborhood of c, so $c \in \mathcal{P}$. Thus $\mathcal{P}$ is open and closed in $\mathcal{O}$, and our proof that $\mathcal{P}$ is closed has also shown that $a \in \mathcal{P}$, so $\mathcal{O} = \mathcal{P}$.

Lemma 5.4.21 has the following standard equivalent: Let f, g be analytic on $\mathcal{O}$, an open, connected set, and let $f(z_n) = g(z_n)$ on some sequence $z_n \to a \in \mathcal{O}$. Then $f = g$.

THEOREM 5.4.22 (Liouville). If $f: \mathbb{C} \to \mathbb{C}$ is bounded and analytic, f is a constant.

Proof: Let $|f(z)| \leq M$ for each $z \in \mathbb{C}$, let $a \in \mathbb{C}$ and let $r > 0$ be infinite. Then by Theorem 5.4.19(b) and comments following 5.4.9,

$$\begin{aligned} |f'(a)^*| &= \left| \left(\frac{1}{2\pi i}\right)^* \int_{C(a^*, r)} f^*(z)(z - a^*)^{-2}\, dz \right| \\ &\leq \left(\frac{1}{2\pi}\right)^* (M^* r^{-2})((2\pi)^* r) \\ &= \frac{M^*}{r} \\ &=_1 0, \end{aligned}$$

but a was arbitrary, so for each $a \in \mathbb{C}$, $f'(a) = 0$.

Problems

‡5.4.1 (a) Show that the inductively defined sets purporting to be $E(P)$, $I(P)$ are open and satisfy conditions (i), (iii) of Lemma 5.4.2.

(b) Show that $I(P)^- = I(P) \cup \mathcal{R}P$ (and $E(P)^- = E(P) \cup \mathcal{R}P$). (HINT: Whether or not x is a vertex of a polygon Q, if $x \in \mathcal{R}Q$ then $m(x)$ is cut into two "connected" pieces by $\mathcal{R}Q^* \cap m(x)$, and if Q has an interior and exterior then one of these pieces is in each.)

(c) Show $I(P)(E(P))$ connected. (HINT: If $I(P) \subset \mathcal{O} \cup \mathcal{P}$, then $\mathcal{R}P \subset I(P)^- \subset \mathcal{O}^- \cup \mathcal{P}^-$. If $SP(0) \in \mathcal{O}^-$, let $t \in [0, 1]$ be the largest number such that $SP[[0, t]] \subset \mathcal{O}^-$ (SP is defined before 5.4.6). If $t \neq 1$, note that $m(SP(t)) \cap I(P)$ can meet only one of $\mathcal{O}$, $\mathcal{P}$.)

(d) Show the comments following 5.4.2.

(e) Show the comments following 5.4.12.

‡5.4.2 (a) Let $x \in \mathbb{C}^*$, $\mathcal{R}P \subset \mathbb{C}^*$, P a polygon. Show that the definition

$$d(x, P) = \inf \{|x - z| \mid z \in P\}$$

is good because the inf mentioned always exists.

Below let S, P, C be as in the fifth paragraph of the proof of Theorem 5.4.7.

(b) Note that for some $w' \in E(S^*) \cap \mathcal{R}P$, $z' \in I(S^*) \cap \mathcal{R}P$,

$$d(w', P) \neq_1 0 \qquad \text{and} \qquad d(z', P) \neq_1 0,$$

and show by induction on the number of intervals in $\mathcal{R}S^* \cap I(P)$ that for some $r, s \in [0, 1]^*$ there are points

$$x \in SS^*[(r, s)] \cap I(P), \qquad y \in SS^*[(s, r)] \cap E(P)$$

such that

$$d(x, P) \neq_1 0 \neq_1 d(y, P).$$

(c) Now show that $st(x) \in I(C) \cap \mathcal{R}S$, $st(y) \in E(C) \cap \mathcal{R}S$, x, y as in (b).

5.4.3 (DeMorera's Theorem) If $f: \mathcal{O} \to \mathbb{C}$ is continuous, $\mathcal{O}$ bounded and simply connected, and $\int_C f\,dz = 0$ for every rectifiable Jordan curve with $\mathcal{R}C \subset \mathcal{O}$, then f is analytic on $\mathcal{O}$. (HINT: This is enough to insure $\int_D f\,dz = 0$ for every closed HV-gon with range contained in $\mathcal{O}$. Now find $g: \mathcal{O} \to \mathbb{C}$ with $g' = f$ and use the derivatives of the terms of local power series for g to get such series for f.)

5.4.4 (Singularities) Let $f: \mathcal{O} \to \mathbb{C}$ be analytic on $\mathcal{O}$; $a \in \mathbb{C} \sim \mathcal{O}$ is called an isolated singularity of f iff $m(a) \sim \mathcal{O}^* = \{a^*\}$ (thus $\mathcal{O} \cup \{a\}$ is open, and connected, bounded, simply connected, etc., if $\mathcal{O}$ is).

Among isolated singularities a is called removable iff there is a $g: \mathcal{O} \cup \{a\} \to \mathbb{C}$ analytic and such that $g \mid \mathcal{O} = f$, a pole iff for some $1 \le k \in \omega$, $(z - a)^k f(z)$ has a removable singularity at a, and the least such k is called the order of the pole at a. All other isolated singularities are called essential.

(a) If f is bounded on some neighborhood of the isolated singularity a, then a is a removable singularity. (HINT: First show $\int_C f\,dz = 0$ for any rectifiable Jordan curve C with $\mathcal{R}C \subset \mathcal{O}$, $\mathcal{R}C \cup I(C) \subset \mathcal{O} \cup \{a\}$, and note that this implies that $\int_C f(z)(z - b)^{-1}\,dz = 0$ for any Jordan curve C with

$$\mathcal{R}C \cup I(C) \subset (\mathcal{O} \cup \{a\}) \sim \{b\}$$

(here considering $g(z) = f(z)(z - b)^{-1}$ on $\mathscr{P} = \mathscr{O} \sim \{b\}$). Thus

$$f(b) = \left(\frac{1}{2\pi i}\right) \int_C f(z)(z - b)^{-1}\, dz$$

for any positively oriented Jordan curve C with $b \in I(C)$, $\mathscr{R}C \cup I(C) \subset \mathscr{O} \cup \{a\}$. Use this to show that

$$f(a) = \left(\frac{1}{2\pi i}\right) \int_C f(z)(z - a)^{-1}\, dz$$

continuously extends f to $\mathscr{O} \cup \{a\}$. Finally show that this extension has the property that $\int_C f\, dz = 0$ for any rectifiable Jordan curve C with $I(C) \cup \mathscr{R}C \subset \mathscr{O} \cup \{a\}$, and use DeMorera's theorem.)

(b) If a is a pole, $b =_1 a^*$, $b \neq a^*$, then $b \in \mathscr{O}^*$ and $|f^*(b)|$ is infinite, thus if a is a pole, $\lim_{z \to a} |f(z)| = \infty$.

(c) If f is analytic on $\mathscr{O}$, every singularity of $1/f$ on $\mathscr{O}$ is isolated and a pole.

(d) If a is essential, $st\,[f^*[m(a)]] = \mathbb{C}$. (HINT: Otherwise for some $c \in \mathbb{C}$, $1/[f(z) - c] = g(z)$ is analytic on $\mathscr{O} \sim \{a\}$ and bounded on some neighborhood of a, thus can be extended analytically to a. Thus $1/[g(z)] = f(z) - c$ is analytic at or has a pole at a, a contradiction.)

5.4.5 (Residues and the counting of poles and zeros.) Let $f\colon \mathscr{O} \to \mathbb{C}$ be analytic, $a_1, \ldots, a_n \in I(C)$, $I(C) \cup \mathscr{R}C \subset \mathscr{O} \cup \{a_1, \ldots, a_n\}$, C positively oriented. Then

$$(R_{a_j} f)^* = \left(\frac{1}{2\pi i}\right)^* \int^*_{C(a_j^*, r)} f^*\, dz \qquad \text{for any } r -_1 0,\ r > 0.$$

Note that by 5.4.17 (c),

$$\frac{1}{2\pi i} \int_C f\, dz = \sum_{j=1}^{n} R_{a_j} f.$$

(a) If f is analytic at a_j, then $R_{a_j} f = 0$, and if f has a pole of order k at a_j, then

$$R_{a_j} f = \lim_{z \to a_j} \frac{((z - a_j)^k f(z))^{(k-1)}}{(k - 1)!}.$$

Let f be analytic on $\mathscr{O}$,

$$\mathscr{P} = \mathscr{O} \cup \{a \mid a \text{ is a pole of } f\}.$$

For $a \in \mathscr{P}$, we define $\mu_f(a)$ as follows: If $a \in \mathscr{O}$, $\mu_f(a) = n$, where $n \in \omega$ is such that $f(z) = (z - a)^n g(z)$, g analytic on $\mathscr{O}$, $g(a) \neq 0$ (show that such an n exists), if a is a pole, $\mu_f(a) = -k$, where k is the order of that pole.

(b) $\mu_f(a) = R_a(f'/f)$, thus if C is a positively oriented curve with $I(C) \cup \mathscr{R}C \subset \mathcal{O}$, $\mathscr{R}C \subset \mathcal{O}$ then

$$\frac{1}{2\pi i}\int_C \left(\frac{f'}{f}\right) dz = \sum_{a \in I(C)} \mu_f(a),$$

and this is a finite sum. Also note that

$$\mu_{fg}(a) = \mu_f(a) + \mu_g(a) \qquad \text{for each} \qquad a \in \mathcal{O}.$$

(c) Let f, g be analytic on $\mathcal{O}$, $I(C) \cup \mathscr{R}C \subset \mathcal{O}$, and for $z \in \mathscr{R}C$, $|g(z)| < |f(z)|$. Then $f + g$ has exactly as many zeros on $I(C)$ (counting multiplicities) as f. (HINT: For

$$z \in \mathbb{C}+ = \mathbb{C} \sim \{x \in \mathbb{R} \mid x \leq 0\}$$

write

$$z = e^{x+iy}, \qquad -\pi < y < \pi,$$

and note that since $z \to x + iy$ is an inverse to the exponential function on this set, it is analytic; call this map ln. The number we want is

$$\sum_{a \in I(C)} \mu_{f+g}(a) = \sum_{a \in I(C)} \mu_f(a) + \sum_{a \in I(C)} \mu_{1+(g/f)}(a),$$

$$\left(1 + \frac{g}{f}\right) [\mathscr{R}C] \subset \mathbb{C}+,$$

so $\ln \circ (1 + g/f)\colon \mathscr{R}C \to \mathbb{C}$. Now use 5.4.9 (b).)

(d) f is locally one-one at a iff $f^* \mid m(a)$ is one-one. For f analytic in some open set containing, show that f is locally one-one at a iff $f'(a) \neq 0$. (HINT: We can in fact show f locally n-one at a, i.e., $f^* \mid m(a) \sim \{a^*\}$ takes n distinct points onto each point in $m(a) \sim \{a^*\}$, where $f^{(n)}(a)$ is the first nonzero derivative of f at a. Since $f(z) = f(a) + (z - a)^n g(z)$ for some analytic g with $g(a) \neq 0$, let

$$|z - a^*| < r, \qquad 0 < r =_1 0.$$

If $0 < b < |g(a)^*|$, then

$$|(z - a^*)^{n^*} g^*(z)| \geq |z - a^*|^{n^*} b^*,$$

so choose w that satisfies

$$|w - f(a)^*| < |z - a^*|^{n^*} b^*.$$

Then

$$f^*(z) - w = ((z - a^*)^{n^*} g^*(z)) + (f(a)^* - w),$$

so by (c), $f^*(z) - w$ has as many roots, counting multiplicities as $(z - a^*)^{n^*} g^*(z)$ does in $I(C(a^*, r))$, namely n. Why are they distinct and why does this assure us that *each* $w \in m(a) \sim \{a^*\}$ is covered n times?)

5.4.6 Let $f\colon \mathcal{O} \to \mathbb{C}$, $a \in \mathcal{O}$. f is conformal at a iff for every $r > 0$ such that $r =_1 0$, if

$$b = a^* + r(e^{it})^*, \qquad c = a^* + r(e^{i(t+s)})^*,$$

then

$$f^*(b) = f(a)^* + r'(e^{it'})^* \quad \text{and} \quad f^*(c) = f(a)^* + r''(e^{i(t'+s)})^*,$$
$$0 < r', \quad r'' =_1 0.$$

f is conformal on $\mathcal{O}$ iff f is conformal at each $a \in \mathcal{O}$.

(a) Show that the following are equivalent:

(i) f is analytic on $\mathcal{O}$ with nonvanishing derivative.

(ii) f is real-differentiable on $\mathcal{O}$ and conformal on $\mathcal{O}$.

(b) Let C, D be curves, $C(t_1) = D(t_2)$, then $< (C, D, t_1, t_2) = \lim_{h\to 0} \theta_h$, where

$$\frac{C(t_1 + h) - C(t_1)}{D(t_1 + h) - D(t_1)} = r_h e^{i\theta_h}$$

(if this is defined). Show that f is conformal at a iff f is continuous at a and for every pair C, D of curves and t_1, t_2 of points such that $< (C, D, t_1, t_2)$ exists and $C(t_1) = D(t_2) = a$,

$$< (f\circ C, f\circ D, t_1, t_2) = < (C, D, t_1, t_2).$$

(c) If f is analytic show that

$$< (f\circ C, f\circ D, t_1, t_2) = k < (C, D, t_1, t_2)$$

for the first k such that $f^{(k)}(C(t_1)) \neq 0$.

5.4.7 Give examples to justify the comments following Lemma 5.4.5; however also show that if $f \in \mathrm{CON}^*$ is bounded then $st\,[\mathscr{R}f]$ is connected, where

$$\mathrm{CON} = \{g \mid g \text{ is continuous and } \mathscr{R}g \text{ is connected}\}.$$

‡5.4.8 If $D \in C/$, $x, y \in \mathscr{D}D$, $x < y$, show that for some $w, z \in \mathscr{D}C$, $w < z$, $C(w) = D(x)$ and $C(z) = D(y)$.

‡5.4.9 We often take statements true for the set P of polygons and use them for P^* (as in the proofs of Lemma 5.4.5 and Theorem 5.4.7). Use Proposition 5.2.1 (a) to justify this. (Work carefully, recalling the admonition in the last three paragraphs of Section 5.1.)

5.5 The Bernstein-Robinson Theorem

Definition 5.5.1. A normed space is a vector space V over $\mathfrak{F}$ (= $\mathbb{R}$ or $\mathbb{C}$ in this section), together with a function $\|\ \|\colon V \to \mathbb{R}$ such that if $x, y \in V$, $r \in \mathfrak{F}$ then:

(i) $\|x + y\| \leq \|x\| + \|y\|$.

(ii) $\|rx\| = |r|\,\|x\|$.

(iii) If $x \neq 0$, $\|x\| > 0$.

A normed space complete under the metric $d(x, y) = \|x - y\|$ is called a Banach space.

We define * as usual (see, for example, the beginning of Section 5.2), as usual

$$m(x) = \{y \mid \|y - x^*\| =_1 0\} \qquad \text{for} \quad x \in V,$$

and for $y \in \bigcup_{x \in V} m(x)$, $St(y) = x$ for the (necessarily unique) x with $y \in m(x)$. V^* is a vector space over $\mathfrak{F}^*$, thus over $\mathfrak{F}$. The following are clear:

Lemma 5.5.2. (a) $m(0) \subset \mathscr{D}St \subset \{x \in V^* \mid \|x\| \in \mathscr{D}st\}$, and all are $\mathfrak{F}$-subspaces of V^*. From now on we use the notation

$$N_V = \{x \in V^* \mid \|x\| \in \mathscr{D}st\},$$

and refer to N_V as the set of norm-finite vectors.

(b) St is $\mathfrak{F}$-linear on $\mathscr{D}St$ with kernel $m(0)$, and for $x \in V$, $St(x^*) = x$.

(c) For $x \in \mathscr{D}St$, $st(\|x\|) = \|St(x)\|$.

(d) V is a Banach space iff for every $a\colon \omega \to V$, if for every $m, n \in \omega'$, $a_m^* =_1 a_n^*$ (i.e., $a_m^* - a_n^* \in m(0)$), then for every $m \in \omega'$, $a_m^* \in \mathscr{D}St$.

The nonstandard definitions for open and closed remain the same in our setting, and a set X remains compact iff $X^* \subset \mathscr{D}St$ and $X = St[X^*]$ (iff $\langle X, C_i\rangle_{i \in I}$ has the finite satisfaction property for positive formulas for any collection $\{C_i \mid i \in I\}$ of closed subsets of X), but it is no longer true that all closed bounded sets are compact (see Problem 5.5.1).

Conditions for continuity and uniform continuity remain the same here as those stated in Theorem 5.3.3 for $\mathbb{R}^n$, and sums and scalar products of continuous functions remain continuous. In fact, Theorems 5.3.3 and 5.3.4 extend to our case.

Norm is no longer unique, however, and not all linear transformations are continuous, but Lemma 5.3.7 extends to our case (stating that continuity, uniform continuity, continuity at 0, and boundedness are equivalent for linear transformations).

If V, W are normed spaces over the same field,

$$CH(V, W) = \{T\colon V \to W \mid T \text{ linear and continuous}\},$$

and Lemma 5.3.9 largely extends to our case with CH replacing H. It still assures us that $CH(V, W)$ is a normed space, $\|TU\| \leq \|T\|\,\|U\|$ when TU is defined, $CH(V, V)$ is an algebra, and for $U \in U(V)$,

$$\|UT\| \geq \|U^{-1}\|^{-1}\|T\|.$$

It may not be that $U(V)$ is open, however:

Lemma 5.5.3. (a) If W is a Banach space, so is $CH(V, W)$.

(b) If V is a Banach space, $U(V)$ is open and $^{-1}$: $U(V) \to U(V)$ continuous.

Proof: (a) Let T_m be Cauchy, then for $m, n \in \omega'$, $T_m^* =_1 T_n^*$; thus if $x \in V$, $T_m^*(x^*) =_1 T_n^*(x^*)$, since

$$\|(T_m^* - T_n^*)(x^*)\| \leq \|T_m^* - T_n^*\| \, \|x^*\|.$$

$T_m^*(x^*) \in \mathscr{D}St$, so we may define T: $V \to W$ by

$$T(x) = St(T_m^*(x^*)) \qquad \text{for} \quad x \in V, \quad m \in \omega'.$$

Since $| \, \|T_m^*\| - \|T_n^*\| \, | \leq \|T_m^* - T_n^*\|$,

$$\|T_m^*\| =_1 \|T_n^*\| \qquad \text{for} \quad m, n \in \omega';$$

if $x \in V^*$, $x \neq 0$, then

$$\frac{\|T^*(x)\|}{\|x\|} =_1 \frac{\|T_m^*(x^*)\|}{\|x\|},$$

so

$$st\left(\frac{\|T^*(x)\|}{\|x\|}\right) \leq st\|T_m^*\|,$$

thus T is continuous and

$$\|T\| \leq st\|T_m^*\|;$$

however, we can choose $x \in V^*$ with

$$\frac{\|T_m^*(x^*)\|}{\|x\|} =_1 \|T_m^*\|, \qquad \text{thus} \quad \|T\| = st\|T_m^*\|,$$

so in fact $T \in CH(V, W)$ (the linearity of T is easy to check) and $\|T\| = \lim_{n \to \infty} \|T_n\|$.

(b) We have now established all nontrivial facts needed to show $CH(V, V)$ a Banach algebra under the usual multiplication and norm, and the proof of Lemma 5.3.9(d) extends to show this result for Banach algebras, where:

Definition 5.5.4. A Banach algebra is a Banach space together with a multiplication under which it is a ring with identity, and

(i) $\|I\| = 1$, where I is the identity;
(ii) if $x, y \in V$, $\|xy\| \leq \|x\| \, \|y\|$.

5.3.10–5.3.15 establishing calculus and the mean value and implicit function theorems for finite dimensional vector spaces extend with essentially unchanged proofs to the Banach space case provided we replace $H(V, W)$ with $CH(V, W)$ throughout.

We should explain, however, that our interest in this section is not in developing the theories of the structures we glance at, but in proving the Bernstein–Robinson theorem (5.5.14).

Let $T \in H(V, W)$. T is called compact iff for each bounded $X \subset V$ (X is bounded iff for some $r > 0$, if $x \in X$, $\|x\| \leq r$), $T[X] \subset W$ has compact closure.

Definition 5.5.5. *T* is compact iff $T^*[N_V] \subset \mathscr{D}St$ (in W).

Proof: First note that X is bounded iff $X^* \subset N_V$ (see the proof of Proposition 5.2.1(d)), and an application of the formula

$$(\forall v_1)(\|v_1\| < c_n \rightarrow P_X(v_1))$$

in 5.2.1(a) shows that $N_V = \bigcup \{X^* \mid X \text{ bounded}\}$. Also note that X^- is compact iff $X^* \subset \mathscr{D}St$, for if X^- is compact, $X^* \subset X^{-*} \subset \mathscr{D}St$, but if $X^* \subset \mathscr{D}St$, then for $r > 0$, $y \in X^-$, there is an $x \in X$ such that

$$\|y - x\| < r;$$

thus for $y \in X^{-*}$ there is an $x \in X^*$ with $x =_1 y$ but $x \in \mathscr{D}St$ so $y \in \mathscr{D}St$.

Thus if $T^*[N_V] \subset \mathscr{D}St$ and X is bounded,

$$T[X]^* = T^*[X^*] \subset T^*[N_V] \subset \mathscr{D}St$$

so $T[X]^-$ is compact.

Conversely if T is compact, $y \in N_V$, then $y \in X^*$ for some bounded X, thus

$$T^*(y) \in T^*[X^*] \subset T[X]^* \subset \mathscr{D}St.$$

Definition 5.5.6. A Hilbert space is a vector space over $\mathfrak{F}$, H, equipped with a map $\cdot : H \times H \to \mathfrak{F}$ such that for each $x, y, z \in H$, $r \in \mathfrak{F}$,

(i) $(x + ry) \cdot z = x \cdot z + r(y \cdot z)$;

(ii) $x \cdot y = \overline{y \cdot x}$ (the complex conjugate of $x \cdot y$);

(iii) if $x \neq 0$, $x \cdot x > 0$;

and such that H is a Banach space under the norm $\|x\| = \sqrt{x \cdot x}$.

Of course we have not yet shown that $\| \ \|$ is actually a norm.

LEMMA 5.5.7. (a) (Schwarz Inequality) If $x, y \in H$ then $|x \cdot y|^2 \leq (x \cdot x)(y \cdot y)$.

(b) $\| \ \|$ is a norm.

(c) If $\sum_{i \in I} x_i$ converges in a normed space, then for some countable subset $J \subset I$, if $i \notin J$ then $x_i = 0$. Here we say $\sum_{i \in I} x_i = x$ iff for each $r > 0$ there is a finite $I' \subset I$ such that $\|x - \sum_{i \in I'} x_i\| < r$, and $\sum_{i \in I} x_i$ converges iff for some $x \in V$, $\sum_{i \in I} x_i = x$.

(d) Let V, W be closed subspaces of a Hilbert space H, $V \subset W$, X an orthonormal basis for V. Then there is an orthonormal basis Y for W such that $X \subset Y$, where an orthonormal basis Z of a Hilbert space H is a set $Z = \{z_i \mid i \in I\}$ such that for $i, j \in I$,

$$z_i \cdot z_j = \begin{cases} 1 & \text{if } i = j \\ 0 & \text{if } i \neq j \end{cases},$$

and every element of H can be written (necessarily uniquely) in the form $\sum_{i \in I} a_i z_i$ with $\{a_i \mid i \in I\} \subset \mathfrak{F}$.

Any two orthonormal bases of a Hilbert space can be put in one-one correspondence and any one-one correspondence between orthonormal bases can be extended by linearity and completion to a linear isometry between the two spaces (i.e. a linear mapping assumed onto and necessarily one-one such that $\|x\| = \|T(x)\|$ for each $x \in H$; it can be shown that this condition is equivalent to the statement that for each $x, y \in H$, $x \cdot y = T(x) \cdot T(y)$).

Since there is such a basis (ϕ, the orthonormal basis of $\{0\}$ can be extended to one for H) and all are in one-one correspondence, we call their common cardinality the dimension of H. We know by the previous paragraph that any two spaces over $\mathfrak{F}$ of equal dimension are isometrically isomorphic.

(e) Let $T \in CH(H, H)$, $\dim H > \omega$. Then there is a closed subspace V of H such that $\{0\} \neq V \neq H$ and $T[V] \subset V$.

Proof: (a) through (d) are standard fare and, in general, we prefer giving references here to giving the proofs. These proofs may be found on the following pages of Halmos, *Introduction to Hilbert Space*: (a) p. 15, (b) p. 16, (c) p. 19 (however, part of Problem 5.5.2 is devoted to finding a nonstandard proof for this fact), and for (d) the existence of an orthonormal basis is shown by applying Zorn's lemma to Theorem 2, p. 23, of that book (which states that if $V \subset W$, $V \neq W$ there is a vector $x \neq 0$ in W such that $x \cdot y = 0$ for each $y \in V$), the existence of a one-one correspondence between any two such bases of the same space is established on p. 29, while the extension of such a one-one mapping to a linear isometry is shown on p. 30, as well as the fact that it preserves inner products.

For (e), let $x \in H \sim \{0\}$; for $n < \omega$, we construct a vector space V_n and orthonormal basis $Y_n = \{y_1, \ldots, y_m\}$, $m \leq n$ for V_n as follows. Let

$$V_n = \{r_0 x + \cdots + r_{n-1} T^{n-1}(x) \mid r_0, \ldots, r_{n-1} \in \mathfrak{F}\}$$
$$\text{for} \quad n \geq 1 (V_0 = \{0\}, \; Y_0 = \phi),$$
$$Y_n = \{y_1, \ldots, y_m\}.$$

If $T^n(x) \in V_n$, let $Y_{n+1} = Y_n$, otherwise extend Y_n to an orthonormal basis Y_{n+1} for V_{n+1}; since $V_{n+1} \neq V_n$ in this case $Y_{n+1} \neq Y_n$, however, $\dim V_{n+1} = \dim V_n + 1 = m + 1$, thus any independent set of vectors has at most $m + 1$ elements, and since any orthonormal set is independent, Y_{n+1} must have exactly $m + 1$ elements $\{y_1, \ldots, y_{m+1}\}$ and $m + 1 \leq n + 1$.

Let $V = (\bigcup_{n \in \omega} V_n)^-$; it can easily be shown that $\bigcup_{n \in \omega} Y_n$ is a basis for V, so $\dim V \leq \omega$, thus $V \neq H$ and $0 \neq x \in V$, so $V \neq \{0\}$. Also

$$T\left[\bigcup_{n \in \omega} V_n\right] = \bigcup_{n \in \omega} T[V_n] \subset \bigcup_{n \in \omega} V_{n+1} = \bigcup_{n \in \omega} V_n,$$

and since T is continuous, $T[V] \subset V$ (see Problem 5.5.2). Our proof is now complete, and could have been shorter but we intend to use the above construction in the proof of 5.5.14.

LEMMA 5.5.8. Let V be a vector space over $\mathbb{C}$ (or any algebraically closed field), $T \in H(V, V)$, $\dim V = n < \omega$. Then there is a sequence of subspaces $V_1 \subset \cdots \subset V_{n-1}$ of V such that for $1 \leq j \leq n$, $\dim V_j = j$ and $T[V_j] \subset V_j$.

Proof: Consider the map $\varphi_T \colon \mathbb{C}[X] \to H(V, V)$ defined by

$$\varphi_T\left(\sum_{k=0}^{p} r_k X^k\right) = \sum_{k=0}^{p} r_k T^k.$$

This can easily be checked a ring homomorphism. Thus it is, in particular, a linear transformation from an infinite dimensional vector space into a finite dimensional one ($\dim \mathbb{C}[X] = \omega$, any linear algebra text shows

$$\dim H(V, W) = \dim V \cdot \dim W$$

for finite dimensional spaces, by the fact that elements of $H(V, W)$ are essentially matrices—note that in this parenthetical remark we have used dimension to mean cardinality of an algebraic (Hamel) basis rather than an orthonormal basis, but this is the only point in the chapter at which we do this), so there is a nonzero polynomial f such that $\varphi_T(f) = 0$.

Let f_T be such a polynomial of minimal degree; since $\mathbb{C}$ is algebraically closed we may write $f_T = r(X - r_1)\cdots(X - r_m)$; let

$$g = r(X - r_1)\cdots(X - r_{m-1}).$$

Then there is a $z \in V$ such that $y = g(T)(z) \neq 0$ (where we write $f(T)$ in place of $\varphi_T(f)$). Thus

$$(T - r_m I)(y) = (T - r_m I)(g(T)(z)) = f_T(T)(z) = 0,$$

so $T(y) = r_m y$. Thus $V_1 = \{sy \mid s \in \mathbb{C}\}$ has the property $T[V_1] \subset V_1$. Now let $W = V/V_1$ and define $T'\colon W \to W$ by $T'(x + V_1) = T(x) + V_1$ (T' is a map since if $x + V_1 = x' + V_1$, then $x - x' \in V_1$, so

$$T(x) - T(x') = T(x - x') \in V_1, \qquad \text{thus} \quad T(x) + V_1 = T(x') + V_1).$$

We now proceed by induction, assuming that since $\dim V = \dim W + 1$ we have $W_1, \ldots, W_{n-2}$, and for $i = 2, \ldots, n-1$ let

$$V_i = \{x \mid x + V_1 \in W_{i-1}\}.$$

Then for $i = 1, \ldots, n-1$ $\dim V_i = i$, $V_1 \subset \cdots \subset V_{n-1}$, and if $x \in V_i$, $i > 1$, then

$$x + V_i \in W_{i-1}, \qquad \text{so} \qquad T(x) + V_1 = T'(x + V_1) \in W_{i-1},$$

thus

$$T(x) \in V_i, \qquad \text{so} \qquad T[V_i] \subset V_i.$$

Thus we note that if $T \in CH(H, H)$, H a Hilbert space over $\mathbb{C}$ of dimension other than ω (also trivially other than 0, 1), there is a closed subspace $V \neq H$, $V \neq \{0\}$ such that $T[V] \subset V$, and it seems reasonable to ask whether this holds for all Hilbert spaces over $\mathbb{C}$ (note that by Theorem 5.3.4 finite dimensional spaces are complete under the usual norm, essentially unique by Proposition 5.3.6, thus they are complete under our norm, thus closed by comments following Lemma 5.5.2 and Theorem 5.3.2(a); we have assumed this fact here). This question remains open, and our interest in it is due to the fact that the best result to date concerning it (and completely resolving a question due to Halmos and Smith, see Halmos [2]) was proven first by nonstandard means. This is of importance; since standard ("epsilon-delta") methods have been used almost exclusively for the past 150 years, most results in nonstandard analysis have been new proofs of old theorems previously established by standard means. This result shows that new theorems in analysis can be discovered and shown using the intuition and methods of nonstandard analysis.

We now introduce the class of operators studied by Bernstein and Robinson [1] and continue in the direction of their proof. Since our class is a subclass of $CH(H, H)$, our theorem will be true for all Hilbert spaces of dimension other than ω (and 0, 1). Thus from now on we consider, unless otherwise stated only those (all isomorphic) of dimension ω.

DEFINITION 5.5.9.

$$PH(H, H) = \{T \in CH(H, H) \mid \text{for some non-constant } f \in C[X], \ f(T)\ (= \varphi_T(f)) \text{ is compact}\}.$$

If $Y = \{y_1, \ldots\}$ is an orthonormal basis, we can always write $T(y_n) = \sum_{m=0}^{\infty} r_{mn} y_m$, and T is determined completely by its values on Y, thus by the r_{mn}. (r_{mn}) is called the matrix for T; note that formally (r_{mn}) is a map from $(\omega \sim \{0\}) \times (\omega \sim \{0\})$ into our field. T is called almost superdiagonal with respect to Y iff $r_{mn} = 0$ whenever $n + 1 < m$. Finally, V is called an invariant subspace for T iff V is a closed subspace of H other than $\{0\}$ and H itself, and $T[V] \subset V$.

Given any $T \in CH(H, H)$ the construction used in the proof of 5.5.7(e) yields a basis Y with respect to which T is almost superdiagonal, since $y_n \in V_n$ and $T[V_n] \subset V_{n+1}$ for which $\{y_1, \ldots, y_{n+1}\}$ is a basis.

LEMMA 5.5.10. Let $T \in PH(H, H)$. Then for some $n \in \omega'$, $r^*_{n+1,n} =_1 0$.

Proof: If $T' = c_0 + \cdots + c_k T^k$ is compact, $c_k \neq 0$, let (s_{mn}) be the matrix of T'. Note that $s^*_{m,n} =_1 0$ for $m \in \omega'$, because $T'(y^*_n) \in \mathscr{D}St$. For any $h > 0$, we see by direct computation that

$$s^*_{h+k^*,h} = (c_k)^* r^*_{h+1,h} \cdots r^*_{h+k^*,h+k^*-1}$$

and since for $h \in \omega'$, $c_k \neq 0$, $s^*_{h+k^*,h} =_1 0$, we must have

$$r^*_{h+j,h+j-1} =_1 0 \text{ for some } \quad j \in \{1, \ldots, k^*\},$$

so

$$\text{if} \quad n = h + j - 1, \qquad \text{then} \quad r^*_{n+1,n} =_1 0.$$

Now note that if $V \subset H$ is a closed subspace then there is a projection $P_V \colon H \to V$, i.e., a $P_V \in CH(H, H)$ such that $P_V \mid V$ is the identity map on V,

$$P_V^2 = P_V, \qquad P_V[H] = V \qquad \text{and} \qquad \|P_V\| = 1 \qquad (\text{if } V \neq \{0\});$$

in fact, P_V may be defined by extending an orthonormal basis $X = \{y_j \mid j \in J\}$ for V to one $Y = \{y_i \mid i \in I\}$ for H and defining

$$P_V\Big(\sum_{i \subset I} a_i y_i\Big) = \sum_{i \in J} a_i y_i.$$

It is easy to check the properties listed above as well as the important property: If $h \in H$, $v \in V$, then

$$\|h - P_V(h)\| \leq \|h - v\|;$$

for if $z \in V$, then

$$(h - P_V(h)) \cdot z = 0,$$

so if $v \in V$, let $z = v - P_V(h)$, then

$$\begin{aligned}(h - v) \cdot (h - v) &= (h - P_V(h) - z) \cdot (h - P_V(h) - z) \\ &= (h - P_V(h)) \cdot (h - P_V(h)) - (h - P_V(h)) \cdot z \\ &\qquad - z \cdot (h - P_V(h)) + z \cdot z \\ &= (h - P_V(h)) \cdot (h - P_V(h)) + z \cdot z \\ &\geq (h - P_V(h)) \cdot (h - P_V(h)).\end{aligned}$$

Thus if $V \in CLS^*$, where CLS is the set of all closed subspaces of H, then $x \in St[V]$ iff for some $y =_1 x^*$, $y \in V$ iff $\|x^* - P_V(x^*)\| =_1 0$, i.e. iff $x = St(P_V(x^*))$.

We shall also find it convenient to denote by FLS the set of finite dimensional subspaces of H and by LS the set of all subspaces.

Since every subspace of a finite dimensional space is finite dimensional, $(FLS)^*$ has this property as well, thus if $V \subset W \in FLS^*$, $V \in LS^*$, then $V \in FLS^* \subset CLS^*$.

LEMMA 5.5.11. Let $V \in CLS^*$. Then $St[V]$ is a closed subspace of H.

Proof: $St[V]$ is clearly in LS, since if $x_1 = St(y_1)$, $x_2 = St(y_2)$, y_1, $y_2 \in V$, then

$$\|x_1^* - y_1\| =_1 0 =_1 \|x_2^* - y_2\|,$$

so if $r \in \mathfrak{F}$,

$$\|(x_1 + r^*x_2) - (y_1 + r^*y_2)\| \leq \|x_1^* - y_1\| + |r^*|\, \|x_2^* - y_2\| =_1 0,$$

so

$$x_1 + rx_2 = St(y_1 + r^*y_2) \in St[V].$$

Now let $x \in St[V]^-$, $x_n \to x$. Then for every $m \in \omega'$, $x_m^* =_1 x^*$. However, for each $n \in \omega$,

$$\|x_{n^*}^* - P_V(x_{n^*}^*)\| =_1 0,$$

thus by Problem 5.2.12 there is an $m \in \omega'$ such that $x_m^* =_1 P_V(x_m^*)$. Thus

$$x^* =_1 P_V(x_m^*) \qquad \text{so} \qquad x = St(P_V(x_m^*)) \in St[V].$$

Assume that $\{y_n \mid n \in \omega \sim \{0\}\}$ is a basis for H, and for $m \in \omega^*$ let

$$H_m = \left\{ \sum_{j=1}^{m} r_j y_j^* \mid j = 1, \ldots, m, r_1, \ldots, r_m \in \omega^* \right\} \text{ if } m \neq 0, \; H_0 = \{0\},$$

$H_m \in FLS^*$ thus is in CLS^*, thus there is a projection, which we shall call P from H^* onto H_m. If $m \in \omega'$, $x \in H$, then $x^* =_1 P(x^*)$. If $T \in CH(H, H)$, let $T' = PTP$, $T_m = T' \mid H_m$. Then

$$\|T_m\| \leq \|T'\| \leq \|P\|^2 \|T\| \leq \|T\|,$$

$$T_m \colon H_m \to H_m, \qquad \text{and} \qquad PT' = T' = T'P.$$

PROPOSITION 5.5.12. Let $V \in CLS^*$, $m \in \omega'$, $T_m[V] \subset V$. Then

$$T[St[V]] \subset St[V].$$

Proof: Let $x \in St[V]$; then

$$\begin{aligned} \|T(x)^* - T_m(x^*)\| &\leq \|T(x)^* - PT(x^*)\| + \|PT(x^*) - T_m(x^*)\| \\ &\leq \|T(x)^* - P(T(x)^*)\| + \|PT(x^* - P(x^*))\| \\ &\leq \|T(x)^* - P(T(x)^*)\| + \|P\| \, \|T\| \, \|x^* - P(x^*)\| \\ &=_1 0 \end{aligned}$$

by the above discussion, so

$$T(x)^* =_1 T_m(x^*) \in V, \qquad \text{thus} \qquad T(x) \in St[V].$$

LEMMA 5.5.13. Let $E \subset V \subset H_m$, E, $V \in LS^*$, $\dim V \leq \dim E + 1$. Then $St[V]/St[E]$ is a vector space of dimension at most 1.

Proof: Let x_1, $x_2 \in St[V] \sim St[E]$ (if $St[V] = St[E]$ we are clearly through), then $x_j = St(y_j)$ with $y_j \in V$ for $j = 1, 2$. By our assumption, for some r_1, $r_2 \in \mathfrak{F}^*$, e_1, $e_2 \in E$, $y_{3-j} = r_j y_j + e_j$ for $j = 1$ or 2 (not necessarily both). For any such expression, $r_j \neq_1 0$ since otherwise

$$x_{3-j} = St(r_j y_j + e_j) = St(e_j) \in St[E]$$

because

$$st\|y_j\| = \|x_j\| \in \mathbb{R} \qquad \text{so} \qquad \|r_j y_j\| = |r_j^*| \, \|y_j\| =_1 0.$$

However this implies that $r_j \in \mathscr{D}st$ as well, for otherwise

$$y_j = \left(\frac{1}{r_j}\right) y_{3-j} - \left(\frac{1}{r_j}\right) e_j$$

is an expression of the form

$$y_j = r_{3-j} y_{3-j} + e_{3-j} \qquad \text{with} \quad r_{3-j} =_1 0,$$

contradicting the previous sentence.

Thus for $j = 1$ or 2,

$$y_{3-j} = r_j y_j + e_j \qquad \text{with} \quad 0 \neq r_j \in \mathscr{D}st,$$

so

$$\begin{aligned} x_{3-j} &= St(y_{3-j}) = St(r_j y_j + e_j) = st(r_j)St(y_j) + St(e_j) \\ &= st(r_j)x_j + St(e_j), \end{aligned}$$

so

$$x_{3-j} \in st(r_j)x_j + St[E],$$

completing the proof (note that $e_j \in \mathscr{D}St$ because $e_j = y_{3-j} - r_j y_j$).

We now look once again at the construction used in the proof of 5.5.7(e). If for some n, $T^n(x) \in V_n$, then let

$$y = r_0 x + \cdots + r_{n-1}T^{n-1}(x) \in V_n,$$

so

$$T(y) = T(r_0 x + \cdots + r_{n-1}T^{n-1}(x)) = r_0 T(x) + \cdots + r_{n-1}T^n(x) \in V_n,$$

so $T[V_n] \subset V_n$. Thus if $\dim H = \omega$, $0 \neq x \in V_n \neq H$ so V_n is an invariant subspace for T.

THEOREM 5.5.14. If $T \in PH(H, H)$ and $\dim(H) \geq 2$, then T has an invariant subspace.

Proof: Let $0 \neq x \in H$ and construct as in the proof of 5.5.7(e) a subspace V and basis Y for V. By previous comments, we know that T is almost superdiagonal with respect to Y, and that we may assume that $\dim H = \omega$, $V = H$. We also know that for some $m \in \omega'$, $a_{m,m+1} =_1 0$. Now consider H_m and the P, T' and T_m constructed from it in the comments preceding 5.5.12. Let

$$y = \sum_{j \in \omega^*} r_j y_j^* \in N_H,$$

then

$$\|y\| = \sqrt{\sum_{j \in \omega^*} |r_j|^2} \in \mathscr{D}st,$$

so $r_j \in \mathscr{D}st$ for each $j \in \omega^*$. Thus

$$\begin{aligned} (T^*P - T')(y) &= (I - P)T^*P(y) \\ &= (I - P)T^*\left(\sum_{j=0}^{m} r_j y_j^*\right) \\ &= (I - P)\left(\sum_{j=0}^{m} r_j \left(\sum_{k=0}^{j+1} a_{kj}^* y_k^*\right)\right) \\ &= r_m a_{m+1,m}^* y_{m+1}^* \\ &=_1 0. \end{aligned}$$

We now show by induction on deg(p) that if $y, y' \in N_H$, $y =_1 y'$, $p \in \mathbb{C}[X]$ then

$$p(T)^*P(y) =_1 p^*(T')P(y'),$$

noting that by the above for such y, y',

$$T^*P(y) =_1 T'(y) =_1 T'(y')$$

(the last $=_1$ is due to the fact that $\|T'\| \in \mathscr{D}st$, for if $\|U\| \in \mathscr{D}st$, $y =_1 y'$, then

$$\|U(y) - U(y')\| \leq \|U\| \, \|y - y'\| =_1 0).$$

If $p \in \mathbb{C}[X]$, $p = gX + r$ for some $g \in \mathbb{C}[X]$ with $g = 0$ or $\deg(g) = \deg(p) - 1$, $r \in \mathbb{C}$, thus we may assume our result for g, so

$$\begin{aligned} p(T)^*P(y) &= (gX + r)(T)^*P(y) \\ &= (g(T)T + rI)^*P(y) \\ &= g(T)^*T^*P(y) + r^*P(y) \\ &=_1 g(T)^*T'(y') + r^*P(y') \\ &= g(T)^*PT'(y') + r^*P(y') \\ &=_1 g^*(T')PT'(y') + r^*P(y') \\ &= g^*(T')T'P(y') + r^*P(y') \\ &= p^*(T')P(y'). \end{aligned}$$

By Lemma 5.5.8 we have $H_1 \subset \cdots \subset H_{m-1}$ subspaces of H_m with $\dim H_j = j$ and $T[H_j] \subset H_j$ for $j = 1, \ldots, m - 1$. The H_j's are in FLS^* so we may choose projections P_j, $j = 1, \ldots, m - 1$ of H^* on H_j, and let $P_m = P$. Now let $f(T)$ be compact. If $z \in H \sim \{0\}$, we may assume that $f(T)(z) \neq 0$, for otherwise $z, \ldots, T^n(z)$ are linearly dependent, where $n = \deg(f)$, establishing the theorem by replacing x by z in the comments preceding its statement:

Thus let $z \in H$, $\|z\| = 1$. Then $z^* =_1 P(z^*)$, so

$$0 \neq_1 f(T)(z)^* =_1 f(T)^*P(z^*) =_1 f^*(T')P(z^*) =_1 f^*(T')(z^*),$$

so for some $r > 0$, $r^* < \|f^*(T')(z^*)\|$. Consider

$$r_j = \|f^*(T')(z^*) - f^*(T')P_j(z^*)\|, \qquad j = 1, \ldots, m,$$

and note that

$$r_j \leq \|f^*(T')\| \, \|z^* - P_j(z^*)\|.$$

$r_0 = \|f^*(T')(z^*)\| > r^*$, $r_m =_1 0$, so $r_m < r^*/2$. Thus for some $n \in \omega^*$,

$$r_{n-1} \geq \frac{r^*}{2}, \qquad r_n < \frac{r^*}{2}.$$

$St[H_{n-1}] \neq H$ because

$$\frac{r^*}{2} \leq \|f^*(T')\| \, \|z^* - P_{n-1}(z^*)\|,$$

so $0 \neq_1 \|z^* - P_{n-1}(z^*)\|$, thus $z^* \notin H_{n-1}$, $\{0\} \neq St[H_n]$ because

$$f^*(T')P_n(z^*) =_1 f(T)^*P_n(z^*) \in \mathscr{D}st,$$

but

$$\frac{r^*}{2} \geq \|f^*(T')(z^*)\| - \|f^*(T')P_n(z^*)\| > r^* - \|f^*(T')P_n(z^*)\|,$$

so

$$\|St(f^*(T')P_n(z^*))\|^* =_1 \|f^*(T')P_n(z^*)\| > \frac{r^*}{2},$$

thus $St(f^*(T')P_n(z^*)) \neq 0$. Because

$$St[H_{n-1}] \subset St[H_n] \qquad \text{and} \qquad \dim St[H_n] \leq \dim St[H_{n-1}] + 1,$$

one of the two must be neither H nor $\{0\}$, but since both are invariant under T (because $T'[H_j] \subset H_j$, using 5.5.12), that one must be our invariant subspace.

The above ends our formal discussion of nonstandard analysis. However, nonstandard analysis can be carried out for metric and general spaces, and problems devoted to this will be found at the end of this section. In fact, uniform spaces and virtually all other systems studied in analysis can be treated by these methods.

While a look into nonstandard analysis does not simplify every proof met in analysis (notably the Baire category theorem, which has not yet been proved more simply by the methods of nonstandard analysis; in one of our problems we ask the reader to mimic the usual standard proof in nonstandard terms) it always provides an alternative point of view, and one which we hope this chapter has shown often useful. Measure theory has proven a difficult subject for nonstandard analysis, but an interesting approach making the measure of a point infinitesimal is developed in a paper by Bernstein and Wattenberg to be found in *Applications of Model Theory to Algebra, Analysis and Probability*, edited by W. A. J. Luxemburg, a collection of papers virtually all of which (other than that by yours truly) should be of interest to the reader studying nonstandard analysis. Luxemburg's collection and Robinson's *Non-Standard Analysis* are the major references for the reader who has read all of Chapter 5. The formalism used in these works is somewhat different from ours, but the reader should not have much difficulty if he keeps the following points in mind: The theory of types is a method alternative to our construction of $\langle A, \in, \phi\rangle^*$

(see Section 5.1) for constructing sets, and sets of sets, etc., used in non-standard analysis, while a set $S \subset A^*$ is called internal if $S \in A^*$ (such as our spaces H_n in the proof of 5.5.14), external otherwise (such as $^*[\omega]$, ω').

Problems

‡5.5.1 (a) Show Lemma 5.5.2.

(b) $\{x \mid \|x\| \leq 1\}$ is a closed and bounded set, but not compact provided H is an infinite dimensional Hilbert space. (HINT: Let $x \in X^* \sim {}^*[X]$, where X is a basis for H.)

‡5.5.2 (a) If $T \in CH(B, B)$, B a Banach space, $V \subset B$ is a subspace, and $T[V] \subset V^-$, then $T[V^-] \subset V^-$.

(b) If D is a nonprincipal ultrafilter on ω, $X \in \mathrm{FIN}^*$, where FIN in the set of finite subsets of our universe A, then

$$c(\{x \in A \mid x^* \in X\}) \leq \omega.$$

(HINT: For $x^* \in X$, let $n(x) = \min\{n \mid x \in X_n\}$.)

(c) Use (b) to show 5.5.7 (c).

5.5.3 Show that if $T \in PH(H, H)$, H a Hilbert space of dimension > 2 over $\mathbb{R}$, then T has an invariant subspace (Bernstein, in his thesis, extended 5.5.14 to the case of a continuous operator in a Banach space, some non-constant analytic function of which is compact. In this thesis he also showed the spectral theorem by nonstandard means. Recently Bernstein has established the existence of common invariant subspaces for certain pairs of commuting continuous operators, one of which is compact.)

5.5.4 Let X be an arbitrary topological space, $\mathscr{T}$ its topology, $x \in X$. Then $m(x) = \bigcap\{\mathcal{O}^* \mid x \in \mathcal{O} \in \mathscr{T}\}$, $St \subset (\bigcup_{x \in X} m(x)) \times X$ is defined by $\langle y, x\rangle \in St$ iff $y \in m(x)$, and for $S \subset X$,

$$m(S) = \bigcap\{\mathcal{O}^* \mid S \subset \mathcal{O} \in \mathscr{T}\}.$$

Show:

(a) If $x^* \in m(y)$, then $m(x) \subset m(y)$.

(b) $\mathcal{O} \in \mathscr{T}$ iff $\bigcup_{x \in \mathcal{O}} m(x) \subset \mathcal{O}^*$.

(c) C is closed (i.e., of the form $X \sim \mathcal{O}$ for some $\mathcal{O} \in \mathscr{T}$) iff for each $x \notin C$, $m(x) \cap C^* = \phi$.

(d) $C^- = St[C^*]$.

5.5.5 Separation properties. Consider the situation described in 5.5.4. The separation properties we discuss here are listed on pages 67, 112, and 113 of Kelley.

(a) X is Hausdorff iff St is a map iff $m(x) \cap m(y) = \phi$ for $x \neq y$.

(b) X is normal iff for each closed C, D, if $C \cap D = \phi$ then $m(C) \cap m(D) = \phi$, regular iff for each $x \in X$, C closed, if $x \notin C$ then $m(x) \cap m(C) = \phi$.

(c) X is compact iff $X^* = \bigcup_{x \in X} m(x)$.
(d) If $Y \subset X$ is equipped with the subspace topology (i.e., $\mathscr{T}_Y = \{\mathscr{O} \cap Y \mid \mathscr{O} \in \mathscr{T}\}$), then $m_Y(x) = m(x) \cap Y^*$ for each $x \in Y$. Thus Y is compact iff Y is closed and $Y^* \subset \mathscr{D}St$.
(e) If C, D are two compact sets in a Hausdorff space or a compact and a closed set in a regular space and $C \cap D = \phi$, then $m(C) \cap m(D) = \phi$. Thus compact Hausdorff spaces are normal.

5.5.6 (Product spaces) We continue our study of general topological spaces. Show that:
(a) in the product topology (see Kelley, p. 90) if $f \in \prod_I X_i$, then

$$m(f) = \{g \in (\textstyle\prod_I X_i)^* \mid \text{if } i \in I \text{ then } g(i) \in m(f(i))\}.$$

(b) products of Hausdorff spaces are Hausdorff.
(c) (Tychinoff) products of compact spaces are compact.

5.5.7 We continue with the study begun in Problem 5.5.4. Prove the following:
(a) $f\colon X \to Y$ is continuous at $a \in X$ iff $f(m(a)) \subset m(f(a))$.
(b) The continuous image of a compact set is compact.
(c) A subset of a compact Hausdorff space is compact iff it is closed. Thus if X is compact space, Y a Hausdorff space, and $f\colon X \to Y$ continuous, onto Y and one-one, then f is a homeomorphism.

5.5.8 We continue the study begun in Problem 5.5.4. Show the following:
(a) If X is a metric space with distance d, the $y \in m(x)$ iff $d^*(x^*, y) = {}_1 0$ (thus for the spaces studied in this chapter, then m defined in Problem 5.5.4 reduces to the ones we studied earlier).
(b) For metric spaces if $m(x) \in A^*$, (A as in the last discussion of this section) then $m(x) = \{x^*\}$ and $\{x\}$ is open.
(c) Recall that a metric space is bounded iff there is an $r > 0$ such that if $x, y \in X$ then $d(x, y) < r$, and the smallest such r is called the diameter of X. $x \in X^*$ is called finite iff

$$\text{for some} \quad y \in X,\ d^*(x, y^*) \in \mathscr{D}st.$$

Show X bounded iff every point of X^* is finite.
(d) Every compact metric space is bounded.

5.5.9 (a) Let $\mathscr{O}$ be open and dense, $\mathscr{P}$ open; show there is an open $\mathscr{Q}$ of diameter $\leq 1/n$ with $\mathscr{Q}^- \subset \mathscr{O} \cap \mathscr{P}$. Thus if $\mathscr{O}_1, \ldots, \mathscr{O}_n, \ldots$ is a countable collection of open dense sets, $\mathscr{P}$ open, there is a sequence $\mathscr{Q}_0, \ldots, \mathscr{Q}_n, \ldots$ of open sets that satisfy: $\mathscr{Q}_0 = \mathscr{P}$, $\mathscr{Q}_{n+1} \subset \mathscr{Q}_n \cap \mathscr{O}_{n+1}$ and the diameter of $\mathscr{Q}_n \leq 1/n$.
(b) If $m \in \omega'$, show that $\mathscr{Q}^*_m \subset \mathscr{D}St$ and for $x \in \mathscr{Q}^*_m$, $St(x) \in \bigcap_{i=1}^\infty \mathscr{Q}_i$. (This establishes the Baire category theorem, which asserts that $(\bigcap_{i=1}^\infty \mathscr{O}_i) \cap \mathscr{P} \neq \phi$ for every open $\mathscr{P}$. HINT: Show any sequence in the $\mathscr{Q}_i$ Cauchy.)

5.5.10 The concept of local group is defined in Montgomery and Zippin [1]. Show that if G is a local group then $m(e)$ (e the identity element of G) is a group, and that for $x \in G^*$, if x^{-1} exists then $x^{-1}m(e)x \subset m(e)$.

Bibliography

Abian, A., *The Theory of Sets and Transfinite Arithmetic*. Philadelphia: W. B. Saunders Company, 1965.

Artin, E., *The Collected Papers*. Reading, Mass.: Addison-Wesley Publishing Co., Inc.

Ax, J., "Zeroes of Polynomials over Finite Fields," *Am. J. Math.*, Vol. 86 (1964), 255–261.

Ax, J. and S. Kochen,

[1] "Diophantine Problems over Local Fields: I," *Am. J. Math.*, Vol. 87 (1965), 605–630.

[2] "Diophantine Problems over Local Fields: II," *Am. J. Math.*, Vol. 87 (1965), 631–648.

[3] "Diophantine Problems over Local Fields: III," *Ann. Math.*, Vol. 82 (1966), 432–456.

Bernstein, A., "Almost Commuting Matrices and Invariant Subspaces in Hilbert Space," *Notices of the A.M.S.*, Vol. 17 (1970), 439–440.

Bernstein, A. and A. Robinson, "Solution of an Invariant Subspace Problem of K. T. Smith and P. R. Halmos," *Pac. J. Math.*, Vol. 16 (1966), 421–437.

Birkhoff, G., "On the Structure of Abstract Algebras," *Proc. Cambridge Phil. Soc.*, Vol. 31 (1935), 433–454.

Birkhoff, G. and S. MacLane, *A Survey of Modern Algebra*, 3rd ed. New York: The Macmillan Company, 1965.

Chang, C. C. and A. Morel, "On Closure under Direct Product," *J. Symb. Logic*, Vol. 23 (1958), 149–154.

Cohen, P. J., "Decision Procedures for Real and p-Adic Fields," *Communications on Pure and Applied Mathematics*, Vol. 22 (1969), 131–151.

Dean, R. A., *Elements of Abstract Algebra*. New York: John Wiley & Sons, Inc., 1966.

Ehrenfeucht, A. and A. Mostowski, "Models of Axiomatic Theories Admitting Automorphisms," *Fund. Math.*, Vol. 43 (1956), 50–68.

Eilenberg, S. and N. Steenrod, *Foundations of Algebraic Topology*. Princeton, N.J.: Princeton University Press, 1952.

Fraleigh, J., *A First Course in Abstract Algebra*. Reading, Mass.: Addison-Wesley Publishing Co., Inc., 1967.

Frayne, T., A. Morel, and D. Scott, "Reduced Direct Products," *Fund. Math.*, Vol. 51 (1962), 195–228.

Gödel, K.,

[1] *The Consistency of the Axiom of Choice and the Generalized Continuum Hypothesis with the Axioms of Set Theory*. Princeton, N.J.: *Ann. of Math. Studies*, 1940.

[2] "Die Vollständigkeit der Axiome des Logischen Funktionenkalküls," *Monatsh. für Math. und Physik*, Vol. 37 (1930), 349–360.

Halmos, P.,

[1] *Introduction to Hilbert Space*, 2nd ed. New York: Chelsea, 1957.

[2] "A Glimpse into Hilbert Space," *Lectures in Modern Mathematics*, Vol. 1 New York–London (1963), 1–22.

Henkin, L., "The Completeness of the First Order Functional Calculus," *J. Symb. Logic*, Vol. 14 (1949), 159–166.

Horn, A., "On Sentences Which are True of Direct Unions of Algebras," *J. Symb. Logic*, Vol. 16 (1951), 14–21.

Jacobson, N., *Lectures in Abstract Algebra*, Vol. 1, Princeton, N.J.: D. Van Nostrand Co., Inc., 1951.

Kaplansky, I., "Maximal Fields with Valuations," *Duke J. Math.*, Vol. 9 (1942), 313–321.

Keisler, H. J.,

[1] "Limit Ultrapowers," *Trans. of the A.M.S.*, Vol. 107 (1963), 382–408.

[2] "Limit Ultraproducts," *J. Symb. Logic*, Vol. 30 (1965), 212–234.

[3] "Reduced Products and Horn Classes," *Trans. of the A.M.S.*, Vol. 117 (1965), 307–328.

[4] "A Characterization of Horn Classes," Notices of the A.M.S., Vol. 6 (1959), 521.

[5] "Good Ideals in Fields of Sets," *Ann. Math.*, Vol. 79 (1964), 338–359.

[6] "Ultraproducts and Elementary Classes," *Indag. Math.*, Vol. 233 (1961), 477–495.

Kelley, J., *General Topology*. Princeton, N.J.: D. Van Nostrand Co., Inc., 1955.

Kochen, S., "Ultraproducts in the Theory of Models," *Ann. Math.*, Vol. 74 (1961), 221–261.

Krull, W., "Allgemeine bewertungstheorie," *J. Reine Angew. Math.*, Vol. 167 (1962), 160–196.

Lang, S., "Theorems and Conjectures on Diophantine Equations," *Bull. of the A.M.S.*, Vol. 66 (1960), 240–249.

Łos, J., "Quelques Remarques, Théorèmes, et Problèmes sur les Classes Définissables d'Algèbres," *Mathematical Interpretation of Formal Systems*. Amsterdam: North-Holland Publishing Co., 1955.

Luxemburg, W. A. J.,
[1] *Non-Standard Analysis.* Pasadena, Calif.: Calif. Inst. of Technology, 1962.
[2] (editor) *Applications of Model Theory to Algebra, Analysis, and Probability.* New York: Holt, Rinehart and Winston, Inc., 1969.
McCarthy, P., *Algebraic Extensions of Fields.* Waltham, Mass.: Ginn-Blaisdell, 1966.
Montgomery, D. and L. Zippin, *Topological Transformation Groups.* New York: John Wiley & Sons, Inc., 1955.
Morley, M., "Categoricity in Power," *Trans. of the A.M.S.*, Vol. 114 (1965), 514–538.
Morley, M. and R. Vaught, "Homogeneous Universal Models," *Math. Scand.*, Vol. 11 (1962), 37–57.
Ostrowski, A., "Untersuchungen zur arithmetischen Theorie der Körper," *Math. Z.*, Vol. 39 (1934), 269–404.
Rabin, M.,
[1] "Classes of Models and Sets of Sentences with the Intersection Property," unpublished notes.
[2] "Arithmetical Extensions with Prescribed Cardinality," *Proc. Roy. Acad., Amsterdam*, Ser. A, Vol. 62 (1961), 439–446.
Ramsey, F., "On a Problem of Formal Logic," *Proc. Math. Soc. (London)*, Vol. 30 (1929), 291–310.
Robinson, A.,
[1] *Complete Theories.* Amsterdam: North-Holland Publishing Co., 1956.
[2] *Introduction to Model Theory and to the Metamathematics of Algebra*, 2nd ed. Amsterdam: North-Holland Publishing Co., 1965.
[3] *Non-Standard Analysis.* Amsterdam: North-Holland Publishing Co., 1966.
Robinson, A. and E. Zakon, "Elementary Properties of Ordered Abelian Groups," *Trans. of the A.M.S.*, Vol. 96 (1960), 222–236.
Rubin, J., *Set Theory for the Mathematician.* San Francisco: Holden-Day, 1967.
Rubin, H. and J. Rubin. *Equivalents of the Axiom of Choice.* Amsterdam: North-Holland Publishing Co., 1963.
Shelah, S.,
[1] "Any Two Elementarily Equivalent Models have Isomorphic Ultrapowers," to appear, *Israeli Journal of Math.*
[2] "Solution of Łos' Conjecture for Uncountable Languages," *Notices of the A.M.S.* 17 (1970), p. 968.
Suppes, P., *Axiomatic Set Theory.* Princeton, N.J.: D. Van Nostrand Co., Inc., 1960.
Terjanian, G., "Un Contre-example à une Conjecture d'Artin," *Compt. Rend.*, Acad. Sc., Paris, Ser. A, Vol. 262 (1966), 612.
Van der Waerden, B., *Modern Algebra*, Vol. 1. New York: Ungar, 1949.
Vaught, R., "Applications of the Löwenheim-Skolem-Tarski Theorem to Problems of Completeness and Decidability," *Proc. Roy. Acad. Sci. (Amsterdam)*, Ser. A, Vol. 57 (1954), 467–472.

Weinstein, J. M.,
[1] "Sentences Preserved under Direct Products," *Notices of the A.M.S.*, Vol. 12 (1965), 230.
[2] "Sentences Preserved under Unions," *Notices of the A.M.S.*, Vol. 12 (1965), 365.

Appendix:

Glossary of Symbols

Symbols which always (or almost always) begin with a given letter are listed by that letter; others follow the alphabet.

$A(F, n)$	31	D_i	75
$a(F, n)$	31	$D(f)$	173
$\mathfrak{A}_p$	184	D^n	254
$B^-(0, m)$	276	e_i	7
$BV(F)$	16	EC	25
$B(S)$	53	$EC_\triangle$	25
$\mathfrak{B}_p$	184	EC^t	25
$c(A)$	2	$EC_\triangle^t$	25
$cf(A)$	4	$E(F)$	30
$c(\mathfrak{A})$	9	$e(F)$	30
capital German letters	7	$eq(F)$	125
C_t	13	$eq(\mathfrak{A})$	125
$C(F)$	16		
$\mathbb{C}$ (complex numbers)	88	$FV(F)$	16
$char(\mathfrak{F})$	175	f_a	81
$C(a, r)$	296	FLS	315
$CH(V, W)$	308		
CLS	315	Γ	74
$\mathscr{D}$	2	$H(\mathbb{R}^n, \mathbb{R}^m)$	259
$Dg(\mathfrak{A})$	42	$\mathfrak{H}$	172
		$\mathfrak{H}_{\mathfrak{A}}$	172

Unalphabetical

Index